NEUTRON INELASTIC SCATTERING
1977
VOL. I

The following States are Members of the International Atomic Energy Agency:

AFGHANISTAN	HOLY SEE	PHILIPPINES
ALBANIA	HUNGARY	POLAND
ALGERIA	ICELAND	PORTUGAL
ARGENTINA	INDIA	QATAR
AUSTRALIA	INDONESIA	ROMANIA
AUSTRIA	IRAN	SAUDI ARABIA
BANGLADESH	IRAQ	SENEGAL
BELGIUM	IRELAND	SIERRA LEONE
BOLIVIA	ISRAEL	SINGAPORE
BRAZIL	ITALY	SOUTH AFRICA
BULGARIA	IVORY COAST	SPAIN
BURMA	JAMAICA	SRI LANKA
BYELORUSSIAN SOVIET	JAPAN	SUDAN
SOCIALIST REPUBLIC	JORDAN	SWEDEN
CANADA	KENYA	SWITZERLAND
CHILE	KOREA, REPUBLIC OF	SYRIAN ARAB REPUBLIC
COLOMBIA	KUWAIT	THAILAND
COSTA RICA	LEBANON	TUNISIA
CUBA	LIBERIA	TURKEY
CYPRUS	LIBYAN ARAB JAMAHIRIYA	UGANDA
CZECHOSLOVAKIA	LIECHTENSTEIN	UKRAINIAN SOVIET SOCIALIST
DEMOCRATIC KAMPUCHEA	LUXEMBOURG	REPUBLIC
DEMOCRATIC PEOPLE'S	MADAGASCAR	UNION OF SOVIET SOCIALIST
REPUBLIC OF KOREA	MALAYSIA	REPUBLICS
DENMARK	MALI	UNITED ARAB EMIRATES
DOMINICAN REPUBLIC	MAURITIUS	UNITED KINGDOM OF GREAT
ECUADOR	MEXICO	BRITAIN AND NORTHERN
EGYPT	MONACO	IRELAND
EL SALVADOR	MONGOLIA	UNITED REPUBLIC OF
ETHIOPIA	MOROCCO	CAMEROON
FINLAND	NETHERLANDS	UNITED REPUBLIC OF
FRANCE	NEW ZEALAND	TANZANIA
GABON	NICARAGUA	UNITED STATES OF AMERICA
GERMAN DEMOCRATIC REPUBLIC	NIGER	URUGUAY
GERMANY, FEDERAL REPUBLIC OF	NIGERIA	VENEZUELA
GHANA	NORWAY	VIET NAM
GREECE	PAKISTAN	YUGOSLAVIA
GUATEMALA	PANAMA	ZAIRE
HAITI	PARAGUAY	ZAMBIA
	PERU	

The Agency's Statute was approved on 23 October 1956 by the Conference on the Statute of the IAEA held at United Nations Headquarters, New York; it entered into force on 29 July 1957. The Headquarters of the Agency are situated in Vienna. Its principal objective is "to accelerate and enlarge the contribution of atomic energy to peace, health and prosperity throughout the world".

Printed by the IAEA in Austria
April 1978

PROCEEDINGS SERIES

NEUTRON INELASTIC SCATTERING
1977

PROCEEDINGS OF A SYMPOSIUM
ON NEUTRON INELASTIC SCATTERING
HELD BY THE
INTERNATIONAL ATOMIC ENERGY AGENCY
IN VIENNA, 17–21 OCTOBER 1977

In two volumes

VOL.I

INTERNATIONAL ATOMIC ENERGY AGENCY
VIENNA, 1978

NEUTRON INELASTIC SCATTERING 1977, VOL. I
IAEA, VIENNA, 1978
STI/PUB/468
ISBN 92—0—030078—2

FOREWORD

In the series of symposia on neutron inelastic scattering the International Atomic Energy Agency identifies trends in neutron scattering techniques and promotes their application in various branches of applied science and technology. The present symposium was largely devoted to fundamental science. The use of neutron scattering in applied research was reviewed recently by an Advisory Group Meeting held by the Agency in 1976 in Ljubljana, and the results of that meeting were published in 1977 in the Agency's Atomic Energy Review, Vol.15, pp. 755–777.

Since the last IAEA International Symposium at Grenoble in 1972, considerable developments in neutron scattering have taken place. It is generally conceded that much information in this field is presented most appropriately at topical conferences dealing with a specific subject, and this fact was borne in mind when the present symposium was being organized. Phonons to a large extent are not referred to here, since recent material on this topic was presented at the International Conference on Lattice Dynamics, held in Paris in September 1977 by the International Union of Pure and Applied Physics.

On the matter of new neutron sources for condensed matter studies, a high demand continues for both steady-state and pulsed sources. With medium flux reactors – the traditional source of neutrons for using the neutron scattering technique – there is clearly much work still to be done. Applications for the technique are determined mainly by the inventiveness of the investigators, and not so much by the intensity of the sources. On the development of new instrumentation, many novel approaches to spectrometer design have been adopted at various laboratories, and these are discussed in the present Proceedings. Perhaps the most interesting new trends and developments reported in the Proceedings concern studies of polymers and molecular crystals; other applications described in the book deal with hydrogen in metals, surface phenomena, liquids, magnetic excitations and phase transitions.

For the success of the Symposium the Agency gratefully acknowledges the assistance of the organizing committee and the chairmen of the sessions, who contributed much to the discussions on the various aspects of neutron inelastic scattering.

EDITORIAL NOTE

CONTENTS OF VOLUME I

SOURCES AND INSTRUMENTS (Sessions I and II)

LIQUID CRYSTALS AND POLYMERS (Session V)

Sessions I and II

SOURCES AND INSTRUMENTS

Chairmen

H. RAUCH
Austria

J.W. WHITE
Institut Laue-Langevin

PULSED NEUTRON SOURCES FOR EPITHERMAL NEUTRONS

C.G. WINDSOR
Atomic Energy Research Establishment,
Harwell, Didcot, Oxfordshire,
United Kingdom

Abstract

PULSED NEUTRON SOURCES FOR EPITHERMAL NEUTRONS.

We show how accelerator based neutron sources, giving a fast neutron pulse of short duration compared to the neutron moderation time, promise to open up a new field of epithermal neutron scattering. The three principal methods of fast neutron production: electrons, protons and fission boosters will be compared. Pulsed reactors are less suitable for epithermal neutrons and will only be briefly mentioned. The design principle of the target producing fast neutrons, the moderator and reflector to slow them down to epithermal energies, and the cell with its beam tubes and shielding will all be described with examples taken from the new Harwell electron linac to be commissioned in 1978. A general comparison of pulsed neutron performance with reactors is fraught with difficulties but has been attempted. Calculation of the new pulsed source fluxes and pulse widths is now being performed but we have taken the practical course of basing all comparisons on extrapolations from measurements on the old 1958 Harwell electron linac. Comparisons for time-of-flight and crystal monochromator experiments show reactors to be at their best at long wavelengths, at coarse resolution, and for experiments needing a specific incident wavelength. Even existing pulsed sources are shown to compete with the high flux reactors in experiments where the hot neutron flux and the time-of-flight methods can be best exploited. The sources under construction can open a new field of inelastic neutron scattering based on energy transfers up to an electron volt and beyond.

1. PULSED NEUTRON OBJECTIVES

The advantages of using pulsed particle accelerators for neutron scattering were realised in the fifties by Egelstaff [1] and Lowde [2]. They function as an efficient neutron time-of-flight monochromator, and give a low fast neutron and γ background, since the source is effectively switched off during the measurement. During the sixties pulsed neutron scattering programmes using electron linear accelerators were started at General Atomic, U.S.A. [3], Rensselair Polytechnic Institute, U.S.A. [4], Harwell, U.K. [5] and Tohoku, Japan [6], besides the pulsed reactor work in the U.S.S.R. [7]. The objective was to exploit the techniques possible using a pulsed source - an objective still going strong. The principle objection to pulsed sources is still that they impose time-of-flight techniques. The early studies on neutron moderation [2,8-13] bore fruit, and by the early seventies several spectrometers optimised for pulsed

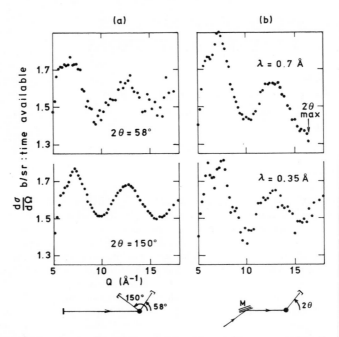

FIG.1.   *The structure factor of liquid nitrogen with scattering vectors Q from 5 to 18 Å⁻¹
measured (a) on the total scattering spectrometer on the 1958 Harwell linac at 58 and 150°
scattering angles, (b) on diffractometer D4 at the Institut Laue-Langevin using a copper
monochromator at 0.7 and 0.35 Å. After Dore and Clarke [15].*

sources had been installed.   In England we recall in figure 1 the total
diffraction from liquid nitrogen performed on the Total Scattering Spectrometer on the 1958 Harwell linac [14].   When compared with the best reactor
measurements, the performance improved as the wavelength decreased and by
0.5 Å the old Harwell linac was out-performing the hot source at the
Institut Laue-Langevin [15].   These results showed that comparisons based
on peak fluxes could be misleading, by beyond two orders of magnitude!
They also showed that time-of-flight methods could be advantageous by, for
example, permitting back scattering at all wavelengths.   A new objective
fired us - to exploit hot neutron science, and to extend upwards the energy
range covered by neutron scattering.   It is an objective which has coloured
our thoughts for instrumentation of the new Harwell linac due to run next
year with 10 times the flux of the old one.

What is the ultimate performance of a neutron source?   To approach this
has been the latest objective, stimulated by the workshops held at the
Argonne [16-18].   Conventional reactors have a performance limit dictated
by heat transfer limitations.   There are no orders of magnitude to spare
there.   They are also expensive and their safety would be questioned at
still higher power densities.   With accelerator based sources the heat is
generated only during the short duration of the pulse, but may be removed

TABLE I. FOUR METHODS OF PULSED NEUTRON PRODUCTION

Method	Electrons linac	Fission + static booster	Fission pulsed reactor	Protons synchrotron
Reaction	$e^- \to \gamma \to n$	fission		spallation
Typical energy	50 MeV			800 MeV
Typical yield	5×10^{-2} n/e	1 n/fission		30 n/proton
	$4 \times 10^{12}\,\mathrm{n \cdot s^{-1} \cdot kW^{-1}}$			$10^{14}\,\mathrm{n \cdot kW^{-1} \cdot s^{-1}}$
Energy deposition	2000 MeV/n	100 MeV/n		40 MeV/n
Typical range	100 mm	400 mm		250 mm
Typical pulse time	2 μs	2 μs	70 μs	0.5 μs
References	[22]	[23]	[26]	[27]
Schematic diagram (by no means to scale)				

at a time-averaged rate slower by the ratio of the period to the pulse
length.   The U.K. Spallation Neutron Source (SNS) [19] and the U.S. Intense
Pulsed Neutron Source (IPNS) [20] both offer over 10^3 times more fast
neutrons than the old Harwell linac. The subject is full of promise.

2.   FAST NEUTRON PRODUCTION METHODS AND THEIR LIMITATIONS

The three principal methods of fast neutron production are given in
table I. We will discuss them in order of typical cost.

2.1 Electrons

Fast neutrons are produced by a two stage process [21]. In the first
few millimetres of the target the electrons are slowed down emitting
energetic rays in the forward direction - the bremsstrahlung. Some γ rays
escape as the "γ flash" but others are converted by γ-n cross-sections into
fast neutrons with roughly a fission spectrum but with a high energy tail
up to the electron energy. In the natural uranium targets often used, the
neutron yield is doubled with little increase in power dissipation from the
photo-fission cross-section. The fast neutron production is closely proportional to the electron beam power for electron energies greater than about
30 MeV. The electron beam current can be as high as one amp within the

pulse and is eventually limited by the electron gun emission or by instabilities in the electron beam. Beam energy is a matter of cost since an
electron linear accelerator can be extended indefinitely in length: the
Stanford Linear Accelerator is some 5 km long! The real limitation with
electron linacs is in the cooling of the target since some 2000 MeV is
dissipated for each neutron produced. An important practical advantage of
electron accelerators is the ease and low cost at which the beams can be
multiplexed or switched rapidly between targets. The 1978 Harwell linac
beam is shared between three other cells besides the condensed matter
cell [22].

2.2 Fission

We discuss only briefly pulsed reactors since from the figure of merit
arguments discussed in section 3, we consider their long pulse times of
order 80 μs make them most appropriate for the longer wavelengths beyond
2 Å. This problem does not occur with neutron "boosters" which are sub-
critical assemblies multiplying the fast neutrons produced by an accelerator. A distinction must also be made between a "static" booster where the
neutron multiplication factor is held constant and a "dynamic" booster
where this is pulsed mechanically in phase with the accelerator pulses. A
static booster of multiplication x 9 for nuclear physics use has been in
operation on the Harwell electron linac since 1958 [23]. The multiplication
feasible with a static booster is limited by delayed neutrons which give a
background between pulses and also broaden the pulse itself. A recent
study for a static booster on the Oak Ridge Electron Linear Accelerator,
U.S.A. [24] showed that a U^{233} booster with x 50 multiplication gave a just
acceptable 10% of its neutron production between pulses. At this multiplication half the target power was generated by the electron beam and half by
fission, and pulse broadening was insignificant. The delayed neutron
problem is largely avoided by the dynamic booster where the multiplication
factor is effectively reduced between the pulses [25]. The IBR 2 pulsed
reactor at Dubna, U.S.S.R. has provision for a booster mode of this kind
using a 200 kW electron linac as injector [26]. The quoted gain factor of
boosters is not wholly realised in neutron brightness at the moderator
since their intrinsic size of order 400 mm is larger than that of an
electron or proton target. They also have an obvious safety problem since
their peak power density is very high. Both cost and safety are less
favourable for a dynamic booster with its problem of mechanically moving
parts of very high reliability in an intense radiation environment.

2.3 Protons

The proton spallation process for pulsed neutron production has been
comprehensively reviewed by Carpenter [27]. Much higher particle energies,
up to 1000 MeV, are required but the 40 MeV heat generated per neutron
produced, with 800 MeV protons, is sufficiently low per unit volume that
target power is not at present a limiting factor. The spallation process
is a two stage one: the energetic protons slow down producing a stream of
sundry particles with an associated "cascade spectrum" of neutrons extending up to the proton energy. Immediately afterwards the excited nuclei
decay giving off more neutrons in the much softer "evaporation spectrum".
Although the cascade component is numerically only a few percent of the
total neutron yield, these energetic neutrons dominate the requirements for
shielding which has to be much more substantial than that for, say, a

fission source of comparable flux. This also degrades the source performance by increasing the minimum possible flight path. Around the energy of
800 MeV the proton yield [28] increases slightly faster than linearly with
proton energy, but so too does the proton range in the target, so that the
fast neutron brightness around the proton beam remains roughly constant.
Energies near 800 MeV have been chosen because the proton range in uranium
is then about 250 mm matching nicely with the moderator assembly dimensions.
Proton current is the important variable. A proton synchrotron of around
52 m diameter gives the required energy in short pulses of order $\frac{1}{2}$ μs when
the beam is extracted in a single turn. Its current is usually determined
by the space charge formed as the protons are first injected into the ring.
This limitation is relaxed by injecting H⁻ ions and stripping off the two
electrons in a thin foil, and by injecting these at a high energy. The SNS
and IPNS both employ injection at around 70 MeV by linear accelerators.
Performance would be enhanced by increasing the injection energy of the
linear accelerator. The ultimate in this process is to reduce the synchrotron to a storage ring, and this is the configuration proposed at the
WNR facility, Los Alamos, U.S.A. [29]. The 800 MeV proton linear accelerator alone gives unacceptably long pulses, although as in the present
mode of operation at the WNR facility, a short pulse from the total beam
may be extracted.

2.4 The Ultimate Source

The heat transfer limitations with electron beams will ensure that the
neutrons will be produced by protons or by fission. Proton sources have
by no means reached the practical limitations of power density. Thus the
SNS source has a peak power density of order 1 MW per ℓ. By the use of
liquid metal coolant with 1 mm uranium plates much higher power densities
of order 10 MW/ℓ might be practicable. Thus it is not impossible to
envisage a booster of modest multiplication installed on a spallation
source. At such relatively low multiplication factor problems of pulse
broadening and delayed neutrons would not be serious.

A more ambitious project would be to use a proton accelerator of say
2.1 GeV energy, which would give a proton range of order 1 m with the
neutron yield concentrated in the first 300 mm of the target. A vertical
proton beam would then give a vertical "line" source of neutrons ideally
suitable for coupling into a rectangular moderator with relaxed vertical
resolution say 300 x 100 mm² in area. Neutron production would be
increased by at least a factor 3, while for many neutron experiments the
degraded vertical collimation of order 3° at 6 m would not be significant.
The power density would not be increased since the range increases with
the proton energy.

3.   TARGET, MODERATOR, REFLECTOR AND CELL DESIGN

These are the crucial components of any pulsed source. The target
produces fast neutrons, the moderator slows them down to the desired energy
by inelastic collisions, and the reflector attempts to scatter into the
moderator fast neutrons escaping either from the moderator or target. These
components are discussed in Carpenter's article [27] with special reference
to proton beam configurations. We shall concentrate on electron beam
designs taking as example that being constructed for the new Harwell linac.

3.1 The Target

The important parameter is the power dissipated, and with it the
choice of coolant method. Water cooling is the cheapest and allows heat
transfer rates up to around 1 kW·cm^{-2}, in 1.5 mm channels. By making the
target of plates having thickness inversely proportional to the heat depos-
ition, the 90 kW rating of the Harwell linac can be accommodated. Water
coolant has the disadvantage of losing some of the neutrons through moderation, particularly in the inlet and outlet manifolds. Heavy water would
alleviate this difficulty, as would a liquid metal coolant. The liquid
sodium coolant technology is well established and would allow a few times
the ratings given above. Uranium targets give the highest neutron yield,
but it is important to ensure that the maximum instantaneous temperature
inside the target plates is kept well below the structural transition at
660°C. For the most highly rated plates in the Harwell design, each
electron pulse raises the temperature inside the plate by some 40°C. This
thermal cycling 10^{10} times per year can cause swelling with inappropriate
alloys and may well be the limiting factor in the target life. Another
problem with uranium is that it must be clad, for example with zircaloy,
with a consequent risk of lack of integrity of the bond. These problems
are largely removed by the use of a non-fissile material such as tantalum,
but Harwell's experience with the old linac suggests that the risks are well
worth taking. The worst eventuality - a target burn out - is no disaster,
and ultrasonic monitoring shows great promise in detecting unusual heat
transfer conditions within the time scale of a single pulse.

3.2 The Moderator

A good neutron moderator has a high scattering cross-section and a low
mass so not surprisingly hydrogen density is the common criteria for
moderators. A most important practical requirement is that its moderating
properties should not change with time either from radiation damage or from
a temperature change caused by the γ or fast neutron heat input. For
ambient moderators water is the straightforward choice although polyethylene
is better in low power conditions where radiation damage is unimportant.
Cold moderators further require an abundance of energy levels in the energy
range around kT. Solid methane and solid ammonia provide good cold moderators [11-13]. At 77K polyethylene provides an adequate practical moderator
in medium radiation levels [3,30]. At the highest radiation levels expected
in the spallation sources and pulsed reactors damage considerations may make
liquid hydrogen the only feasible cold moderator despite its relatively low
hydrogen density.

3.3 The Reflector

Figure 2 shows the two types of moderator geometry which can be used.
(a) is the "slab" geometry used in most pulsed neutron studies so far. It
has the disadvantage that perhaps half the fast neutrons and γ rays stream
past the moderator down the beam tube. The difficulty of shielding energetic
fast neutrons stimulated the reflected wing geometry (b) where the beam
tube is shielded from the target: a geometry first studied by Graham and
Carpenter [12] and used successfully in the ZING P experiment [31]. Since
the moderator is edge on to the target in this case, the direct solid angle
seen at the target is low and it relies on a reflector surrounding the
moderator to direct fast neutrons from the target into the moderator, and

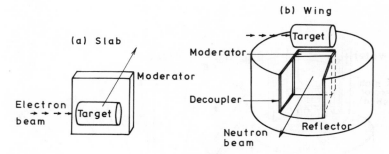

FIG.2.   *Schematic diagrams of (a) slab and (b) wing moderators on a pulsed source.*

to reflect back into the moderator fast neutrons escaping from it. An
essential component of a reflector is the decoupling layer, shown by the
double line in figure 2, which surrounds the moderator aperture. Reflected
epithermal neutrons have a time delay appropriate to their increased flight
path and must be attenuated by a layer of boron carbide or cadmium suitably
thick to transmit the fast neutrons but absorb those of energies which might
broaden the pulse. It is misleading to say that a slab moderator needs no
reflector. Its dimensions are generally of larger size than a wing moderator
and its outer regions function as a reflector, intercepting fast neutrons
from the target and directing them towards the centre of the moderator and
reflecting back fast neutrons escaping from this region.

It is now well established from experiment [12] and calculation [32]
that reflectors give epithermal flux gains of around 10 over a bare wing
moderator. However it is still a point of discussion on how an optimised
wing moderator compares with an optimised slab moderator. It is hoped this
question will be answered by the new Harwell moderator assembly shown in
figure 3. It contains two slab moderators 50 mm above the plane of the
electron beam serving beam holes on either side of the cell. One of these
will be a 77 K polyethylene moderator, the other a water cooled ambient
moderator. Some 200 mm below the electron beam is a lower wing moderator
serving a second set of beam tubes on both sides of the cell. It will be
reflected by a tank of heavy water of average thickness 200 mm and decoupled
by a 4 mm layer of boron carbide powder giving a decoupling energy of 20 eV.

3.4   The Target Cell

In designing a pulsed source shielding it is necessary to distinguish
the biological shield allowing safe working conditions from the neutron
shield giving a satisfactory background in the spectrometers. The situation
is quite different from that of a reactor because although the fast neutron
and γ ray radiation levels near the target are comparable with those near a
reactor core, they occur in a "flash" and do not therefore prevent remote
operation of neutron spectrometers. In a 50 kW electron linac the γ radiation is of order 50 Mrem/hour near the target but can be reduced to below
2.5 mrem/hour by 3 m of concrete which has a ten-fold attenuation length
of about 160 mm. Fast neutron levels are lower but these are much more

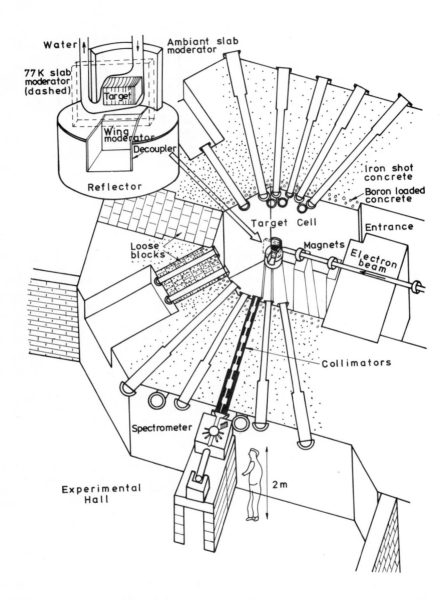

FIG.3. *A sketch of the target cell of the 1978 Harwell linac. We imagine the cell sliced apart through the plane of the upper beam tubes.*

difficult to attenuate - concrete gives a 10 folding length of 500 mm at
30 meV - so that they require an equal shielding requirement of about 3 m
of concrete. Particularly troublesome are the 0.1% or so of neutrons with
energies above 40 MeV, which because the attenuation reduces with energy
dominate the shielding requirement. For a shield broken by numerous beam
holes, the shield must be improved throughout. It is prudent to place
higher quality fast neutron shielding in the neighbourhood of the beam
holes, which should be as numerous as spectrometer geometry allows since
there is no reactivity loss problem as on a reactor. Iron has nearly double
the attenuation of fast neutrons at 15 MeV so that it provides a much better
fast neutron shield.

The target cell designed for the new Harwell linac is shown in figure 3.
The cell generally has concrete walls 3 m thick but loaded with iron shot in
a 1 m high band near the target and around the beam tubes. The inner 0.3 m
is of boron loaded concrete to reduce the activity in the cell, which should
be below 100 mrem/hour after a 24 hour shutdown. The target itself is
retractable into the cell roof. The minimum flight path is 5 m except in
two recessed areas where rotors, collimators or samples may be placed at
a 3 m flight path inside the biological shield.

4.   PULSED SOURCE PERFORMANCE

Two functions of wavelength are necessary to specify the performance
of a pulsed source. Measured variables are typically the flux averaged over
all time $n_L(\lambda)$ per unit wavelength at a given flight path L, and the associated fractional wavelength resolution $R(\lambda) = \Delta\lambda/\lambda = \Delta t(\lambda)/t$ at time-of-
flight t measured for example by Bragg reflection from a single crystal.
These may be expressed in terms of flux per unit area or "brightness" per
unit wavelength, $n_o(\lambda)$ at the surface of the moderator of area A

$$n_L(\lambda) = n_o(\lambda) \cdot \frac{A}{4\pi L^2} \qquad (1)$$

and the neutron pulse length $\Delta t(\lambda)$

$$R(\lambda) = \frac{h}{m} \cdot \frac{\Delta t(\lambda)}{\lambda L} \qquad (2)$$

where for L in mm, λ in Å and Δt in μs, h/m = 3.95603. Alternatively the
flux may be expressed as a function of energy E per unit energy. The
relationship between wavelength in Å and energy in eV is

$$\lambda = \frac{0.28601}{E^{\frac{1}{2}}} \quad \text{or} \quad E = \frac{0.081805}{\lambda^2}, \qquad (3)$$

so that $\Delta\lambda/\lambda = \frac{1}{2}\Delta E/E$ and therefore

$$n_o(\lambda) = N_o(E) \frac{dE}{d\lambda} = \frac{2E}{\lambda} \cdot N_o(E), \qquad (4)$$

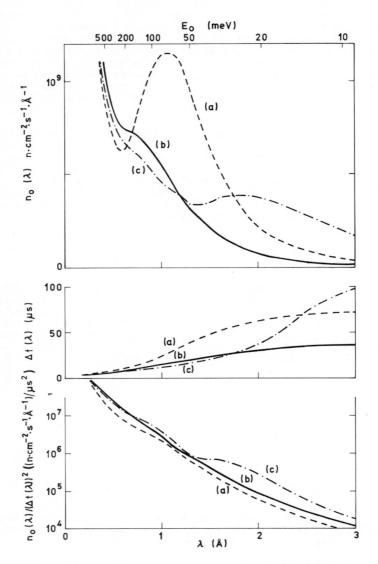

FIG.4.   *The measured performance of several moderators on the 1958 Harwell linac. (a) is a simple polyethylene slab moderator 40 mm thick, at ambient temperature; (b) a 'sandwich' moderator composed of a 13 mm thick slab of polyethylene separated by a 0.025 mm foil of gadolinium from a 26 mm slab; (c) the 40 mm slab of (a) cooled to 77 K. After Ref. [30].*

Thus a typical epithermal flux $N_0(E) = C/E^{1-\alpha}$, where $\alpha \simeq 0.1$ is the small parameter describing leakage from the moderator, becomes $n_0(\lambda) = C'/\lambda^{1+2\alpha}$ Another commonly used definition is the flux ϕ from the whole moderator per unit solid angle, per unit wavelength or energy. For energy fluxes per eV and wavelength fluxes per $\overset{\circ}{A}$, we may summarise the results

$$n_L(\lambda) = n_0(\lambda) \cdot \frac{A}{4\pi L^2} = \frac{\phi(\lambda)}{L^2} = \frac{2E\Phi(E)}{\lambda L^2} . \qquad (5)$$

If we assume the flight path length L to be a variable, which is permissible except at short flight paths where shielding constraints inter-vene, then L may be eliminated in equations (1) and (2) to give

$$n_L(\lambda) = \frac{\lambda^2 R^2}{4\pi (h/m)^2} \cdot \left[\frac{An_0(\lambda)}{\Delta t(\lambda)^2} \right] . \qquad (6)$$

Thus for a specified wavelength and resolution, the flux at the sample depends on the moderator "brightness", its area, and inversely as the square of its pulse length $\Delta t(\lambda)$. This is an important result, and the terms in the square bracket define the "figure of merit" used for example by Michaudon [8]. The usefulness of short pulse times allowing short flight paths becomes even more important in a more practical analysis based on instrumental costs. These might vary as the square of the flight path leading to a figure of merit containing a $\Delta t(\lambda)^{-4}$. In situations where the pulse frequency is limited by "frame overlap" between neutrons from consecutive pulses the figure of merit contains $\Delta t(\lambda)^{-3}$. Early work [8-13] showed that the pulse times for thin hydrogenous moderators approached a limiting value proportional to wavelength, with λ in $\overset{\circ}{A}$, or E in eV

$$\Delta t(\lambda) \simeq 7\lambda \ \mu s \simeq 2/E^{\frac{1}{2}} \ \mu s \qquad (7)$$

Increasing the moderator thickness gives a broad epithermal flux maximum at around $\Delta L = (h/m)\Delta t(\lambda)/\lambda = 28$ mm corresponding to the fixed distance a neutron of any wavelength travels in the time $\Delta t(\lambda)$. However a Maxwellian distribution also builds up leading to much longer time widths: neutrons scatter up and down in thermal equilibrium until they are lost by leakage. This effect is shown in curves (a) of figure 4 which shows some recent measurements made on the 4.5 kW Harwell linac using a 40 mm slab moderator at ambient temperature [30]. That the Maxwellian can be supressed by poisoning the moderator has long been known. Fluharty et al introduced the simple "sandwich" moderator where a thin front moderator is decoupled by a thin sheet of cadmium or gadolinium from a thicker back moderator facing the target [11]. The decoupling energy should be only just above kT if the epithermal flux is not to be attenuated. Curves (b) in figure 4 show a 13 mm polyethylene slab moderator decoupled by 0.023 mm of gadolinium from a 26 mm slab, which halves pulse widths at thermal wavelengths. The alter-native method of avoiding the harmful effects of the Maxwellian distribution is to shift it to longer wavelengths by cooling the moderator [5-9]. Curves (c) in figure 4 show the moderator (a) cooled to 77 K by liquid nitrogen.

Pulse widths in the 1 Å region approach the ideal value, and both flux and pulse length are high in the Maxwellian region near 2 Å.

To assess these moderators we plot the figure of merit $n_o(\lambda)/(\Delta T(\lambda))^2$ as also shown in figure 4. A simple moderator is satisfactory only below 0.5 Å; a cooled moderator is best. However, a cooled moderator is expensive and has a practical difficulty in either slab or wing geometry in requiring vacuum spaces and containment which degrades its performance in the epithermal region by as much as a factor of two. This effect is included in the measurements of figure 4.

We now derive two approximate relationships valid in the epithermal region. The flux distributions approximate to the infinite medium epithermal law $n_o(\lambda) = C/\lambda$, and the pulse widths approach a linear variation with wavelength $\Delta t(\lambda) = B\lambda$ as in equation (7). Assuming these functional forms we note first that the fractional resolution in the incident wavelength $R(\lambda)$ becomes independent of wavelength and depends only on the total flight path L

$$R(\lambda) = \frac{h}{m} \cdot \frac{B}{L} . \qquad (8)$$

Putting $B = 7 \; \mu s \cdot Å^{-1}$ we note that 1% wavelength resolution is achieved for $L \simeq 3$ m. This result is of great practical utility and contrasts with the $1/\lambda$ dependence of the resolution from a crystal monochromator of given plane spacing or rotor of given pulse width. Secondly the neutron intensity $n_L(\lambda) \cdot \Delta\lambda$ at a position distance L per resolution element $\Delta\lambda = R(\lambda) \cdot \lambda$ is given from equations (6) and (8) as

$$n_L(\lambda) \cdot \Delta\lambda = \frac{R^3 AC}{4\pi (h/m)^2 B^2} \qquad (9)$$

and is thus independent of wavelength. For example, an idealised loss-free rotor transmitting the wavelength spread $\Delta\lambda$ would have a percentage resolution and a flux which persist to any selected energy. These two simple results and their breakdown at longer wavelengths are illustrated by the dashed lines in figure 7. They explain the excitement of pulsed sources in promising to open up a new field of higher energy "hot" neutron scattering.

5.   COMPARISONS BETWEEN REACTORS AND PULSED SOURCES

This is a difficult topic. Perhaps the only valid comparisons are those, such as the liquid nitrogen example mentioned in the introduction, between spectrometers designed to measure similar ranges of the scattering law, from similar samples, at similar resolution, with individually optimised spectrometers, using existing "state-of-the art" technology. These conditions are rarely all met, then only after the construction of both sources. Gross errors can arise by comparing the design flux of an idealised spectrometer on an unbuilt source with that from a practical existing one. Technical advances such as position sensitive detectors can easily change counting rates by an order of magnitude. Any particular comparison will be specific to a type of problem, and do not allow a general

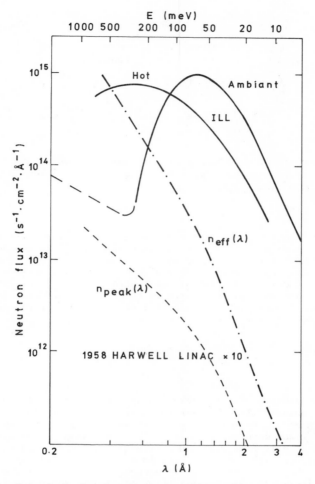

FIG.5.   The flux from the Institut Laue-Langevin ambient and hot sources (from the
Facilities Handbook) compared with the peak and effective fluxes for the 1958 Harwell linac
calculated using Eqs (10) and (11), respectively, using the measured time-average flux and
pulse widths of the sandwich moderator (b) of Fig. 4.

comparison between sources. Also it must constantly be remembered that flux
is by no means the only important parameter in an experiment. Despite these
difficulties, the expense of neutron sources demands that comparisons must
not be ignored, or be so naive that the results are misleading.

    We first clear the air by detailing some methods of comparison which
are manifestly unfair. Many stem from the desire to express pulsed source
performance in terms of a single parameter equivalent total flux - a valid
unit for reactors since their Maxwellian spectra have a well defined area.

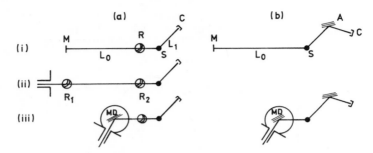

FIG.6. Comparisons between inelastic spectrometers using (i) a pulsed source, (ii) a neutron chopper, and (iii) a crystal monochromator, used for (a) fixed wavelength time-of-flight spectrometry, and (b) crystal analyser spectrometry.

This same procedure has been followed by integrating the Maxwellian component of a bare moderator [12]. It is false because, as we saw in the previous section, the Maxwellian component with its long pulse times gives lower performance than the ignored epithermal component. The obvious remedy is to quote the flux as a function of wavelength per unit wavelength (or energy). The measured flux on a pulsed source is the time averaged flux, so that a peak flux must be calculated knowing the measured pulse width $\Delta t(\lambda)$ and the period τ between pulses from

$$n_{peak}(\lambda) = n_o(\lambda) \cdot \frac{\tau}{\Delta t(\lambda)} \qquad (10)$$

Peak fluxes calculated for the IPNS and of some existing reactors have been given by Carpenter [27]. They exceed those of the high flux reactors except in the cold neutron regime. Figure 5 shows similar measurements for the 1958 Harwell linac compared with ILL. The comparison can be misleading because a beam hole from a pulsed source having the calculated peak flux is not comparable with a reactor beam hole, but rather with the exit port of a neutron chopper or of a crystal monochromator drum. For example as illustrated in figure 6a, inelastic time-of-flight scattering is possible in all three cases by the addition of an extra chopper. The area of a pulsed source moderator corresponds to the chopper aperture rather than that of the reactor source block and the moderator solid angle must be compared with that of the reflected beam from a crystal monochromator.

5.1   A Comparison with Reactor Time-of-Flight Techniques

Just how relevant the peak flux concept is as a measure of pulsed source performance depends on its neutron pulse lengths at the wavelength of interest compared with available neutron chopper burst times. Short burst neutron choppers (< 12 µs) are in use, but suffer from the triple handicaps of low duty cycle, low effective beam area and restricted collimation. A quantitative analysis may be made by applying the "figure of merit" ratio of the square bracket in equation(6) to a given chopper. A typical rotor in use on the Harwell reactors has an effective beam area of A_{rot} = 625 mm^2, a period τ_{rot} = 2000 µs, and a pulse time Δt_{rot} = 12 µs.

Using the Harwell source moderator area $A = 22\ 500\ \text{mm}^2$, period $\tau = 3500\ \mu s$ and pulse time $\Delta t(\lambda)$, we may define an effective flux

$$n_{eff}(\lambda) = n_{peak}(\lambda) \cdot \frac{A}{A_{rot}} \cdot \frac{\tau_{rot}}{\tau} \cdot \frac{\Delta t_{rot}}{\Delta t(\lambda)} \simeq n_{peak}(\lambda) \cdot \frac{247}{\Delta t(\lambda)} \qquad (11)$$

Thus at 500 meV incident energy where $\lambda \simeq 0.4$, and $\Delta t(\lambda) \simeq 4.5\ \mu s$, the peak flux underestimates the performance by a factor 55. The factor is still around 18 at 1 Å but for a poisoned ambient moderator beyond 2 Å, $\Delta t(\lambda) \simeq 35 \mu s$ and it drops towards around seven. For a typical pulsed reactor the moderator area $A \simeq 60\ 000\ \text{mm}^2$, $\tau \simeq 100\ 000\ \mu s$ and $\Delta t(\lambda) \simeq 70\ \mu s$ at all wavelengths and the peak flux may be fairly compared with a steady reactor flux. Figure 5 shows that even the new Harwell linac is expected to exceed the high flux reactors in effective flux at around 500 meV, and implies a spectacular performance to the new spallation sources at epithermal wavelengths.

However, this analysis has two exceptions - poor resolution and long wavelengths. In experiments requiring only modest resolution the sample position may be within the biological shield and so be impractical. If the minimum flight path is L_{min}, resolutions worse than $R = \frac{h}{m} \frac{\Delta t(\lambda)}{\lambda L_{min}}$ would ideally require a flight path L less than L_{min}, and intensity will be reduced by the factor

$$F = \left[\frac{L}{L_{min}}\right]^2 = \left[\frac{h}{m} \cdot \frac{\Delta t(\lambda)}{R\lambda L_{min}}\right]^2 \cdot \qquad (12)$$

This factor is almost independent of wavelength and of order 0.04 for a 5% wavelength resolution using a poisoned moderator with a minimum flight path of 6 m. Some of this considerable loss could be recovered by using a thick unpoisoned moderator.

At long wavelengths the possible use of guide tubes makes the figure of merit inappropriate. These give good ($\sim 50\%$) transmission over many tens of metres, but at the expense of an angular collimation angle α_g determined by the guide tube material and the wavelength. For nickel guides $\alpha_g \simeq 0.2\ \lambda^\circ$ with λ in Å. Thus the guide tube transmission is proportional to λ^2 and favours long wavelengths rather than the short wavelengths at which fast pulsed sources give their best performance relative to reactors. The analogue of equation (1) for the mean flux at the sample position using a nickel guide is

$$n_g(\lambda) = n_o(\lambda) \cdot \frac{\alpha_g^2}{4\pi} = n_o(\lambda) \cdot \left(\frac{0.01}{\pi} \cdot \lambda\right)^2 \qquad (13)$$

WINDSOR

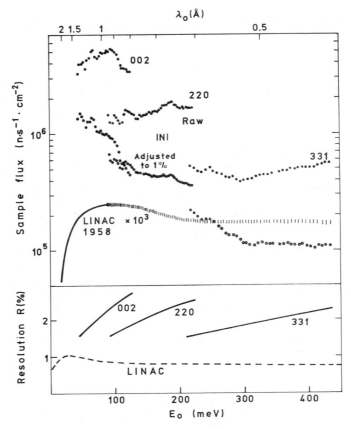

FIG.7.   *The measured sample flux within a selected incident energy or wavelength band ($\Delta\lambda$) of width, defined by the measured resolution $R = \Delta\lambda/\lambda$, for the IN1 hole at the Institut Laue-Langevin and for the 1958 Harwell linac. Open circles show the calculated sample flux for a constant 1% resolution.*

and is independent of wavelength.   Comparison with equation(1) shows that for a moderator area of 0.01 m^2 the guide tube is preferable when the wavelength in Å

$$\lambda < \frac{30}{L} \qquad (14)$$

where L is the flight path in metres.   Thus for 1 Å neutrons a gain occurs only for a 30 m flight path.   For cold neutrons at 6 Å, however, the gain occurs even for the shortest practical paths of order 5 m.

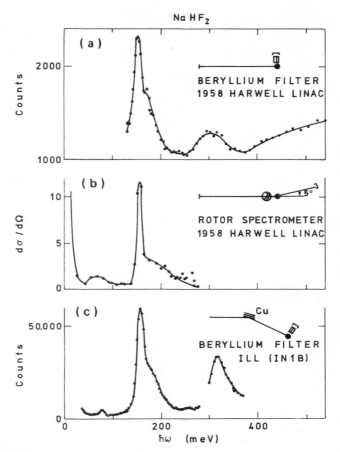

FIG.8. *The inelastic spectrum from sodium bifluoride NaHF₂ measured by (a) a beryllium filter spectrometer on the 1958 Harwell linac, (b) the Inelastic Rotor Spectrometer on the 1958 Harwell linac, (c) the beryllium filter spectrometer IN1B at the Institut Laue-Langevin.*

5.2 Crystal Monochromator Comparisons

There exists on reactors a very important class of instruments using neutrons monochromated by crystals where pulsed neutron sources are least favourable. These include the most important instrument for inelastic neutron scattering - the triple axis spectrometer. In many triple axis experiments the incident and scattered wave-vectors must both be fairly closely defined and the time-of-flight scan is not helpful except as a means of picking out the desired wave-vector $\vec{k}_o$ with the desired wave-vector spread $\Delta\vec{k}_o$. We assume in the following comparison that all other incident wave-vectors will be discarded from the time-of-flight scan just as a crystal monochromator discards all incident wave-vectors except those satisfying the Bragg condition (figure 6b).

The comparison will be made between measured incident beam intensities of the IN1 beam, monochromated by a copper crystal, on the hot source of the Institut Laue-Langevin reactor at Grenoble, France and the 1958 Harwell linac. Reactor beam intensities shown by closed circles in figure 7 were measured using a calibrated fission chamber corrected for the variation of fission cross-section. The measurements were corrected for non-Bragg reflected neutrons but are not corrected for the presence of higher order reflections. Below the flux curve is shown the corresponding fractional wave-vector resolution parallel to the incident beam calculated from $\Delta k_o'' = \cot\Theta.\Delta\Theta$ where the scattering angle Θ is calculated from the known energy and d spacing, and $\Delta\Theta = \sqrt{\alpha_o{}^2 + \alpha_1{}^2}$, where $\alpha_o = \alpha_1 = 0.5^o$ correspond to the collimation present before and after the monochromator crystal. Shown by the dashes is the measured resolution of the poisoned ambient moderator (curves (b) in figure 4) at a 6 m flight path. Although near the shortest practical flight on a pulsed source, the resultant resolution is still good compared with that from typical crystal monochromators. The resolution of a crystal monochromator is seen from the figure to degrade sharply for a given plane spacing as the scattering angle 2Θ reduces. To correct for this effect we show by the open circles in figure 7 an adjusted flux $I(E) . (0.01/R(E))^2$ appropriate to a fixed 1% wavelength resolution. The measured flux $I(E) . \Delta E$ at 6 m on the 4.5 kW Harwell linac per resolution element ΔE is shown by the vertical dashes - each dash represents a single resolution element. As indicated by equation (10) this is almost independent of energy in the epithermal region. However it is roughly 10^{-3} lower than the monochromated reactor beam. Thus to achieve the reactor performance for experiments with a specified incident wave-vector $\vec{k}_o$, as in a triple axis experiment we require a 10^3 performance increase over the old Harwell linac, as we believe will be achieved in the SNS and IPNS projects. By using the constant Q geometry a further x 10 may be gained by allowing an energy scan at constant Q from say 100 to 200 meV to be measured simultaneously. If the time-of-flight scans giving values of Q near the chosen value can be used, the extra gain would be proportional to the number of resolution elements included, x 50 for a scan from 100 to 200 meV.

We illustrate this comparison by showing in figure 8 beryllium filter measurements on $NaHF_2$ made on (a) the 1958 Harwell linac. The filter transmits neutrons of energies less than the beryllium Bragg cut-off energy of 5 meV, and the incident energy is determined by time-of-flight [33]. The disadvantage of the time spread of neutrons transmitted by the filter is reduced by using a scattered flight path of only 150 mm. Clearly this spectrometer, set up literally in a weekend, is not uncompetitive with (c) the beryllium filter spectrometer IN1B at Grenoble [34] .(b) shows measurements of the same sample run on the Inelastic Rotor Spectrometer [35]. This uses a low scattering angle (5°) and high incident neutron energy (300 meV) to give scattering vectors Q as low as 4 $\mathring{A}^{-1}$ for energy transfers $\hbar\omega$ of order 160 meV. The low Q values give reduced line broadening and multiphonon scattering producing very high quality data. Flux is not everything!

6. CONCLUSIONS

We may look forward during the coming years to using pulsed sources of a performance vastly better than our present experience. We shall all have to change our ways of thinking, and rid ourselves of the notion that neutron scattering is limited to the narrow range of thermal energies. We must invent and use the time-of-flight methods until they have the sophistication

of reactor techniques.   If we do this the new sources will lead neutron
scattering as far forward as did the high flux reactors of the sixties.

ACKNOWLEDGEMENTS

Out of many colleagues at the Harwell, Rutherford and Argonne
Laboratories who have helped to crystallise these ideas, it is a pleasure
to thank Roger Sinclair for many fruitful discussions.

REFERENCES

[1]   Egelstaff, P.A., "Third Congress of the International Union of
      Crystallography", Paris (1954), and A.E.R.E. N/M 60 (1953).
[2]   Lowde, R.D., Acta. Cryst. 9 (1956) 151.
[3]   McReynolds A.W., Whitlemore W.L., "Inelastic Scattering of Neutrons",
      p 421, Vienna (1961).
[4]   Moore, M.J., Kasper, J.S., Menzel, J.H., Nature 219 (1968) 848.
[5]   Sinclair, R.N., Day, D.H., "Particles and Nuclii", Ed. Bogolyubov,
      Consultants Bureau (1973).
[6]   "Pulsed Neutrons and their Utilization", Joint meeting, Euratom -
      Japan Atomic Energy Soc., Ispra (1971), EUR 4954e.
[7]   Blokhin, G.E., Blokhintser, D.T., et al. Atomnaja Energia 10 (1961) 437,
      Frank, I.M., "Particles and Nuclii", Ed. Bogolyubov, Consultants
      Bureau (1973).
[8]   Michaudon, A., Reactor Sci. Tech. 17 (1963) 165.
[9]   Ishmaev, S.N., Mostovoi, V.I., Sadikov, I.P., Chernyshov, A.A., "Pulsed
      Neutron Research", Proc. Symp., Karlsruhe, Vol. I, 643, I.A.E.A., Vienna
      (1965).   Report I.A.E.-2019, (1970), I.A.E.-2271(1973).
[10] Day, D.H., Sinclair, R.N., Nucl. Inst. Meth. 72 (1969) 237.
[11] Fluharty, R.G., Simpson, F.B., Russell, G.J., Menzel, J.H., Nucl. Sci.
      Eng. 35 (1969) 45.
[12] Graham, K.F., Carpenter, J.M., Nucl. Inst. Meth. 85 (1970) 163.   Nucl.
      Sci. Eng. 49 (1972) 418.
[13] Sumita, K., Joint Meeting Euratom - Japan Atomic Energy Soc., Ispra,
      p 287, (1971).   Watanabe, N., Kimura, M., Takahashi, H., Tomiyoshi, S.,
      Ibid. p 255 (1971).
[14] Sinclair, R.N., Johnson, D.A.G., Dore, J.C., Clarke, J.H., Wright, A.C.,
      Nucl, Inst. Meth. 117 (1974) 445.
[15] Dore, J.C., Clarke, J.H., Nucl. Inst. Meth. 136 (1976) 79.
[16] Carpenter, J.M., Marmer, G.J., (1972) ANL/SSS-72-1.
[17] Applications of a Pulsed Spallation Source (1973) ANL-8032 (Unpublished).
[18] Uses of Advanced Pulsed Neutron Sources (1975) ANL-76-10 (Unpublished).
[19] "A Pulsed Neutron Facility for Condensed Matter Research", Ed. Hobbis,
      Rees, Stirling, RL-77-064/ C (1977).
[20] Carpenter, J.M., Price, D.L., An Intense Pulsed Neutron Source for
      Argonne National Laboratory, Proc. "Particle Accelerator Conference",
      Washington D.C., IEEE Transactions on Nuclear Science, NS-22 (1975)
      1768.
[21] Groce, D.E., Aller, C.P., Herring D.F., Trans Am. Nucl. Soc. 11 (1968)
      179.
[22] Coates, M.S., Thomas, P.P., Clear, B.P., Sinclair, R.N., Lynn, J.E.,
      Proc. Fourth National Conference on Neutron Physics (1977) Kiev, USSR.
[23] Poole, M.J., Wiblin, E.R., "Peaceful Uses of Atomic Energy", P 59 14
      266-282.   Proc. Second U.N. International Conference, Geneva (1958).

[24] Peele, R.W., Lewis, T.A., Michalezo, J.T., Mook, H.A., (1973) Use of ORELA to Produce Neutrons for Scattering Studies on Condensed Matter ORNL-TM-4987.

[25] Poole, M.J., "Research Applications of Nuclear Pulsed Systems", PL-203/7, pp 104-123 (Proc. Panel Dubna, 1966), IAEA, Vienna (1967).

[26] Pikelner, L.B., Rudenko, V.T., "Research Applications of Nuclear Pulsed Systems", PL 203/11 pp 165-178 (Proc. Panel Dubna, 1966), IAEA, Vienna (1967).

[27] Carpenter, J.M., "Pulsed Spallation Neutron Sources for Slow Neutron Scattering", Nucl. Inst. Meth. 145 (1977) 91.

[28] Fraser, J.S., Green, R.E., Hilborn, J.W., Milton, J.C.D., Gibson, W.A., Gross, E.E., Zucher, A., Phys. in Canada 21 2 (1965) 17.

[29] Fluharty, R.G., Seegar, P.A., Harris D.R., Koelling, J.L., Deutsch, O.L., Nuclear Data in Science and Technology, Vol.I, pp 607, IAEA, Vienna (1973).

[30] Mildner, D.F.R., Boland, B., Sinclair, R.N., Windsor, C.G., Bunce, L.J., "A Cooled Polyethylene Moderator on a Pulsed Neutron Source", submitted to Nucl. Inst. Meth. (1977).

[31] Carpenter, J.M., Mueller, M.H., Beryerlein, R.A., Worlton, T.G., Jorgensen, J.D., Brun, T.O., Skold, K., Pelizzari, C.A., Peterson, S.W., Watanabe, N., Kimura, M., Gunning, J.E., Proc. "Neutron Diffraction", Petten (1975) p 192, RLM/234.

[32] Das, S.G., Carpenter, J.M., Prael, R.E., "Slow Neutron Leakage Spectra from Spallation Neutron Sources", Argonne (1977) ANL-77-76-123.

[33] Taylor, A.D., Windsor, C.G., (1977) To be published.

[34] Waddington, T.C., Private communication.

[35] Boland, B.C., Mildner, D.F.R., Bunce, L.J., Sinclair, R.N., and Windsor, C.G., "High Energy Vibrational Spectroscopy on a Pulsed Neutron Source", submitted to Nucl. Inst. Meth. (1977).

DISCUSSION

B.N. BROCKHOUSE: You have made some glowing predictions regarding the new physical results obtainable with these high neutron energies. Would you please comment on the intensities expected, bearing in mind the magnetic form factors and other things that are involved?

C.G. WINDSOR: Hot neutrons have some of their most important applications in magnetism because of the need to cover a wide range of energy transfers at low scattering vectors. This requires high incident energies compared with the energy transfer, and forward scattering, in order to complete the scattering triangle. For $\hbar\omega \gg \hbar^2 Q^2/2m$, the incident energy required actually varies as the square of the energy transfer.

T.C. WADDINGTON: We ran a spectrum of $NaHF_2$ up to about 300 meV (2400 cm^{-1}) on a beryllium filter spectrometer (IN1B) using the hot source of the ILL reactor. I believe that the quality of this spectrum was much the same as that of a similar compound obtained on a beryllium filter spectrometer using the old Harwell LINAC. This certainly seems to indicate that on the *new* Harwell LINAC, with about 10 times the flux at the sample, such a spectrometer should be most useful for studying high-energy hydrogen vibrations, as in (i) hydrogen bonding, (ii) hydrogen in metals and (iii) hydrogen absorbed on metal surfaces.

C.G. WINDSOR: Yes. Equally true is that by using still higher incident energies and forward scattering to achieve spectra at low scattering vectors, it is possible to obtain vibrational spectra of low intrinsic width uncontaminated by multiphonon contributions.

H. RAUCH *(Chairman):* Your comparisons are based on a pulsed spallation source and a steady state reactor. Have you considered the case of a new type of pulsed reactor source?

C.G. WINDSOR: The neutron pulse times associated with pulsed reactors are in good correspondence with the neutron moderation times for cold neutrons. For epithermal or even thermal neutrons the moderation time is much shorter, so that the effective flux as defined in the paper can be much higher than the peak flux. This in turn leads to shorter flight paths for a given resolution, allowing much cheaper spectrometers.

W. GLÄSER: Do you think that for single crystal work — elastic and inelastic — the new pulsed sources under construction can compete with the steady-state high-flux reactors? I feel that for this one needs peak fluxes an order of magnitude higher than those planned. Can you comment on this?

C.G. WINDSOR: I agree that single crystal diffraction and triple axis spectrometry represent areas where the high-flux reactors still have a role to play even after the construction of the new spallation sources. Extrapolation from Fig.7 confirms your assertion for 100 meV incident neutron energies. The order-of-magnitude gain is lost by going to 250 meV energies, or alternatively by using the 'constant-Q geometry' with 10 counters. In the end the background advantage of a pulsed source may prove equally important.

K. HENNIG: I would like to emphasize the difference in pulse widths between the pulsed reactor with and without accelerator booster. You mentioned a typical width of 70 μs. This holds only for the reactor regime, not for the booster. In the booster regime you will have only a few μs for multiplication factors up to about 100. For epithermal neutron scattering experiments, where you really need the short pulse width, the reactor with accelerator will constitute a very intense epithermal source. I am thinking, in particular, of the IBR-2 with electron accelerator.

C.G. WINDSOR: I agree entirely that for wavelengths less than, say, 2 Å the IBR-2 will be more effectively operated in its booster mode. At cold neutron wavelengths, and for experiments needing only relaxed resolution, the pulsed reactor mode will be preferable. We await the results of IBR-2 operation with great interest.

THE UK PULSED
SPALLATION NEUTRON SOURCE

G.C. STIRLING
Science Research Council,
Rutherford Laboratory,
Chilton, Oxfordshire,
United Kingdom

Abstract

THE UK PULSED SPALLATION NEUTRON SOURCE.

A high intensity pulsed source for neutron scattering research is being constructed at the Rutherford Laboratory. A new 800 MeV proton synchrotron, designed to provide 2.5×10^{13} protons per pulse, with a pulse duration of ~ 400 ns and a repetition frequency of ~ 50 Hz, will replace the present Nimrod accelerator following Nimrod's closure in 1978. In the present design protons from the new machine will be transported to a uranium target to yield 4×10^{16} spallation and fission neutrons per second. The fast neutrons will be slowed to thermal energies by moderator/reflector assemblies close to the target. For a typical target assembly configuration, with an optimized hydrogenous moderator, the time-averaged neutron flux is estimated to be, at 1 eV, 10^{13} neutrons/(eV·sr·s), with a pulse width of about 2 μs. Intensity and pulse width distributions in the thermal region below 1 eV can be adjusted by appropriate moderator design. The new source is some orders of magnitude more powerful than any pulsed source currently being used for condensed matter research, and at this level can equal or out-perform the highest flux steady state reactors, both operating and envisaged. The comparison depends on experimental requirements and conditions, and demonstrates the complementarity that can be achieved in utilization. Detailed comparisons, instrument by instrument, have been carried out for pulsed source instruments and their reactor counter parts. Broadly, it is shown that the under-moderated spectrum from the pulsed source leads to superior performance in the epithermal region of the spectrum compared with the reactor, while at longer wavelengths the gains, although often substantial, are not necessarily so clear cut. Performance details are presented for typical inelastic spectrometers.

1   INTRODUCTION

It has become widely accepted in recent years that the most realistic way to obtain significantly higher effective fluxes for neutron scattering research is via pulsed sources. Technological barriers, not to mention financial and environmental considerations, all point to the impracticability of realising new research reactors which would give substantial gains over the best in use today. Studies in the UK and elsewhere have indicated that the most significant gains are likely to come from pulsed sources based on the spallation production of neutrons (a comprehensive review has recently been given by Carpenter [1]), and it has now been agreed that such a source will be built at the Science Research Council's Rutherford Laboratory.

25

TABLE I. SOURCE PARAMETERS

Proton energy	800 MeV
Proton injection energy	70 MeV
Mean synchrotron radius	26 m
Proton intensity	2.5×10^{13} per pulse
Pulse repetition rate	50 Hz
Proton pulse length	0.4 µs (0.1 µs)
Target	^{238}U, water-cooled
Target heating	350 kW

It is planned to serve the needs of scientists studying the liquid and solid state, including applications in physics, chemistry, biology and materials science. The facility will make use of existing buildings and plant which will be released when the 7 GeV proton accelerator, Nimrod, is closed down in 1978. Design work for the new facility is in progress, and construction and installation will start following the closure of Nimrod. This paper gives an outline description of the project, and indicates those areas of science expected to gain the greatest benefits.

2   DESCRIPTION

The facility is based on a high repetition rate, high intensity proton synchrotron of 800 MeV, giving intense bursts of neutrons from a heavy-metal target[2]. The main parameters of the reference design are given in Table I. A site view of the facility is shown in Figure 1. The target is surrounded by an assembly of moderators and reflectors designed to give optimum epi-thermal and thermal neutron intensities and pulse widths.

2.1 Injector

The injector will be the recently-commissioned 70 MeV linear acceler-ator designed for the present Nimrod synchrotron, with modifications to increase the pulse repetition rate (1 to 50 Hz), and to permit H$^-$ acceler-ation.

2.2 Synchrotron

A new synchrotron magnet ring will be constructed and installed in place of the present Nimrod magnet. H$^-$ ions will be stripped at injection to give a high circulating proton intensity. With a pulse repetition rate of 50 Hz the mean current will be ∿ 200 µA. Extraction will take place within one revolution, giving two 0.1 µs pulses within an overall burst of 0.4 µs.

2.3 Target

Spallation neutron yields increase with target Z, plus an added factor of about two for fissile targets[3,4], leading to the choice of uranium as target material. The target will be in the form of clad uranium plates with

70 MeV INJECTOR   800 MeV SYNCHROTRON

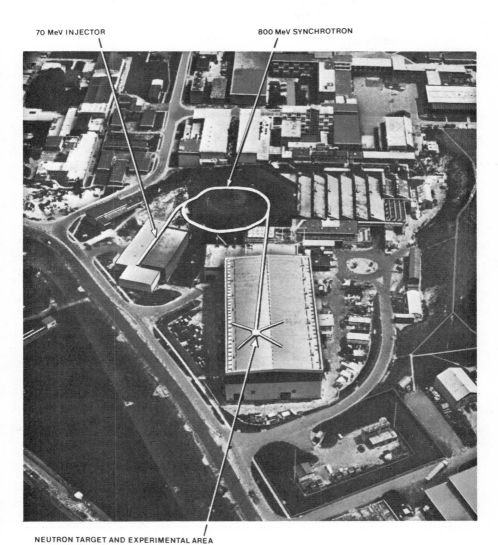

NEUTRON TARGET AND EXPERIMENTAL AREA

FIG.1.   Rutherford Laboratory site showing the layout of the new neutron source.

water cooling; heat dissipation is 350 kW. Reactor fuel technology provides
a firm base for design, and there is operational experience with such
targets, for example on the Harwell linac neutron sources.

2.4 Moderator assembly

Pulsed neutron sources provide an undermoderated spectrum of neutrons
(compared say with a thermal reactor), the neutron behaviour being highly
dependent on the moderator design. An assembly of moderators will be
mounted adjacent to the target to give a range of neutron beam characteristics. It is proposed to use reflectors around the moderators, designed to
maximise neutron yields without prejudicing pulse widths. The target-
moderator-reflector assembly will be mounted within a thick shield, with
conventional beam tubes, appropriately collimated, leading to the experimental area.

3   PERFORMANCE

3.1 Primary neutron production

The synchrotron operates at a repetition rate of $\sim$ 50 Hz producing
2.5×10^{13} protons per pulse at an energy of 800 MeV. With a uranium target
giving 30 neutrons per incident proton, the overall neutron production rate
is then 4×10^{16} neutrons per second. The primary neutrons are emitted
predominantly isotropically from the target, with a spectrum similar to that
from a fission source[4].
The potential effectiveness of such a source can be assessed in various
ways, although comparisons are not straightforward, as most recently pointed
out by Windsor[5]. Table II gives a selection of pulsed sources in use for
condensed matter research for which published experimental data are available. (A more comprehensive list has been given by Carpenter, for example,
and includes both existing and proposed sources[1]).
For the facilities quoted in Table II the primary neutron pulse is
relatively short (< 1 μs); pulse widths at the sample are therefore mod-
erator-dependent rather than source-dependent, and so the primary neutron
production rate provides a fair comparison figure. Clearly the new source
will constitute a potent facility, being some two to three orders of
magnitude more powerful than pulsed facilities used heretofore. The importance of this comparison in the context of reactor-based research is clear

TABLE II. PULSED ACCELERATOR SOURCES IN USE FOR NEUTRON
          SCATTERING RESEARCH

Facility	Fast neutron production rate	Reference
ZING-P (Argonne, USA)	5×10^{11} neutron·s^{-1}	[6]
Toronto e$^-$ linac (Canada)	1×10^{13}	[7]
Tohoku e$^-$ linac (Japan)	1.4×10^{13}	[8]
Harwell e$^-$ linac (UK)	2×10^{13}	[5]

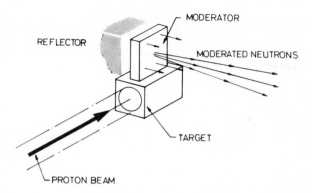

FIG.2. Schematic layout of a target-moderator assembly in 'wing' geometry. The sides and back face of the moderator can be surrounded by reflector to increase fluxes.

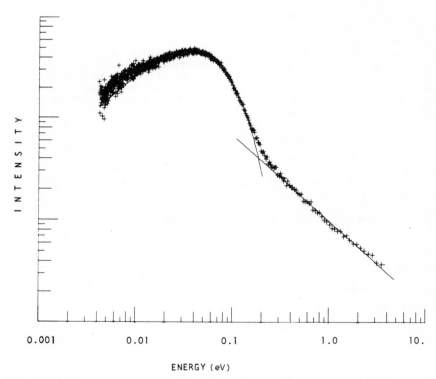

FIG.3. Typical neutron spectrum, measured on Nimrod. 800 MeV protons, uranium target, 10 cm × 10 cm × 5 cm H$_2$O moderator. Smooth curves are a fitted Maxwellian (thermal region), 1/E (epithermal).

from recent neutron scattering experiments where it has been shown that for certain measurements the Harwell linac gives superior performance to that obtained on comparable instruments at the ILL reactor [9]. A more quantitative comparison with reactor-based instruments is given later, see § 3.4 below.

3.2 Estimated intensities and pulse widths

For the performance of the facility to be fully evaluated, neutron intensities, energy spectra, and time distributions must all be taken into account. For the purposes of the following discussion, we shall describe the performance in terms of a compact hydrogenous moderator (nominal dimensions 10 cm x 10 cm x 5 cm) closely coupled to a uranium target, and surrounded by, and suitably decoupled from, an efficient reflector. The moderator is in 'wing' geometry to the target, whereby the target is not viewed directly; the geomtry is shown schematically in Figure 2. (In the alternative 'slab' geometry, the moderator is side-on to the target, the latter being viewed directly through the moderator. The choice of geometry depends on a subtle optimization, where target-moderator coupling is traded off against reflector efficacy; fast neutron shielding can be an important factor. For a discussion see [1], [10]).

The neutron characteristics of the source can conveniently be considered in two regimes - a) the so called slowing-down region, where the spectrum of neutrons has an approximately $1/E$ dependence, corresponding to those neutrons emitted from the moderator with energies above about 5 kT (T = moderator temperature), b) the thermal region, where the emitted neutrons have a Maxwellian distribution appropriate to the moderator temperature, and so corresponding to those neutrons with an energy less than $\sim$ 2 kT. Figure 3, based on some recent measurements at the Nimrod accelerator (see § 3.3 below) shows the distinction between these two regimes. Important factors are the difference in intensity, and time-widths, as a function of energy, which each exhibit characteristic behaviour depending on the neutron energy regime.

In the slowing-down region, the neutron spectrum follows approximately a simple $1/E$ dependence. For the reference design parameters this leads to a time-averaged beam current emitted around the normal to the moderator $\phi(E) = 10^{13}/E$ neutrons $\cdot$ eV^{-1} $\cdot$ sr^{-1} $\cdot$ s^{-1}. The time-widths of the pulses are relatively narrow, given approximately by $\Delta t(\mu s) \sim 2/E^{\frac{1}{2}}$ (eV). In the lower-energy Maxwellian region the situation becomes more complicated as thermalising collisions (up-scattering as well as slowing-down) come into play, resulting in marked spectral and temporal changes according to the nature

TABLE III. MODERATOR PARAMETERS

Moderator	Temperature	kT$_{eff}$	1/E Range
$(CH_2)_n$, H_2O	300 K	$\sim$ 35 meV	> 200 meV
CH_4, NH_3	77 K	$\sim$ 11 meV	> 50 meV
CH_4, H_2	20 K	$\sim$ 3 meV	> 15 meV

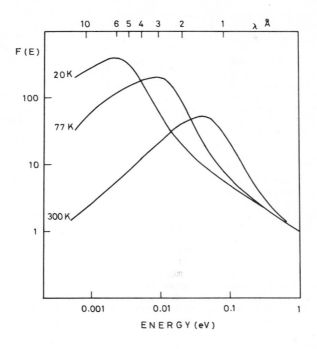

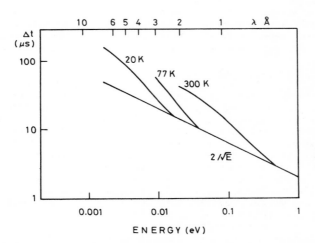

FIG.4. *The dependence of thermal neutron intensities and pulse widths on E for various moderators; based on data from Refs* [11–13].

and temperature of the moderator. An important factor is the significant
time-broadening of pulses giving reduced experimental capability. To off-
set this effect at lower energies, the slowing-down region of the spectrum
can be extended by reducing the moderator temperature. Table III gives the
relevant parameters for various moderators suitable for different temperatures, while Figure 4 shows typical spectra and pulse widths corresponding
to such moderators. In Figure 4(a) the spectra have been normalised to
unity at 1 eV, an energy which is in the slowing-down region for all temperatures; $F(E)$ is the ratio of the flux per unit energy at an energy E to
that at 1 eV. The time-averaged intensity at a specimen at a distance L cm
from the moderator within an energy window ΔE at an energy E is then given
by $I(E)\Delta E = (10^{13}/L^2) F(E) \Delta E$ neutrons·cm^{-1}·s^{-1}, and this expression can be
used for instrument evaluation.

3.3 Prototype measurements

As part of the exercise to optimise the source performance parameters,
in particular those related to the target-moderator-reflector assembly,
measurements have recently been carried out on a prototype target assembly
mounted on the Nimrod accelerator at the Rutherford Laboratory. For the
purposes of these experiments the proton energy was reduced to values
envisaged for the new machine, 0.7 - 0.9 GeV, and a fast kicker magnet on
the extracted proton beam gave pulse widths of a few microseconds. Experiments have been carried out for different targets, both fissile (uranium)
and non-fissile (lead); different moderators (polyethylene, H_2O), reflectors
(combinations of D_2O, beryllium, graphite), and decouplers (boron, cadmium),
in various combinations and geometries. Figure 3 showed the characteristic
undermoderated spectrum of a pulsed source. For measurement of pulse shapes,
discrete neutron energies were selected from the beam by single crystal
diffraction; Figure 5 shows the diffraction pattern from (220) germanium.
The most accurate measurements of pulse shapes were obtained with a water
moderator heterogeneously poisoned with cadmium foil below the surface.
Computer programs being used in the optimisation of the proposed source
target assembly have been shown to be fully consistent with the results,
even though the experiments were carried out with neutron intensities some
five orders of magnitude lower than those expected on the new facility.

3.4 Experimental facilities

It is aimed to have about a dozen instruments operational for the
inauguration of the new source, closely followed by a further half-dozen.
Detailed assessments, both scientific and technical, are currently in progress to establish the first priorities, with the aim of providing a balanced
group of instruments to cover a wide range of research. It is currently
envisaged that about half these instruments will be for inelastic scattering,
exploiting where possible the unique characteristics of the source, in
particular the advantageous fluxes at higher energies. It is hoped to
envelop polarized neutron research by using polarized filters. For illust-
rative purposes we will consider here two different instrument types, both
designed for inelastic neutron scattering, to give a quantitative indication
of the relative potential of the facility. It should be emphasised that the
designs are schematic, with little attempt at optimisation.

3.4.1 Intermediate energy transfer spectrometer

An inelastic chopper spectrometer, analogous in performance to the
rotating crystal spectrometer IN4 at ILL is shown in Figure 6(a). A monochromatic beam is defined by the phase relationship between the pulsed

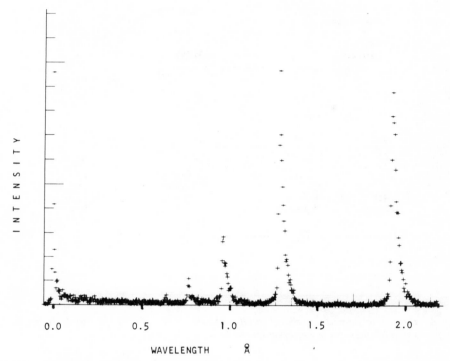

FIG.5.   *Diffraction pattern measured on Nimrod (800 MeV protons, uranium target),*
unpoisoned H_2O moderator, 300 K.

source and the chopper. The secondary spectrometer is taken to be identical
with that of IN4, so that the intensity at the sample may be taken as a
figure for comparison. The chopper is situated 7 m from the source, with
burst widths which vary from 7 μs at 200 meV to 50 μs at 12 meV. The
neutron intensity at the sample is given by

$$I(E)\Delta E = \frac{10^{13}\ F(E)\ \Delta E}{L^2}\ \eta_c$$

where   L is the moderator-chopper distance, 7 m
         F(E) is the spectral intensity (see, for example, Figure 4)
         η_c is the chopper transmission
         ΔE is the transmitted energy

The overall time uncertainty includes contributions from the primary
pulse width, the chopper burst width, and uncertainties in the flight path.
Table IV gives estimated intensities at the sample position for a range of
incident energies, together with the corresponding (elastic) resolutions.
An important feature is the high intensity obtainable at high incident
energies. Measurements at intermediate to high energy transfer can be made,

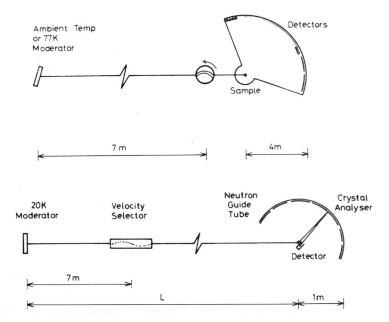

FIG.6. *Conceptual designs for (above) an intermediate energy transfer spectrometer,(below) a high resolution quasi-elastic scattering spectrometer.*

TABLE IV. CHOPPER SPECTROMETER PERFORMANCE

Incident Energy (meV)	Intensity at Sample (n·cm^{-2}·s^{-1})	Resolution (meV)
12	2 10^5	0.62[†]
12	9 10^5	0.52*
80	5 10^5	2.7 [†]
200	1 10^5	6.7 [†]

* 77 K moderator.

[†] 300 K moderator.

TABLE V. HIGH RESOLUTION QUASI-ELASTIC SPECTROMETER PERFORMANCE

	Intensity at sample $(n \cdot cm^{-2} \cdot s^{-1})$	Rate of Data Acquisition (Intensity/ Unit Energy Channel)	$\hbar\omega$ (μeV)	$\hbar\omega$ Range (μeV)
IN10	1×10^4	1	1	20
SNS (L=25m)	8×10^6	8	15	2000
SNS (L=75m)	2×10^6	6	5	600
SNS (L=100m)	1×10^6	5	2	400

and at low Q, by using high incident energies and low scattering angles, and such a spectrometer should permit measurements at lower values of Q than can be obtained on conventional instrumentation available on steady state reactors.

3.4.2   High resolution quasi-elastic spectrometer

The basic principle of the spectrometer is similar to that of ILL's back-scattering spectrometer IN10, with the difference that the incident energy spread is achieved by allowing a broad band of wavelengths, selected from the moderator pulse by a velocity selector, to separate in energy during flight along a neutron guide of length L. Scattered neutrons are analysed by back-scattering from crystal analysers, as at IN10. The use of neutron guides allows long flight paths to give adequate time resolution without a dramatic loss in intensity. Some form of shielding is required around the detector to prevent neutrons scattered directly from the sample being detected. The arrangement is shown schematically in Figure 6(b).

High resolution is obtained by going to long flight paths, but at the expense of reducing the energy window allowed before frame overlap occurs. The intensity of neutrons at the sample is calculated as for the chopper spectrometer, substituting the guide efficiency for the chopper transmission. Assuming a cold moderator (20K), for neutrons in the wavelength range $4 < \lambda < 8$ Å we obtain the intensity figures given in Table V, with those for a conventional back-scattering instrument included for comparison. A valuable feature is the large energy window which covers the entire quasi-elastic region without serious loss in resolution. It should be noted that for this comparison identical analysing systems have been assumed; for the pulsed spectrometer, matching the analyser resolution to the inherent time resolution should give an increased count rate without significantly degrading the overall resolution.

4   SCIENTIFIC PROGRAMME

The impact of the new facility on inelastic neutron scattering is most easily summarised by considering the ranges of momentum and energy transfer which can be covered in relation to present sources. Performance estimates

along the lines described above, particularly those in which specific
instruments, or experiments, are compared with present-day capability,
clearly show that the pulsed source will equal or out-perform the best
steady state reactors over a wide range, although the different nature of
the techniques means that each retains certain unique features, ensuring a
degree of complementarity. An important area is certain to be the presently
inaccessible high energy transfer region, relating to studies of molecular
vibrations, magnetic excitations, etc. As a speculative example we mention
the possibility of directly determining the dispersion curves for electronic
excitations. An important class of materials is the large group of semi-
conductors having band excitation energies up to say 5 eV throughout the
Brillouin zone. Other techniques (optical absorption, electron scattering..)
provide accurate information for specific parts of the zone, but the ability
to measure more complete dispersion curves would be a major advance both in
the study of the electronic states of semi-conductors and in the growing
possibilities of 'electronic design' of materials. More generally, it is
clear that the overall higher effective fluxes which will become available
with the new source will benefit a wide range of science, particularly those
areas which today prove intractable due to difficult sample materials, for
example 'dilute' specimens such as liquid solutions, matrix-isolated systems,
or surface adsorbates, all of which are now taking an increasing part in inelastic neutron scattering.

R E F E R E N C E S

[1] CARPENTER, J.M., Nucl. Instrum. Meth. 145 (1977) 91.
[2] HOBBIS, L.C.W., REES, G.H., STIRLING, G.C., Rutherford Laboratory Rep.
     RL-77-064 (1977).
[3] FRASER, J.S., GREEN, R.E., HILBORN, J.W., MILTON, J.C.D., GIBSON, W.A.,
     GROSS, E.E., ZUCKER, A., Phys. Canada 21 (1965) 17.
[4] FULLWOOD, R.R., CRAMER, J.D., HARMAN, R.A., FORREST, R.P.,
     SCHRANDT, R.G., Los Alamos Scientific Laboratory Rep. LA-4789 (1972).
[5] WINDSOR, C.G., these Proceedings, Vol. 1, IAEA-SM-219/83.
[6] CARPENTER, J.M., MUELLER, M.H., BEYERLEIN, R.A., WORLTON, T.G.,
     JORGENSEN, J.D., BRUN, T.O., SKÖLD, K., PELIZZARI, C.A., PETERSON, S.W.,
     WATANABE, N., KIMURA, M., GUNNING, J.E., New Methods and Techniques in
     Neutron Diffraction (Proc. Neutron Diffraction Conf. Petten, 1975)
     Rep. RCN-234 (1975).
[7] EGELSTAFF, P.A., GRAHAM, W.G., HAHN, L., SUZUKI, K., WINFIELD, D.J.,
     Can. J. Phys. 52 (1974) 2093.
[8] KIMURA, M., KUBOTA, T., NIIMURA, N., OYAMADA, M., OZORA, A., SATO, K.,
     TAKAHASHI, F., TAKEDA, TOMIYOSHI, S., YAMADA, Y., WATANABE, N., Pulsed
     Sources and their Utilisation (Proc. Joint Meeting Euratom-Japan Atomic
     Energy Society, Ispra, 1971) Rep. EUR 4954e (1973) 75.
[9] DORE, J.C., CLARKE, J.H., Nucl. Instrum. Meth. 136 (1976) 79.
[10] RUSSELL, G.J., SEEGER, P.A., FLUHARTY, R.G., Los Alamos Scientific
     Laboratory Rep. LA-6020 (1977).
[11] FLUHARTY, R.G., SIMPSON, F.B., RUSSELL, G.J., MENZEL, J.H., Nucl. Sci.
     Engng. 35 (1969) 45.
[12] GRAHAM, K.F., CARPENTER, J.M., Nucl. Sci. Engng. 49 (1972) 418.
[13] INOUE, K., KIYANAGI, Y., KONNO, H., J. Nucl. Sci. Technol. 14 (1977) 195.

DISCUSSION

W. SCHMATZ: You showed a slide comparing different methods, such as
light, X-rays, neutrons, etc., in q,ω regions. I think the comparison should also

include electron spectroscopy. This method is especially suitable for high-resolution work in electronic excitations ($\Delta\hbar\omega \cong 0.1$ eV, q-range approximately 0 to 4 Å^{-1}).

B.N. BROCKHOUSE: Will experimenters be able to work in the main hall when the accelerator is in operation, bearing in mind the spallation neutron background, or will the apparatus be remotely controlled?

G.C. STIRLING: The facility is being designed in such a way as to allow access to the experimental area during operation.

W.J.L. BUYERS: How often does the target have to be changed?

G.C. STIRLING: We plan to change the target approximately every six months.

W.J.L. BUYERS: What is the operating cost of the facility including the cost of support accelerator engineers and physicists?

G.C. STIRLING: The operating cost will depend on the level of exploitation, but is at present estimated at about £3M per annum, including some continuing capital expenditure on experimental facilities.

W.J.L. BUYERS: If you compare a reactor and a spallation source, which has the cheaper operating cost per neutron?

G.C. STIRLING: Per useful neutron, the pulsed spallation source is cheaper to operate.

ПОЛУЧЕНИЕ И ХРАНЕНИЕ УЛЬТРАХОЛОДНЫХ НЕЙТРОНОВ

В.В. ГОЛИКОВ, В.И. ЛУЩИКОВ,
А.В. СТРЕЛКОВ
Объединенный институт ядерных исследований,
Дубна*

Abstract—Аннотация

THE PRODUCTION AND STORAGE OF ULTRA-COLD NEUTRONS.

The paper presents experimental results obtained using gaseous hydrogen, deuterium and frozen hydrogen-containing liquids as ultra-cold neutron (UCN) converters. It is shown that, whereas with zirconium hydride and polyethylene the increase in the UCN yield associated with cooling of the converter is not as high as the calculated value, in the case of gaseous hydrogen the observed increase in UCN yield (by a factor of 3.2), when the hydrogen is cooled from 300 to 80 K, corresponds to the calculated value. It is found that the UCN yield from gaseous deuterium differs only slightly from that from hydrogen in the temperature range considered. Relationships are established between the UCN intensity and the thickness of the frozen layer of water, ethyl alcohol or butyl alcohol. The UCN yield from frozen water exceeded that from aluminium by a factor of 23. The yield becomes saturated at converter thicknesses of ∼0.05 g/cm^2. During two years of work with freezable converters no decrease in the UCN yield from the neutron guide was observed which could have been attributed to possible corrosion of the copper walls of the tube. The practical convenience, the possibility of regeneration, the fact that there is no additional corrosion of the walls of the neutron guide due to water vapour, and the ease with which the thickness of the converter can be changed, make the frozen water converter one of the most promising UCN sources at the present time. The paper gives the results of research carried out in 1976—77 on the storage of UCNs.

ПОЛУЧЕНИЕ И ХРАНЕНИЕ УЛЬТРАХОЛОДНЫХ НЕЙТРОНОВ.

Приводятся экспериментальные результаты использования газообразного водорода, дейтерия и намороженных водородосодержащих жидкостей в качестве конверторов ультрахолодных нейтронов (УХН). Показано, что в отличие от гидрида циркония и полиэтилена, где эффект увеличения выхода УХН при охлаждении конвертора не достигает расчетной величины, для газообразного водорода наблюдаемое увеличение в 3,2 раза выхода УХН при его охлаждении от 300 К до 80 К соответствует расчетному значению. Установлено, что выход УХН из газообразного дейтерия незначительно отличается от выхода УХН из водорода в рассматриваемом интервале температур. Получены зависимости интенсивности УХН от толщины намороженного слоя воды, этилового и бутилового спирта. Выход УХН из намороженной воды превысил выход УХН из алюминия в 23 раза. Насыщение выхода достигалось при толщинах конвертора ∼0,05 г/см^2. Установлено, что в течение двух лет работы с намораживаемыми конверторами не было

---

* ОИЯИ, п/я 79, Москва, СССР.

замечено уменьшения выхода УХН из нейтроновода в связи с возможной коррозией стенок медного нейтроновода. Практическое удобство, регенерация, отсутствие дополнительной коррозии стенок нейтроновода от паров воды, возможность легкого изменения толщины конвертора делают намораживаемый водяной конвертор в настоящее время одним из наиболее перспективных источников УХН. Приводятся результаты исследований по хранению УХН, выполненных в 1976-1977 гг.

В работе [1] дан обзор используемых в экспериментальной практике способов получения ультрахолодных нейтронов (УХН).

В настоящее время наибольшее распространение получили способы непосредственного извлечения УХН из замедлителя реактора и дальнейшая их транспортировка к экспериментальной установке с помощью горизонтального или вертикального нейтроновода. Поскольку из замедлителя могут выходить практически только УХН, образовавшиеся в поверхностном слое толщиной порядка средней длины свободного пробега УХН, то этот слой замедлителя (так называемый конвертор УХН) обычно отделяется от основной массы замедлителя. К материалу для конвертора предъявляется ряд специфических требований: а) в случае использования горизонтального транспортного нейтроновода граничная скорость конвертора (или его оболочки) $v_{гр}^{к}$ должна быть меньше граничной скорости нейтроновода $v_{гр}^{н}$ ($v_{гр}$ — некоторая критическая скорость для данного материала, ниже которой нейтрон при любом угле падения отражается от границы раздела вакуум-среда); б) для увеличения выхода УХН из конвертора при его охлаждении до низких температур сечение поглощения УХН $\sigma_{с}$ должно быть много меньше сечения нагрева УХН $\sigma_{ну}$; в) поскольку конвертор находится близко к активной зоне реактора, он должен обладать высокой радиационной стойкостью и низким газовыделением в вакуумную полость нейтроновода.

Предъявляемые требования значительно сужают круг подходящих материалов для конверторов. Например, такие вещества, как бериллий, графит, удовлетворяющие последним двум условиям, из-за своей высокой граничной скорости не могут быть эффективно использованы в горизонтальных нейтроноводах.

В работах [2, 3] было показано, что открытая поверхность гидрида циркония является сравнительно хорошим конвертором УХН, однако с течением времени постепенное

обеднение водородом поверхностного слоя под действием
радиации приводит к уменьшению выхода УХН, а охлаждение
гидрида циркония до температуры 80 K увеличивает выход
УХН всего в 1,5-2 раза [3,4].

В данной работе рассматриваются возможности использования в качестве конверторов УХН газообразного водорода,
дейтерия и тонких слоев намороженных водородосодержащих
летучих веществ.

1. ГАЗООБРАЗНЫЕ КОНВЕРТОРЫ

Для расчета выхода УХН из газообразных конверторов
был использован метод, описанный в работе [4]. Согласно
этой работе полный поток УХН Ф в интервале энергий от 0
до $E_{гр}^{н}$, выходящий с 1 см^2 конвертора, можно представить
в следующем виде:

$$\Phi = \frac{\Phi_0}{8} \left(E_{гр}^{н} \right)^2 G(T_н , T_к) \tag{1}$$

где Φ_0 — полный поток тепловых нейтронов с Максвеллов-
ским спектром с температурой $T_н$, $T_к$ — температура конвертора, $E_{гр}^{н}$ — граничная энергия нейтроновода, а функция

$$G (T_н , T_к) = \frac{1}{T_н^2} \times \frac{\int\limits_0^\infty E' \left[\sigma (E' \to E) E^{-1/2} \right] \exp(-E'/T_н) dE'}{\left[\sigma_c (E_0) E_0^{1/2} \right] + \int\limits_0^\infty \left[\sigma (E \to E') E^{1/2} \right] dE'} \tag{2}$$

не зависит от энергии E выходящих из конвертора УХН и
определяется только характеристиками конвертора. Здесь
E' — энергия тепловых нейтронов, падающих на конвертор;
$\sigma (E' \to E) dE$ — сечение неупругого рассеяния нейтронов с
энергией E' в интервал энергий E, E + dE (сечение охлаждения тепловых нейтронов); $\sigma (E \to E') dE'$ — сечение неупругого
рассеяния УХН с энергией E в интервал энергий E', E' + dE'
(сечение нагрева УХН); $\sigma_c (E_0)$ — сечение поглощения нейтронов с некоторой фиксированной энергией E_0.

Для расчета $G (T_н , T_к)$ использовались теоретические
выражения для сечений неупругого рассеяния медленных

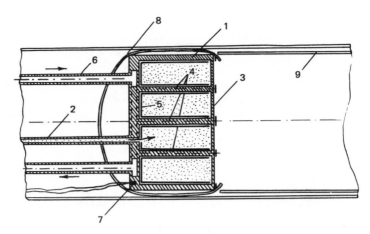

Рис.1. Схема газового конвертора УХН. 1 – алюминиевый корпус конвертора; 2 – трубка для подачи газа в конвертор; 3 – окно для выхода УХН из газа в нейтроновод; 4 – поддерживающие стержни; 5 – медная фольга; 6 – трубки системы охлаждения; 7 – термопара; 8 – пружина; 9 – нейтроновод УХН.

нейтронов молекулярным водородом и дейтерием, полученных в работе [5] при описании движения молекулы моделью твердого ротатора с учетом спиновых корреляций между атомами молекулы. Результаты расчетов [6] показывают, что выход УХН из указанных веществ при фиксированной температуре падающих нейтронов должен заметно возрастать при охлаждении конвертора, при этом выход УХН из водорода при комнатной температуре практически не отличается от выхода УХН из воды.

Частичная экспериментальная проверка проведенных расчетов была выполнена совместно с группой физиков Института ядерной физики АН Казахской ССР (г.Алма-Ата) на реакторе ВВР-К[6].

Газовый конвертор УХН (рис.1) представлял собой герметичный алюминиевый цилиндрический сосуд (1) диаметром 17,5 см и длиной 9 см, помещаемый в сквозном касательном канале реактора ВВР-К в потоке тепловых нейтронов $5 \cdot 10^{12}$ см$^{-2}$с$^{-1}$ при мощности реактора ~ 10 МВт[2].

По трубке (2) от системы наполнения внутрь конвертора под различным давлением подавался газ. УХН, образованные в наполняющем конвертор газе, проходили в вакуумную полость нейтроновода через тонкую алюминиевую стенку (3) толщиной 0,3 мм. Применением специальных внутренних стержней (4)

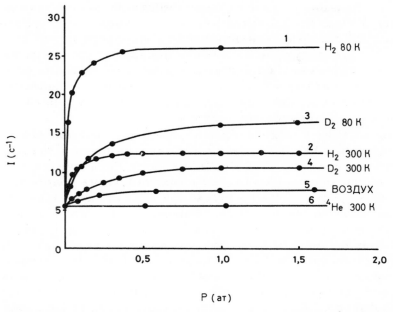

Рис.2. Зависимость интенсивности регистрации УХН $I(c^{-1})$ от $P(aт)$ — давления и температуры наполняющих конверторов газов.

достигалась достаточная механическая прочность тонкой передней стенки (конвертор выдерживал давление до 5 ат) и осуществлялся отвод радиационного тепла от этой стенки.

Влияние внутренних алюминиевых стенок на результаты измерений исключалось путем покрытия всей внутренней поверхности конвертора, кроме передней стенки (3), медной фольгой (5) толщиной 50 мкм. Для охлаждения конвертора по трубкам (6) подавался жидкий азот, либо проточная вода. С помощью проволочных пружин из нержавеющей стали (8) производилась центровка конвертора в канале, чем предотвращался теплоприток к конвертору от стенок нейтроновода при охлаждении конвертора жидким азотом.

Выходящие из конвертора УХН по электрополированному медному нейтроноводу (9) диаметром 17,5 см и общей длиной 6 м попадали на детектор УХН. Нейтроновод имел два прямоугольных поворота, позволяющих расположить детектор вне видимости прямого пучка. УХН регистрировались парой фотоумножителей ФЭУ-52 со сцинтилляторами ZnS(Ag) диаметром 6 см, на поверхность которых наносились слои гидроокиси ^{6}Li.

На рис.2 представлены зависимости интенсивности регистрации УХН от P — давления некоторых газов в конверторе. Выход УХН при откачанной полости конвертора (P = 0) составил 5 с⁻¹. Последующие измерения показали, что такой же выход наблюдается и из сплошного толстого алюминиевого диска. Это указывает на то, что при P = 0 интенсивность регистрации определяется УХН, выходящими из тонкой передней стенки корпуса конвертора.

Насыщение в выходе УХН из водорода, охлажденного до температуры 80 К, наступает при давлении вдвое меньшем, чем для водорода при 300 К. Это хорошо согласуется с расчетными значениями λ — глубины выхода УХН из водорода: $\lambda(300\,К) \sim 5,5$ см, $\lambda(80\,К) \sim 3,3$ см при P = 1 ат (изменение λ от температуры происходит по причине изменения концентрации модификаций водорода с температурой и температурного изменения сечений неупругого рассеяния на водороде). Наблюдаемое увеличение в 3,2 раза выхода УХН при охлаждении водорода от 300 К до 80 К находится в пределах расчетных значений увеличения выхода при таком изменении температуры: фактор 2,6 для равновесной концентрации водорода при 300 К и фактор 3,3 для равновесной концентрации при 80 К. Для дейтерия (кривые 3 и 4, рис.2) давление насыщения выхода УХН заметно превышает давление насыщения для водорода. Несколько неожиданным является то, что выход из дейтерия незначительно отличается от выхода УХН из водорода, несмотря на то, что сечение захвата для водорода в 600 раз больше, чем для дейтерия.

Кривая 5 на рис.2 показывает, что наблюдается незначительное количество УХН, образующихся на воздухе, заполняющем полость конвертора. Практическое отсутствие выхода УХН из He (кривая 6) объясняется малой вероятностью рождения УХН в гелии при используемых давлениях.

При полном заполнении внутренней полости конвертора дистиллированной водой интенсивность составила 12,5 с⁻¹, что подтверждает теоретически рассчитанный результат о незначительной разнице в выходе УХН из газообразного водорода и воды.

2. НАМОРАЖИВАЕМЫЕ КОНВЕРТОРЫ

Во избежание потерь УХН при их отражении от алюминиевого окна корпуса конвертора (фактор $\sim 2,5$ [3,4]) пред-

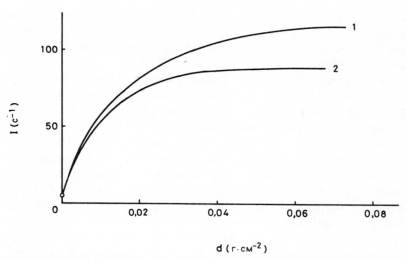

Рис.3. Зависимость интенсивности регистрации УХН I(c⁻¹) от толщины d(г·см⁻²)
намороженных жидкостей.   1 — вода при Т ~ 80 К; 2 — этиловый и бутиловый
спирты при Т ~ 80 К.

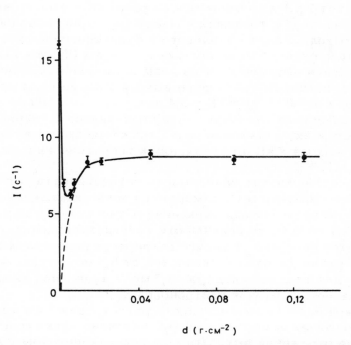

Рис.4. Зависимость интенсивности регистрации УХН I(c⁻¹) от толщины d(г·см⁻²)
намороженной тяжелой воды на поверхность гидрида циркония при Т ~ 80 К.

ставляет особый интерес использование некоторых летучих водородосодержащих веществ в качестве конверторов УХН путем их намораживания на какую-либо охлажденную поверхность.

На реакторе ВВР-К [6] намораживание летучих водородосодержащих веществ происходило на поверхность помещенного на место установки конвертора алюминиевого диска (ϕ 175 мм и толщиной 5 мм), охлаждаемого жидким азотом.

При начале работы после достижения рабочего вакуума в полости нейтроновода 10^{-6} торр на конвертор подается жидкий азот. После достижения конвертором температуры 80 K перекрывались вентили высоковакуумных насосов и необходимое количество воды или спирта дозирующим образом порциями вводилось в вакуумную полость нейтроновода. Наблюдалось ухудшение вакуума до 10^{-2} торр, однако через несколько минут он восстанавливался до прежнего значения, после чего открывались насосы для поддержания вакуума.

На рис.3 представлена зависимость выхода УХН от толщины намороженного слоя воды, этилового и бутилового спирта. Выход УХН из намороженной воды (кривая 1) превысил выход УХН из алюминия в 23 раза. Насыщение выхода достигалось при толщинах конвертора $\sim 0,05$ г/см^2 (500 микрон). Выходы УХН из этилового и бутилового спиртов оказались несколько меньшими, чем из воды (кривая 2). Приняв отношение выходов УХН из воды и алюминия (при 300 K) 1:0,14 [4], получаем увеличение выхода УХН из воды при охлаждении от 300 K до 80 K $\sim 3,4$ раза, что составляет $\sim 0,6$ от теоретического значения. Для полиэтилена и гидрида циркония при их охлаждении ранее также наблюдался только 60% рост выхода УХН по отношению к теоретически предсказанному [4].

На рис.4 показана зависимость интенсивности регистрации УХН от толщины D_2O, намороженной на охлажденную до 80 K поверхность гидрида циркония. Относительно малый выход УХН из D_2O, по сравнению с гидридом циркония и H_2O, объясняется тем, что от такого конвертора получаются УХН только в узком диапазоне скоростей от 5,5 мс$^{-1}$ — граничной скорости для тяжелого льда, до 5,7 мс$^{-1}$ — граничной скорости меди — материала стенок нейтроновода.

Резкое падение интенсивности регистрации УХН при малых толщинах намороженной D_2O наглядно иллюстрирует появление отражения выходящих из гидрида циркония УХН от тончайших слоев D_2O.

В принципе, введение паров воды в вакуумную полость
нейтроновода должно вызвать коррозию полированных стенок
нейтроновода, однако, в течение двух лет работы с намораживаемыми конверторами не было замечено уменьшения
выхода УХН из нейтроновода.

Таким образом, суммируя данные по конверторам для
УХН, можно сказать, что конвертор из газообразного водорода является практически удобным источником УХН при
использовании его на высокопоточном реакторе, так как
такой конвертор не подвержен радиационному разложению
под действием излучения реактора. В отличие от гидрида
циркония, полиэтилена и воды, где эффект увеличения выхода УХН при охлаждении не достигает расчетной величины,
для газообразного конвертора эффект охлаждения соответствует расчетному значению.

Потери в результате отражения УХН от стенки алюминиевого окна конвертора не позволяют получить выход УХН из
обычного водорода, существенно превышающий выход УХН с
открытой поверхности гидрида циркония. Согласно расчету[6]
выход УХН из газообразного параводорода при температуре
20 К почти в 30 раз должен превышать выход УХН из обычного водорода при комнатной температуре. Этот факт еще
требует экспериментальной проверки. В то же время, согласно полученным экспериментальным данным, намороженная вода при температуре жидкого азота обладает максимальным
выходом УХН. Практическое удобство, регенерация, отсутствие дополнительной коррозии стенок нейтроновода от паров
воды, возможность легкого изменения толщины конвертора
делают намораживаемый водяной конвертор в настоящее время одним из наиболее перспективных источников УХН на горизонтальных каналах.

3. ХРАНЕНИЕ УЛЬТРАХОЛОДНЫХ НЕЙТРОНОВ

Основной особенностью УХН является возможность их
длительного хранения в замкнутых объемах в виде своеоб-
разного квантового газа с характерной температурой
$T \sim 10^{-3}$ К. Главной характеристикой этого газа является
время его хранения, поскольку, во-первых, этот параметр
служит прямым критерием для сопоставления экспериментов
с теоретическими расчетами поведения УХН и, во-вторых,
целесообразность использования газа УХН в различного рода

физических экспериментах определяется достижимым временем их хранения.

Как отмечалось в обзорах [1, 7], максимальное получаемое время хранения УХН значительно меньше теоретически предсказываемого. Измеренный коэффициент поглощения УХН при отражении от стенки сосуда μ соответствует предсказываемому выражению

$$\mu \sim \frac{\pi}{2} \cdot \frac{\sigma(k)\,k}{4\pi b}$$

где b — амплитуда когерентного рассеяния; k — волновой вектор падающего на стенку нейтрона; $\sigma(k)$ — эффективное сечение потерь, пропорциональное $1/k$. Однако, минимальное, получаемое из экспериментов по хранению УХН, сечение потерь σ составляет $\sim 10^3$ барн (при $\lambda = 2\pi/k = 500 \overset{\circ}{A}$) даже для материалов с низкими сечениями захвата и неупругого рассеяния нейтронов, такими как пирографит или стекло. Более того, это сечение не обнаруживает какой-либо температурной зависимости в диапазоне температур от -150 °C до ~ 400 °C.

За последний год было выполнено несколько экспериментальных и теоретических работ, значительно сузивших направление поисков причин утечки УХН из ловушек.

В экспериментах, проведенных Стрелковым и Хетцельтом [8], сосуд для хранения УХН окружался многонитевым пропорциональным счетчиком тепловых нейтронов. С помощью наружной защиты фоновый счет этого детектора удалось снизить до уровня $\sim 0,1$ имп/с. При наполнении внутреннего сосуда УХН этим детектором удалось четко зарегистрировать появление нейтронов вне сосуда, причем скорость счета нейтронов была пропорциональна количеству УХН, находящихся в сосуде. Более того, количество нейтронов, регистрируемое детектором, с учетом геометрии эксперимента и эффективности детектора, хорошо соответствовало убыли УХН в сосуде. Изменением эффективности детектора за счет изменения давления гелия-3 удалось установить, что энергия вытекающих из сосуда нейтронов близка к тепловой энергии. Эксперименты выполнялись с сосудами из меди и стекла с напыленным тонким слоем бериллия, т.е. из материалов с низким сечением неупругого рассеяния. Тем не менее, эксперименты однозначно указывают, что основным процессом, выводящим УХН из сосуда, является неупругое рассеяние на поверхности ловушки.

Единственно реально возможной причиной быстрого нагрева УХН может быть примесь водорода в материале стенки сосуда или в его поверхностном слое толщиной $\sim 100\overset{\circ}{A}$ в количестве ~ 10 ат% в силу большого неупругого некогерентного сечения водорода ($\sim 10^4$ барн при $\lambda = 500\overset{\circ}{A}$). Однако обычно неупругое рассеяние резко падает с понижением температуры, чего не наблюдается в экспериментах по хранению УХН. Игнатовичем и Сатаровым [9] было высказано предположение, что водород, адсорбированный на поверхности сосуда, почти свободно мигрирует вдоль поверхности, будучи сильно связанным с нею в направлении нормали к поверхности, и его можно рассматривать как свободный двумерный газ. В этом случае упругое рассеяние нейтрона на атоме водорода приводит к обмену энергией между нейтроном и протоном, т.е. нейтрон при упругом рассеянии приобретает тепловую энергию. Сечение такого процесса $\sigma \simeq \dfrac{\sigma_0 k_0}{k}\sqrt{\dfrac{T}{T_0}}$, где $\sigma_0 = 20$ барн — сечение упругого рассеяния на свободном протоне, k_0 = волновой вектор теплового нейтрона, $T_0 \simeq 300$ К, T — температура стенки сосуда. Из этого выражения следует, что нагревание УХН может быть по-прежнему объяснено примесью 10 ат% водорода на поверхности, что при разветвленной поверхности может соответствовать одному монослою. Кроме того, температурная зависимость такого сечения является довольно слабой и в эксперименте может оказаться незамеченной, если количество адсорбированного водорода растет с понижением температуры. Существующие литературные данные о количестве адсорбированного водорода и тем более о его динамических свойствах весьма противоречивы и не дают возможности окончательного решения проблемы хранения УХН в пользу "водородной гипотезы". По-видимому, ответ на вопрос о влиянии водорода может быть получен в новых экспериментах по хранению УХН в максимально чистых сосудах или при дейтерировании их поверхности.

Если основной причиной уменьшения времени хранения УХН являются поверхностные загрязнения стенок сосудов, то этот фактор полностью устраняется при хранении УХН в магнитных бутылках. Первый эксперимент по магнитному хранению УХН был выполнен Морозовым и др. [10] на высокопоточном реакторе СМ-2. Нейтроны с энергией 0-10 нэВ хранились в магнитной "тарелке" с внутренним диаметром 640 мм, сформированной магнитными зеркалами по типу предложенных Владимирским [11] с максимальным полем 2,5 кГс.

Гравитационное поле не позволяло нейтронам подниматься выше боковых зеркал "тарелки" высотой 15 см. Полученное время хранения нейтронов составило 35 ± 10 с. За одно наполнение в "тарелку" попадал ~ 1 нейтрон. Этот эксперимент доказывает возможность хранения УХН в магнитных ловушках, хотя полученное время хранения является разочаровывающе малым, поскольку теми же авторами ранее было получено время хранения УХН в медной "тарелке" ~ 360 с. Хотя авторами и не обсуждаются причины столь быстрой утечки УХН из магнитной ловушки, очевидно, что в первую очередь это связано с деполяризацией хранящихся нейтронов.

Вопрос о скорости деполяризации УХН при магнитном хранении рассматривался Владимирским в его оригинальной работе [11]. Предполагалось, что деполяризация в основном происходит при прохождении нейтроном области перемены знака магнитного поля. Поскольку, однако, скорости УХН чрезвычайно малы, спин нейтрона успевает следить за направлением поля и адиабатически поворачивается вместе с полем, почти не испытывая деполяризации, и Владимирским были получены оптимистические оценки скорости деполяризации УХН при магнитном хранении.

Более строгий расчет движения нейтрона в магнитном шестиполюснике, выполненный Игнатовичем [12], показал, что в некоторых случаях скорость деполяризации может быть весьма высокой.

Хотелось бы отметить, что деполяризация нейтронов может иметь место не только при хранении УХН в знакопеременном поле, но и в недостаточно однородном магнитном поле. Качественно эта возможность следует из того, что при движении в неоднородном поле нейтрон "видит" переменную во времени компоненту поля $H_\perp(t)$, нормальную к основному полю H_0. Фурье-компонента $H_\perp^\omega$ с частотой $\omega = \gamma H_0$ ($\gamma / 2\pi = 3 \cdot 10^3$ Гц/Гс – гиромагнитный фактор нейтрона) вызывает резонансный поворот спина нейтрона и время деполяризации будет порядка $T = 2\pi / \gamma H_\perp^\omega$, откуда следует, что достаточно неоднородности поля с $H_\perp^\omega \approx 10^{-5}$ Гс, чтобы деполяризировать нейтроны за время порядка 100 с. Хорошо известно, например, что при поляризации газообразного гелия-3 методом "оптической накачки" газ быстро деполяризуется, если не принять особых мер по устранению малой неоднородности магнитного поля в лабораторном помещении.

Заключая обзор работ по хранению УХН, следует сделать вывод, что несмотря на многолетние усилия эксперимента-

ров и теоретиков, в настоящее время еще нет окончательной
ясности в причинах быстрой утечки УХН из ловушек.

ЛИТЕРАТУРА

[1]   ШАПИРО, Ф.Л., Препринт ОИЯИ Р3-7135, Дубна, 1973.
[2]   АХМЕТОВ, Е.З. и др., Препринт ОИЯИ Р3-7457, Дубна, 1973.
[3]   ГРОШЕВ, Л.В. и др., Препринт ОИЯИ Р3-7282, Дубна, 1973.
[4]   ГОЛИКОВ, В.В., ЛУЩИКОВ, В.И., ШАПИРО, Ф.Л., Ж. Эксп. Теор.
      Физ.64 (1973) 73.
[5]   YOUNG, J.A., KOPPEL, J.U., Phys. Rev. 135 (1964) 603.
[6]   АХМЕТОВ, Е.З. и др., Препринт ОИЯИ Р3-8470, Дубна, 1974.
[7]   ЛУЩИКОВ, В.И., Материалы конференции по взаимодействию нейтро-
      нов с ядрами, Лоуэлл, США, 1976.
[8]   СТРЕЛКОВ, А.В., ХЕТЦЕЛЬТ, М., Препринт ОИЯИ Р3-10815, Дубна,
      1977.
[9]   ИГНАТОВИЧ, В.К., САТАРОВ, Л.М., Препринт ИАЭ 2820, Москва,
      1977.
[10] АВЕРЬЯНОВ, П.Г., КОСВИНЦЕВ, Ю.Ю., КУШНИР, Ю.А., МОРОЗОВ,В.И.,
      ПЛОТНИКОВ, И.А., Труды IV-ой конференции по нейтронной физике,
      Киев, 1977, Изд-во г. Обнинска, 1977.
[11] ВЛАДИМИРСКИЙ, В.В., Ж. Эксп. Теор. Физ. 12 (1961) 740.
[12] ИГНАТОВИЧ, В.К., Препринт ОИЯИ Е4-8404, Дубна, 1974.

DISCUSSION

H. RAUCH *(Chairman):* Is the depolarization caused by inhomogeneous
magnetic fields, resonance depolarization, or incoherent scattering?

V.I. LUSHCHIKOV: Inhomogeneity of the magnetic field is responsible
for depolarization.

J.W. WHITE: Professor Paul and his team from Bonn were recently successful
in storing ultracold neutrons in a hexapole toroidal bottle at the Laue-Langevin
Institute, and they were able to demonstrate the natural decay time for neutrons.
Could you suggest any urgent experiments on UCN/surface interactions which
could be done by deliberately introducing samples into the circulating UCN beam?

V.I. LUSHCHIKOV: Unfortunately, I have not heard about this successful
work before. I have no proposals regarding the use of the magnetic ring for
surface contamination problems.

A. STEYERL: If hydrogenous contamination on the bottle surface is the
reason for the low experimental containment lifetimes, one should expect the
lifetime to be temperature dependent. In previous experiments, however, Strelkov
observed an experimental lifetime nearly independent of temperature. Have any
new measurements been made in order to clarify this point?

V.I. LUSHCHIKOV: No new experiments have been done, but we have many old results which show that the lifetime is independent of temperature to within 10%.

R. GOLUB: Can you tell us a bit more about the energy of the neutrons which are observed to escape from the UCN storage vessel when it is surrounded by a neutron detector?

V.I. LUSHCHIKOV: By changing the ^{3}He pressure in the counter we estimated that the energy of the escaping neutrons is a little lower than thermal.

O. SCHÄRPF: What experimental arrangement is used to obtain the magnetic field at the surface of your containment?

V.I. LUSHCHIKOV: The walls of the magnetic bottle are formed by magnetic mirrors of a type designed by Vladimirsky. The magnetic field on the surface is 2.5 kG.

A. STEYERL: In the magnetic bottle used in your experiments there are regions where the magnetic field is very small. Neutron depolarization is likely to occur in such zones. In the magnetic storage ring of Paul's group, which is now operating at the ILL, zones of zero magnetic field are excluded from the working volume. Perhaps this explains why they apparently obtain the theoretical lifetime corresponding to β-decay.

V.I. LUSHCHIKOV: You are right. The low field regions are very dangerous, and they may be responsible for the short lifetime in Morozov's experiment.

PRELIMINARY MEASUREMENTS OF THE PERFORMANCE OF THE SOURCE OF ULTRA-COLD AND VERY COLD NEUTRONS AT ILL

P. AGERON, M. HETZELT, W. MAMPE
Institut Laue-Langevin,
Grenoble

R. GOLUB, M. PENDELBURY, K. SMITH
University of Sussex,
Sussex,
United Kingdom

J. ROBSON
Mc Gill University,
Montreal,
Canada

Abstract

PRELIMINARY MEASUREMENTS OF THE PERFORMANCE OF THE SOURCE OF ULTRA-COLD AND VERY COLD NEUTRONS AT ILL.

The ultra-cold (UCN) and very cold neutron (VCN) source, which has been put into operation in April 1977 at the high-flux reactor of the Institut Laue-Langevin (ILL), provides a beam of neutrons with velocities lower than 50 m·s⁻¹ (wavelength longer than 80 Å) which do not exist in the other beams. A description is given of the different parts of the source: the in-pile guide, in an inclined beam tube, with a room-temperature water converter in a flux of 6×10^{14} n·cm⁻²·s⁻¹, the curved guide inside an external shield, and the distribution system to three experimental sites. Theoretical neutron spectra of such a source are indicated. The measurements of the flux and of the spectra are made by means of four different methods: conventional time-of-flight over the whole range, time-of-flight with a pre-selection of UCN, gravity spectrometer, and UCN storage in a 'bottle', for the UCN range. The total flux in the beam is 2×10^5 n·cm⁻²·s⁻¹ with the maximum of the spectra at 60 m·s⁻¹. The total UCN flux (velocity lower than 6.2 m·s⁻¹) is, after correction of the TOF and 'bottle' measurements, evaluated at about 300 n·cm⁻²·s⁻¹.

1. THE SOURCE OF ULTRA-COLD AND VERY COLD NEUTRONS

Ultra-cold neutrons (UCN) and very cold neutrons (VCN) define neutrons with velocities $0 < v < 6.2$ m·s⁻¹ and $6.2 < v < 50 - 100$ m·s⁻¹, respectively, where the limit, $v_1 = 6.2$ m·s⁻¹, has been chosen arbitrarily as the limit velocity in stainless steel.

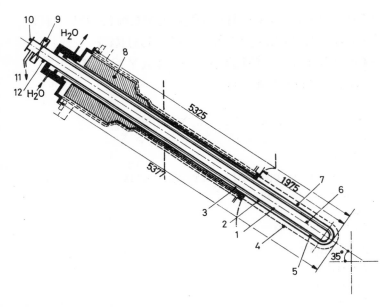

FIG.1. *Sketch of the in-pile part:*
(1) polished stainless-steel guide; (2) water barrier; stainless steel with Zircaloy spacers;
(3) external aluminium tube; (4) reactor thimble; (5) water; (6) vacuum; (7) helium;
(8) shielding plug; (9) safety valve; (10) membrane; (11) vacuum pump; (12) leak detection.

Such neutrons, which are practically missing in the other, even cold, beams of the high-flux reactor, are extracted from the reactor reflector (without any cold moderator) and guided to experiments by the different sections of the instrument:

1.1. In-pile guide

An in-pile guide (Fig.1) installed in an inclined (35°) beam tube with the end in a thermal-neutron flux of $6 \times 10^{14}\,\mathrm{n \cdot cm^{-2} \cdot s^{-1}}$. It is a 6.7-cm-inner-diameter stainless-steel tube polished internally (mechanically and electrolytically). At the inner end, a thin (0.6 mm) Zircaloy dome is connected to the tube by a "diffusion" weld (Fig.2).

At the other end, it is closed by a thin (0.1 mm) aluminium sheet. Just before, a safety valve, controlled by a water detector, will automatically be closed in case of tube rupture. In the normal open position it is equipped with a ring maintaining the continuity of the guide.

The nuclear heat (5 kW total, 2.5 $\mathrm{W \cdot g^{-1}}$ maximum) is removed by a flow (300 $\mathrm{g \cdot s^{-1}}$) of ordinary water which acts also as a converter (3–4 mm thick, at a temperature of 50°C).

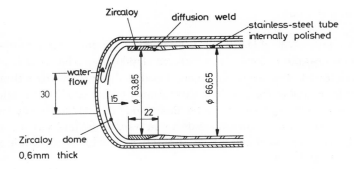

FIG.2.   Detail of the converter.

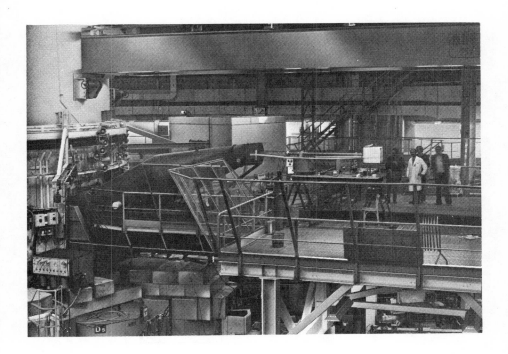

FIG.3.   View of the curved guide and the TOF set-up.

1.2. Out-of-pile guide

A main out-of-pile guide, which is a square (7×7 cm²) curved tube
($R = 9.82$ m) made of nickel-coated, borated glass plates. The guide is adjusted
inside a stainless-steel vacuum container, closed at the entrance by a thin (0.1 mm)
aluminium sheet and at the exit by a valve similar to the safety valve, which
prevents a membrane from isolating the main guide during interference with the
experiments. This guide is placed inside a removable shielding with a maximum
thickness of 20 cm of steel and 50 cm of paraffin. A view of this guide and of its
shield is shown in Fig.3.

The gap (30 mm) between the windows of the in-pile and the out-of-pile
parts is equipped with a short guide section sealed by a compressible seal and
evacuated.

A clean, secondary vacuum ($10^{-5} - 10^{-4}$ torr) is maintained both in the in-pile
and the out-of-pile guides by means of sorption pumps and ion pumps.

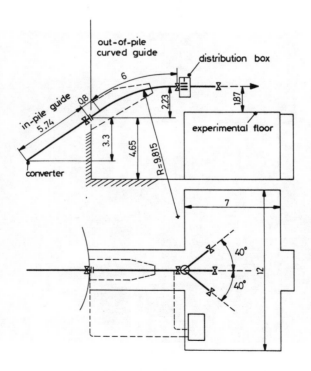

FIG.4.   General lay-out of instrument.

1.3. "Distribution box"

A "distribution box" which contains movable sections of guides, which could distribute, in time sharing, the beam in three directions, 40° left and right and straight on. The curved sections (R = 0.5 m) are made of thin nickel-coated glass sheets fixed in grooves inside nickel-coated plastic plates, with a spacing of 2−3 cm.

The lay-out and the dimensions of the instrument and its experimental area are shown in Fig.4.

2. THEORETICAL SPECTRA

The neutron spectra which could theoretically be obtained by an ideal rectangular curved guide are:

for UCN: $\lambda > \lambda_1$ of the reflecting material,

$$\frac{d\phi}{d\lambda} = \frac{\phi}{4\pi} \frac{2\lambda_T^4}{\lambda^5}$$

for VCN: $\lambda \ll \lambda_1$ [1],

the spectra vary according to the vertical abscissa in the section (x = 0 at the top, x = a at the bottom):

$$\frac{d\phi}{d\lambda} = \frac{\phi}{4\pi} \frac{8\lambda_T^4}{\lambda^3 \lambda_1^2} \sqrt{1 - \frac{x}{a} \frac{\lambda_*^2}{\lambda^2}}$$

When averaged over the whole section, the mean spectra are given by

$$\frac{d\phi}{d\lambda} = \frac{\phi}{4\pi} \frac{16\lambda_T^4}{3\lambda_1^2 \lambda_*^2 \lambda} \left[1 - \left(1 - \frac{\lambda_*^2}{\lambda^2}\right)^{3/2}\right] \text{ for } \lambda_* < \lambda < \lambda_1$$

and

$$\frac{d\phi}{d\lambda} = \frac{\phi}{4\pi} \frac{16\lambda_T^4}{3\lambda_1^2 \lambda_*^2 \lambda} \text{ for } \lambda < \lambda_*$$

where ϕ is the thermal flux at the moderator at a reactor power of
57 MW = 6×10^{14} n·cm^{-2}·s^{-1}, λ_T is the wavelength of neutrons at temperature T
of the moderator ($\lambda_T = 1.69$ Å for T = 333 K), λ_1 is the limit wavelength for the
reflecting material (= 645 Å for stainless steel); λ_* is the "characteristic" wavelength of the guide (= $\lambda_1 \sqrt{2a}/R = 77$ Å for the main curved guide with a = 7 cm
and R = 981.8 cm).

Example:

for UCN: $\lambda > 645$ Å, $\dfrac{d\phi}{d\lambda} = 2.45 \times 10^{15}/\lambda^5$ cm^{-2}·s^{-1}·Å^{-1}

for VCN: $100 < \lambda < 400$ Å, the flux is homogeneous over the guide section

$$\frac{d\phi}{d\lambda} = 7.5 \times 10^9/\lambda^3 \text{ cm}^{-2}\cdot\text{s}^{-1}\cdot\text{Å}^{-1}$$

3. EXPERIMENTAL SPECTRA

3.1. The "direct" time-of-flight (TOF) measurements

The TOF set-up, as seen in Fig.3, includes:

A chopper: the thin (5 mm) disc has a circular opening of 6.7 cm diameter
at a radius of 20 cm; thus, the duty cycle is 4.25%. The angular velocity may be
varied between 60 and 300 rev/min in order to provide an acceptable resolution in
the whole TOF range.

A 200-cm flight path made of an internally polished stainless-steel tube of
6.7 cm diameter.

A 5-cm-thick detector, filled with helium-3 at a pressure of 11 torr, diluted in
argon at a pressure of 1.2 b in order to have a low efficiency at small wavelengths
(lower than about 1.5% at 2.38 Å). The entrance window is a thin (50 μm)
aluminium sheet supported by a stainless-steel grid. Its estimated efficiency for
UCN is about 60%.

The conventional TOF method, which measures flux per unit of the axial
component v_z of the velocity, gives reliable results as long as the neutron velocities
are high (say, more than 30 m·s^{-1}). The measured spectra of such VCN are given
in Fig.5, either an averaged spectrum over the whole section, or detailed spectra
according to the abscissa x from the top of the guide section. The spectra are
corrected for the detector efficiency. A rough extrapolation of the spectrum of
the cold beam H 18 of HFR is added to indicate the domain where the VCN
source provides higher intensities.

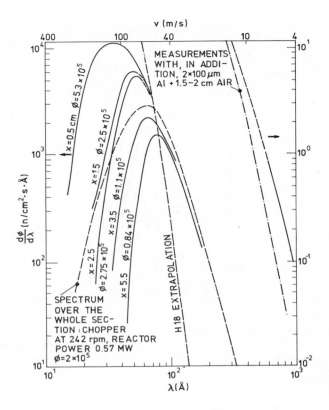

FIG.5.   VCN spectra, corrected for detector efficiency.

For UCN and VCN, with velocities not high compared to v_1, the angle θ of the zigzag path in the flight path guide is no longer negligible. For example, a spectrum at $v_z < v_1$ for an incident flux ϕ with a Maxwellian distribution and in the extreme case of a cosine angular distribution will be given by

$$\frac{d\varphi}{dv_z}\,dv_z = \int_\theta \frac{\phi}{4\pi}\,\frac{2v^3}{v_T^4}\,dv\,\cos\theta\,2\pi\sin\theta\,d\theta$$

and, with $v_z = v\cos\theta$ and v_T at temperature T of the converter:

$$\frac{d\varphi}{dv_z} = \frac{\phi}{2v_T^4}\left[(v_z v_1^2 - v_z^3) + v_z^3\right] = \frac{\phi}{2v_T^4}\,v_1^2 v_z$$

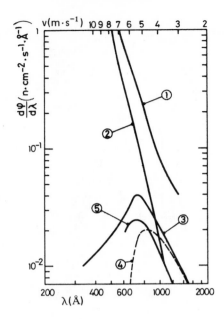

FIG.6.   *UCN spectra, without correction:*
(1) TOF uncollimated; (2) TOF collimated; (3) "filtered" TOF, measured; (4) "filtered"
TOF, calculated with the same asymptote as (3); (5) gravity spectrometer.

where the first term in the bracket represents the UCN contribution and the
second one the VCN one.

Then, $d\varphi/dv_z$ (or $d\varphi/d\lambda$) is proportional to v_z(or λ^{-3}) and φ integrated between
$0 < v_z < v_1$ would be $\varphi = (\phi/4)\ v_1^4/v_T^4$ in contrast to the opposite extreme case of
monodirectional neutrons ($v_z = v$), where $d\varphi/dv$ (or $d\varphi/d\lambda$) is proportional to v^3 (or
λ^5) and $\varphi = (\phi/8)\ v_1^4/v_T^4$, thus just half of the value for the other case.

Figure 6 shows the spectra taken without and with rough collimator (polyethylene coating of the end of the flight guide over a length of 1.25 times the tube
diameter). A fit with a λ^n curve gives, respectively, $n = 4.06$ without and $n = 6.02$
with collimator; these values are higher than expected, but can be explained by a
contribution of the estimated overall transmission of the instrument (roughly
proportional to $\lambda^{-1.6}$) as well as by the fact that the UCN flux is more forward-
anisotropic than a cosine distribution.

The integrated UCN flux is

$\approx\ 107\ cm^{-2} \cdot s^{-1}$ in the uncollimated case with a proportion of VCN; and

$\approx\ \ \ 31\ cm^{-2} \cdot s^{-1}$ in the collimated case with no VCN, but loss of UCN.

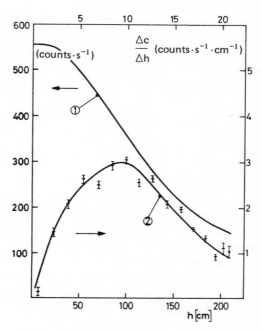

FIG.7. Gravity spectrometer:
(1) integral counting rate; (2) spectrum $\Delta c/\Delta h$.

3.2. The "filtered" TOF measurement

An attempt has been made to measure a TOF spectrum of UCN after elimination of VCN and re-homogenization of the angular UCN distribution. For this purpose, a U-shaped guide, constructed with four 90° elbows (rough, but electro-polished stainless steel) was inserted before the chopper.

The measured spectrum given in Fig.6 is still above the theoretical TOF spectrum of a pure-UCN TOF spectrum with cosine distribution. Thus, it includes a VCN contribution further demonstrated by the counting rate below the λ_1 cut-off. The integrated flux for $\lambda > \lambda_1$ is about 18 cm$^{-2} \cdot$s^{-1}.

3.3. The gravity spectrometer

This is an alternative to the TOF methods for UCN spectra measurements [2]. It is also a U-shaped guide, constructed with the elbows described previously, but having, in addition, straight guide sections. It can be rotated about the horizontal axis of the main beam so that the elevation h of the axis of its upper part, above the horizontal plane of the beam, can be varied from 0 to + 211.3 cm, which is more than the maximum elevation which neutrons reflected at any angle by stainless steel can reach : h_1 = 196 cm plus the tube diameter, 6.7 cm.

The total UCN flux is taken as the difference in the counting rates at h = 0 and at h = 211.3 cm, i.e. φ = 12 n·cm^{-2}·s^{-1}; the UCN spectrum defined as dc/dh is given in Fig.7.

3.4. Bottle experiment

A neutron bottle experiment may be used to measure the UCN flux. Such a bottle has been made with a 224-cm-long, 6.7-cm-diameter polished stainless-steel tube (cross-section 35 cm^2, volume 7840 cm^3) with two valves, V_1 and V_2, at both ends. One end is fitted to the main guide and the other one to a 90°-elbow followed by a 79-cm guide tube leading to the detector.

The UCN are no longer selected by the geometry (the steady-state counting rate of about 9000 counts per second, with the two valves open, is mainly background, when compared to the 560 counts per second of the gravity spectrometer in horizontal position), but by storing UCN during times where faster neutrons are eliminated. For this purpose, V_1 is first held open and V_2 closed for the

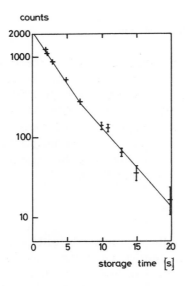

FIG.8.   Stored neutron counts as a function of storage time.

TABLE I. CALCULATED LOSS FACTORS IN THE DIFFERENT PARTS
OF THE INSTRUMENT

$v_z (m \cdot s^{-1})$		5	10	20	40
Flux depression in light water of converter		1.5	1.5	1.5	1.5
Converter window (0.7 mm Zircaloy)		1.46	1.27	1.13	1.06
Lack of reflecting surface at the diffusion weld, 22 mm		1.11	1.09	1.06	1.04
Gap at reactor face: (a) 0.1 mm Al foil, 0.2 mm AG3 foil, 30 mm without guide, 37 mm air		2.66	1.90	1.41	1.19
(b) two 0.1 mm Al foils		(1.19)	(1.09)	(1.03)	(1.02)
Miscellaneous gaps, holes, etc... equivalent to 13 mm without guide		1.11	1.08	1.05	1.03
Enlargement from 35 cm^2 (round) to 49 cm^2 (square) cross-section		1.4	1.4	1.4	1.4
Reflection losses (1.25% per reflection) of the different guides		5.86	3.13	1.9	1.4
Overall loss	(a)	58.9	18.6	6.9	4
	(b)	(26.3)	(10.7)	(5.2)	(3.4)
Detector efficiency in TOF experiment		0.63	0.62	0.5	0.33
Ratio of theoretical to measured TOF values (corrected for detector efficiency)		47	25	9.5	4.7

(a) State at the time of the TOF measurements.
(b) Present state after improvement.

filling of the bottle. Then, V_1 is closed and V_2 opened after a variable time. The
counting rate as a function of time gives the emptying time (i.e. the UCN lifetime in the bottle with one valve open: T open) and the total number of UCN
still in the bottle after a given storage time. These numbers, as a function of the
storage times, give the decay time of UCN in the closed bottle, T closed, and, by
extrapolation to the storage time equal to zero, the equilibrium density of UCN,

ρ_0 in the filling phase. Then, the input UCN flux may be deduced from the measurements by using the formula:

$$\varphi = \frac{\rho_0 V}{S T_{open}}$$

Total counts as a function of the storage time are given in Fig.8. The extrapolated value to $t_{storage} = 0$ is 2200, i.e. we have an equilibrium density of 0.28 cm^{-3}. The decay time in the closed bottle varies from 3.4 s at $t_s < 7$ s to 5.2 s for $t_s > 10$ s. Besides, T_{open} has been measured as 1.7 s. Thus, the input flux is 37 cm$^{-2} \cdot$ s^{-1}.

4. DISCUSSION

The various raw experimental results presented here are directly representative of the final performances of the instrument only for VCN with velocities higher than 20–30 m·s^{-1}. For VCN of lower velocities, and mainly for UCN, important corrections have to be made to the experimental results in order to take into account:

(1) the fact that, at the times of the various experiments, the states of the instrument were different from the final one and, moreover, different from one experiment to the next one.

(2) specific reasons for losses in each type of experiment (gaps, valves, elbows, efficiency of the detector, etc...)

Only the cases of direct TOF and of bottle experiments for which the corrections are easier to make will be considered here.

4.1. Direct TOF measurements

Table I presents the calculated loss factors for the various parts of the instrument. In TOF measurements the gap at the reactor face was in state (a) and has been improved to state (b) for the other experiments. The overall loss factors agree with the experimental values (i.e. the ratio of theoretical to experimental values corrected for detector efficiency).

The actual UCN flux in the final state will be obtained by multiplying the experimental value by:

the inverse of detector efficiency = 1.59;
the factor due to improvement of the gap 2.66/1.19 = 2.23.

Thus, the upper and lower limits of the UCN flux ($v < 6.2$ m·s^{-1}) are given by:

380 n·cm^{-2}·s^{-1} (uncollimated case)
120 n·cm^{-2}·s^{-1} (collimated case)

4.2. Bottle measurements

The various reasons for loss in this measurement and their corresponding loss factors are:

During bottle filling:
Losses into walls and holes in the bottle:	1.4
Losses through the V_1 valve gap when open:	1.7

During emptying:
Losses into walls and holes in the bottle and in the guide to the detector:	1.6
Losses through the V_2 valve gap when open:	2.1
Inverse of detector efficiency:	1.22
overall factor	9.75

Thus, the corrected UCN flux ($v < 6.2$ m·s^{-1}) deduced from the bottle experiment is 360 n·cm^{-2}·s^{-1}.

REFERENCES

[1]   MAIER-LEIBNITZ, H., SPRINGER, T., Reactor Sci. Technol. (J. Nucl. Energy A/B) **17** (1963) 216.
[2]   GROSHEV, L.V., et al., JINR preprint. P3–5392.

DISCUSSION

W. SCHMATZ: Is it possible to provide this UCN source with a cold moderator and/or a converter?

P. AGERON: In principle, yes.

V.I. LUSHCHIKOV: How stable is the intensity in the channel?

P. AGERON: The intensity has not yet been monitored because the many changes that had to be made in the set-up would have made monitoring meaningless. Now that the set-up is in its final state monitoring will be carried out.

L.A. VINHAS: What kind of detectors were used in the various methods, and why do you have a different efficiency factor for each case?

P. AGERON: We used detectors with helium-3 diluted in argon. They differed in their entrance windows, which were either 50 μm aluminium foil or 12 μm titanium foil.

LIQUID ORTHO-DEUTERIUM AS A CONVERTER FOR ULTRA-COLD NEUTRONS

M. UTSURO[†], M. HETZELT
Institut Laue-Langevin,
Grenoble

Abstract

LIQUID ORTHO-DEUTERIUM AS A CONVERTER FOR ULTRA-COLD NEUTRONS.
   Theoretical calculations of UCN gain factors of liquid ortho- and para-deuterium are performed, taking into account the effects of intermolecular interferences and liquid dynamics in deuterium. Calculated results of UCN production and total cross-sections give very different values from those based on the gas model. The calculation gives a UCN gain factor of 100 for a liquid ortho-deuterium converter if used in combination with a Maxwellian neutron spectrum of 50 K. An experiment to measure the UCN gain factor of liquid ortho-deuterium at 20 K was carried out. The experimental gain factor is about 3 times larger than the value calculated on the basis of the gas model and in good agreement with the result of the present calculation.

1. INTRODUCTION

   Recent interest in ultra cold neutron (UCN) experiments is leading us to think in terms of more intense UCN sources. A number of solid converter materials have already been used to produce UCN [1-3] and with these UCN sources a number of experiments have been carried out.
   However, from the theoretical point of view, the most attractive materials for converters are low temperature molecular liquids such as liquid hydrogen or liquid deuterium, since they can give a large inelastic scattering cross section to produce UCN due to the excitation of molecular rotations and to the nearly free translational motions of the molecules. This fact is already shown in the high UCN gains obtained from calculations on liquid hydrogen and deuterium [4], and also from the recent experimental result on liquid hydrogen [5].
   In the present paper, various important properties of an UCN converter material are studied in detail, and the advantages of low temperature molecular liquids are recognized. In particular, the coherent contribution to the scattering cross section due to the liquid structure of liquid deuterium, which was ignored in the previous theoretical study [4], is taken

---

[†] On leave from Research Reactor Institute, Kyoto University, Osaka, Japan.

into account in estimating the UCN gain factor[1] . Further, a
measurement of the UCN gain factor of liquid deuterium is also
reported and the result indicates that the coherent effects
are important. Ortho-deuterium is preferable to normal deuterium as an UCN converter material since most of the molecules
in this liquid are taking the rotational ground state. Thus
an UCN converter of liquid ortho-deuterium inserted in cold
neutron flux gives one of the highest UCN gain factors ever
reported.

2. DESIRABLE PROPERTIES OF UCN CONVERTER MATERIALS

We consider here a sufficiently thick UCN converter with
a flat surface inserted in an isotropic homogeneous flux
$\Phi_o(E_o)$ of thermal or cold neutrons. Then the UCN flux extracted from the converter surface into a solid angle $\Delta\Omega$ is
written as

$$\Phi_u(E_u) = \frac{\Delta\Omega}{4\pi} \frac{1}{\Sigma_t(E_u)} \int_0^\infty \Phi_o(E_o)\Sigma_s(E_o \to E_u)dE_o, \tag{1}$$

E_o: energy of the incident neutron; E_u: energy of the UCN;
$\Sigma_s(E_o \to E_u)$: macroscopic cross section for UCN production;
Σ_t: total macroscopic cross section.
This equation leads to the following general properties
desirable for the converter material:

2.1 UCN production

The inelastic cross section $\Sigma_s(E_o \to E_u)$ should be as big
as possible. From this point low temperature liquid of light
molecules is attractive since it will have a larger production cross section than solids from heavy molecules. The
energy transferred in the downscattering process, from thermal
to ultra cold, is generally larger than the energies of the
intermolecular interactions in low temperature liquids, therefore the application of the gas model will give a rough picture. This is obtained by putting the energy and momentum
transfers in the formula [6] equal to the energy and momentum
of the incident neutrons, respectively, and the conditions
for a big production cross section become as follows

(i)   for rotational elastic processes: low incident
      neutron energy as well as low molecular mass and a
      large coherent scattering amplitude are advan-
      tageous.

(ii) for rotational inelastic processes: near the peak
      of the cross section for rotational transitions,
      the UCN production cross section is, roughly
      speaking, inversely proportional to the incident
      energy; therefore molecules with low energy rota-
      tional excitations are advantageous.

---

[1] UCN gain factor is defined here as the ratio between the UCN intensities from the converter of the
selected material and from that of light water at room temperature with the same geometry.

2.2   UCN removal

A small total cross section $\Sigma_t(E_u)$ for ultra cold neutrons is desirable, which makes a converter made of a coherent scatterer at low temperatures attractive. Especially, in the case of liquid para-hydrogen and liquid deuterium considerable decrease of the total cross section has been observed [7] in the energy region below 3 meV, due to intermolecular interference. This fact should give a large improvement in UCN gain as compared to the simple gas model, which ignores intermolecular interference.

We conclude that liquid ortho-deuterium can be a very good converter when used in combination with an incoming spectrum of cold neutrons.

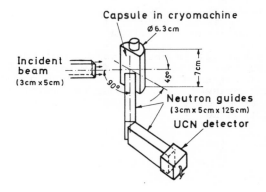

FIG.1.   Experimental set-up.

3.   THEORETICAL CALCULATION OF THE UCN GAIN

The following theoretical calculation for the UCN flux takes the actual experimental geometry shown in Fig. 1 into account. So, Eq. (1) should be modified a little and becomes as follows:

$$\Phi_u(E_u) \cong \Delta\Omega \int_0^\infty \frac{\Phi_o(E_o)\Sigma(E_o \to E_u; 90^\circ)}{\Sigma_t(E_o) + \Sigma_t(E_u)} \, dE_o , \tag{2}$$

where $\Sigma(E_o \to E_u; 90^\circ)$ means the differential scattering cross section in the converter material with a scattering angle of 90°. In Eq. (2), the converter is supposed to be sufficiently thick and illuminated by a large incident beam, while the solid angle of detection $\Delta\Omega$ is assumed to be narrow.

The differential scattering cross section for a molecule in liquid ortho-deuterium with the assumption of free molecular rotation and neglecting the intermolecular interference can be written as [6]:

$$\frac{d^2\sigma}{d\Omega d\epsilon}\Big|_{self}^{ortho} = \frac{k}{k_o} \sum_{J=0,2,4..} P_J \Big[(4\ a_{coh}^2 + \frac{5}{2}\ a_{inc}^2) \sum_{J'=0,2..} +$$

$$+ \frac{3}{2}\ a_{inc}^2 \sum_{J'=1,3..} \Big] \cdot (2J'+1) S_t(\kappa,\omega) \sum_{\ell=|J'-J|}^{J'+J} C^2(JJ'\ell;00) j_\ell^2(\kappa b), \tag{3}$$

where a_{coh} and a_{inc} are the coherent and incoherent scattering amplitudes, respectively, for a deuterium atom, 2b is the interatomic distance in the molecule, C the Clebsch-Gordan coefficient, and j_ℓ is the spherical Bessel function of ℓ-th order. Further, only the vibrational ground state is considered in Eq. (3).

$S_t(\kappa,\omega)$ in Eq. (3) is the translational part of the molecular scattering law. If we assume free translation of the molecules in $S_t(\kappa,\omega)$ then the results of the gas model are obtained. In the present calculation, we employ the Fourier transform of a model of the translational intermediate scattering function Eq. (4) [8]:

$$I_t(\kappa,t) = \exp(-A_o\alpha^2)\ \Big\{\exp\Big[-2d\alpha^2(\sqrt{t^2+c^2+1/4}-c)\Big]+$$

$$+ \exp\Big[-d\alpha^2/c\cdot(t^2+1/4)\Big]\Big[\exp(A\alpha^2 e^{-\omega_o^2\ t^2/4})-1\Big]\Big\}, \tag{4}$$

where $\alpha^2 = \hbar^2\kappa^2/(2MkT)$, with M the molecular mass; t,d and c are similar dimensionless quantities representing time, the self-diffusion coefficient and the time delay for achieving the asymptotic diffusive motion in the liquid [9]. Further, ω_o is a parameter concerning intermolecular excitations in the liquid [8].

We now consider the intermolecular interference.

$$\frac{d^2\sigma}{d\Omega d\epsilon} = \frac{d^2\sigma}{d\Omega d\epsilon}\Big|_{self} + \frac{d^2\sigma}{d\Omega d\epsilon}\Big|_{int.} \tag{5}$$

Here the second term on the right-hand side represents the contribution from intermolecular interferences. For the calculation of this term, we employ the convolution approximation for the dynamics of liquids [10], which can be written in the present case as

$$\frac{d^2\sigma}{d\Omega d\epsilon}\Big|_{int.} = \frac{k}{k_o}4a_{coh}^2[S(\kappa)-1]\cdot S_t(\kappa,\omega)\cdot[\sin(\kappa b)/(\kappa b)]^2. \tag{6}$$

In Eq. (6), $S(\kappa)$ denotes the static structure factor in the liquid.

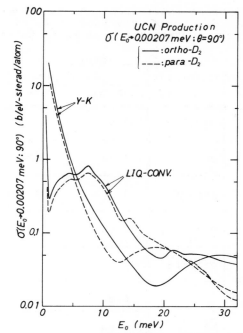

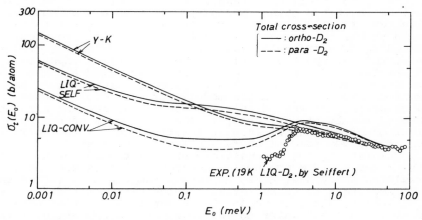

FIG.2.   Theoretical UCN production cross-sections for liquid deuterium at 20 K.
Y-K: gas model [6]; LIQ-CONV.: calculation based on liquid model [8] with the convolution
approximation [10] for the intermolecular interference term.

FIG.3.   Theoretical total cross-section for liquid deuterium at 20 K.
Y-K: gas model [6]; LIQ-SELF: liquid model [8] neglecting intermolecular interferences;
LIQ-CONV.: liquid model [8] considering the interference effects in the form of convolution
approximation [10]. Open circles: experimental results on liquid deuterium at 19 K by
Seiffert [7].

TABLE 1. Comparison of theoretical and experimental UCN gain factors for liquid deuterium converter at 20 K. The temperature of the incident neutron spectrum T_n is taken to be 300 K and 50 K.

Method	Geometry	Converter material	Gain factor		Remarks
			T_n = 300 K	T_n = 50 K	
	Eq. (1)	Equil.-D_2	3.5	60	Ref. [4]
Gas model	Eq. (2)	ortho-D_2	4.24	87.2	UCN velocity v_u=20m/s
		para-D_2	4.16	81.2	
Liquid model	Eq. (2)	ortho-D_2	13.6	101	
		para-D_2	14.2	89.0	
Experiment	Eq. (2), but finite size converter	Equil.-D_2	6.88	–	$\bar{v}_u$=49m/s
			9.63	–	$\bar{v}_u$=25m/s
			10.2	–	$\bar{v}_u$=20m/s

The theoretical differential and total scattering cross sections in liquid ortho- and para-deuterium are calculated using Eqs. (3)-(6). For the parameters which enter into the liquid model, the values for liquid hydrogen [8] are used, reduced for the molecular mass difference. For $S(\kappa)$ in liquid deuterium the reported result of the diffraction experiment [11] is used[2] . In Fig. 2 the results calculated for the UCN production cross sections from the present liquid model are compared with those from gas model. Further, Fig. 3 shows the comparison of the calculated total cross section with the measured result of Seiffert [7]. The importance of the contribution of the intermolecular interference for the estimation of the UCN removal cross section is apparent.

Theoretical UCN intensities were calculated using these results for the UCN production and removal cross sections. Maxwellian spectra with two different temperatures (300 K and 50 K) were used to characterize the incoming neutrons.

Similar calculations on UCN intensities are also performed for a light water converter at room temperature, using a simplified scattering formula for light water [12]. From the comparisons between the calculated results of these two

---

[2] The values for $S(\kappa)$ near $\kappa = 0$ were a little modified with respect to the reported result to make them consistent with the compressibility derived from P-V-T data [11].

different converter materials, the theoretical UCN gain
factors for liquid ortho- and para-deuterium are obtained,
and compared with the experimental values in TABLE 1.

4.   MEASUREMENT OF UCN GAIN FACTOR ON LIQUID ORTHO-DEUTERIUM

An experiment to measure the UCN gain factor of liquid
ortho-deuterium was carried out, and the result is compared
with the accurate theoretical calculation taking the effects
of intermolecular interferences and of liquid dynamics into
account.

The most important difference is brought about in the
UCN removal cross section by the effects of intermolecular
interferences as mentioned above. Therefore, according to
Eq. (1), an experiment with incident neutrons of thermal
energies is equally apt to reveal the significance of the
effect on the UCN gain factor. In the present experiment,
the thermal neutron beam from the guide tube H22 of ILL-HFR
was used. The outline of the experimental arrangement is
shown in Fig. 1.

The size of the converter capsule (6.3 cm$^{\emptyset}$ x 7 cm) is
determined by the mean free path of the incident neutrons in
liquid deuterium ($\sim$ 4 cm) and the restriction coming from
the cryomachine. The straight surface of the aluminium capsule of semi-circular cross section is placed 45° to the
axis of the incoming beam. The capsule is mounted in a cryomachine and kept at 20 K. The equilibrium concentration of
ortho-deuterium (98 % is ortho at 20 K) is obtained in the capsule by insertion of some water-free Cr_2O_3 catalyst into the
capsule before the experiment. To detect UCN emerging from
the surface of the converter, a neutron guide is placed
under 90° to the axis of the incoming beam as close as
possible to the capsule, covering about 7 % of the solid
angle of the neutrons scattered. This UCN guide was made from
two sections, and the second half could be placed at an
angle with respect to the first half, thus cutting off faster
neutrons. Data were taken at three different angles (8°, 17°,
25°). The neutrons were detected at the exit of the guide
tube by a thin-walled UCN detector [5]. The mean velocity of
the neutrons was determined from the transmission ratio of
copper foils inserted in front of the detector. Foils with
a thickness of 0.1 mm and 0.2 mm were used. A thickness of
1.8 mm was used to measure the contribution of faster
neutrons. These measurements were repeated for each angle
between two sections of neutron guide. The results obtained
for the mean velocity by this absorption method agreed well
with the value calculated from the angle between the two
sections of the neutron guide.

After the measurements with liquid deuterium were accomplished, liquid deuterium was replaced by light water at
room temperature, without changing the geometry of the set-
up, and the whole set of measurements was repeated with
light water. From these two sets of measurements the UCN
gain factor for the case of an incident spectrum of thermal
neutrons was obtained, as shown in TABLE 1.

It is obvious that there remains some difference between measurement and calculation, but this can be explained with the finite dimensions of the converter capsule which was assumed infinite in the theoretical calculation, and with the fact that the real incoming spectrum was not quite a Maxwellian spectrum, with the deviation from the Maxwellian form occurring especially in the low energy tail of the distribution.

5. CONCLUSIONS

The calculated result of the UCN gain factor for a liquid ortho-deuterium converter in combination with an incident thermal neutron beam shows good agreement with the measured results. The large difference between the calculated gain factors for the liquid model and for the gas model indicates that it is important to consider the liquid effects for the correct understanding of the performance of a liquid deuterium converter. Doing so, the liquid ortho-deuterium converter combined with an incoming beam of cold neutrons gives a very large theoretical UCN gain factor, about a hundred, which is one of the highest values ever reported. Thus, the combination of a liquid deuterium converter with a cold neutron source in a reactor is a very attractive concept for an intense UCN source.

ACKNOWLEDGEMENT

The authors would like to thank Dr. P. Ageron for his support and encouragement to the present study. Further, much valuable contribution by Mr. R. Ritter who carried out the whole of the technical preparations in the present experiment should be acknowledged. We are also much indebted to Mr. G. Germain for his kind supply of the equipment.

REFERENCES

[1] KOSVINTSEV, Yu. Yu., KULAGIN, E.N., KUSHNIR, Yu.A., MOROZOV, V.I., STRELKOV, A.V., Nucl. Instr. Methods 143 (1977) 133.

[2] ALTAREV, I.S., et al., Communications of the Leningrad Inst. of Nucl. Phys. to the name of B.P. Konstantinov No. 246 (1976).

[3] STEYERL, A., Nucl. Instr. Methods 101 (1972) 295.

[4] AKHMETOV, E.Z., GOLIKOV, V.V., KAIPOV, D.K., KONKS, V.A., STRELKOV, A.V., JINR Communications R3-8470, Dubna (1974).

[5] GERMAIN, G., "Contribution au Développment à la Réalisation et aux Essais d'une Source de Neutrons Ultra-Froids" Memoire, Grenoble (1977).

[6] YOUNG, J.A., KOPPEL, J.U., Phys. Rev. 135 (1964) A603.

[7]   SEIFFERT, W.D., EUR 4455d (1970).

[8]   UTSURO, M., Z. Phys. B27 (1977) 111.

[9]   EGELSTAFF, P.A., SCHOFIELD, P., Nucl. Sci. Eng. 12
       (1962) 260.

[10] VINEYARD, G.H., Phys.Rev. 110 (1958) 999.

[11] TALHOUK, S.J., HARRIS, P.M., WHITE, D., ERICKSON, R.A.,
       J. Chem. Phys. 48 (1968) 1273.

[12] UTSURO, M., J. Nucl. Sci. Technol. 10 7 (1973) 428.

DISCUSSION

G.L. SQUIRES: How long did you wait to achieve the ortho/para equilibrium ratio at 20 K?

M. UTSURO: Measurement of UCN intensities was started about 15 hours after the beginning of condensation. Constancy of the intensity was assured for several hours by the completely filled capsule.

G.L. SQUIRES: How did you measure the ortho/para ratio?

M. UTSURO: The ortho/para ratio was not measured in our experiment. In the experiment by Germain, who used a similar device on liquid hydrogen, the neutron transmission ratio shows that the equilibrium para/ortho ratio is attained within about 10 hours.

A. STEYERL: The gain factor calculated for ortho-deuterium is about 100 at room temperature. How does this compare with the value for a Maxwell spectrum at the converter temperature of 20 K?

M. UTSURO: The gain factor for a 20 K Maxwell spectrum is 225, which means that about half the thermal factor for 20 K was obtained in the present calculation on a 50 K incident spectrum.

A. STEYERL: Do I understand that the reason for the suggested two-stage process with a converter at 20 K and an incident spectrum at about 50 K is that it is technologically much easier to have a small converter — which allows a thin window — and a small cold source providing a 50 K spectrum, rather than to use a large D_2 cold source for the cold Maxwell spectrum?

M. UTSURO: That is correct.

V.I. LUSHCHIKOV: Do you plan to carry out new experiments with a cold initial neutron spectrum?

M. UTSURO: I am not planning any experiments with a cold initial neutron spectrum at present.

V.I. LUSHCHIKOV: What will be the gain factor for the 20 K initial spectrum?

M. UTSURO: About 200.

STUDY OF A COLD NEUTRON SOURCE

M.J. VALO
Reactor Laboratory,
Technical Research Centre of Finland,
Espoo,
Finland

Abstract

STUDY OF A COLD NEUTRON SOURCE.

A hydrogen cold neutron source has been constructed allowing wide variation of density, temperature and ortho-hydrogen concentration. The maximum cold neutron flux was obtained with pararich hydrogen at the lowest temperature attained. Substitution of normal hydrogen by parahydrogen doubled the cold neutron flux. The effect of density and orthoconcentration is explained qualitatively.

Description of the apparatus

A hydrogen cold neutron moderator was installed in the centre of the tangential beam tube of our 250 kW Triga Mark II reactor. The moderator chamber was designed to withstand pressures up to 25 atm allowing for fluid dense enough even around 33 K near the critical point of hydrogen. Figure 1 shows the details of the moderator chamber. The moderator chamber is cooled by a Philips PGH 105 cryogenerator. Thermal connection between the cryogenerator and the moderator chamber is provided by circulated helium gas. A double cylindrical construction aims at a low moderator temperature and the safe use of hydrogen. Such a massive construction is possible in a low flux reactor with moderate gamma heating only. The material of the moderator chamber is Al+3 % Mg, the hydrogen volume being 2600 cm^3. Thermal insulation is provided by vacuum and highly polished surfaces.

Hydrogen begins to condense into the moderator after about 2 hours from the start of the cryogenerator. The condensation takes about 1 hour. The temperature of the moderator chamber is controlled by appropriate heat input to the helium heat transfer system. The hydrogen storage consists of 12 bottles of 40 litres each with hydrogen at about 25 atm. The number of connected bottles determines the pressure-temperature path the moderator will follow during the cooling. In order to be able to change the orthohydrogen concentration a 10 cm^3 NiO-cathalyzer was placed inside the moderator chamber at the construction stage. The rate of change of ortho-% after condensation of room temperature equilibrium gas is about 2 %/h at 30 K.

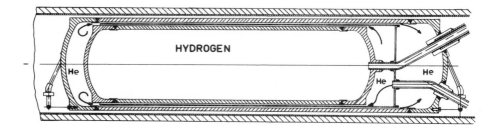

FIG.1. Moderator chamber.

Measurements

The pressure of the moderator is directly measured by a capacitive pressure gauge[1]. The moderator chamber, the storage space and the connecting pipes constitute a constant volume system. From the known partial volumes, the initial state, the temperature of the room temperature parts and the pressure of the system the average molar volume of the moderator can be calculated using known thermodynamic data for hydrogen /1/. Around the critical point, where the molar volume is sensitive to pressure and temperature, the accuracy of the temperature determination is good. The crucial assumption in converting molar volumes to temperatures is thermal equilibrium in the moderator, i.e. no bubbles exist in the moderator except at the liquid-gas phase separation curve. The estimated temperature difference between the centre and the surface of a cylindrical liquid hydrogen moderator is about 2.5 K, when the radiation absorbed in hydrogen is evaluated according to ref. /2/ and if only conduction of heat is considered. A temperature inhomogeneity of ±1.2 K does not lead to bubble formation.

The measurement of orthoconcentration of hydrogen is based on the difference in the thermal conductivity of the two forms. A standard room temperature thermal conductivity cell is employed[2]. Hydrogen sample from the moderator is drawn through a 0.3 mm i.d. stainless steel tube. A tube with 50 % ortho-flow was heated for checking whether back-conversion will appear in the capillary. The first signs of back-conversion were seen at temperatures higher than 200 ℃. It is belived that the orthohydrogen concentration in the measuring cell indicates the right value in the moderator. Well cathalyzed room temperature and liquid N_2-temperature reference hydrogen was used to span the ortho-scale.

---

[1] Bofors TYP TDS-1.
[2] Gow-Mac Instr.Co.Mod.10—454.

The neutron spectra were measured by the time-of-flight method. A curved-slit Cd-plated chopper with maximum transmission at 4.3 Å and a cut-off at 12 Å was used. To eliminate the back-ground caused by the broad chopper transmission for epicadmium and fast neutrons, a separate spectrum measured with 0.6 mm Cd in the beam was subtracted from the open beam spectrum. The difference spectrum is our slow neutron spectrum. We have no filters in the beam and use a flight path of 0.8 m, a multichannel analyzer channel width of 20 μs and detectors of the fission type. Except for the flight path of 0.8 m at 1 atm pressure the neutrons travel about 4 meters inside the insulation vacuum between the cold moderator and the fission detector.

The following corrections were made for the spectra: A dead time correction for the multichannel analyzer for both the open and the Cd-filtered beam. This correction amounted to from 8 % to 20 %. A correction for the detector efficiency assuming that the efficiency is proportional to $\Sigma(U235)_{fiss}$ and a standard correction for chopper transmission /3/. Finally the spectra were scaled to the reactor power and the relative efficiency of the detector used.

Results

Some general physical considerations apply to the problem of neutron moderation. Decrease of temperature always lowers the neutron temperature the more effectively the nearer the neutron temperature is to the moderator

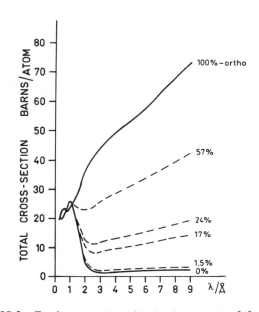

FIG.2.   Total cross-section of molecular hydrogen [4].

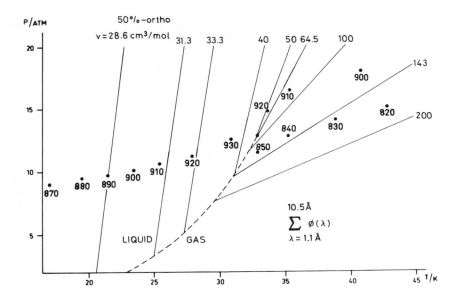

FIG.3. Total neutron flux from 1.1 to 10.5 Å in relative numbers.

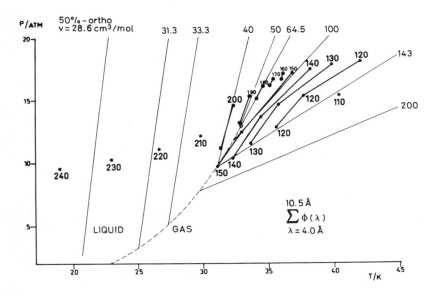

FIG.4. Total neutron flux from 4.0 to 10.5 Å. The numbers in Figs 3 and 4 are comparable.

temperature. The growth of density leads to a greater number
of neutron collisions which promotes good thermalization but
increases absorption. High density means also a small
leakage of neutrons and a change of the effective beam
source point usually towards a lower flux area in the reactor.
The effect of orthoconcentration on the neutron beam is not
obvious, either. Figure 2 shows the total neutron cross-
section of a hydrogen molecule. It is generally claimed
that the form of this figure leads to a great leakage of
cold neutrons. Unfortunately, the independent change of
temperature, density and orthoconcentration is strongly
limited by the thermodynamical properties of hydrogen.
Thus, without experiment little can be said about the optimum
condition of a cold moderator.

Figure 3 shows the integrated flux between 1.1Å and
10.5Å averaged over adjacent pressure and temperature points
and extrapolated to 50%-orthohydrogen. The total number has
a broad maximum around the critical point of hydrogen. Still
at v=620 cm^3/mole (T=130 K) the value is about 70 % from the
maximum value.

The slow decrease below the temperature corresponding
to the maximum can be explained as a combined effect of
increased absorption and the change of the effective beam
source point from the centre of the tangential beam tube to a
smaller flux. The decrease of the total flux at higher
temperatures is a result of the decrease in the scattering
power of the moderator. The fact that the position of the
maximum total flux is at a temperature low enough shows that a
total moderator length of 30 cm is not excessive. The
broadness of the maximum is a result of the slow change of flux
near the centre of the tangential beam tube.

Figure 4 depicts the total number of neutrons from 4Å to
10.5Å averaged the same way as in figure 3. The number of
cold neutrons grows continuously as the temperature decreases.
It can be concluded from the measurements around the critical
point where only density changes that density is the primary
parameter affecting the number of cold neutrons at temperatures
below about 45 K. This is understandable as the measured
spectra are not equilibrium spectra. If two Maxwellian
spectra are fitted to the measurements, the proportion of
the cold neutrons at about 30 K is from 15 % to 30 %, the warm
neutrons having a temperature > 100 K. Thus the principal
mechanism for increasing the number of cold neutrons is to
increase the moderating power, i.e. to increase the density
rather than to lower the moderator temperature.

The effect of orthoconcentration on the spectra can be
seen from figure 5, where the ratio of spectra of different
orthoconcentrations are drawn as a function of wavelength.
The reference spectrum contains 57 % orthohydrogen. The
detector intensity of the Cd-filtered beam was found to be
independent of orthoconcentration. The form of the total
neutron cross-section of molecular hydrogen gas shown in the
figure 2 can qualitatively explain the effect of orthoconcentration on the spectra. The increase of neutrons of
wavelength longer than 2Å can be said to be a result of
increasing leakage of these neutrons, i.e. of the increase of
the effective beam neutron source volume. The decrease in

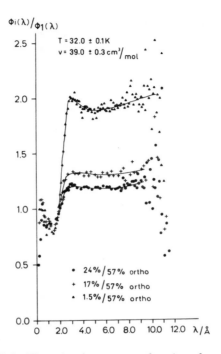

FIG.5.   The ratio of spectra as a function of wavelength.

the number of neutrons from 1Å to 2Å is due to moderation of
these neutrons to longer wavelengths. This is evident from
the calculated slowing-down power of parahydrogen /4/, which
has a pronounced peak between 1Å and 2Å. Figure 6 shows the
effect of orthocomposition at some other measuring points.
The effect does not seem to depend on temperature/density in
the limited range shown. Finally in figure 7 a few typical
time-of-flight spectra are given. This figure shows the
nonequilibrium character of the spectra.

Discussion

        Before the construction of the cold neutron source
H. Kalli made Monte Carlo simulations of hydrogen as moderator
in our geometry /5/. His purpose was mainly to find an optimum length for the moderator, but there is one point, T=35 K,
v=78 cm³/mole and 6.4 % ortho, where a comparison can be made
between a measured and a calculated spectrum in a limited
wavelength range from 2.5Å to 9.0Å. The agreement is
satisfactory, maximum discrepancy being about 10 %.

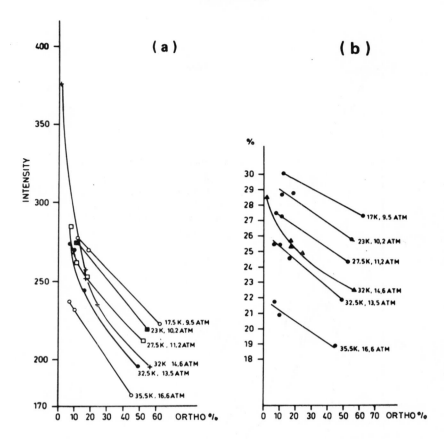

FIG.6. (a) The total neutron flux from 4.0 to 10.5 Å, and (b) the ratio of neutrons from 4.0 to 10.5 Å and from 1.1 to 10.5 Å in different operation points of the moderator.

Good neutron moderation and easy diffusion of neutrons from the moderator are both necessary when intense cold neutron beams are wanted. In pulsed neutron sources a short pulse is often an advantage. That is why the good neutron leakage properties of a parahydrogen cold moderator are sressed in this connection /6/, /7/. On the other hand, the high orthohydrogen cross-section for cold neutrons leading to small leakage but good moderation is considered as an advantage, even if the scattered neutrons gain energy in a transition from ortho to para /4/. The measurements concerning the effect of paraconcentration are also contradictory. Webb observed a 10 % increase in the flux of neutrons of longer wavelength than 8Å /8/. Ageron et.al. on the other hand found that the para form is inferior to the ortho form as a moderator /9/.

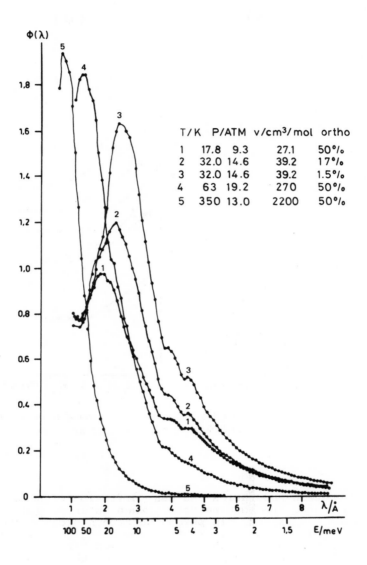

FIG. 7.   *Typical time-of-flight spectra.*

The calculations of Moon and Beynon are consistent with our observation of the neutron flux increase resulting from paraconcentration growth /10/. They calculated the transient cold neutron flux near a cold and a room temperature moderator surface. They found that even if the peak cold neutron flux on the cold moderator side is a bit larger in the ortho- than paramoderator, the opposite is true for longer distances than about 3 cm away from the surface if graphite or heavy water is the room temperature moderator. This should in big sources together with increased leakage favour a para-rich moderator. The inconsistent effect of para-% on the available cold neutron beam is perhaps mostly due to different geometries and even to different reactor moderators.

Conclusions

It is shown that density and orthohydrogen concentration are the important parameters in characterizing the neutron moderation in hydrogen. The effect of these two parameters is explained qualitatively. It was experimentally found that the hydrogen moderator should be as cold as possible and its paraconcentration as high as possible in our moderator shape and geometry. Parahydrogen looks like a good choice of a moderator if the available space in the reactor and costs rule out the use of deuterium.

References

/1/ Roder, H.M., Weber, L.A., Goodwin, R.D., NBS Monograf 94 (1965).

/2/ Leyers, H.J., Nukleonik 7 (1965) 300.

/3/ Marseguerra, M., Pauli, G., Nucl.Instr.Meth. 4 (1959) 140.

/4/ Koppel, J.U., Young, J.A., Nukleonik 8 (1966) 40.

/5/ Kalli, H., Acta Polytechnica Scandinavica PH 88 (1972).

/6/ Riccobono, G., Ardente, V., Rossi, G., EUR-4954e (1972) 427.

/7/ Rief, H., Hartman, J., Annals of Nucl.Energy 8 (1975) 521.

/8/ Webb, F.J., Reactor Science and Technology 17 (1963) 187.

/9/ Ageron, P., De Beaucourt, Ph., Harig, H.D., Lacaze, A., Livolant, M., Cryogenics 9 (1969) 42.

/10/ Moon, J.R., Beynon, T.D., J.Phys.D:Appl.Phys. 6 (1973) 427.

DISCUSSION

H. RAUCH *(Chairman)*: Have you also done experiments with deuterium, and do you expect deuterium to have definite advantages?

M.J. VALO: We have not done such experiments. I think the diameter of our source is too small for deuterium experiments.

ДВОЙНОЙ СПЕКТРОМЕТР
МЕДЛЕННЫХ НЕЙТРОНОВ ДИН-2К

В.А.ПАРФЕНОВ, П.С.КЛЕМЫШЕВ,
И.Г.МОРОЗОВ, А.Ф.ПАВЛОВ
Физико-энергетический институт,
Обнинск,
Союз Советских Социалистических Республик

Представлен М.Г.ЗЕМЛЯНОВ

Abstract—Аннотация

THE DIN-2K DOUBLE SLOW NEUTRON SPECTROMETER.
The paper describes a spectrometer based rigorously on the time-of-flight method. This method is used for monochromatization of the neutrons incident upon the sample and for analysis of the neutrons scattered by it. The DIN-2K double slow neutron spectrometer is being installed on the IBR-2 pulsed fast reactor at the Joint Institute for Nuclear Research, Dubna. The spectrometer is for a wide range of experiments on the physics of condensed media and achieves a resolution of 1 μs/m in the neutron energy range 0.001−1 eV.

ДВОЙНОЙ СПЕКТРОМЕТР МЕДЛЕННЫХ НЕЙТРОНОВ ДИН-2К.
В докладе представлен спектрометр, построенный последовательно на основе метода времени пролета (МВП). Монохроматизация падающих на исследуемый образец нейтронов и анализ рассеянных им нейтронов осуществляется МВП. Двойной спектрометр медленных нейтронов ДИН-2К создается на импульсном быстром реакторе ИБР-2 в Объединенном институте ядерных исследований в г.Дубне. Комплекс спектрометра позволит осуществить широкий класс экспериментов по физике конденсированных сред с разрешением 1 мкс/м в области энергий нейтронов 0,001-1 эВ.

1. ВВЕДЕНИЕ

Анализ исследований по физике конденсированных сред убедительно показывает, что экспериментальное и теоретическое исследование более тонких особенностей спектра неупругого рассеяния медленных нейтронов — ширин пиков, температурной зависимости их положения и формы, концентрационных зависимостей особенностей и т.п. — позволит получить ценную информацию не только о спектрах элементарных возбуждений, но также об их релаксационных характеристиках, о неоднородностях реальных кристаллов, о механизме диффузии и других микроскопических характеристиках реальных кристаллов. Исследования по физике реального кристалла представляют в настоящее время значительный интерес не только фундаментальный, но и прикладной в связи с широким применением в технике и промышленности достижений физики полупроводников, квантовых явлений в конденсированных средах, искусственных кристаллов и др. Современные ядерно-физические (в значительной степени нейтронные) методы исследований по физике твердого тела означают качественный переход от классических макроскопических исследований к исследованиям по физике реального кристалла, конденсированных сред на микроскопическом уровне. Эти исследования открывают новое направление изучения глубокой связи указанных выше микроскопических характеристик реального кристалла и конденсированных сред с их макроскопическими свойствами (термодинамическими, физико-механическими, электрофизическими) и, следовательно, дают возможность получения в будущем материалов с предельными свойствами.

Убедительную иллюстрацию этой глубокой связи микроскопических свойств конденсированных сред с макроскопическими явлениями в них представляют собой квантовые явления сверхтекучести и сверхпроводимости, связанные с микроскопическими характеристиками: спектром элементарных возбуждений и Бозе-Эйнштейновской конденсацией.

Указанное направление исследований требует все более совершенных методов и экспериментальной техники. Достаточно сказать, что со времени первого симпозиума по неупругому рассеянию медленных нейтронов (1960 г.) разрешение нейтронных спектрометров улучшилось примерно на два порядка. В то же время достигнутый к настоящему времени уровень разрешения ($\sim 10^{-4}$ эВ) не удовлетворяет современным требованиям и, тем более, перспективе исследований по физике реального кристалла и применению результатов этих исследований в различных областях науки и техники. Однако, отмеченная тенденция улучшения разрешения не может сохраняться сколь угодно долго без создания принципиально новых источников нейтронов, т.к. разрешение спектрометров в лучшем случае обратно пропорционально корню квадратному из интенсивности источника нейтронов, а источники нейтронов первого поколения (реакторы постоянной мощности) близки к своему пределу по потоку после пуска Гренобльского исследовательского пучкового реактора (предел определяется удельным энерговыделением

и ограниченной кампанией). Таким образом, первый путь
дальнейшего повышения параметров спектрометров, связан-
ный с созданием мощных реакторов постоянной мощности,
не может обеспечить перспективу исследований по физике
конденсированных сред. Второй путь связан с созданием
нейтронных источников второго (импульсные быстрые реакторы, бустеры) и третьего поколений (реакция (p,n) или,
возможно, термоядерная реакция с лазерным инициированием реакции). На такую перспективу указал в своем со-
общении на франко-советском симпозиуме в 1964 г.
А.П.Александров, а в докладах на японо-американском
симпозиуме [1] эта перспектива получила дальнейшее обо-
снование.

    В настоящем докладе представлен физический проект
спектрометра ДИН-2К на строящемся в г.Дубне реакторе
ИБР-2 [2]. Этот спектрометр является дальнейшим развитием спектрометров второго поколения, перспектива которых связана с импульсными источниками нейтронов и впервые была обоснована в работах на втором симпозиуме по
неупругому рассеянию медленных нейтронов в Чок-Ривере [3].

2. МЕТОД ВРЕМЕНИ ПРОЛЕТА В ИССЛЕДОВАНИЯХ ПО
ФИЗИКЕ КОНДЕНСИРОВАННЫХ СРЕД

    МВП, как метод спектрометрии нейтронов, применительно
к реакторам постоянной мощности развивался в условиях
конкуренции с нейтронными дифрактометрами, а позднее с
трехкристальными спектрометрами в исследованиях нейтронных спектров, ядерных сечений, атомной структуры и
динамики конденсированных сред [3,4].
    До применения в исследованиях по физике конденсиро-
ванных сред импульсных источников нейтронов (1960 г.)
кристалл-дифракционные методы в общем случае имели пре-
имущество в интенсивности монохроматических нейтронов,
поступающих в канал регистрации, на фактор

$$\frac{S}{2\pi R} \cdot f(v) \qquad\qquad (2.1)$$

где S — ширина щели ротора механического прерывателя,
R — радиус ротора, $f(v)$ — функция пропускания вращающейся
щели в зависимости от скорости нейтрона. Этот фактор в

зависимости от динамической скважности ротора и отличия от единицы коэффициента отражения кристалла в кристалл-дифракционном методе составляет величину 10^{-3}- 10^{-2}. Однако, в некоторых задачах МВП, даже применительно к реактору постоянной мощности, имеет равные или лучшие возможности. Это относится, в частности, к задачам измерения спектров нейтронов или закона рассеяния, в которых в МВП число каналов регистрации больше на фактор 10^2- 10^3, а одновременность измерений по всем каналам существенно улучшает качество результатов. Таким образом, интенсивность монохроматических нейтронов не является единственным критерием в определении спектрометрических возможностей или качества спектрометра и более того, в конечном счете, физическая задача определяет требования к параметрам спектрометра. Следовательно, создание прибора с рекордными параметрами не является самостоятельной задачей. Именно потребности ядерной физики и физики твердого тела положили начало разработке в конце 40-х годов спектрометрических методов исследования, без которых немыслимо дальнейшее развитие современной физики конденсированных сред и ядерной физики.

Уже в первые годы применения импульсных источников нейтронов в исследованиях по физике конденсированных сред (1960-1963 гг.) была экспериментально подтверждена широкая перспектива развития МВП применительно к нейтронным источникам второго поколения [2,3,5,6]. Созданные в эти годы на импульсных источниках мощностью несколько кВт спектрометры по МВП позволили сделать вывод о том, что они эквивалентны спектрометрам подобного типа на реакторах постоянной мощности с потоками до 10^{14} см$^{-2}$с$^{-1}$, а спектрометры, созданные на импульсном реакторе ИБР-30 [7], близки по своим возможностям к подобным приборам на реакторах постоянной мощности с потоками до 10^{15} см$^{-2}$с$^{-1}$. В этом можно качественно убедиться, сравнив потоки тепловых нейтронов на расстоянии 5 м от светящей поверхности для Гренобльского реактора ($\sim 3 \cdot 10^{10}$ см$^{-2}$с$^{-1}$ и реактора ИБР-30 ($\sim 3 \cdot 10^{7}$ см$^{-2}$с$^{-1}$). Именно на этот фактор $\sim 10^{-3}$, как отмечалось выше, необходимо умножить поток нейтронов реактора постоянной мощности для случая МВП с тем, чтобы получить полезный поток.

Как отмечалось во введении, современные исследования требуют все более совершенных методов и техники эксперимента с дальнейшим улучшением разрешения, увеличением интенсивности нейтронов и повышением точности эксперимента, а также с существенным расширением спектра используемых нейтронов. Исследование квазиупругого рассеяния нейтронов в связи с изучением диффузии и квантовой диффузии в конденсированных средах и исследование глубоко неупругого рассеяния в связи с изучением Бозе-Эйнштейновской конденсации требуют расширения спектра используемых нейтронов соответственно в область 1 МэВ и ниже, и в область 1 эВ и выше, а также дальнейшего существенного улучшения разрешения на 2-3 порядка. Исследование тонкой структуры фононных спектров, локальных и квазилокальных мод, формы пиков когерентного неупругого рассеяния и других, требуют дальнейшего улучшения разрешения на 1-2 порядка.

Современные экспериментальные исследования требуют высокой точности эксперимента и в этой связи многоканальных и многомерных измерений. Необходимые условия для выполнения столь высоких и многосторонних требований удовлетворяются в МВП в сочетании с импульсным источником нейтронов:

— весь спектр медленных нейтронов источника может быть использован в эксперименте, т.к. функция пропускания ротора может быть сколь угодно близкой к единице для исследуемой области энергий, а изменение энергии нейтронов в ходе эксперимента осуществляется простым изменением фазы вращения ротора без каких-либо геометрических изменений в спектрометре;

— предельное разрешение спектрометра определяется только интенсивностью источника нейтронов и может улучшаться за счет уменьшения длительности импульса источника и увеличения пролетного расстояния;

— в области энергий, где размер образца незначительно влияет на разрешение прибора, возможно максимальное использование пучка нейтронов до предельной площади образца, что существенно для повышения статистической точности измерений;

— многоканальные и многомерные измерения являются естественным следствием самого принципа МВП.

Достаточные условия для выполнения современных требований к эксперименту могут быть созданы дальнейшим развитием нейтронных источников второго поколения и созданием новых источников третьего поколения. Динамика развития импульсного реактора в Дубне (ИБР-1, 1 кВт,

1960 г.; ИБР-30, 25 кВт, 1970 г.; ИБР-2, 4 МВт, ~1980 г.),
материалы японо-американского симпозиума по импульсным
источникам [1] позволяют сделать вывод об устойчивой перспективе МВП в сочетании с импульсными источниками нейтронов для создания мощной экспериментальной базы исследований по физике конденсированных сред.

2.1. Импульсные источники нейтронов

В исследованиях по физике конденсированных сред на-
шли применение фотоядерные источники нейтронов и бустеры (подкритические сборки с размножением нейтронов) на
пучках ускоренных электронов [3] и импульсные реакторы
периодического действия ИБР-1 и ИБР-30 [2]. До последнего времени мощности этих источников были невелики и
составляли несколько киловатт или несколько десятков киловатт, соответственно. Естественно, что при таком уровне
мощности не возникало материаловедческих и теплофизичес-
ких проблем. Однако, при дальнейшем росте интенсивности
нейтронов эти проблемы становятся существенными и определяют предел по интенсивности источника. Так, существующие реакторы постоянной мощности при мощности 50-
100 МВт позволяют получать потоки тепловых нейтронов на
уровне 10^{15} см$^{-2}$с$^{-1}$. Этот уровень, по-видимому, близок
к практическому пределу, определяемому стойкостью материалов в радиационных и температурных полях и скоростью
теплосъема. Следовательно, дальнейшее повышение интенсивности импульсных источников приведет к тому, что наиболее перспективными будут те источники, для которых энер-
говыделение (энергия диссипации) в активной зоне или мише-
ни-конверторе на один нейтрон утечки будет минимальным.
В этой связи малоэффективными будут фотоядерные источники на электронных пучках, т.к. в этих реакциях на каждый
полученный нейтрон в мишени диссипируется несколько ГэВ
энергии электронов. На один нейтрон утечки в делящихся
нейтронных конверторах выделяется немногим более 200 МэВ,
а в реакции расщепления тяжелых ядер под действием протонов с энергией ≲ 1 ГэВ выделяется 20-30 МэВ (подобные же
возможности открываются при использовании термоядерной
реакции с импульсным лазерным инициированием реакции [2]).
По-видимому, можно построить последовательный перспек-
тивный ряд импульсных источников: бустер-импульсный бы-
стрый реактор — реакция расщепления на протонах. Достаточно сказать, что при среднем токе протонов ~1 мА пара-

метры импульсного нейтронного источника будут близки к
спектрометрическим параметрам ИБР-2 [8,9].

Спектрометрические возможности или качество импульсного источника определяются не только и не столько его
интенсивностью, сколько длительностью импульса. Как известно, время жизни нейтронов в замедляющей кассете импульсного источника существенно влияет на формирование
импульса тепловых нейтронов и его длительность. Оптимизации выхода нейтронов из кассеты и длительности импульса посвящено много работ, в частности [9-11]. Результаты
этих работ указывают на оптимальную (по выходу нейтронов)
толщину кассеты (для воды) ~40-50 мм. Время жизни
тепловых нейтронов для таких толщин ~40 мкс. Применение гомогенного отравления, гетерогенного отравления или
охлаждения замедлителя позволяет получить длительности
импульса тепловых и холодных нейтронов $\lesssim$ 30 мкс в широкой области энергий Е $\gtrsim$ 0,001 эВ. Заметим, что длительность импульса быстрых нейтронов ИБР-1 (36 мкс) и
ИБР-30 (70 мкс) близки к характерным временам жизни тепловых нейтронов в кассете замедлителя. Таким образом,
применение тепловых и холодных нейтронов в исследованиях по физике конденсированных сред приводит к сложной за-
даче оптимизации нестационарной термализации по спек-
трометрическому качеству источника. Как следствие этой
задачи, на пути улучшения спектрометрического качества
источника уменьшением длительности импульса имеется
естественный предел — время жизни используемых нейтронов в оптимизированной кассете.

2.2. Спектрометрическое качество импульсного источника

Экспериментальные возможности, качество импульсного источника нейтронов в МВП определяется двумя связан-
ными параметрами: интенсивностью и длительностью импульса. Поэтому естественно связать эти два параметра
в одном функционале, одной характеристике источника. Такое определение применительно к спектрометрии быстрых
нейтронов было сделано в работе [12]:

$$K_0 \sim \frac{I}{t_и^2} \qquad (2.2)$$

где I — средняя интенсивность источника, $t_и$ — длительность
импульса источника. Спектрометрия резонансных и быст-

рых нейтронов за последнюю четверть века прошла путь по разрешению от уровня 0,1 мкс/м до 0,001 нс/м. Такой успех естественно связан с оптимизацией качества источников. Очевидно, что при $L \to \infty$ (длина пролетной базы) можно получить сколь угодно хорошее разрешение, однако, при этом катастрофически ($\sim L^{-3}$) уменьшается интенсивность счета. Таким образом, имеется предел по величине пролетной базы, который будет определяться отношением измеряемого эффекта к фону. Отсюда следует, что в (2.2) необходимо учесть параметр

$$r = \frac{I_\Phi}{I_\text{э}}$$

где I_Φ — число зарегистрированных отсчетов фона, $I_\text{э}$ — число зарегистрированных отсчетов эффекта. Если учесть этот параметр [7] при оптимальном распределении полного времени измерения между измерением эффекта и измерением фона для получения эффекта с заданной точностью, то получим

$$K \sim \alpha(r) \cdot \frac{I}{t_\text{и}^2} \tag{2.3}$$

$$\alpha(r) = \left\{ 1 + 2 \left[r + \sqrt{r(1+r)} \right] \right\}^{-1}$$

К настоящему времени можно считать установившимся общий подход к основным параметрам двойных спектрометров: поток монохроматических нейтронов на образце — I_0, полное разрешение спектрометра, измеряемое для определенности по ширине пика упруго рассеянных ванадием нейтронов R (для случая МВП разрешение удобно выражать величиной $\Delta t / L_2$, где L_2 — величина второй пролетной базы от образца до детектора) и отношение фона к эффекту в пике упруго рассеянных ванадием нейтронов. Таким образом, для спектрометра можно ввести по аналогии с формулой (2.3) качество:

$$K \sim \alpha(r) \cdot \frac{I_\text{м}}{R^2} \cdot n_\tau \cdot n_\theta \tag{2.4}$$

где $I_\text{м}$ — полный поток монохроматических нейтронов, n_τ — число каналов регистрации, n_θ — число углов регистрации.

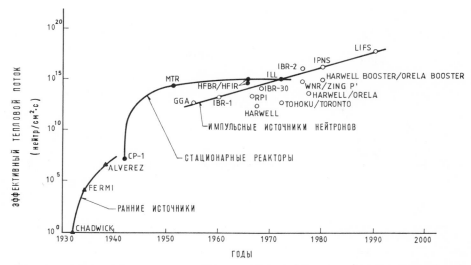

Рис.1. Эффективные нейтронные потоки источников первого, второго и третьего поколений.

При этом принято, что в любом спектрометре можно обеспечить равным телесный угол и эффективность регистрации рассеянного нейтрона.

Если сравнивать спектрометры по времени пролета, то в формуле (2.4) без потери общности можно опустить множители n_τ и n_θ, т.к. в таких спектрометрах технически всегда возможно обеспечить равное число каналов и углов регистрации.

В заключение следует еще раз заметить, что второе поколение мощных источников нейтронов для исследований в области физики конденсированных сред вероятнее всего будет основано на импульсных быстрых реакторах и линейных ускорителях с бустерами, а третье поколение — на реакциях расщепления на протонах или термоядерных реакциях с лазерным инициированием реакции. Наглядной и убедительной иллюстрацией к такому заключению является рис.1. из работы Р.Браггера [1]. Такие оценки перспективы импульсных источников имели место и в ранних работах [13,6], что и позволило своевременно (в 1966 г.) приступить к созданию комплекса спектрометра ДИН-2К.

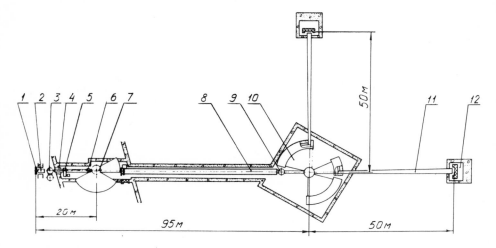

Рис.2. Схема комплекса спектрометра ДИН-2К: 1 — источник нейтронов ИБР-2, 2 — жидко-водородный замедлитель, 3 — вращающийся коллиматор, 4 — коллиматор, 5 — дисковый прерыватель, 6 — основной прерыватель спектрометра ДИН-2ПИ, 7 — спектрометр ДИН-2ПИ (вакуумная камера образца и нейтроноводы 2-ой пролетной базы), 8 — зеркально-вакуумный нейтроновод, 9 — основной прерыватель спектрометра ДИН-2ПР, 10 — спектрометр ДИН-2ПР (вакуумная камера образца и нейтроноводы 2-ой пролетной базы), 11 — вакуумный нейтроновод (50 м), 12 — измерительный бокс.

3. КОМПЛЕКС СПЕКТРОМЕТРА ДИН-2К

На принципе работы и принципиальной схеме спектрометра мы останавливаться не будем в связи с тем, что они близки к таковым для спектрометра ДИН-1 [14] и других спектрометров на импульсных источниках. Заметим только, что спектрометр построен существенно на основе МВП: на первой пролетной базе L_1 от активной зоны реактора до исследуемого образца по МВП осуществляется монохроматизация медленных нейтронов с помощью фазированного с импульсным источником механического прерывателя; на второй пролетной базе L_2 от образца до детекторов для каждого угла рассеяния по МВП анализируется спектр рассеянных исследуемым образцом нейтронов.

Комплекс спектрометра ДИН-2К, представленный на рис.2, включает в себя спектрометры ДИН-2ПР и ДИН-2ПИ и оборудование, обеспечивающее формирование пучка нейтронов по геометрии и энергии на первой пролетной базе;

оборудование вакуумной камеры образца, обеспечивающее установку исследуемого образца, создание необходимого состояния (температура, давление, электрические и магнитные поля и т.п.) и управление им; оборудование второй пролетной базы; детекторный и измерительный модули. Кроме того, комплекс включает в себя вспомогательные системы и оборудование, такие, как система вакуумирования; система вытеснения воздуха из газовых нейтроноводов и заполнения их гелием; система поддержания постоянной плотности газа в нейтроноводах; система криогенная; система электроснабжения и контрольно-измерительных приборов; система заполнения защиты спектрометра водой и охлаждения некоторых узлов оборудования; различное оборудование и устройства, обеспечивающие отладку и юстировку всего комплекса спектрометра и удобство его эксплуатации. Предусмотрены защитные устройства и блокировки, обеспечивающие безопасность обслуживания всего комплекса.

Пучок нейтронов, выходящий из реактора ИБР-П, на всем своем протяжении в комплексе спектрометра ДИН-2К коллимируется, а вся система, начиная с коллиматора в стене, разделяющей кольцевой коридор и экспериментальный зал реактора, нейтроноводов и оборудования, соединена герметично и вакуумирована за исключением двух секторов нейтроноводов второй пролетной базы спектрометра ДИН-2ПР, которые заполнены гелием.

Оборудование, предназначенное для формирования пучка нейтронов в определенном энергетическом интервале, состоит из замедлителя вращающихся коллиматоров, зеркально-вакуумного нейтроновода, дискового прерывателя и основного (роторного) прерывателя. Все они фазируются с импульсами мощности реактора. Система магнитной записи, использованная на прерывателях, позволяет как управлять ими в процессе фазировки, так и давать старт для системы регистрации.

Весь комплекс спектрометра ДИН-2К имеет как биологическую, так и фоновую защиту.

Краткое описание основного оборудования комплекса спектрометра ДИН-2К дано ниже, в последовательности, по пути формирования пучка нейтронов, начиная от источника — реактора ИБР-2.

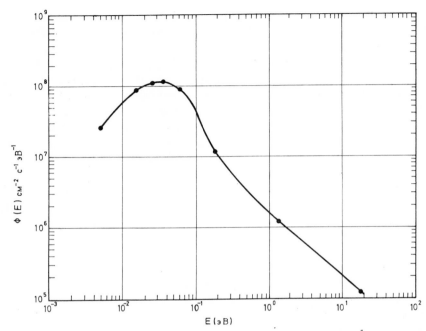

Рис.3. Энергетическая зависимость потока $\Phi(E)\,\text{см}^{-2}\text{с}^{-1}\text{эВ}^{-1}$ на пучке реактора ИБР-2 при пролетном расстоянии $L_1 = 95$ м и мощности реактора 4 МВт. Нейтроновод вакуумирован.

3.1. Источник нейтронов

В качестве источника нейтронов в экспериментальном комплексе ДИН-2К используется реактор ИБР-2 [2], пусковые работы которого начинаются в конце 1977 г. Одновременно начинаются пусковые работы комплекса ДИН-2К.

Основные проектные параметры реактора:

Средняя мощность — $\overline{W} = 4$ МВт;

Длительность импульса быстрых нейтронов — $t_и = 90$ мкс;

Средняя интенсивность быстрых нейтронов —
$I = 1,75 \cdot 10^{17}\ \text{с}^{-1}$;

Средний поток тепловых нейтронов с поверхности замедлителя — $\Phi_0 = 5,8 \cdot 10^{12}\ \text{см}^{-2}\text{с}^{-1}$;

Поток тепловых нейтронов в импульсе с поверхности замедлителя — $\Phi_{0,\text{пик}} = 1 \cdot 10^{16}\ \text{см}^{-2}\text{с}^{-1}$.

На рис.3 приведена ожидаемая энергетическая зависимость потока нейтронов в центре камеры образца спектрометра ДИН-2ПР. Энергетическая зависимость потока нейтронов получена в предположении, что температура замедлителя будет ~310К и тогда спектр утечки для ИБР-2 будет близок к спектру утечки ИБР-30 [7]. В дальнейшем некоторые расчеты и оценки параметров ДИН-2К будут основаны на экстраполяционной процедуре параметров спектрометров ДИН-1, ДИН-1М и ДИН-2. Интегральный поток тепловых нейтронов на расстоянии 5м от поверхности замедлителя составит величину $\sim 4 \cdot 10^9$см$^{-2}$с, что лишь на порядок меньше соответствующего потока в пучках Гренобльского реактора.

3.2. Конструкция комплекса спектрометра ДИН-2К

3.2.1. Жидководородный замедлитель

Жидководородный замедлитель (ЖВЗ) предназначен для увеличения интенсивности холодных нейтронов с поверхности замедлителя в области энергий 1-5 МэВ. ЖВЗ представляет собой сосуд, заполненный жидким водородом, снабженный конструкцией и инженерными коммуникациями, обеспечивающими его надежную работу. ЖВЗ устанавливается в выводном канале защиты реактора сечением 200×200 мм^2. Установка в выводной канал ЖВЗ и его извлечение производится дистанционно. При необходимости выводной канал в защите реактора может перекрываться специальным шибером барабанного типа.

3.2.2. Вращающийся коллиматор

Вращающийся коллиматор предназначен для снижения уровня фона до проектной величины (см. ниже) и устранения коррелированного фона сателлитов реактора [2]. Вращающийся коллиматор, представленный на рис.4, выполнен в виде цилиндрического ротора диаметром 500 мм с коллимирующим каналом сечением 200×400 мм^2 (400 — по вертикали вдоль оси ротора), разделенным на три щели сечением 63,3×400 мм^2. Частота вращения ротора — до 3000 об/мин. Для фазирования вращения ротора с импульсами мощности реактора на роторе предусмотрены две кольцевые дорожки с магнитной записью, на корпусе установлены электромагнитные головки, считывающие магнитную запись и передающие информацию в систему управления. Вращающийся коллиматор конструктивно входит в коллимирующую установку, объединяющую в себе два вращающихся коллиматора, которые могут попеременно дистанционно устанавливаться на

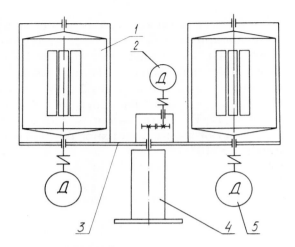

Рис.4. Схема установки вращающихся коллиматоров: 1 – вращающийся коллиматор, 2 – электропривод для смены положения коллиматоров, 3 – рама, 4 – станина, 5 – электропривод вращающегося коллиматора.

пучке нейтронов или полностью освобождать его. Коллимирующая установка расположена в кольцевом коридоре реактора ИБР-2 (между защитой реактора и защитой, разделяющей кольцевой коридор и экспериментальный зал) на расстоянии 4,6м от источника нейтронов.

3.2.3. Дисковый прерыватель

Дисковый прерыватель является одной из систем комплекса, предназначенной для получения предельных параметров спектрометра. Он предназначен для получения предельного разрешения 0,1 мкс/м путем сокращения импульса тепловых и холодных нейтронов для ИБР-2 до величины 10 мкс.

3.2.4. Зеркально-вакуумный нейтроновод

Зеркально-вакуумный нейтроновод предназначен для увеличения интенсивности нейтронов в области энергий 0,001-0,1 эВ и установлен между дисковым прерывателем и прерывателем спектрометра ДИН-2ПР. Длина зеркально-вакуумного нейтроновода – 73,24 м.

В данном спектрометре целесообразно использовать зеркальный нейтроновод для энергий нейтронов 0,001-1 эВ, а для энергий 0,1-1 эВ – вакуумированный нейтроновод (трубопровод) для сечения пучка 200×400 мм^2.

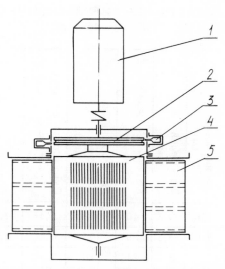

Рис.5. Схема основного прерывателя спектрометра ДИН-2К: 1 – электропривод основного прерывателя, 2 – диск с магнитной записью, 3 – магнит-
ная головка, 4 – ротор основного прерывателя, 5 – щелевой коллиматор.

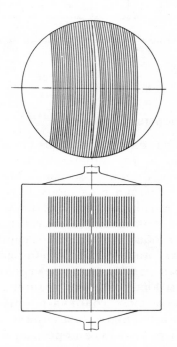

Рис.6. Двухпакетный ротор основного прерывателя спектрометра ДИН-2К.

ТАБЛИЦА I. ГЕОМЕТРИЧЕСКИЕ И ФИЗИЧЕСКИЕ ХАРАКТЕРИСТИКИ РОТОРОВ

Диаметр ротора (мм)	Площадь щелевого пакета (мм²)	Ширина щели (мм)	Шаг щелей (мм)	Количество щелей в пакете	Радиус кривизны щелей (мм)	Скважность щелевого пакета	Область энергий нейтронов (мм)	Длительность импульса на половине высоты (мкс)
250	141,1×180	1,6	3,5	40	5000	0,46	0,15-1,00	5-50
	136,6×180	1,6	3,5	39	2000	0,46	0,04-0,15	5-50
	73,6×180	1,6	3,5	21	1100	0,46	0,01-0,04	5-50
	73,6×180	4,6	3,5	21	350	0,46	0,001-0,0005	5-50
250	50,0×180	1	2	25	750	0,45	0,005-0,02	3-32
	50,0×180			25	350	0,45	0,001-0,0005	3-32
250	151×180	8	11	14	∞	0,75	0,15-1,00	25-100

* Скважность — отношение суммарной площади сечения щелей к площади пакета.

3.2.5. Основной прерыватель

Основной прерыватель (роторный) спектрометра ДИН-2, изображенный на рис.5, установлен на входе нейтронного пучка в камеру образца спектрометра. Максимальное удаление прерывателя от образца в сторону источника нейтронов — 10 м. В отличие от общепринятой схемы механических прерывателей, данный прерыватель имеет так называемые сменные головки, т.е. на общей плите смонтированы: ротор в подшипниковых узлах, диск с дорожками магнитной записи и электромагнитными головками, электродвигатель, вибродатчики и термопары для контроля температуры в подшипниковых узлах. В таком виде головка прерывателя может быть подготовлена на специальном стенде для соответствующего эксперимента и в результате перехода на последующий эксперимент позволит до минимума сократить время перена-

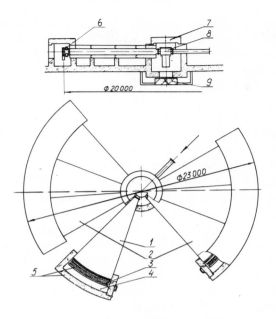

Рис.7. Схема спектрометра ДИН-2ПР (центральный зал): 1 — вакуумный нейтроновод, 2 — гелиевый нейтроновод, 3 — нейтронные детекторы, 4 — туннель для обслуживания детекторного модуля, 5 — защита детекторов, 6 — регулируемые коллиматоры, 7 — защита камеры образца, 8 — камера образца, 9 — откатный шибер.

ладки. Конструктивно прерыватель выполнен таким образом, что ротор может эксплуатироваться в условиях вакуума или газа (гелия).

Для проведения различных экспериментов в комплект прерывателя входит шесть роторов, отличающихся щелевыми пакетами. В одном из роторов, изображенном на рис.6, вмонтировано два геометрически различных пакета для расширения энергетического диапазона в области холодных нейтронов без смены ротора (скорость вращения роторов — 12 000 об/мин). В табл.I приведены геометрические и физические характеристики указанных роторов.

3.2.6. Спектрометр ДИН-2ПР (центральный зал)

Спектрометр ДИН-2ПР предназначен для обеспечения прецизионных экспериментов с предельным разрешением 1 мкс/м или лучше и абсолютным предельным разрешением $10^{-7} - 10^{-6}$ эВ. Спектрометр ДИН-2ПР размещен в зале экспериментального павильона (рис.7). На первом этаже павильона под спектрометром размещается пульт управления спектрометром и различное оборудование.

Центральная часть спектрометра состоит из камеры образца, нейтроноводов второй пролетной базы и детекторного модуля.

Камера образца представляет собой полость цилиндрической формы диаметром 1 м, высотой 0,6 м. С нейтроноводом первой пролетной базы и нейтроноводами второй пролетной базы камера разделена диафрагмами из ванадия — в камере поддерживается остаточное давление $1 \cdot 10^{-6}$ мм.рт.ст. Снизу камеры на специальной сменной плите установлена гониометрическая головка для крепления образца, термостат-криостат и другие системы. Внутри камеры смонтирован механизм с загрузочным устройством, позволяющий дистанционно менять образцы. Управление гониометрической головкой и регистрация положения образца производится дистанционно. Для визуального наблюдения за состоянием в камере имеются смотровые люки и подсветка.

Нейтроноводы второй пролетной базы (от образца до детекторов) из конструкционных соображений выполнены в виде отдельных секторов, соединенных с камерой образца через компенсаторы. Нейтроноводы обеспечивают длину пролетной базы 10 м в вакууме или в среде гелия. Область углов, охватываемых нейтроноводами, составляет $0,5^\circ - 25^\circ$ в вакуумируемом нейтроноводе, $15^\circ - 165^\circ$ в двух нейтроноводах, заполненных гелием с автоматическим поддержанием плотности гелия и $155^\circ - 178^\circ$ в атмосфере воздуха. Перед детекторами нейтроноводы герметизируются с помощью алюминиевых диафрагм. Между счетчиками и диафрагмами нейтроноводов, по всему периметру нейтроноводов, установлены подвижные блоки-коллиматоры, позволяющие дистанционно изменять регистрирующую площадь по высоте счетчиков в пределах 0-460 мм. Блоки выполнены из алюминия и заполнены поглощающими материалами. Для обслуживания детекторов в защите предусмотрен туннель.

Для проведения прецизионных измерений (разрешение 1 мкс/м или лучше) по оси пучка и под углом 90° имеющиеся нейтроноводы с пролетной базой 10 м удлиняются с помощью вакуумированных нейтроноводов. Вторая пролетная база в этом случае составляет 50 м и позволяет производить измерения в диапазоне углов $1^\circ 30'$. Пучок нейтронов на входе в нейтроноводы и выходе из них коллимируется. В конце

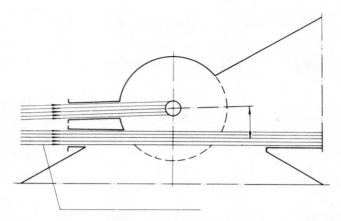

Рис.8. Схема центральной части спектрометра ДИН-2К.

нейтроноводов, в специально оборудованных боксах, установлены детекторы и ловушки.

3.2.7. Спектрометр ДИН-2ПИ

Спектрометр ДИН-2ПИ предназначен для обеспечения экспериментов с умеренным разрешением ~ 7 мкс/м и предельным потоком монохроматических нейтронов на образце — до 10^7 см$^{-2}$с$^{-1}$. Принципиально конструкция центральной части спектрометра ДИН-2ПИ не отличается от спектрометра ДИН-2ПР. Установлен спектрометр ДИН-2ПИ в экспериментальном зале реактора ИБР-2 на общем пучке со спектрометром ДИН-2ПР на расстоянии 15 м от кассеты замедлителя. Из-за ограничения площади в зале спектрометр имеет вторую пролетную базу 7,5 м.

Взаимное расположение специально отколлимированных пучков нейтронов спектрометров ДИН-2ПР и ДИН-2ПИ изображено на рис.8. На входе в спектрометр ДИН-2ПИ установлен прерыватель, аналогичный прерывателю спектрометра ДИН-2ПР.

В перспективе предусматривается на некоторых углах спектрометра ДИН-2ПИ увеличение второй пролетной базы до 50 м.

3.2.8. Система фазировки

Для спектрометра ДИН-2К к настоящему времени испытаны две системы фазировки. Система фазировки, основан-

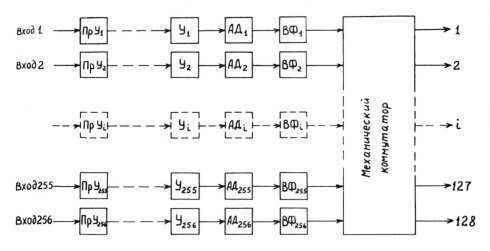

Рис.9. Функциональная схема детекторной системы спектрометра.

ная на принципе точного слежения за переходом импульсов
мощности реактора, описана в нашей работе на симпозиуме
в Чок-Ривере[5]. Эта система обладает свойством автофа-
зировки, крайне важным для надежности работы установки.
Однако, достигнутая к настоящему времени механическая
точность изготовления диска с магнитными вкладышами не
позволила получить точность фазировки лучше 0,2-0,3°.
В этой связи эту систему фазировки предполагается использовать для фазировки вращающихся коллиматоров, где указан-
ная точность фазировки удовлетворительна, а свойство авто-
фазировки и высокая надежность работы позволяет отдать
ей предпочтение. В перспективе, с повышением точности
изготовления диска, возможно использование этой системы
также и для фазирования основного прерывателя.

Другая система фазировки, основанная на принципе слежения за задаваемым кварцевым генератором сдвигом фазы,
равным времени пролета нейтронов от кассеты замедлителя
до основного прерывателя, осуществлена в работе [19] и
испытана многолетней эксплуатацией на спектрометре ДИН-1М.
Система показала удовлетворительную надежность (эффективное время работы >90%) и высокую точность фазировки ≤ 0,03°.
Эта система будет использована для фазирования основного
и дискового прерывателей.

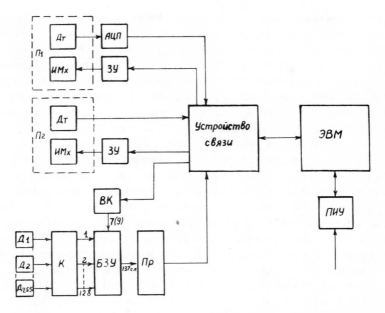

Рис.10. Блок-схема измерительного модуля спектрометра.

3.2.9. Детекторный модуль спектрометра

На рис.9 приведена функциональная схема детекторной системы спектрометра. Она состоит из следующих устройств:

1. 256 детекторов, включая мониторы;
2. 256 предусилителей ($П_pУ_i$), находящихся рядом с детекторами;
3. 256 электронных блоков, каждый состоящий из усилителя ($У_i$), амплитудного дискриминатора ($АД_i$), выходного формирователя ($ВФ_i$).

Все блоки размещены на отдельной панели, установленной на расстоянии ~ 30 м от предусилителей. Здесь же установлен коммутатор ручного выбора детекторов, позволяющий выбирать любые 128 детекторов. Из коллиматора сигналы по 128 высокочастотным кабелям (длиной ~ 600 м) поступают в измерительный модуль спектрометра ДИН-2К.

3.2.10. Измерительный модуль спектрометра

На рис.10 приведена блок-схема измерительного модуля спектрометра ДИН-2К. Учитывая требования независимости

регистрации сигналов по каждому тракту, а также импульс-
ный характер поступления информации, была принята измери-
тельная система, прототипом которой является анализатор-
ная часть спектрометра ДИН-1. Выходы всех детекторов(Д)
спектрометра ДИН-2К заведены на механический коммутатор (К), позволяющий выбрать определенную,необходимую в
данном эксперименте,часть детекторов для записи их информации в буферное запоминающее устройство (БЗУ). Одновременно с линейным кодом камера детектора в одно и то же слово
БЗУ заносится и временный код, определяющий время прихода
сигналов из детектора. Синхронизирующие устройства обеспечивают "привязку" случайно появляющихся во времени детекторных сигналов к импульсам опроса, задаваемым времен-
ным кодировщиком. Период этих импульсов определяет бы-
стродействие измерительной системы. Емкость БЗУ должна
быть выбрана достаточно большой, чтобы потери счета из-за
конечной емкости БЗУ были пренебрежимо малы. Выход
БЗУ связан с преобразователем линейного кода камеры детектора (Пр) в двоичный код. Информация о номере детектора
и времени поступления из этого детектора в измерительную
систему сигнала заносится в оперативную память ЭВМ в качестве адреса, по которому добавляется единица (если идет
измерение "эффект + фон") или вычитается некоторое наперед
заданное число (если идет измерение фона), зависящее от
продолжительности обоих измерений.

Наряду с регистрацией детекторных сигналов, измерительный модуль ДИН-2К должен решать задачи контроля и
управления параметрами эксперимента. Перед началом
измерений должны быть установлены требуемые значения
параметров и в ходе эксперимента они должны автоматичес-
ки поддерживаться в допустимых пределах или изменяться
по программе, заранее заложенной в ЭВМ или выработанной
в ходе эксперимента (управление "на линии"). Объекты контроля и управления могут выдавать текущие значения своих
параметров как в аналоговой,так и в цифровой форме в зависимости от типа датчика ($Д_т$), используемого в системе контроля. Выдаваемые сигналы или через аналого-цифровой
преобразователь (АЦП), или прямо поступают в устройство
связи.

В процессе измерений может возникнуть необходимость
измерения какого-либо параметра эксперимента. В этом
случае в соответствующей ячейке оперативной памяти ЭВМ
заменяется программным путем (либо с пульта ЭВМ) эталон-

ное значение изменяемого параметра. Возникающий при этом
сигнал ошибки приведет в действие через запоминающее устройство (ЗУ) соответствующий исполнительный механизм (ИМ$_x$),
который изменит текущее значение параметра.

Используемая в измерительном модуле ДИН-2К ЭВМ,
кроме этого, ведет постоянный контроль за правильностью
работы детекторной аппаратуры, временного кодировщика
к БЗУ; обеспечивает сжатие накопленной информации и ее
предварительную обработку, перезапись ее для хранения во
внешние устройства с использованием организующей (центральной) ЭВМ и большой ЭВМ, обеспечивающей окончательную
обработку информации. Пульт индикации и управления, кроме
сигнальных приборов и переключателей ручного управления,
содержит осциллограф со световым карандашом, который
позволяет более оперативно управлять процессом набора
информации и ходом эксперимента.

Все блоки выполняются в механическом и электрическом
стандартах САМАС, позволяющих более гибко изменять структуру измерительного модуля.

3.2.11. Проблема надежности

Необходимо специально остановиться на этой проблеме.
И это естественно, т.к. возрастающая точность и сложность
современных спектрометров приводит к большому количеству
основных и вспомогательных систем, в том числе электронных, и у каждой системы есть конечная вероятность выйти
из строя за время эксперимента. Таким образом легко
свести к нулю эффективность спектрометра с высоким каче-
ством и предельными параметрами, если надежность приме-
няемых в нем систем невелика. Для спектрометра ДИН-2К
эта проблема решается следующим образом. Наряду с высо-
кими параметрами, высокой точностью, каждой системе предъ-
являются требования: высокая надежность, высокая устойчи-
вость к помехам и модульный принцип построения (от микромодулей интегральных схем до макромодулей взаимозаменя-
емых блоков и систем).

Жидководородный замедлитель может быть дистанционно удален при выходе его из строя с пучка нейтронов.

Вращающийся коллиматор дистанционно без остановки
реактора за время короткой остановки измерений заменяется
на резервный.

Дисковый прерыватель может быть удален с пучка нейтронов за время короткой остановки измерений при выходе его из строя. В зависимости от опыта эксплуатации может быть изготовлен резервный дисковый прерыватель.

Зеркальный нейтроновод может быть выведен из пучка нейтронов простым поворотом зеркально-вакуумного нейтроновода на $40°$ вокруг его оси за время короткой остановки измерений.

Основной прерыватель легко заменяется на резервный заменой стандартной головки с ротором.

Детекторный модуль в связи с его микро- и макромодульным построением исключает остановку измерений. Опыт эксплуатации такого модуля на спектрометрах ДИН-1 и ДИН-1М показал, что выход из строя даже одного из микромодулей относится к разряду редких событий.

Система фазировки построена по микро- и макромодульному принципу. Опыт ее эксплуатации на спектрометре ДИН-1М показал ее удовлетворительную надежность. При повышении требований может быть изготовлена резервная система или касса резервных блоко-макромодулей.

Измерительный модуль по глобальной стратегии построения измерительного центра Лаборатории нейтронной физики ОИЯИ может быть заменен на один из резервных измерительных модулей центра.

Ряд других систем и узлов спектрометра ДИН-2К построен на тех же принципах.

4. ОСНОВНЫЕ ПАРАМЕТРЫ СПЕКТРОМЕТРА ДИН-2К

4.1. Интенсивность монохроматических нейтронов

Рассмотрим прежде всего счетную характеристику спектрометра, т.к. в конечном счете она определяет предельное разрешение спектрометра. Ожидаемая длительность тепловых нейтронов для реактора ИБР-2 составляет 95 мкс. Эта величина и определяет в основном монохроматизацию нейтронов на первой пролетной базе. Следовательно, можно получить

$$\frac{\Delta t_{\text{м}}}{L_1} = 1 \, \text{мкс/м}$$

— для спектрометра ДИН-2ПР,

$$\frac{\Delta t_{\text{м}}}{L_1} = 7 \text{ мкс/м}$$

— для спектрометра ДИН-2ПИ.

На рис.11 приведена интенсивность монохроматических нейтронов для спектрометра ДИН-2ПР. Для спектрометра ДИН-2ПИ приведенные на рис.11 интенсивности необходимо увеличить на коэффициент $2{,}5 \cdot 10^2$.

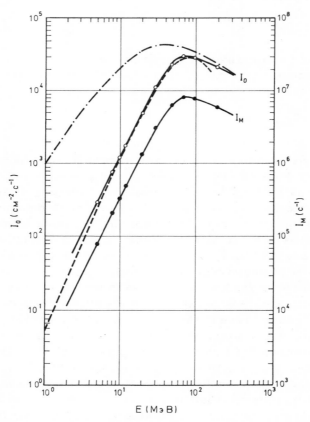

Рис.11. Энергетическая зависимость интенсивности монохроматических нейтронов $I_{\text{м}}(E) \text{ с}^{-1}$ и потока $I_0(E)$ в камере образца спектрометра ДИН-2ПР. Сплошная кривая — расчет из экспериментальных данных для спектрометра ДИН-1М на ИБР-30. Пунктирная кривая — расчет по формуле (4.1). Штрих-пунктирная кривая — ожидаемый поток монохроматических нейтронов для случая применения зеркального нейтроновода и жидко-водородного замедлителя.

Приведенные на рисунке в виде сплошной линии данные получены расчетом из имеющихся экспериментальных данных по интенсивности монохроматических нейтронов для спектрометра ДИН-1М на ИБР-30 и независимо вычислены из данных, приведенных на рис.3. Оба расчета удовлетворительно согласуются и дали результат

$$I_м = 8,3 \cdot 10^6 \, c^{-1}$$

— интенсивность монохроматических нейтронов на полную площадь образца для энергии 0,07 эВ.

$$I_0 = 3,1 \cdot 10^4 \, см^{-2} c^{-1}$$

— поток монохроматических нейтронов.

Приведенные на рис.11 пунктирной линией данные получены по формуле

$$I_м \sim E^{5/2} \exp \left(\frac{E}{T} \right) \qquad (4.1)$$

Температура нейтронного газа T получена из описания максвелловской формой спектра нейтронов утечки из кассеты замедлителя ИБР-30 [8] с учетом поглощения в 10 м слое воздуха и оказалась равной 0,035 эВ. Такое описание, очевидно, некорректно, т.к. "нагревание" нейтронного газа при утечке с поверхности замедлителя вызвано зависимостью транспортной длины пробега нейтрона от энергии [15], а не повышением температуры нейтронного газа. Однако, т.к. точного расчета указанного эффекта нет, а согласие максвелловского распределения с температурой нейтронного газа 0,035 эВ с экспериментальным распределением [8] удовлетворительно, мы используем для экстраполяции данных в область энергий E < 0,005 эВ приближение (4.1). В разделе 3 отмечалось, что вторая очередь спектрометра ДИН-2К предусматривает пуск жидко-водородного замедлителя (ЖВЗ) и зеркального нейтроновода для значительного увеличения интенсивности в области холодных нейтронов. Однако экспериментальные данные [3,16-18] по выигрышу интенсивности, вследствие неполной термализации в ЖВЗ, существенно отличаются от расчетных, а выигрыш интенсивности при применении зеркального нейтроновода зависит от качества его изготовления. Поэтому на рис.11 дана лишь мыслимая оценка (штрих-пунктирная кривая) суммарного выигрыша от

применения зеркального нейтроновода и ЖВЗ. Однако
эта оценка сделана на основе имеющихся в различных лабо-
раториях экспериментальных данных по термализации в ЖВЗ
и прохождению нейтронов через зеркальный нейтроновод.
Для полной термализации и идеального зеркального нейтроновода (оптимистическая оценка) выигрыш в области холодных
нейтронов по крайней мере на порядок выше принятого на
рис.11.

4.1.1. Детекторы спектрометра ДИН-2К

Рассмотрим кратко счетные характеристики спектрометра. Детекторы представляют собой кассеты, собранные из
стандартных счетчиков СНМ-33, наполненных гелием-3 до
10 ат с 3% примеси углекислого газа. Диаметр счетчика — 32 мм,
длина — 500 мм (рабочая длина — 460 мм). Кассеты содержат
от одного до пяти счетчиков, в зависимости от угла рассеяния.

На рис.12 представлена амплитудная характеристика
одного из таких счетчиков. Наличие щели между шумами и
минимальными нейтронными импульсами, а также близость
амплитудных характеристик различных счетчиков, позволяют
без затруднений формировать кассеты из нескольких счетчиков с хорошим счетным плато.

На рис.13 приведены расчетные эффективности детектора для счетчиков с абсолютно прозрачной для нейтронов стен-
кой ($\epsilon_0(E)$) и для счетчиков СНМ-33 ($\epsilon(E)$). Для $\epsilon_0(E)$ получена точная формула

$$\epsilon_0(\mu) = \frac{\pi}{2} \cdot \frac{I_1(\mu) - L_1(\mu)}{1 + \left(\dfrac{n-1}{n}\right) \cdot \dfrac{d}{R}} \tag{4.2}$$

где $I_1(\mu)$ — функция Бесселя мнимого аргумента, $L_1(\mu)$ — функция Струве.

$$\mu \equiv 2KNR\sigma$$

где K — число рядов счетчиков в направлении пучка нейтронов,
n — число счетчиков в ряду, N — число ядер гелия-3 в единице
объема, R — внутренний радиус счетчика, d — толщина стенки
счетчика, σ — сечение поглощения гелия-3.

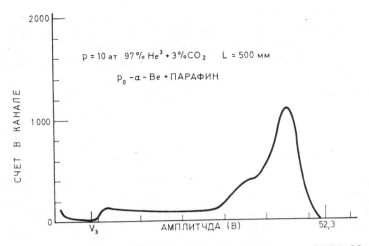

Рис.12.   Амплитудная характеристика счетчика СНМ-33.

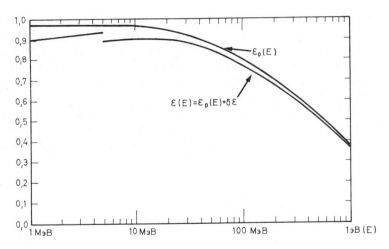

Рис.13.   Эффективность детектора из счетчиков СНМ-33.

Поправка на полное сечение взаимодействия нейтронов со стенкой счетчика вычислена в приближении изотопного упругого рассеяния нейтронов с последующей их регистрацией с эффективностью $\epsilon_0(\mu)$[1]. Приведенные результаты полезны при экспериментальной градуировке эффективности детекторов.

---

[1] Поправка получена Н.М.Благовещенским.

4.2. Разрешение спектрометра

Разрешение спектрометра по начальной энергии E_0 или монохроматизация на первой пролетной базе L может быть записано в следующем виде, справедливом для случая одномерной спектрометрии:

$$\frac{\Delta E_0}{E_0} = 2 \frac{\sqrt{(\Delta t_\text{м})^2 + (\Delta t_L)^2}}{t} \qquad (4.3)$$

где $\Delta t_\text{м}$ — неопределенность по времени пролета на первой пролетной базе, Δt_L — неопределенность по времени пролета, определяемая неопределенностью пролетной базы.

$$\Delta t_L \equiv \frac{\Delta L_1}{v_0} \qquad (4.4)$$

где v_0 — скорость нейтрона.

Очевидно, что в области больших энергий нейтрона ($v_0 \to \infty$) монохроматизация полностью определяется неопределенностью времени пролета и, следовательно, строго выполняется соотношение

$$\Delta E_0 = 2,76 \cdot 10^{-2} \cdot E_0^{3/2} \cdot \frac{\Delta t_\text{м}}{L_1} \qquad (4.5)$$

где $\Delta t_\text{м}/L_1$ — ширина функции монохроматизации на половине высоты (мкс/м), E_0 — начальная энергия нейтрона (эВ). В области низких энергий нейтрона ($v_0 \to 0$) монохроматизация полностью определяется неопределенностью пролетной базы

$$\Delta E_0 = 2 E_0 \cdot \frac{\Delta L_1}{L_1} \qquad (4.6)$$

Определим максимальный размер образца, для которого в рабочей области энергий спектрометра ДИН-2К неопределенность пролетной базы будет несущественной. Из формулы (4.3) получим

$$\Delta L_1 \lesssim v_0 \cdot \Delta t_\text{м} \qquad (4.7)$$

Подставив в это выражение скорость нейтрона, соответству-
ющую нижней границе области начальных энергий ($E_0 = 0,001$ эВ),
и принимая $\Delta t = 100$ мкс, получим

$$\Delta L_1 \lesssim 4,4 \text{ см}$$

За редкими исключениями (например, толщина образца
жидкого гелия-4 достигает величины ~ 10 см) неопределенность пролетной базы, обусловленная конечной толщиной
образца, длиной свободного пробега нейтрона в замедлителе,
координатой точки вылета нейтрона с поверхности замедлителя, менее 1 см. Следовательно, для исследуемых образцов
с линейным размером < 5 см во всей области начальных энергий $E_0 \gg 0,001$ эВ удовлетворительно выполняется соотношение
МВП (4.5). За редкими исключениями такой размер образца
удовлетворяет современный эксперимент. Таким образом,
для разрешения по начальной энергии (монохроматизация)
спектрометра ДИН-2ПР получим

$$10^{-3} < \frac{\Delta E_0}{E_0} < 3 \cdot 10^{-2}$$

$$10^{-6} \text{ эВ} < \Delta E_0 < 0,03 \text{ эВ}$$

для $0,001$ эВ $< E_0 < 1$ эВ

Поправка в расчете, обусловленная длительностью импульса
механического прерывателя, учтена при округлении полученных значений. Для рабочего диапазона $5 - 50$ мкс длительности импульса прерывателя эта поправка составляет величину
менее 10%. Приведенные параметры будут получены при пус-
ке реактора ИБР-2. В дальнейшем пуском зеркального нейтроновода, жидко-водородного замедлителя и прерывателя для
укорачивания импульса (или бустера с инжектором) будут
созданы необходимые условия для получения предельных параметров спектрометра ДИН-2ПР и расширения области начальных энергий

$$10^{-4} < \frac{\Delta E_0}{E_0} < 10^{-1}$$

$$10^{-7}\,\text{эВ} \ll \Delta E_0 \ll 1,0\,\text{эВ}$$

для $0,001\,\text{эВ} \ll E_0 \ll 10\,\text{эВ}$

Разрешение спектрометра ДИН-2ПР при анализе энергии рассеянного исследуемым образцом нейтрона МВП на второй пролетной базе L_2 может быть получено также на уровне или лучше 1 мкс/м. При использовании $L_2 = 50$ м и $L_2 = 10$ м длительность импульса механического прерывателя находится в диапазоне 5-100 мкс, в зависимости от задачи эксперимента.

Таким образом, для разрешения спектрометра ДИН-2ПР по конечной энергии Е получим

$$10^{-3}(10^{-2}) \ll \frac{\Delta E}{E} \ll 3\cdot 10^{-2}$$

$$10^{-6}\,\text{эВ}(10^{-5}\,\text{эВ}) \ll \Delta E \ll 0,03\,\text{эВ}$$

для $0,001\,\text{эВ} \ll E \ll 1\,\text{эВ}$

В скобках на нижней границе области энергий приведены значения разрешения для $L_2 = 10$ м и линейного размера образца 5 см. Из этого примера видно, как существенно влияет на разрешение неопределенность пролетной базы при уровне разрешения по времени пролета ~ 1 мкс/м и сколь существенна в этой связи оптимизация пролетных баз.

Поскольку снизить неопределенность L_2 до величины менее 1 см (диаметр детектора, толщина образца) трудно, то при измерениях на пролетной базе $L_2 = 10$ м разрешение при граничной энергии Е = 0,001 эВ будет не лучше 0,2%. Однако с вводом в строй плоско-параллельных детекторов неопределенность L_2 можно свести до величины менее 0,5 см (для ограниченного диапазона углов рассеяния) и, следовательно, на пролетной базе $L_2 = 10$ м можно получить разрешение 0,1% при Е = 0,001 эВ.

В соответствии с центральной предельной теоремой вероятностей, свертывая большое число функций произвольной формы, мы получим функцию, близкую к гауссовой функции, причем, средний квадрат отклонения (дисперсия) равен сумме квадратов отклонений всех исходных функций. Выше при

элементарном рассмотрении задачи о разрешении на первой
и второй пролетных базах мы исходили из этой теоремы и,
следовательно, для полного разрешения спектрометра
ДИН-2ПР (определяемого, как отмечалось выше, в области
упругого рассеяния) можно записать

$$\frac{\Delta E_R}{E} = 2{,}76 \cdot 10^{-2} \cdot E^{1/2} \cdot \sqrt{R_1^2 + R_2^2} \qquad (4.8)$$

Если считать $R_1 = R_2 = 1$ мкс/м, то получим

$$\frac{\Delta E_R}{E} = 4 \cdot 10^{-2} E^{1/2}$$

где E измеряется в эВ. Следует заметить, что при вычислении ширины функции разрешения через дисперсию, как
сумму дисперсий исходных функций, получается удовлетвори-
тельная точность. Например, если сравнить вычисленную
точно ширину функции монохроматизации с вычисленной через
дисперсию, то расхождение не превышает 7%. Такая точность
удовлетворительна при вычислении параметров спектрометров.

4.3. Фон

Выше отмечалось, что при заданной мощности источника
уровень фона существенно влияет на качество спектрометра
и определяет реально достижимые параметры (в том числе и
разрешение). Очевидно, что в условиях импульсного источника по сравнению с условиями на реакторах постоянной мощности можно достигнуть значительно более низкого уровня
фона, т.к. в момент регистрации нейтронов эффекта мощность реактора близка к нулю (на 4-5 порядков ниже амплитудного значения мощности).

На спектрометре ДИН-2К, в связи с применением вращающихся коллиматоров, а также в связи с удаленностью
экспериментального павильона спектрометра ДИН-2ПР от
реактора, предполагается достигнуть следующего уровня
фона

$r < 10^{-3}$ — для спектрометра ДИН-2ПИ,

$r \ll 10^{-3}$ — для спектрометра ДИН-2ПР.

Указанные значения приведены для максимума спектра нейтронов и образца ванадия с 90% пропусканием. Точность измерений эффекта зависит не только от уровня фона, но и от методики его измерения. Разработанные для спектрометра ДИН-1М методики предполагается развить применительно к спектрометру ДИН-2К до уровня безмониторного измерения фона при относительных измерениях спектра рассеянных нейтронов. Эти методики основаны на периодическом чередовании измерений эффекта и фона, причем, период чередования существенно меньше периода дрейфа мощности реактора и параметров измерительного модуля (коэффициент усиления, пороги и т.п.).

В заключение этого раздела в табл.II приведены имеющиеся литературные данные по параметрам некоторых спектрометров на высокопоточных реакторах и ожидаемым параметрам спектрометра ДИН-2ПР.

В связи с тем, что нет некоторых данных по приведенным в таблице спектрометрам (полное разрешение, отношение эффекта к фону) или в них имеется неточность, не исключены ошибки в вычисленных данных по качеству спектрометров (К). По-видимому, эти ошибки невелики, т.к. качество спектрометра ДИН-2ПР уступает примерно на порядок качеству трехкристальных спектрометров и примерно на порядок превосходит качество спектрометров по времени пролета. Этот результат логичен, т.к. при равном разрешении потоки нейтронов на образце для высокопоточного реактора превосходят поток нейтронов на образце для реактора ИБР-2 на порядок. Естественно, что различие в спектрах нейтронов и геометрии спектрометров приводит к некоторой неадэкватности приведенных оценок. Приведенные в таблице параметры ДИН-2ПР вычислены для первой очереди спектрометра (пунктирная кривая для интенсивности на рис.11 и разрешение 1,4 мкс/м). В результате полной оптимизации (вторая очередь) пучка нейтронов на первой пролетной базе (зеркальный нейтроновод, ЖВЗ и дисковый прерыватель), приведенные в таблице параметры будут существенно улучшены. В частности, значительно увеличится интенсивность холодных и тепловых нейтронов, что позволит улучшить примерно на порядок разрешение спектрометра.

ТАБЛИЦА II. СРАВНИТЕЛЬНЫЕ ХАРАКТЕРИСТИКИ СПЕКТРОМЕТРА ДИН-2ПР И СПЕКТРОМЕТРОВ ILL И BNL

Параметры спектрометра	ILL пучок H1	ДИН-2ПР	ILL пучок H2	ДИН-2ПР	ILL пучок H4	ДИН-2ПР	BNL	ДИН-2ПР	ДИН-2ПР
I_M (c^{-1})	$2,9 \cdot 10^8$	$6 \cdot 10^6$	$2,5 \cdot 10^8$	$3 \cdot 10^6$	$3,6 \cdot 10^6$	$3 \cdot 10^6$	$8 \cdot 10^6$	$8 \cdot 10^4$	$7,5 \cdot 10^3$
I_0 $(c^{-1} см^{-2})$	$1,15 \cdot 10^7$	$2,2 \cdot 10^4$	$5 \cdot 10^6$	10^4	$4 \cdot 10^4$	10^4	$1,2 \cdot 10^6$	$3 \cdot 10^2$	28
R $(\%)$	6,6 (E = 0,25 эВ)	2,1 (E = 0,25 эВ)	1,7 (E = 0,025 эВ)	0,7 (E = 0,025 эВ)	3,2 (E = 0,025 эВ)	0,7 (E = 0,025 эВ)	6,0 (E = 0,005 эВ)	0,31 (E = 0,005 эВ)	0,2
K	$6,7 \cdot 10^{10}$	$1,5 \cdot 10^{10}$	$8,5 \cdot 10^{11}$	$6 \cdot 10^{10}$	$3,5 \cdot 10^9$	$6 \cdot 10^{10}$	$2,2 \cdot 10^9$	$8,3 \cdot 10^9$	$1,5 \cdot 10^9$
S $(см^2)$	5×5	15×18	7×7	15×18	9×9	15×18	$1,3 \times 5$	15×18	15×18
Область энергий (эВ)	0,1 - 0,5	0,1 - 0,5	0,005 - 0,1	0,005 - 0,1	0,01 - 0,1	0,01 - 0,1	0,005	0,005	0,002

ЗАКЛЮЧЕНИЕ

В результате пуска спектрометра ДИН-2К будет создана перспективная (10-15 лет) экспериментальная база для широкой программы исследований по физике конденсированных сред:

— фундаментальные исследования по физике реального кристалла; исследование детальной структуры фононных спектров; исследование релаксации элементарных возбуждений; исследование взаимодействия фононов со статическими неоднородностями, друг с другом и другими квазичастицами; релаксация и сдвиг частоты фононов за счет электрон-фононного взаимодействия в сверхпроводниках, релаксация элементарных возбуждений в квантовых жидкостях (гелий-4, гелий-3); исследование Бозе-Эйнштейновской конденсации в квантовых жидкостях; исследование квантовой диффузии и др.;

— исследование влияния макроскопических факторов (в том числе в экстремальных условиях) — примеси, температура, давление, магнитные и электрические поля и др. — на спектры элементарных возбуждений; исследование связи микроскопических свойств конденсированных сред (фононные спектры и их особенности, структура кристалла) с макроскопическими свойствами и явлениями (физико-механические, термодинамические, электрофизические, квантовые явления — сверхтекучесть, сверхпроводимость); поиск путей получения материалов с предельными параметрами и свойствами, обусловленными межатомными взаимодействиями;

— прикладные исследования по физике реакторов и энергетике; измерение дважды-дифференциальных сечений рассеяния перспективных замедлителей и композиций в широком диапазоне энергий нейтронов (0,001-10 эВ) и температур образца (4-2000 К) для тепловых реакторов и тепловых конверторов быстрых реакторов; исследование фононных спектров сверхпроводников в связи с проблемой технической сверхпроводимости, по-видимому, является перспективным путем для определения предельной температуры сверхпроводящего перехода в случае низкотемпературной сверхпроводимости; исследование фононных спектров в связи с проблемой прямого преобразования в случае существенного вклада фононной теплопроводимости; исследование фононных спектров в приповерхностных слоях стенки и теплоносителя в связи с зарождением кризиса и др.

Указанные и другие прикладные исследования, по-видимому, в ближайшие годы дадут практически полезные результаты для промышленного реакторостроения и энергетики.

Спектрометр ДИН-2К позволит измерять с высокой эффективностью и точностью детальную структуру спектра неупругого рассеяния медленных нейтронов — ширины пиков, температурную зависимость их положения и форму, концентрационные зависимости особенностей и т.п. Эффекты взаимодействия фононов со статическими неоднородностями, ангармонизм колебаний проявляются в неупругом рассеянии в виде локальных и квазилокальных пиков, в уширении однофононных пиков, отклонении их формы от лоренцовской, сдвиге пиков и т.п. Эти тонкие эффекты при современных требованиях к точности измерений могут быть измерены МВП в сочетании с импульсным источником нейтронов значительно успешнее, чем другими методами (например, форма пика когерентного неупругого рассеяния может быть измерена значительно точнее МВП, чем известным методом трехкристального спектрометра). Таким образом, МВП с развитием мощных импульсных источников получает новые возможности и в целом ряде экспериментов, отмеченных выше, становится предпочтительнее других методов.

Авторы глубоко благодарны сотрудникам и организациям, способствовавшим успешному созданию спектрометра ДИН-2К.

ЛИТЕРАТУРА

[1] Японо-американский семинар по быстрым импульсным реакторам, Токио, 19-23 января 1976 г.
[2] ФРАНК, И.М., Развитие и Применение в Научных Исследованиях Импульсного Реактора ИБР, Проблемы Физики Элементарных Частиц и Атомного Ядра, том 2, вып.4, Атомиздат, М., 1972.
[3] Рассеяние Тепловых Нейтронов, Под ред. П. Энельстаффа, Атомиздат, М., 1970.
[4] Сб. "Исследование радиоактивных излучений кристалл-дифракционным методом", Изд-во ИЛ, М., 1949.
[5] Proc. Symp. Chalk River, 1962, IAEA, Vienna, 1963.
[6] ЛИФОРОВ, В.Г. и др., Метод времени пролета в исследованиях по физике конденсированного состояния, ФЭИ, Препринт-140, 1968.
[7] ГОЛИКОВ, В.В. и др., Параметры нейтронных пучков ИБР-30, ОИЯИ, Препринт 3-5736, 1971.
[8] BARTHOLOMEW, G.A., TUNNICLIFFE, P.R., Intensive neutron generator, AECL-2600, 1966.
[9] CARPENTER, J.M., MARMER, G.J., Evalution of the ZGS Injector-booster as an intense neutron generator, ANL/SSS-72, 1972.

[10]   ARROTT, A., et al., Application of a pulsed spallation neutron source,
        ANL-8032, 1973.
[11]   СИНКЛЕР, Р.Н., ДЕЙ, Д.Г., Эксперименты по Рассеянию Медленных
        Нейтронов, Проводимые с Помощью Линейного Ускорителя в Харуэле,
        Проблемы Физики Элементарных Частиц и Атомного Ядра, том 2,
        вып.4, Атомиздат, М., 1972.
[12]   BARTHOLOMEW, G.A., MILTON, I.C.D., VOGHT, E.W, AECL-Rep.,
        AECL-2059, 1964.
[13]   BRUGGER, R.M., Phys. Today 21 12 (1968) 23.
[14]   ЛИФОРОВ, В.Г. и др., Двойной спектрометр медленных нейтронов
        ДИН-1, ФЭИ, Препринт-129, 1968.
[15]   ТОЛСТОВ, К.Д. и др., "Средние скорости нейтронов в различных
        средах", Сессия АН СССР по мирному использованию атомной энер-
        гии,1-5 июля 1955 г., Изд-во АН СССР, М., 1955.
[16]   ГУРЕВИЧ, И.И., ТАРАСОВ, Л.В., Физика Нейтронов Низких Энергий,
        Изд-во "Наука", М., 1965.
[17]   DAVIES, F., et al., "The design and performance of the HERALD cold
        source", Neutron Inelastic Scattering (Proc. Symp. Copenhagen, 1968)
        IAEA, Vienna 2 (1968) 341.
[18]   Оптимизация Нейтронных Пучков, Под ред. О.Д. Казачковского,
        Атомиздат, М., 1965.
[19]   БОГДАСАРОВ, Р.Э., Приб. Тех. Эксп., 4 (1969) 204.

DISCUSSION

K. HENNIG: In connection with the papers of C.G. Windsor and
G.C. Stirling (IAEA-SM-219/83 and 118), it is interesting to note that the time-
of-flight spectrometer has been successfully used on the IBR-30 reactor for
studies in the epithermal range. I am thinking of the experiments on neutron
scattering in liquid ^{4}He. I should like to ask whether any further experiments
are planned with ^{4}He and, also, what other studies are to be performed with the
new spectrometer.

M.G. ZEMLYANOV: The present spectrometer on the IBR-30 reactor has
also been used to study the temperature behaviour of the ^{4}He Bose condensate.
Experiments of this kind on ^{4}He will also be continued on the new spectrometer,
but with bigger pulses and higher resolving power. In addition, the higher resolution
of the spectrometer ($10^{-6}-10^{-7}$ eV) will make it possible to study low energy
transitions, which is of special interest in the study of phase transitions, the
electron-phonon interaction, anharmonic processes, hydrogen diffusion mobility
in metals, complex molecular systems, and so on.

T. RISTE: When will the IBR-2 pulsed reactor be operating?

M.G. ZEMLYANOV: By the end of 1978.

NEUTRON SPIN ECHO
AND POLARIZED NEUTRONS

F. MEZEI
Institut Laue-Langevin,
Grenoble
and
Central Research Institute for Physics,
Budapest,
Hungary

Abstract

NEUTRON SPIN ECHO AND POLARIZED NEUTRONS.

The Larmor precession of polarized neutrons provides an intrinsic measure of a selected component of the momentum of a given neutron, and a way of storing this information on the same neutron via a neutron spin memory effect. These phenomena are utilized in the neutron spin echo approach to neutron scattering, which consists of replacing the classical measurement of ingoing and outgoing neutron momenta by a single measurement of a quantity related directly to the change of momentum of a given neutron in the scattering process, in much the same way as selected parts of the scattering function depend on the momentum change. This technique breaks the strong relation between resolution and neutron intensity which the other methods are submitted to. Consequently, the neutron spin echo approach offers a much improved resolution capability and better neutron economy even for moderate resolutions for the major part of inelastic scattering and for certain classes of elastic scattering experiments. Its application could substantially improve the utilization efficiency of continuous beam reactors, or eventually, help to improve resolution on pulsed sources. For illustration, sample experimental results are presented, which were obtained with the instrument built and operating at the Institut Laue-Langevin (ILL).

1. Larmor Precessions in Polarized Neutron Beams

The behaviour of the spins of free neutrons can be described in an essentially classical mechanical way[1]: The spin of a given neutron is represented by a classical unit vector $\vec{S}$ defined e.g. by the polar angles θ and ϕ. The polarization of a given ensemble of neutrons is then defined by the ensemble average

$$\vec{P} = <\vec{S}>$$

The components of $\vec{P}$ are the expectation values, i.e. first moments of the distributions of the components of the $\vec{S}$ vectors in the ensemble and the only quantum mechanical restriction to this classical picture is that higher moments of these distributions cannot be measured, so they do not make sense.

The equation of motion for $\vec{S}$ is simply given by

$$\frac{d\vec{S}}{dt} = \gamma[\vec{B}(t) \times \vec{S}(t)] \tag{1}$$

where $\vec{B}(t)$ is the magnetic field seen by the given pointlike neutron following the trajectory $\vec{r}(t)$, i.e. for static fields

$$\vec{B}(t) = \vec{B}(\vec{r}(t))$$

Therefore the equation of motion for P can only be given if the $\vec{B}(t)$ is the same for all neutrons in the ensemble.

This picture breaks down in all cases where the neutron wave-functions play a role, i.e. the neutrons cannot be considered as pointlike. Examples for this are the scattering processes. On the other hand, neutron beams can be treated in the above manner. It has to be kept in mind, however, that the precise definition of the ensemble of neutrons characterized by $\vec{P}$ is essential, e.g. we can speak of the polarization of a neutron beam at a given point in space.

If $\vec{B}$ and $\vec{S}$ are not parallel, eq.(1) will describe the well known Larmor precession, which in turn will be a measure of $\vec{B}(t)$. Since for a static field the time dependence in $\vec{B}(t)$ only comes from the neutron velocity, we have here an intrinsic measure of this latter quantity. A very essential feature of this Larmor precession velocity determination is that it is made for all individual neutrons in the beam separately and the result of this "measurement", the Larmor precession angle, is stored on the neutron (as the direction of the spin) and can either be read out by 3-dimensional polarization analysis or can be used to compare with what will happen to the same neutron later. Thus we have a handy neutron spin memory effect.

It is of particular interest to use the Larmor precession technique to determine a selected component of the neutron velocity, as shown in Fig. 1. The neutron spin is parallel to the magnetic (guide) field before the 90° turn coil, which initiates the precession. The total angle of Larmor precession between the 90° coil and the reference surface F is given as

$$2\pi N = \frac{A}{\vec{n}\,\vec{k}}$$

where $\vec{n}$ is the unit vector perpendicular to the magnet faces, $\vec{k}$ is the momentum of the neutron, and the constant A is proportional to the line integral of the field across the magnet. For example, for a $\lambda = 4$ Å neutron and a magnet of 20 cm width and of 500 Oe field, $2\pi N \simeq 2000$ rad (for $\vec{n} \parallel \vec{k}$) which illustrates the resolution power of the Larmor precession velocity determination method.

2. The Spin Echo Approach to Neutron Scattering

The usual way neutron scattering experiments are performed consists of two basic steps: preparation of the incoming beam and analysis of the outgoing beam. (This applies to all elastic and inelastic experiments with the exception of single crystal diffractometry). The preparation of the beam means the selection of neutrons with momenta within a given range, and it represents a first measurement in the quantum mechanical sense (projection to a subspace). The analysis is a second similar process. Both of these processes involve selecting out a small fraction of the neutrons present. (In time-of-flight methods the chopping basically makes part of the analysis and not the beam preparation).

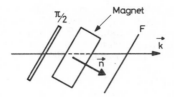

FIG.1.   The Larmor precession measurement of a given component of the neutron velocity.

However, the relevant parameters of the scattering function S are not the ingoing and outgoing neutron momenta $\vec{k}_o$ and $\vec{k}_1$, respectively, but the combinations $\vec{\kappa} = \vec{k}_1 - \vec{k}_o$ and $\omega = \hbar^2(k_1^2 - k_o^2)/2m$. This is why the usual approach to neutron scattering is a poorly adapted one, with the main drawbacks:

   a) The resolution in κ and ω depends on the scatter of $\vec{k}_o$ and $\vec{k}_1$, i.e. both have to be severely restricted. High resolution is difficult to achieve;

   b) These resolution restrictions affect the neutron intensity very sensitively, particularly since they apply twice, both for $\vec{k}_o$ and $\vec{k}_1$. Neutron intensity is inversely proportional to a high power of the resolution.

   A more adequate method of measuring $S(\vec{\kappa},\omega)$ has to be related to the change of the state of a given neutron in the scattering process, the same way as it is in $S(\vec{\kappa},\omega)$. In other words, the two quantum mechanical measurements, that of $\vec{k}_o$ and that of $\vec{k}_1$ have to be replaced by a single one related to the difference between $\vec{k}_1$ and $\vec{k}_o$. Such a method a priori offers the advantages that

   a) In measuring directly a quantity related to the difference between $\vec{k}_1$ and $\vec{k}_o$, better resolution can be achieved;

   b) The resolution and neutron intensity become, in principle, independent.

   For the practical realization of such a difference method, we need a neutron memory effect, i.e. a way to have stored on each scattered neutron the information on its state before the scattering. The only available coding parameter for information storage on individual neutrons is the spin, and, as pointed out before, the neutron spin memory effect is easily controllable. The resulting experimental method has a strong formal, but no conceptual resemblance to the NMR spin echo technique. This is why in the first place, with a superficial understanding of the phenomenon, the name Neutron Spin Echo was chosen [2].

   It has to be emphasized that the Neutron Spin Echo (NSE) is not just another method in neutron (inelastic) scattering, but a conceptually different approach to all the others. It could be defined in the following way: Direct, single measurement of the change of the neutron state in the scattering process using the spin memory effect, as opposed to the classical way of measuring incoming and outgoing neutron momenta in two, separate steps. Consequently there is no common measure in the resolution and neutron intensity relations for the two cases. Whereas for all of the classical methods the Liouville space considerations give roughly identical resolution-intensity conditions (depending on monochromatizations, collimations etc), for the NSE, these restrictions do not apply at all. The crucial, and only real problem for intensity in the NSE is the luminosity and efficiency of the neutron polarizer and polarization analyser. This problem, constituting for a long time the main obstacle to the proliferation of polarization analysis studies, is now solved by the development of neutron supermirrors [3].

It is obvious that the NSE approach will be superior in neutron economy
to any of the classical methods in any type of experiment where the phase
space limitations due to resolution requirements become essential.
A consideration of the technical details suggests that this is the case
generally if either the required momentum or energy resolution is better
than about 2 - 5% of the incoming value. In addition, the practical
limits of the resolution for the NSE are better than for the classical
methods, namely 10^{-3} to 10^{-5}, depending on the case, and this is achieved
with a neutron intensity constant over the whole resolution range.

2.1. Formal Theory of NSE

There is a theoretical possibility of coding more than one component
of $\vec{k}_o$ into the neutron spin direction. However, the way of doing this is
very impractical, and in addition, the gain in information is not too useful
anyway. Instead, we will only consider the case when only a given component
of $\vec{k}_o$ is taken, in the way described above, and compared to another given
component of $\vec{k}_1$ for each scattered neutron. The essential thing is the
appropriate choice of these components, which makes in most cases a more
general approach unnecessary.

Thus, in general, the quantity we can measure, the Larmor precession
angle of neutron spins is given by the equation

$$2\pi N = \frac{A}{\vec{n}_o \vec{k}_o} + \frac{B}{\vec{n}_1 \vec{k}_1}$$

where N is the total number of Larmor precession which is the algebraic
sum of precessions before the scattering (first term) and after the scattering (second term). The unit vectors $\vec{n}_o$ and $\vec{n}_1$ defining the components of
$\vec{k}_o$ and $\vec{k}_1$ which are considered, are freely chosen together with the parameters A and B (which can be positive and negative), within practical limits,
of course.

It is easy to see that a given value of N corresponds to a 5-dimensional
surface (which we shall call a NSE surface) of the 6-dimensional variable
space $(\vec{k}_o, \vec{k}_1)$. Under certain special conditions the N = const. equation
describes a 3-dimensional surface also in the 4-dimensional space of the
relevant variables $(\vec{\kappa}, \omega)$. For simplicity, let us assume for the moment that
this is the case. So in a NSE scan (below we will come back to what this
means in practice) one essentially probes the scattering function $S(\kappa, \omega)$
by moving the NSE surface around in the $(\vec{\kappa}, \omega)$ space, which surface now
replaces the classical resolution ellipsoid. This situation is schematically illustrated in 2 dimensions in Fig. 2, where the scattering function
$S(\kappa, \omega)$ is represented by a phonon dispersion surface. It is obvious that
a single scan, in which the NSE surface "moves" parallel to itself, does
not give a point by point map of $S(\kappa, \omega)$, which in fact is rarely needed
either. This limited, one-dimensional NSE information can be very eff-
iciently used, as illustrated in Fig. 2 by the shaded area. Within this
area the dispersion surface and the NSE surface are parallel, so the NSE
scan can give precise measurement of the width, position and slope of the
dispersion relation. In practice such a measurement is a combination of a
very rough resolution classical, selection-type procedure (e.g. triple axis)
that singles out the shaded area, and a fine NSE scan within this area.
It remains to be shown that the slope of the NSE surface can be tuned to
any given direction in the $(\vec{\kappa}, \omega)$ space. (In principle, scanning the same
area with different NSE surfaces of, say, perpendicular slopes gives an
equivalent to a point by point map).

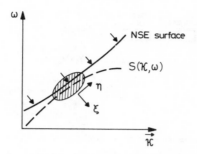

FIG.2.   *The principle of the NSE focussing.*

Using a series expansion around the centre of gravity values $\vec{k}_0^o$, $\vec{k}_1^o$, $\vec{\kappa}^o = \vec{k}_1^o - \vec{k}_0^o$, $\omega_o = \hbar^2((k_1^o)^2 - (k_0^o)^2)/2m$, the NSE surface and the dispersion relation are given by the equations (2) and (3), respectively,

$$dN = - \frac{A}{(\vec{n}_o \vec{k}_o^o)^2} \vec{n}_o d\vec{k}_o - \frac{B}{(\vec{n}_1 \vec{k}_1^o)^2} \vec{n}_1 d\vec{k}_1 = 0 \qquad (2)$$

$$\vec{\alpha} \, d\vec{\kappa} + d\omega = 0 \qquad (3)$$

where $d\vec{k}_o = \vec{k}_o - \vec{k}_o^o$, etc.

The equivalence of (2) and (3) requires that

$$\vec{n}_o = - \frac{\vec{\alpha} + \hbar^2 \vec{k}_o/m}{|\vec{\alpha} + \hbar^2 \vec{k}_o/m|}$$

$$\vec{n}_1 = + \frac{\vec{\alpha} + \hbar^2 \vec{k}_1/m}{|\vec{\alpha} + \hbar^2 \vec{k}_1/m|} \qquad (4)$$

$$\frac{A}{B} = - \frac{|\vec{\alpha} + \hbar^2 \vec{k}_o/m|}{|\vec{\alpha} + \hbar^2 \vec{k}_1/m|} \cdot \frac{(\vec{n}_o \vec{k}_o^o)^2}{(\vec{n}_1 \vec{k}_1^o)^2}$$

Obviously the set of equations (4) automatically assures that to first order the NSE surface fulfils the conditions to be represented also in the $(\vec{\kappa}, \omega)$ space, which we assumed above for Fig.2.

We conclude that the first order focussing, i.e. the tuning of the vector slope of the NSE surface to a dispersion surface is generally possible. Consequently, the resolution of the corresponding NSE scan will only be limited by second order effects, i.e. by eventual differences in the curvatures of these two surfaces. It turns out that for typical acoustic dispersion relations these second order effects will be equivalent to about $10^{-5} - 10^{-6}$ eV resolution broadening, while for quasi-elastic scattering and dispersionless excitations (flat part of optical branches, molecular transition etc), i.e. when $\vec{\alpha} = 0$, they vanish, and the resolution is only limited by the details of magnetic precession field configuration, to about $10^{-7} - 10^{-8}$ eV (see below).

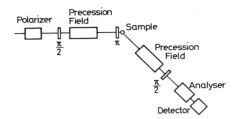

FIG.3.   The general lay-out of the NSE Spectrometer IN11 of the ILL.

2.2. The Fourier Aspects of the NSE Measurements

In the original paper[3] introducing the NSE, it was shown that inherently the NSE means the measurement of a Fourier transform of the scattering function. Here we will only point out the basic features of this.

Obviously, the quantity that is physically measured is not N itself, but the vector polarization of a scattered beam at a given surface, which defines the end limit of the Larmor precession region. This way a directly measured component of this polarization will be given e.g. by

$$P_X = < \cos(2\pi N) >$$

where the average is taken over all the neutrons in the analysed beam. Since N varies in the direction perpendicular to the NSE surface, which direction is taken as the ξ axis of a new coordinate system (see Fig. 2), the distribution of N in the beam is proportional to the cross section of $S(\kappa,\omega)$ taken in the ξ direction.   Hence

$$P_X(t) = \int S_\eta(\xi) \cos(2\pi t\xi) d\xi$$

where $$S_\eta(\xi) = \int S(\xi,\eta)d\eta$$

and the integrals are taken over the shaded selection area (properly weighted with the pertinent transmission function). The proportionality constant t is obviously proportional to A (or B) which is the only experimental parameter left free by eqs.(4), which determine only A/B.

In first approximation, this proportionality constant t can be taken as independent of η . So by scanning A and B so that A/B stays constant, the Fourier transform of $S_\eta(\xi)$ can be determined. As mentioned above, there is a way of obtaining the full two-dimensional Fourier transform of $S(\xi,\eta)$. It consists, in principle, of independent scanning of A and B. However, if $S(\xi,\eta)$ has a very different behaviour in ξ and η directions, the scan has to be asymmetric too. Practically this means scanning say A in the first place, and then B around the value calculated from the last equation of the set (4).

Finally there is a remark to be made about Fourier transform measurements. The relatively discouraging experiences with mechanical Fourier choppers are due to two facts. Namely, that the Fourier signal was contaminated by higher order harmonics, (or other frequencies), and that the whole scattering function with a number   of different structures (elastic and different inelastic scattering processes) were to be sorted out simultaneously. None of these difficulties emerge here. The Larmor precessions

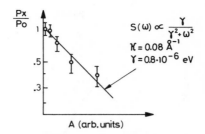

FIG.4. NSE spectrum of the quasi-elastic diffuse scattering of water.

give a perfectly pure cosine or sine modulation, and, as it was made clear
above, we only use the NSE-Fourier method inside a pre-selected $(\vec{\kappa},\omega)$
domain (the shaded area in Fig. 2.).

3. Experimental Examples

A Neutron Spin Echo spectrometer has recently been completed at the
Institut Laue-Langevin in Grenoble. It was designed for the very high
resolution study of quasi-elastic scattering (Fig. 3). In this case, as it
follows from Eqs.(4) for $\vec{\alpha} = 0$ and $|\vec{k}_o| = |\vec{k}_1|$, $\vec{n}_o \| \vec{k}_o$, $\vec{n}_1 \| \vec{k}_1$ and
$A/B = -1$. Since these solutions are independent of k_o and k_1, eqs.(2) and
(3) can be integrated, and the focussing conditions are seen to be fulfilled
exactly, not only to first order. So the resolution will be limited by
(second order) effects concerning the neutron passage through the precession
fields. These are basically the cross-sectional inhomogeneities of these
fields and the neutron path length differences in the precession region due
to finite divergence. For the 200 cm long solenoidal precession fields
actually these effects give, for a 3 cm beam and sample diameter 8×10^{-5}
and 2×10^{-5}, respectively, resolution broadening relative to the incoming
energy. (The first of these effects will be reduced by shimming   the
solenoids). The spectrometer operates from $4 - 8$ Å incoming wavelength.
The limiting resolution, taking into account also neutron statistics for a
10% (coherent) diffuse scattering sample in a $1 - 2$ days NSE scan, is
actually 2×10^{-8} eV, and should be improved by a factor of 5 within the
next year. The maximum polarized neutron flux at the sample is 7×10^6
n/cm^{2}sec, which uniquely high value at long wavelengths is due to the use
of a supermirror polarizer (though a temporary one), and the poor monochromatization required by the NSE (±20%). This flux will be improved by
a factor of about $3 - 4$ in the next 6 months by improving the incoming
beam and polarizer geometry. The instrument is interactively on line
controlled by a PDP 11/20 computer, which is capable of performing basic
data reduction, including the calculation of Fourier transforms of up to
1k data point spectra immediately. The construction costs of the apparatus
were much inferior ($ 200.000) to those of other types of inelastic
spectrometers. This spectrometer was developed in collaboration with J.B. Hayter and
P.A. Dagleish.

Fig. 4 shows the NSE spectrum of the diffuse, low angle scattering
of water. For spin incoherent scattering the polarization of the scattered beam is $- 1/3$ of that of the incoming one, which reduces the data
collection rate by about a factor of 10 as compared with   coherent or

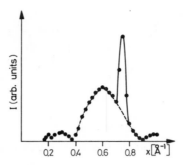

FIG.5. An elastic scattering spectrum measured by a two-dimensional NSE-Fourier scan.

isotopic incoherent scattering. The data presented here was collected at $2\theta = 4°$ scattering angle in about 1 hour per point. The observed behaviour of $P_x(A)$ is consistent in this logarithmic plot with the straight line representing the diffusion constant of water extrapolated from measurements at higher κ values, assuming that the Lorentzian width γ follows the classical $\gamma = D\kappa^2$ relation (D is the diffusion constant). Note that the measured cosine Fourier transform of a Lorentzian line is the exponential function, which is easier to evaluate than the direct Lorentzian spectrum. It is also important that the instrumental resolution broadening only affects the value of P_o, i.e. the polarization of the NSE signal for elastic scattering, which is used to normalize P_x. In other words, the instrumental resolution, which broadens the direct spectra via a convolution, turns up in the NSE spectra only as a simple multiplicative normalization factor, just due to the Fourier transform performed naturally by the NSE. This is a very important general advantage, which in effect improves the information collection rate.

Finally, Fig. 5 shows an example of the above-mentioned two-dimensional NSE scan, with $\xi = \omega$ and $\eta = \kappa$ in this case. The small angle scattering spectrum of an Al sample holder is shown here, calculated as the Fourier transform of the NSE spectrum obtained by scanning B for a fix A, which corresponds to the measurement of κ in this case. The focussing NSE scan for $\xi = \omega$ (A/B = const.=-1) was used here only to establish that the scattering was elastic, and to filter out the inelastic air scattering. The broad peak (dashed line) approximately reproduces the incoming spectrum, and it comes from the diffuse part of the scattering. (To obtain the slow κ dependence of this, the data has to be normalized to the exact incoming spectrum, actually measured by the same NSE-Fourier method). The sharp peak is due to a double Bragg reflection effect. This spectrum gives a nice illustration of the good two-dimensional, both ω and κ resolution (10^{-4} and 2×10^{-2}, respectievly), achieved with a very poorly monochromated beam. This is at the same time an example of how to use the NSE method in elastic scattering.

4. <u>Conclusion</u>

The Neutron Spin Echo approach to neutron scattering, by breaking the close, unfavourable relation between resolution and neutron intensity, offers substantial improvements both in neutron economy and resolution as compared to the other techniques based on the usual concepts. These predictions have

been experimentally verified in a few cases, and the systematic work in this
field is under way now at the Institut Laue-Langevin in Grenoble. The
systematic use of the NSE principle would substantially enhance (by an
estimated factor of 3 - 10) the efficiency of the use of available neutron
flux at continuous reactors, which has to be taken into consideration in
the comparisons with pulsed sources. On the other hand, the use of the
NSE can be interesting to improve resolution on pulsed sources too, by
using the pulsed time-of-flight as the rough pre-selection for the finer
NSE analysis.

REFERENCES

[1] For an introduction to 3-dimensional neutron polarization and for
     references on experimental methods see MEZEI, F., Physica 86-88B,
     (1977) 1049. The technique used for Spin Echo is described in
     Ref.[2].
[2] MEZEI, F., Z. Phys. 255 (1972) 146.
[3] MEZEI, F., Comm. on Physics 1 (1976) 81;
     MEZEI, F. and DAGLEISH, P.A., Comm. on Physics 2 (1977) 41.

DISCUSSION

W. SCHMATZ: Are the analogies between the spin echo method and the
TOF technique based on statistical choppers?   In particular, does the spin echo
method need sharp signals even against a negligible background?

F. MEZEI: The analogy is that both methods measure an integral transform
of the direct spectrum. Consequently, the optimal data collection rate is achieved
by an appropriate mixture of the direct and the transform methods, depending
on the structure of the measured spectra. For statistical choppers this means
the use of less than 50% duty cycle sequences. For spin echo, the equivalent
optimization involves using classical preselection in combination (shaded area
in Fig.2).

B.N. BROCKHOUSE: Has your very promising instrument already been
used for actual experiments, or just for the demonstration experiments you
mentioned in your talk?

F. MEZEI: The instrument has just been completed. The only real experiment performed so far involved looking for a dynamic width for the familiar
central peak in $SrTiO_3$ antiferrodistorsive phase transitions. The central peak
was found to be elastic to within 2×10^{-8} eV experimental error. More experiments are to be performed during the next few months.

D.K. ROSS: Can you distinguish between incoherent and coherent
scattering?

F. MEZEI: Spin incoherent scattering changes the polarization to $-1/3$
as compared with coherent and isotopic incoherent scattering. In particular,

this is a powerful way of distinguishing between proton incoherent scattering and coherent scattering in hydrogenous samples.

J.W. WHITE *(Chairman)*: Would you comment on the use of the spin echo technique to get energy resolutions in the range 10 to 100 μeV without the intensity penalties which normally accompany crystal techniques?

F. MEZEI: This is one of the main points I wanted to make with the illustration of a phonon line in Fig.2. The advantage of spin echo in such a case is that the monochromatization on the incoming and outgoing sides can be very relaxed as compared with the resolution of 10 to 100 μeV, e.g. 13 ± 2 meV.

POLARIZATION AND DIFFRACTION
OF ULTRACOLD NEUTRONS

R. HERDIN, H. SCHECKENHOFER,
A. STEYERL
Fachbereich Physik,
Technische Universität München,
Munich,
Federal Republic of Germany

Abstract

POLARIZATION AND DIFFRACTION OF ULTRACOLD NEUTRONS.

Using the 'neutron turbine' at the FRM reactor, Munich, as a pulsed or continuous source of ultracold neutrons, experiments have been performed on their polarization by perpendicular transmission through monocrystalline iron foils prepared epitaxially in a magnetic field, and on their diffraction by an optical ruled grating. The polarization experiments yielded a high polarization efficiency of 95 to 98% within the interval $4.5 < v < 8.2$ m/s of neutron velocity, at almost no loss in intensity. In our diffraction experiments several orders of diffraction could be observed. The peak positions, line widths, and intensities were found to agree with expectation. Further investigations of ultracold neutron reflection from mirrors yielded, for glass with a thin gold coating, the interference pattern well known from optics, and for a pure glass mirror, a reflectivity curve which is sensitive to surface contamination. The data reveal an impurity quantity on glass which, if assumed to be of hydrogenous composition, could explain the 'anomalously' high containment losses in 'neutron bottles' reported in a number of previous works.

1. POLARIZATION OF ULTRACOLD NEUTRONS

The development of efficient methods of polarization and polarization analysis of ultracold neutrons (UCN) is of particular interest for planned experiments where polarized, very low energy neutrons confined in a "neutron bottle" are to be used for a high-sensitivity search for an electric dipole moment of the neutron (for a review of such efforts see, e.g., [1]).

In our polarization experiments we made use of the fact that slow neutrons experience total reflection when they fall on matter from vacuum if their kinetic energy E of motion perpendicular to the surface lies below the "optical potential"

$$U_{\pm} = 2\pi\hbar^2 N b_{coh}/m \pm \mu B. \qquad (1)$$

N is the number of atoms in unit volume, b_{coh} the coherent-scattering length for the bound nucleus, m the neutron mass, μ its magnetic moment, and B the magnetic induction. The "+" ("−") sign stands for parallel (antiparallel) orientation

of spin and induction. In consequence of the spin dependence
of the effective potential U, UCN may be polarized by perpendicular transmission through a thin, magnetized ferromagnetic film, since in the interval $U_- < E < U_+$ (or $0 < E < U_+$, if
$U_- < 0$) only those neutrons with spin antiparallel to magnetization can pass the foil. The other ones will be totally reflected. This method of UCN polarization has been pioneered
by Egorov et al. [2], who reported to have achieved a polarization efficiency of ≈75 % using polycrystalline ferromagnetic
films. Similar results were obtained by Taylor with Fe-Co
films on plastic foil [3]. In our experiments we employed
monocrystalline iron films in order to improve the homogeneity
of magnetization within the films, and in this way to reduce
depolarization effects associated with fluctuations of
magnetization.

1.1 Film preparation

The monocrystalline films of thickness 1500 - 3000 Å and
area 3 x 4 cm² were prepared by epitaxial evaporation on
rock-salt substrate in a magnetic field of 600 G which was
applied in order to facilitate the growth of α-Fe crystals
with the desired orientation Fe (001) [100] ∥ NaCl (001) [110].
The films were removed from the substrate in distilled water.
X-ray topographic analysis revealed that the foils obtained
in this way consisted of pure monocrystalline α-Fe oriented
in the desired direction.

1.2 Principle of polarization analysis

For polarization analysis we used a modification of the
conventional scheme which consists of a polarizer and an
analyzer and some space in between where the neutron spin may
be flipped relative to the guiding magnetic field. With such
an arrangement, the polarization efficiency can be determined
only if the flipping probability is known. Instead, we used
two identical spin flippers in series because then both the
polarization efficiency and the flipping probability may be
determined from the intensities measured under the various
conditions of flippers in operation or not.
For the transmission geometry considered here the relevant mechanism for imperfect polarization seems to be partial
depolarization of the spin state which is able to penetrate
the film, due to fluctuations of magnetization within the
foil. Neglecting other, presumably less important, possible
reasons for depolarization (like surface stray fields) and
assuming equal efficiencies for polarizer and analyzer as
well as for both spin flippers, the polarization efficiency p
and flipping efficiency f may be written [3-5].

$$p = (I_a - I_b)^2 / (I_a I_c - I_b^2), \tag{2}$$

$$f = (I_a + I_c - 2I_b) / (2I_a - 2I_b), \tag{3}$$

where I_c, I_b, and I_a are respectively the intensities
measured when both flippers are in operation, or one, or

none. As usual, the polarization efficiency is defined, both
for polarizer and analyzer, as the degree of polarization
that would be attained when used as a polarizer for initially
unpolarized neutrons. It should be noted that, for $f \rightarrow 1$
(which is usually assumed if no experimental value is available), expression (2) does not reduce to the conventional
relation

$$p' = \sqrt{(I_a - I_b)/(I_a + I_b)}, \tag{4}$$

which applies to the situation where both polarizer and analyzer are used in the reflection geometry. Instead, $p \rightarrow p'^2$.
This difference is due to the different mechanisms for imperfect polarization in reflection and transmission, which
has also been noted by Taran [6][1].

1.3 Experimental arrangement

The apparatus used for the polarization experiments
(Fig. 1) was set up inside the vacuum casing of the "neutron
turbine" [7] which was employed as a pulsed source of ultra-
cold neutrons, with a pulse duration of ≈ 9 ms as determined
by the length of the packet of turbine blades in operation
(the remainder of the circumference of the turbine wheel being
shielded). The pulse repetition frequency is given by the
frequency of 4.5 cps of turbine rotation. The experimental
set-up consists of a polarizer foil and an analyzer foil,
magnetized in the [100]-direction by permanent magnets
(600 G), and two spin flipper coils. The UCN beam was channel-
ed by straight guide tubes, composed of two stainless steel
sections and a glass section (in the flipping region where
the walls must be transparent to the radio-frequency field).
For spin reversal we employed the method of "fast adia-
batic spin flip" [2,8]. This technique requires a static
magnetic field $H_o(x)$ with a gradient in the direction x of
the neutron beam, provided in our experiment by the permanent
magnet stray fields. In addition, a rotating field of
frequency ω with amplitude H_1 is provided perpendicular to $\vec{H}_o$.
Neutrons traversing the resonance region where $H_{oo} = H_o(x_r) = \omega/\gamma$
(where γ is the gyromagnetic ratio of the neutron) will reverse their spin, provided that their velocity v is low
enough to satisfy the condition of adiabaticity $\omega_1 \tau \gg 1$.
$\omega_1 = \gamma H_1$ is the Larmor frequency for H_1, and $\tau = H_1/(v|dH_o/dx|)$
is the effective reversal time. We chose the following data
for the spin flipping coils: $H_o = 30$ G, $\omega = 4.498 \times 10^5$ s^{-1},
$H_1 = 0.9$ G, and $|dH_o/dx| = 4$ G/cm. For these parameters the condition of adiabaticity is satisfied very well in the whole
velocity interval of polarizable neutrons ($\omega_1 \tau \geq 4.5$).

1.4 Results

Fig. 2 shows the results of time-of-flight measurements
performed under the various conditions of spin flippers on

---

[1] Egorov et al. [2], however, used Eq.(4) also in their transmission geometry. As a
consequence, their value $p' \approx 75\%$ for the polarization efficiency seems to be on the opti-
mistic side, since $p = p'^2 \cong 0.56 < p'$.

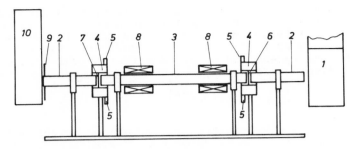

FIG.1. *Scheme of the apparatus used for the ultracold neutron polarization experiments;*
1 – blades of the 'neutron turbine'; 2 – stainless steel guide tubes; 3 – glass guide tube;
4 – permanent magnets; 5 – iron bars for field trimming; 6 – polarizer foil; 7 – analyser
foil; 8 – spin flipper coils; 9 – Cd shield; 10 – BF₃ detector.

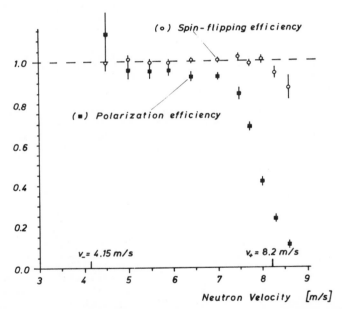

FIG.2. *Experimental spin flipping probability f (open circles) and polarization efficiency p*
(full squares) plotted versus neutron velocity v.

or off. The data shows that the flipping probability f (open
circles) is practically 100 % for velocities up to ≈8 m/s.
The polarization efficiency p (full squares) is constant at
(95 ± 2) % within the theoretical region of polarization
$4.15 < v < 8.2$ m/s (which corresponds to the values $U_- = 0.90 \times 10^{-7}$
eV and $U_+ = 2.50 \times 10^{-7}$ eV for iron in natural isotopic composition), except near the upper limit. Measurements with a
different, thicker analyzer foil yielded an even higher

value p=(98+3) % for the polarization efficiency. The decline
of the data for p in Fig. 2 somewhat below the theoretical
limit 8.2 m/s is a spurious effect due to the finite resolution ($\Delta v/v \cong 15$ % at v=8.2 m/s), which is about 50 % deteriora-
ted compared to the time-of-flight value, due to diffuse
reflections from the guide tube walls which are not ideally
smooth. This broadening of the resolution function was determined experimentally from the measured steepness of the
transmission edges at U_- and U_+ in the transmission of unpolarized UCN through a single iron foil [4,5]. These
measurements also showed that the foils are nearly 100 %
transparent to neutrons with proper spin orientation in the
intermediary region 4.15<v<8.2 m/s. This indicates that practically no loss of intensity occurs for such polarizer foils.

2.   DIFFRACTION OF ULTRACOLD NEUTRONS

In the following we report on experimental investigations of the diffraction of ultracold neutrons from an optical
ruled grating and on their reflection from neutron mirrors.
The idea behind these studies was to, perhaps, gain some insight into possible anomalies at very low neutron energies,
especially in connection with the idea of an "intrinsic
coherence length of the neutron wave train", about which
there has been speculation [9,10] stimulated by the curious
experimental containment data for UCN in material "neutron
bottles" [11,1], which thus far have persistently yielded
shorter containment lifetimes than expected.

2.1   Gravity diffractometer for ultracold neutrons

In the apparatus which we used for our experiments and
which we may call "gravity diffractometer", we make use of
the fact that the motion of UCN is strongly affected by
gravity since the neutron gravitational potential $U' \cong 10^{-7}$ eV
per m of height is of the same order as the kinetic energies
considered. Furthermore, the special features of the flight
parabola described by particles under the influence of
gravity, are utilized for beam focusing in two space dimensions.

Fig. 3 shows the principle arrangement. A continuous
beam of neutrons slowed down by the neutron turbine (with the
whole wheel circumference covered by blades) is channelled by
neutron guides to the horizontal entrance slit, which is
placed $\approx$60 cm above the turbine exit for geometrical reasons.
Two additional adjustable beam stoppers, arranged symmetrically to the entrance slit, select a horizontal UCN beam with
small vertical divergence. The neutrons with proper initial
velocity around 3 m/s at the entrance slit fall in the gravitational field along parabolic trajectories through 50 to
80 cm and hit a first vertical mirror consisting of nickel-
coated glass. This mirror can be replaced by a ruled grating
for the diffraction experiments discussed later. In case of
the vertical mirror the vertical component of neutron velocity, $v_\perp = \sqrt{2gh}$, where h is the height of fall and g the gravitational constant, remains unchanged in the reflection process,

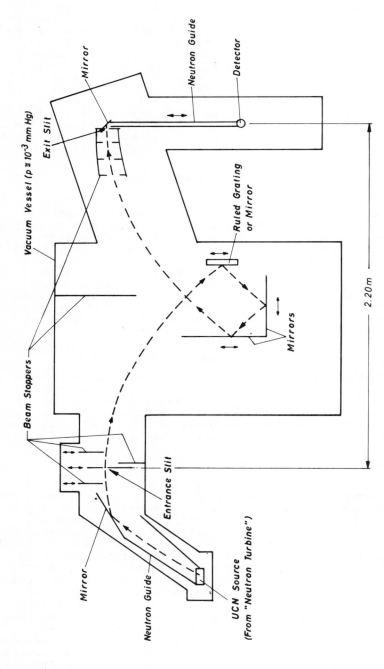

FIG.3. Scheme of the 'gravity diffractometer'. A change of the neutron vertical momentum due to diffraction may be sensitively analysed by measuring the change of culmination height of the secondary, ascending flight parabola.

whereas the horizontal component changes sign. So the neutrons
continue to fall until they hit a horizontal glass mirror whose
vertical position may be changed. After reflection (either
total or partial, depending on the height of fall below or
above the limiting value h_{cr} for total reflection) from this
horizontal mirror the neutrons start to move upwards with
their vertical velocity component reversed. Their horizontal
direction of motion is also reversed once more by means of a
second vertical mirror (nickel-coated glass) before they
arrive at the horizontal exit slit. The horizontal position
of the second vertical mirror can be adjusted properly such
that the rising neutrons pass the exit slit just at the culmination point of their ascending flight parabola.

The culmination point is chosen because it is the focusing
point for the beam, where the spatial beam width is a minimum,
and the angular divergence is a maximum, as it must be in
accordance with Liouville's theorem. In fact, for negligible
angular divergence and neutron velocity spread at the entrance
slit, the theoretical beam width at the exit slit should be
the same as at the entrance slit, that is 2 cm in our experiment. In this way all the useful neutrons can be collected
by a narrow slit. However, since the neutron velocity at this
point is only about 3 m/s, as it was at the entrance slit,
direct detection would be difficult because neutrons with
velocities less than 3.2 m/s would be unable to penetrate the
aluminium wall (0.1 mm) of our BF_3 detector, but would be
totally reflected from it. So the neutrons having passed the
exit slit are allowed to acquire sufficient energy by falling
through about 80 cm of vertical distance before they reach
the detector.

Along the whole flight path the neutron beam is confined
to a lateral width of 10 cm by glass mirrors. The apparatus
is designed to work in a vacuum vessel joined directly to the
vacuum system of the turbine.

The guide tube including the exit slit and the detector
may be moved vertically in order to scan the beam profile.
For a system which consists only of vertical and horizontal
mirrors, as described above, there is no interference between
the horizontal and vertical components of velocity, and
therefore the exit culmination should be the same as the
entrance culmination. Thus the experimental resolution may
be determined by variation of the exit slit position about
this point.

Fig. 4 shows the resolution curve as determined in this
way. It is nearly triagonal as expected for the convolution
of two rectangular resolution functions of the same width,
respectively for the entrance and exit slits. The full width
of 3 cm at half-maximum intensity, which corresponds to ≈3 neV
of energy resolution for the vertical motion, is very nearly
as expected for the slit widths of 2 cm, allowing for some
contributions due to the angular beam divergence and finite
velocity spread, which also explain the slight asymmetry of
the resolution curve. The same resolution was obtained when
the glass mirror was lowered to an overcritical height of fall
such that the reflectivity amounted to about 0.5.

The measured high resolution indicates that the fairly
large number of reflections (say, 10-50) along the flight

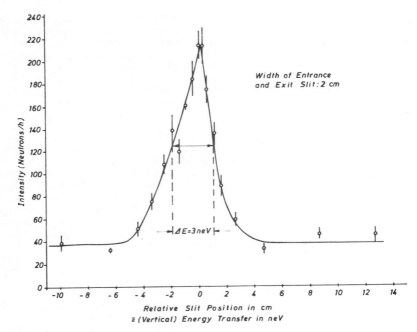

FIG.4. *Resolution curve for the energy of vertical neutron motion in the gravity diffractometer. Background is included.*

path, mainly from the lateral mirror plates, has little effect on the resolution, although some beam attenuation of ∼20 %/m takes place due to diffuse reflections (Sect. 2.3).

It should be noted that in spite of the very high resolution of this instrument, $\Delta E_\perp = 3$ neV (i.e. $\Delta v_\perp / v_\perp = 1.5$ %), the intensity at the detector is still appreciable, even at the FRM reactor with a thermal flux of only 10^{13} cm^{-2}s^{-1}, because one can use a fairly wide interval of horizontal neutron velocities and a significant beam divergence without deterioration of the resolution of $E_\perp$. This is because no interference between horizontal and vertical motion occurs, and because at the culmination point $E_\perp$ is stationary with respect to a variation of angle about the horizontal direction.

Nevertheless, care was taken to keep the detector background low. By proper shielding with B_4C and by using a BF_3 detector (1" diam. x 10 cm) with depleted ^{10}B content, thus reducing sensitivity for faster neutrons, we obtained a minimum background of 24 counts/h.

2.2 Diffraction experiments

The gravity diffractometer was used to study the diffraction of UCN by an optical ruled grating. In these experiments the first vertical mirror was replaced by the

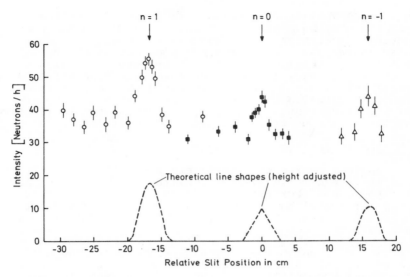

FIG.5. Measured diffraction peaks for the ruled grating as compared to the theoretical line shapes for the instrumental resolution. Background is included.

grating (Fig. 3). We used an ordinary, mechanically ruled grating coated with a thin nickel layer in order to enhance reflectivity for neutrons. The following specifications were chosen: 1200 grooves/mm, blazing for first-order diffraction and wavelength ~1500 Å, effective size 10 x 20 cm².

In the diffraction process the component of wavenumber k parallel to the grating surface, which in our case is the vertical component $k_\perp = mv_\perp/\hbar$ of neutron wavenumber (m: neutron mass), will change by $2\pi n/t$, where n is the order of diffraction and t is the groove spacing. So the grating can be understood as a device which gives the neutron a well-defined push up or down (unless n = 0).

The momentum transfer at the grating may be analyzed sensitively by measuring the change of culmination height of the secondary, ascending flight parabola by a vertical intensity scan. In Fig. 5 the measured UCN intensity is plotted versus the exit slit position relative to the entrance slit. The diffraction orders n=1, 0, and -1 were observed. (By n= -1 we mean first-order diffraction with reversed grating. The vertical position of the grating was adjusted to the various diffraction orders in such a way as to ensure optimum resolution and diffraction efficiency.) The intensity in the predominant diffraction peak n=1 is nearly as high as expected. The other orders are further away from the exact blazing condition and, therefore, less pronounced. The linewidths may be fully explained by the experimental resolution which is slightly worse in the first and, even more, the minus first order diffraction than in zeroth order, because for n≠0

there is some contribution to the resolution due to the finite
size of the grating. This effect occurs as the grating causes
a constant momentum transfer, whereas eventually the energy
transfer is analyzed, which depends somewhat on the vertical
position on the grating where the diffraction took place.

From the absence of any detectable line broadening beyond
the resolution limit it may be concluded that any "intrinsic
neutron coherence length" should be at least of the order
of 10^2 groove spacings, i.e. 10^6 Å or more, which is $\gtrsim 10$ times
larger than previous limits reported by Shull [12].

2.3 Mirror reflection experiments

In another series of experiments the diffractometer was
used to study the reflectivity of mirrors both of glass and of
gold-coated glass. For this purpose the intensity reflected
from the horizontal sample mirror was measured as a function
of the neutron height of fall by varying the vertical position
of this mirror.

The reflection curve obtained for glass is shown in
Fig. 6. The data shows the typical steep edge at the critical
height of fall $h_{cr} = 93.6$ cm, which agrees with the calculation
for the glass composition used. However, the measured slope
is much steeper than the simple theory for reflection from a
potential step predicts. The most plausible assumption was
that there may be a relation to surface contamination which
always exists on technical solid surfaces. Contamination
layers with small scattering potential, as for hydrogenous
substances, tend to soften the potential step. Calculations
show that smoothing of the potential apparently always leads
to steepening of the overcritical reflection curve. The lower,
dashed curve in Fig. 6 represents a fit curve for a soft
potential of the form

$$U(z) = \frac{U_o}{1 + e^{-z/d}} ,$$

where z is the coordinate perpendicular to the wall and d is
a measure of the thickness of the transition region. For this
potential the Schrödinger equation can be solved analytically.
A good fit to the data is achieved for $d = (73 \pm 3)$Å. This seems
to be a plausible result for a possible hydrogenous adsorption layer (H_2O, etc., with a concentration dimishing with
depth), since corresponding quantities of hydrogen both have
been observed on technically "clean" glass [13] and would be
sufficient to account for the empirical UCN containment lifetimes, at least at room temperature [14-17], due to the large
cross section of hydrogen for inelastic neutron scattering.

The reflectivity should be practically equal to one below the critical height of fall. Thus the slope of the intensity curve in this region should be determined only by the
slight variation of beam losses due to a variation of the
length of flight path. This variation was measured directly
using, instead of the glass mirror, a nickel mirror for which
the critical height of fall is more than twice that for glass.
The data for nickel yield a loss rate of about 0.2 per m of
flight path which is consistent with the measured slope for
glass.

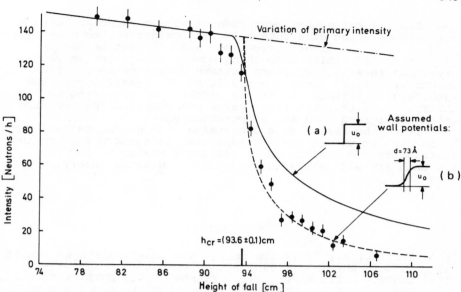

FIG. 6. *Measured intensity reflected from a glass mirror (points) compared to theoretical curves for (a) a step function, (b) a smoothed step function for the wall scattering potential. — — — calculation for monoenergetic neutrons;* ——— *for the instrumental resolution. Assumption (b) may be a model for a hydrogenous surface contamination.*

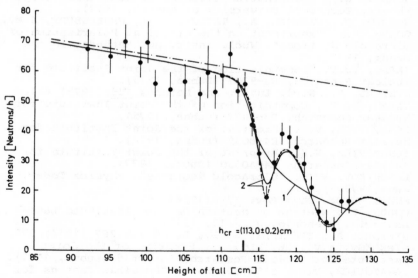

FIG. 7. *Intensity reflected from glass mirror with gold coating (points) showing interference pattern characteristic of thin films. The data is compared to calculations for thick, homogeneous gold showing no interference (curve 1), and for a thin homogeneous gold film (2680 Å) on homogeneous glass exhibiting the observed pattern (curve 2). — — — calculation for mono- energetic neutrons;* ——— *for the instrumental resolution.*

Similar reflection measurements were carried out with a mirror consisting of a thin gold film evaporated on glass. It is well known in light optics (but also in neutron optics [18]) that reflection from thin, homogeneous films should give rise to an interference pattern sensitive to the film thickness. Fig. 7 shows the result of our measurements. The interference pattern is clearly established according to theory. The fitted numerical value d=(2680±60)Å for the film thickness agrees with the evaporation data.

It may be stated as a conclusion that no "anomalies" must be invoked to understand our experimental results both on the diffraction and reflection of ultracold neutrons, but that the data are well explained by ordinary quantum theory.

REFERENCES

[1]   STEYERL, A., "Very low energy neutrons", Springer Tracts in Mod. Phys. 80 (1977) 57.
[2]   EGOROV, A.I., EZHOV, V.F., IVANOV, S.N., KNYAZ'KOV, V.A., LOBASHOV, L.M., NAZARENKO, V.A., PORSEV, G.D., SEREBROV, A.P., Sov. J. Nucl. Phys. 21 (1975) 153.
[3]   TAYLOR, A.R., "Transmission, Polarisation and Detection of Ultracold Neutrons" (Dissertation, University of Sussex, Falmer, Brighton, 1977).
[4]   HERDIN, R., "Polarisation ultrakalter Neutronen" (Diploma thesis, Technical University of Munich, 1977).
[5]   HERDIN, R., STEYERL, A., TAYLOR, A.R., PENDLEBURY, J.M., GOLUB, R., "Experiment on the Efficient Polarization of Ultracold Neutrons", Nucl. Instr. and Methods (in the press, 1977).
[6]   TARAN, Yu.V., Communication of the Joint Institute for Nuclear Research, R3-9307 (Dubna, 1975).
[7]   STEYERL, A., Nucl. Instr. and Methods 125 (1975) 461.
[8]   TARAN, Yu.V., Communication of the Joint Institute for Nuclear Research, R3-8577 (Dubna, 1975).
[9]   IGNATOVICH, V.K., Preprint of the Joint Institute for Nuclear Research, E4-8039 (Dubna, 1974).
[10]   IGNATOVICH, V.K., Preprint of the Joint Institute for Nuclear Research, R4-10650 (Dubna, 1977).
[11]   LUSCHIKOV, V.I., "Ultracold Neutrons", Physics Today, June 1977.
[12]   SHULL, C.G., Phys.Rev. 179 (1969) 752.
[13]   GOLUB, R., Meeting on Neutron Optics (Institute Laue-Langevin, Grenoble, June 17, 1977).
[14]   STEYERL, A., TRÜSTEDT, W.-D., Z. Physik 267 (1974) 379.
[15]   STRELKOV, A.V., HETZELT, M., Preprint of the Joint Institute for Nuclear Research, R3-10815 (Dubna, 1977).
[16]   IGNATOVICH, V.K., SATAROV, L.M., "Possible Reasons for the Anomalous Losses of Ultracold Neutrons in Bottles" (Kurchatov Institute of Atomic Energy, Moscow, 1977).
[17]   BLOKHINTSEV, D.I., PLAKIDA, N.M., Communication of the Joint Institute for Nuclear Research R4-10381 (Dubna, 1977).
[18]   STEYERL, A., Z. Physik 252 (1972) 371.

DISCUSSION

T. SPRINGER: You mentioned the concept of neutron 'coherence length'. Are we to infer that this is some special or intrinsic property of the neutron? I believe that the coherence length is simply related to the spread in energy or momentum given by the neutron monochromatizer or, if these spreads are very small, the neutron lifetime.

A. STEYERL: I think so too. However, some workers are reluctant to accept the idea that the neutron wave could be spread out over a distance of, say, 5 km, which corresponds to the β-decay lifetime and a neutron velocity of 5 m/s. Hence the speculation has arisen that there might be an intrinsic property of the neutron which limits its coherence length to a smaller value. However, I do not think that any convincing experimental evidence exists in support of such a hypothesis.

H. RAUCH: I think the coherence length is mainly related to the energy resolution of the beam. But how can you determine the number of grooves seen by the neutron for such a high value as 100? Can the broadening be determined to this accuracy?

A. STEYERL: If only a few grooves contributed to the diffraction, the broadening would be approximately equal to the separation of adjacent diffraction orders, which in the present case corresponds to about 10 cm. The accuracy of line width determination for the diffraction data is about 1 mm, i.e. one hundredth of the peak separation. This is the reasoning which leads to the limit of coherence length given.

F. MEZEI: It seems that the coherence length in an experiment is intrinsically determined by the selection of a given component of neutron velocity in the experiment itself. For example, in total reflection on ordinary neutron mirrors, we can have Fresnel zones of up to 1 mm reflecting coherently over the whole surface.

A. STEYERL: I doubt whether a limitation of the wave packet size due to any cause — resolution effects or 'intrinsic effects' — could be easily detected by mirror reflection since symmetry arguments will always lead to mirror reflection without beam broadening, if the mirror surface is plane. An idea promoted by Ignatovich in Dubna is that, if the wave packet size were limited intrinsically — which would require a modification of the Schrödinger equation — then there would be a small probability of deep penetration into the wall even in conditions where total reflection should occur. This idea was conceived to try to account for the reduced containment lifetimes in material neutron bottles.

J.W. WHITE (Chairman): Have you observed diffraction peaks of higher order than the first? Could their intensities be used to get information on the profile of the diffracting surface for finely ruled gratings?

A. STEYERL: We searched for higher-order diffractions but could not observe any owing to their low intensity. In principle, higher-order reflections could perhaps yield information on the quality of the groove profile through the form factor.

T.C. WADDINGTON: I accept that your experimental results with plane mirrors indicate that you have a considerable departure from a square well potential, but do you believe that in your experimental conditions, with a vacuum of 10^{-3} torr, you can have a 72 Å layer of physisorbed water on your mirrors? This would correspond to more than 10 molecular layers of physisorbed water.

A. STEYERL: Such amounts seem to be quite possible and have certainly been observed. I understand that it would require high temperatures ($>400°C$) and much better vacuum to reduce significantly the amount of physisorbed H_2O, or other hydrogenous contaminations.

SOME APPLICATIONS OF A HORIZONTALLY CURVED ANALYSER CRYSTAL

R. SCHERM, V. WAGNER †
Institut Laue-Langevin,
Grenoble

Abstract

SOME APPLICATIONS OF A HORIZONTALLY CURVED ANALYSER CRYSTAL.

The use of curved crystals as monochromator or analyser is still a novel and rather undeveloped technique in neutron scattering. We discuss basic principles of 'Bragg-optics' with neutrons, the influence of various parameters as curvature, mosaic, crystal thickness and detector size on resolution. Examples are given how to apply the method with plate-like isotropic samples or small single crystals. The combination of a curved analyser with a multidetector permits to subdivide the extended resolution element typical to the focussing technique. A particular simple application of this principle is a CONSTANT-E-MARX, an arrangement capable to perform energy scans at many fixed Q values simultaneously.

1. INTRODUCTION

Spherical or parabolic mirrors are known as optical elements since Archimedes set fire to the enemy's ship. He instructed soldiers to reflect the sun onto the sail by carefully orienting their polished shields : the first composite mirror.

Why neutron optics ? By simple analogy : Imagine your holiday pictures taken with a pinhole camera; imagine optical spectroscopy or any particle accelerator without optical elements such as mirrors and lenses.

Compared to all these techniques, neutron scattering is still living in a pre-Archemedian age. To find an example for a concave mirror we do not need to climb Mt. Palomar; it is sufficient to dismantel a torch. Nevertheless it took nearly 20 years of neutron scattering before vertically curved monochromators were used [1-3]. Here a high beam is focussed onto a small sample, thus increasing the flux at the expense of the angular divergence. The application of vertical focussing is very straightforward because the vertical resolution is generally nearly completely decoupled from the definition of energies, etc. in the scattering plane.

In principle one can proceed similarly in the scattering plane. One can focus a wide beam onto a small sample or investigate with a big curved analyzer neutrons scattered into a large solid angle. However, the correlation of angular variations with the definition of energy and momentum renders focussing in the scattering plane much more complicated and defines its natural limits.

---

† Guest scientist from the Physical Institute of the University of Würzburg, Federal Republic of Germany.

Basic principles of Bragg optics in neutron scattering have been discussed by Maier-Leibnitz [4-6] , Egert and Dachs [7] and Kalus [8]. Different
methods have been employed to construct curved crystals : thermal bending
[9], elastic or plastic bending of ideal crystals [10,11].

Our approach starts from the simplest possible technique of construc-
ting a curved crystal : an analyzer composed of properly aligned mosaic
crystals. For the time being we omit discussion of curved monochromators
in the first place to avoid the additional restrictions imposed by collimation and size of the white beam; furthermore the low radiation renders
practical experimenting on the analyzer site quite preferable.

A first account of results obtained with a curved composite analyzer
has been published recently [12]. In the present paper we want to emphasize
the combination of a curved analyzer with a space sensitive multidetector.

2. THEORETICAL CONSIDERATIONS

In order to apply curved crystals in neutron spectroscopy a complete
theory describing the resolution of a curved crystal spectrometer will be
needed. An excellent basis is the formalism presented by POPOVICI [13].
He generalized the approach of Cooper and Nathans to include spatial
effects into a theory which defines the resolution in terms of Gaussian
distributions in $\vec{Q}$-ω space. To include a space sensitive detector in
Popovici's formalism should not present too much difficulty. Another
possibility would be to calculate the resolution by means of a Monte Carlo
program.

We present here a completely different approach based on ideas
developed by Maier-Leibnitz [5] and Kalus [8] . The following does not
claim to constitute a complete formulation of the resolution problem. It is
rather a loose collection of simplified first order calculations to estimate the influence of each individual element independently. We believe
that this approach offers advantage at the stage of testing and optimizing
the new method; it can however not replace a more rigorous treatment later
on.

A sample (or source) of diameter s emits neutrons toward an analyzer
at distance L_A with lattice spacing d, thickness D, mosaic width η, curved
to a radius R. The reflected neutrons will be detected in a detector at
distance L_D which is space sensitive along the direction z perpendicular to
the beam. For simplicity, we regard only crystals with the reflecting
planes parallel to the crystal plane; we ignore lattice gradients and
arbitrary orientations of the detector plane. We want to emphasize that
these parameters offer four additional useful degrees of freedom to
optimize an experiment.

2.1. Point sample and ideal thin analyzer with zero mosaic

An ideal thin crystal, bent to a radius R acts exactly like a mirror
with the focal length

$$f_o = \frac{R}{2} \sin \Theta_o \tag{1}$$

The object S is imaged at a distance b given by the usual lens formula

$$\frac{1}{b} + \frac{1}{L_A} = \frac{1}{f_o} \tag{2}$$

The curve $f(\Theta)$ is a circle with diameter R/2 tangential to the curved
mirror (fig. 2). In contrast to usual near axis optics we deal here with
reflexions far from the symmetry line $\Theta = 90°$. Consequently an object

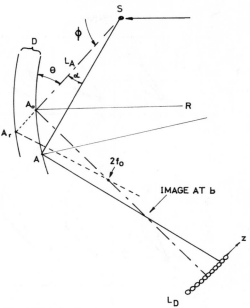

FIG.1.   *Geometry for curved analyser.*
(The index o is used for the reference ray, i.e. nominal spectrometer setting.
For nomenclature see text).

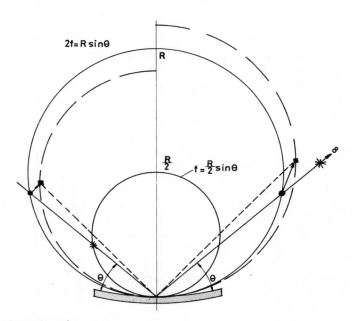

FIG.2.   *The image in real space*
∗ the circle with diameter R/2 represents the focal length $f = \frac{R}{2} \sin \theta$. Image at infinite.

TABLE I. The "zoom-mirror"

	curvature ρ	focus f	image at b	k-element orientation χ	real space	k-space
plane	0	∞	$-L_A$	θ_o		
sample in focus	$\dfrac{\sin \theta_o}{2L_A}$	L_A	∞	$\operatorname{ctg} \chi = \dfrac{1}{2} \operatorname{ctg} \theta_o$		
monochromatic focussing	$\dfrac{\sin \theta_o}{L_A}$	$L_A = 2f \therefore b$		$90°$		

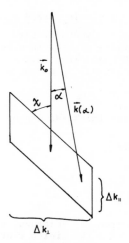

FIG.3. $\vec{K}$-space element, as reflected from sample via real analyser.

perpendicular to SA_0 in fig. 1 creates an image in a plane inclined with respect to the reference direction.

A curved crystal is a dispersive element. Because of Bragg's law

$$k = \frac{\pi}{d \sin \Theta} \qquad (3)$$

The wavevector $\vec{k}$ of the reflected radiation depends on the angle of incidence $\alpha = \phi - \phi_0$. $k(\alpha)$ is most conveniently represented in polar coordinates (fig. 3). In the case of an ideal thin analyzer we obtain in first order a "thin" line inclined by the angle χ with respect to $\vec{k}_0$.

$$ctg \; \chi = ctg \; \Theta_0(1 - \frac{L_A}{2f_0}) \qquad (4)$$

The variation of the image in real space and of the resolution in $\vec{k}$-space with curvature $\rho = 1/R$ is illustrated in table I.

Generally equ. (4) allows the rotation of the resolution ellipsoid in $\vec{k}$-space and therefore in $\vec{Q},\omega$ space to match it to the slope of the dispersion curve under investigation. The method works, however, only within reasonable limits. Furthermore both monochromator and analyzer contribute and have to be optimized independently.

The second case in table I is of interest if one wants to concentrate a wide beam from a neutron guide onto a small sample. With a curved monochromator the neutron distribution obtained in this way is not monochromatic which sets practical limits to the useful solid angle.

The third case, monochromatic focussing is much easier to undertand and therefore to use than arbitrary focussing. In practice it is convenient to keep the spectrometer distances constant and to vary rather the curvature ρ with energy in case of monochromatic focussing :

$$R^x = \frac{L_A}{\pi} \cdot d \cdot k \qquad (5)$$

2.2.   The realistic analyzer : mosaic spread η and thickness D

The mosaic spread η is the width of the statistical distribution of the orientation of reflecting planes. In a bent crystal of finite thickness D the lattice planes exhibit a systematical tilt varying between the front and rear surfaces (points A_o and A_r in fig. 1) by

$$\eta_D = D\rho \; ctg \; \Theta_o \qquad\qquad (6)$$

Both effects generate a finite thickness $\Delta k_{\|}$ of the volume element (fig. 3).

$$\Delta k_{/\!/} = |\; k_o \; ctg \; \Theta_o \; \cdot \; \eta_{eff} \;| \qquad\qquad (7)$$

with the effective mosaic

$$\eta^2_{eff} = \eta^2 + 0.68^2 \eta^2_D \qquad\qquad (8)$$

Here the factor 0.68^2 comes from the rectangular distribution of η_D. Slits of collimators finally determine the finite width $\Delta k_\perp$ of the k-element perpendicular to $\vec{k}_o$ as shown on fig. 3.

Up to now we have constructed the k-resolution of neutrons reflected by a curved analyzer into a wide open detector. We now turn to the question of where and how widely does the reflected beam impinge on the detector ? or : How does a finte size detector modify the resolution ?

Firstly again the idealized, thin crystal : A well defined ray of direction α is reflected into a well defined direction β after the crystal and hits the detector at

$$z = -\alpha \; (L_A + L_D - \frac{L_A L_D}{f_o}) \qquad\qquad (9)$$

The multidetector can be calibrated in terms of the scattering angle $\phi = \phi_o + \alpha$, or in other words the multidetector subdivides the extended k-element. This does not apply if the detector coincides with the image $L_D = b$, where obviously $z = 0$ for all α.

To investigate the effect of the mosaic we follow a well collimated white ray of direction α : it leaves the analyzer with an angular spread 2η , which causes a spot on the detector centered at $z(\alpha)$ as given by (9) and with a width

$$\Delta z_{\eta} = 2L_D \cdot \eta \qquad\qquad (10)$$

Within this spot the spatial coordinate $\delta z = z - z(\alpha)$ (still for a sharp fixed α !) is uniquely correlated to a variation of wavevector

$$\delta k_{\eta} = -k_o \; ctg \; \Theta_o = \frac{\delta_z}{2L_D} \qquad\qquad (11)$$

A quite similar effect is caused by the crystal thickness D. The direction β of the reflected beam is related to the depth of the reflexion point within the crystal. This leads to a (rectangular) width

$$\Delta z_D = |\, 2(L_D - 2f_o) \cdot \eta_D \,| \qquad\qquad (12)$$

and implies, similar to (11), a variation of k with the detector-coordinate

$$\delta k_D = - k_o \text{ ctg } \Theta_o \frac{\delta_z}{2(L_D - 2f_o)} \tag{13}$$

It is interesting to note that at a distance $2f_o$ the crystal thickness causes no broadening of the image $\Delta z_D = 0$, it always contributes fully, however to the k-width in equ. (7).

The image on the detector is of course the convolution of the width, corresponding to the finite acceptance angle (9), the mosaic (10) and crystal thickness (12). At $L_D \gg b$ or $L_D \ll b$ the detector coordinate z can be calibrated in terms of ϕ (equ. 9), whereas at $L_D = b$ the multidetector resolves energy rather at constant ϕ.

2.3. The multidetector

In order to resolve the problem of how to calibrate the multidetector at arbitrary L_D we ask : which is the trace in k-space corresponding to a point sample $\rightarrow$ infinite mosaic analyzer $\rightarrow$ point detector at z ? For a fixed incident angle α the detector coordinate z means a variation of the Bragg angle $\Delta(2\Theta) = z/L_D$ and hence of the wave vector

$$\delta k_{/\!/} = k_o \text{ ctg } \Theta_o \cdot \frac{z}{2L_D} \tag{14}$$

On the other hand, a detector at z receives the nominal k_o from an incident angle $\alpha = z/(L_D - L_A)$. This implies a lateral shift in k of

$$\delta k_\perp = k_o \frac{z}{L_D - L_A} \tag{15}$$

The trace in k-space corresponding to one detector point is therefore a line as indicated in fig. 4 with inclination

$$\text{ctg } \chi = \text{ctg } \Theta_o \cdot \frac{1}{2} \left(1 - \frac{L_A}{L_D}\right) \tag{16}$$

The resolution of a realistic system, finite size mosaic analyzer and multidetector is visualized by a superposition of fig. 3 and fig. 4. Finally to obtain the total resolution, the contributions due to the monochromator and the finite sample size have still to be added.

For practical use of the multidetector analyzer, the experimenter disposes of the curvature ρ and the detector distance L_D as the main parameters for optimization. Of all possible combinations of ρ and L_D, we discuss three particularly simple cases (see fig. 5).

1. Monochromatic focussing $\rho = \rho^x$, detector in image $L_D = 2f_o = L_A$. The analyzer accepts a wide solid angle $\Delta\phi$ which is focussed onto the detector. The detector width w can cut down the spot caused by the mosaic and thus influence the energy resolution, while the contribution from the analyzer thickness remains unchanged. In this case equ. (8) is to be replaced by

$$\eta^2_{eff} = 0.68^2 \left(\eta^2_D + \left(\frac{w}{2L_D}\right)^2\right) \tag{17}$$

2. Monochromatic focussing $\rho = \rho^x$, $L_A = 2f_o$, detector at $L_D \gg L_A$. The multidetector resolves different ϕ i.e. Q all at the same energy. We believe that this extension of the "Multi Angle Reflecting X-tal" spectrometer [14] might be of considerable interest.

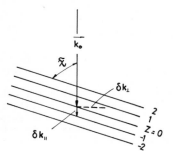

*FIG.4. $\vec{K}$-space element, as defined by sample and point detector via a ' $\eta \rightarrow \infty$ analyser'.
Resolution from sample via real analyser into small detector is superposition of Figs 3 and 4.*

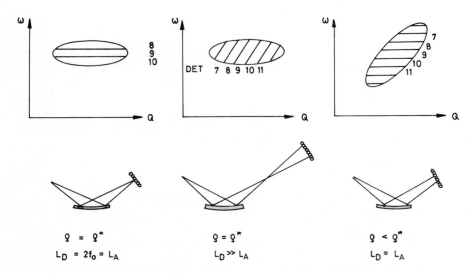

FIG.5. Spatial focussing and resolution depend on curvature ρ and detector distance L_D.

    3.   Oblique focussing $\rho \neq \rho^x$, multidetector at $L_D = L_A$. We try
to focus a dispersion curve with arbitrary slope by tuning the analyzer
curvature. Provided focussing is possible within the instrumental limits
which is by no means obvious, we then will end up with a k-element at some
inclination, say χ. As can be seen from equ. (16), a detector point at
$L_D = L_A$ receives monochromatic radiation only regardless of the curvature
of the analyzer. With equ. (14) z can be calculated in terms of energy,
independently of Q.

Focussing in k-space means collecting intensity from an ellipsoid long along the dispersion surface $\omega(q)$. The danger, however, of picking spurious scattering or of suffering from second order effects rises with the acceptance angle $\Delta\phi$. The multidetector subdivides the large volume element and makes possible the decision whether or not to integrate the data <u>after</u> the experiment.

3. TECHNIQUE

We now describe the instrumentation used for the experimental studies. IN3 is a three axis spectrometer installed at a thermal guide tube at the High Flux Reactor in Grenoble. While operated normally as a classical spectrometer it is nevertheless specially designed to study optical methods : the low fast background after the guide permits a rather compact shielding and quick and easy access to the monochromator. All distances are simply and reproducibly variable. Collimators, slits, filter, monochromator and analyzer crystals are prealigned and can easily be exchanged. This enables us to perform comparative scans on the same sample at various instrumental configurations without the need to perform acrobatic realignments. As a special feature, IN3 is equipped with a multidetector consisting of 18 ^{3}He detectors in a staggered arrangement with 0.75 cm spacing; the detectors cover an area of 14 x 12 cm^2. This fairly large detector can be conveniently operated in the low background of the guide hall.

The monochromators in use are a Graphite (002) and a Cu(111) crystal, both vertically curved. The curvature of the latter can be adjusted. Two curved analyzers have been constructed. The first consists of a series of graphite strips glued on a flexible steel plate , it has been described in detail in [12] . Its curvature is automatically controlled by the instrument computer. The second analyzer offers better resolution. Eight Ge(220) crystals of 0.8 x 0.8 cm^2 section and 9 cm high can be aligned manually to form a plane or curved arrangement. Unfortunately a single element is 8 mm wide, too much compared with its mosaic spread of $\eta = 0.2°$, to be homogeneous.

4. THE SAMPLE SIZE EFFECT

The main reason for the use of curved analyzers is to accept a big solid angle from a small sample and thus to increase intensity. The method quickly loses all virtues when the sample exceeds a certain size of typically 1 cm. There is however one exception to this rule : monocrystalline or liquid samples of plate geometry. KJEMS and REYNOLDS [14] have demonstrated that a properly oriented plate sample does not alter the energy resolution of their MARX-spectrometer. We extend here their formalism to the case of an arbitrary dispersion (Q).

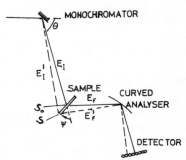

FIG.6. *Focussing with an extended flat sample: ψ is chosen such that Q, ω for both rays lay on the dispersion curve $\omega(Q)$.*

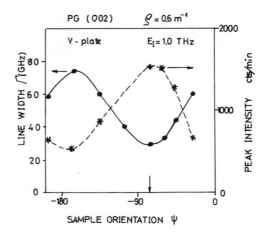

FIG. 7.   *The peak intensity and line width depends on the orientation ψ of a plate sample.*
Focussing occurs at $\psi = -76°$
Monochromator: PG(002) $E_I = 1.0$ THz
Sample: Vanadium plate 1 mm
Analyser: PG(002) $\rho = 0.6\ m^{-1}$ at $L_A = 1$ m.

Moving from the center point s_o of the sample in fig. 6 onto an off center point S, the Bragg angles Θ_M and Θ_A as well as the scattering angle ϕ change with respect to the center ray.

This generally implies a variation of both Q and ω. The angular orientation ψ of the sample can be chosen in such a way that Q,ω lies on the dispersion curve $\omega(Q)$ like $Q_o\omega_o$ for the center ray.

$$\text{ctg}\ \psi = \frac{1}{\sin\ \phi_o}\left[P\ \frac{L_A}{L_S} + \cos\ \phi_o\right] \tag{18}$$

with

$$P = \frac{2\ Q_oK_F^2\ \text{ctg}\ \Theta_A + \frac{2m}{\hbar}\frac{\partial\omega}{\partial Q}\cdot\left[k_F^2\ \text{ctg}\ \Theta_A(1-\cos\ \phi_o) - K_IK_F\ \sin\ \phi_o\right]}{2\ Q_oK_I^2\ \text{ctg}\ \Theta_M - \frac{2m}{\hbar}\frac{\partial\omega}{\partial Q}\cdot\left[k_I^2\ \text{ctg}\ \Theta_M(1-\cos\ \phi_o) - K_IK_F\ \sin\ \phi_o\right]} \tag{19}$$

One easily sees that for the simple case of elastic scattering with $\partial\omega/\partial Q = 0$, $L_A = L_S$ and $\Theta_M = \Theta_A$, this leads to the obvious half angling arrangement.

To illustrate this const-Q scans have been performed from a 1 mm thick vanadium plate at different orientations ψ using the curved graphite analyzer with curvature $\rho = 0.6\ m^{-1}$ at an energy $E_I = 1$ THZ. Fig. 7 shows the variation of peak intensity and resolution width with ψ. The minimal resolution occurs exactly at the calculated value $\psi = -76°$, the maximal intensity of 1500 n/min being 5 times larger than the intensity obtained with 40' collimation at equal resolution.

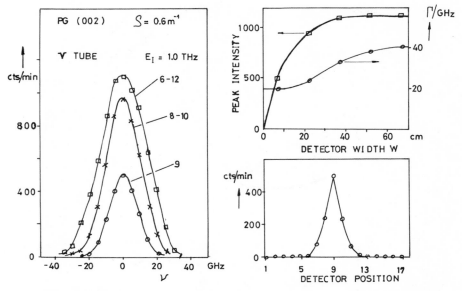

FIG. 8. *The influence of the detector width w on resolution in the case of monochromatic*
focussing: $\rho = \rho^*$, $L_D = 2f_0 = L_A$.
   Monochromator: PG(002) $E_I = 1.0$ THz
   Sample: V 1.5 cm dia.
   Analyser: PG(002), $\rho = 0.6$ m^{-1}
      $L_A = 1$ m $L_D = 1$ m

This method has been employed in an experiment investigating rotons
in a thin layer of superfluid helium adsorbed on grafoil [15]. Because
of multiple scattering from the grafoil substrate the sample was restricted
to be not thicker than 1 cm. Rotons could be observed down to a coverage
of 6 monolayers. In this case the intensity increase from the bent analyzer
turned out to be crucial for the sensitivity of the experiment.

5. THE DETECTOR WIDTH

We now turn to the question of how the resolution can be influenced
by a proper choice of the detector width. For the sake of simplicity we
restrict the discussion to monochromatic focussing, a case which applies
very often to optical phonons. Fig. 8 shows results obtained from a
vanadium sample, a tube of 15 mm diameter and volume of 3.8 cm^3. The
graphite monochromator was kept fixed at $E_I = 1.0$ THz. The analyzer,
curved to $\rho^x = 0.6$ m^{-1}, was fully illuminated over a width of 6 cm, thus
accepting 3.4° horizontal and 2.9° vertical divergence. In fig. 8 the
intensity distribution across the multidetector is displayed. Its width
of 15 mm FWHM is about the same as the sample diameter. This is in fact
smaller than one would expect from eq. (10) : $\Delta z_\eta = 2L_\eta \cdot \eta = 2.3$ cm.
This full width would only occur if the sample were illuminated with white
radiation. In fig. 8 is displayed the linewidth Γ and peak intensity I as
a function of the detector width w. Both Γ and I level off at $w \geqslant 2\Delta z_\eta \approx 5$ cm

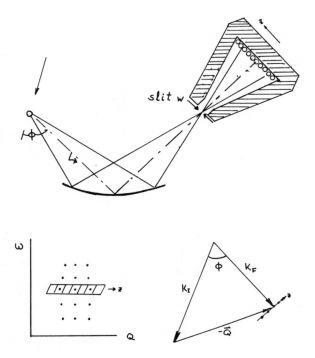

FIG.9.   'CONSTANT-E-MARX'
      Data are taken simultaneously at constant ω along a trace perpendicular to k_F.

i.e. the whole distribution caused by the mosaic is accepted. On the other
hand diminishing w cuts down the "visible" mosaic, thus adjusting Γ
without much loss in intensity.

      The best detector width, balancing intensity versus resolution and
background, can very conveniently be chosen <u>after</u> the experiment, simply
by adding channels of the multidetector.

      This method has been employed in an experiment to measure the temper-
ature dependence of the transverse optical mode in the narrow band semi-
conductor $Pb_{1-x}Sn_xSe$ [16]. A clear indication could be found for the vanishing of the band gap around 40 K.

6.   THE CONSTANT E-MARX (Fig.9)

      Let us now deal with the most complex application, the combination of
the curved analyzer with a true multidetector, and the interpretation of data
in many channels. An analyzer system of this kind consisting of a big plane
crystal and a space sensitive detector has been presented by KJEMS and
REYNOLD [14]. Their MARX takes data simultaneously along a trace oblique
in $\vec{Q},\omega$.

If one curves the analyzer such that $\rho = \rho^x$, monochromatic radiation
from the sample will be focussed on an image point at $b = L_A$. The multidetector being placed at a distance sufficiently far from that image $L_D > L_A$
receives the same energy but distinguishes ϕ

$$\phi - \phi_o = \frac{z}{L_D - L_A} \tag{20}$$

Data are collected simultaneously along a trace at constant ω, but along
a direction perpendicular to k_F which generally does not coincide with a
symmetry direction in $\vec{Q}$.

We believe that this concept might be simpler to use than the original
MARX, because one of the main variables, $\omega_{\bullet}$ is kept constant. Instead of
having the spectrometer standing still we rather scan ω at fixed E_F, thus
performing many const–Q scans at once. Strictly speaking only the center
detector sees Q_O = constant, whereas Q varies slightly for the other channels
during the scan.

Note that the center group of detectors performs exactly the usual
scan. The information in the other detector channels is free : it can
be added to the center group, regarded as additional information in neighbouring Q or discarded.

The image at b is the ideal place to limit the scattered beam by a slit,
which plays exactly the role of the width w in the previous chapter. It
ameliorates the ω-resolution and considerably facilitates the shielding of
the large multidetector.

In the following we present a few preliminary experimental results.
The curved analyzer was in this example the composite Ge(220) analyzer with
a curvature of $\rho = \rho^x = 0.5$ m^{-1} at $K_F = 3.0$ A^{-1}.

Fig. 10 shows the scattering from vanadium with the detector in the
image plane $L_D = b = L_A$. In view of the typical uncertainties : sample 6 mm,
one analyzer element 8mm, one detector 7 mm the image having 11 mm FWHM
cannot be expected to be any better. We further observe that during an
energy scan adjacent detectors at different z produce peaks which are
shifted in ν. The slope $d\nu/dz = -0.5$ THz/detector interval corresponds
exactly to what one expects from equ. (11)

$$dk = - k_o \ ctg \ \Theta_o \ \frac{z}{2L_D}$$

A Q scan at $\nu = 0$ across a powder line (fig. 10b) calibrates the reflectivity of the analyzer. As expected the image appears for all ϕ in the
center of the detector. The structure in I(Q) can be attributed to individual elements of the composite arrangement. A better composite analyzer
should have more elements of smaller size and bigger mosaic spread.

The instrument has been transformed into a CONST E-MARX by inserting
a 1 cm wide diaphragm at the image at b = 1 meter and pushing the detector
out to $L_D = 2$ m. At IN3 the distances can easily be varied without upsetting
the alignment. First inspect the vanadium scan in fig. 10c. The spot at the
detector is now 37 mm wide in good agreement with the divergence of 2.1°
subtended by the analyzer. According to (20) individual detectors can be
calibrated in terms of ϕ, here

$$\phi - \phi_o = \frac{z}{L_D - L_A} = 0.43°/det.interval$$

This has been tested by performing a Q-scan at $\nu = 0$ across a
reflexion from a Al_2O_3 powder sample. The peaks labelled detector 8, 9,
10 etc. in fig. 10d are spaced precisely 0.44°. The intensity I(Q) summed

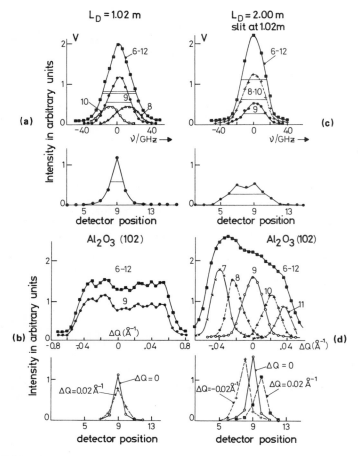

FIG.10.   Calibration scans
          Monochromator: Cu(111)
          Samples: V or Al₂O₃
          Analyser: Ge(220) $\rho = 0.5\ m^{-1}$.
          Scans are shown for detectors 6−12 with detector 9 in centre.
          (a,b) Monochromatic focus; $L_D = L_A = 1\ m$; multidetector resolves ℏω.
          (c,d) Const-E-MARX; $L_D = 2L_A = 2\ m$; multidetector resolves Q.

up over a wide detector should ideally be a trapeze.The fluctuations in
this curve are again caused by imperfections of the analyzer.

CONCLUSION

    It is not our intention to praise curved crystals as a new miracle
weapon. Without any doubt the happy owner of a large sample will employ
plane monochromator and analyzer with Soller collimators and profit from
the simplicity of the conventional method.

Applying Bragg optics will be of interest either for plate like iso-tropic samples or for small single crystals. The first domain concerns problems usually tackled by time of flight techniques, where data are taken in a large solid angle simultaneously. Curved crystal analyzers might become of special importance in connection with pulsed sources : time of flight analysis of the incoming beam and analysis of scattered neutrons at fixed energy in big solid angles.

In the second domain, inelastic scattering from small single crystals, we think of two typical applications. Measurement of optical phonons with a monochromatically focussing analyzer operated at fixed energy and the investigation of effects like line shifts or line broadening at a few selec-ted $\vec{q}$-values as a function of an internal variable of the sample like tem-perature, pressure, field, etc. Here the additional effort which has to be payed for alignment and optimizing the experiment may be more than compen-sated by a considerable intensity increase for repetitive measurements.

The curved crystal spectrometer uses unusually large solid angles. This inherently implies the danger to spoil resolution by a too wide Q-range and to suffer far more from spurious processes. The multidetector subdivides the enlarged resolution-"cigars" into many cells, it permits to adjust after the experiment the data treatment to the actual result.

It cannot be expected that after the fairly moderate effort which has been developed up to now to the development of neutron Bragg optics a full-proof system would be available for everyday use. We showed that with fairly moderate technical effort one can already achieve considerable ameliorations in particular cases. We are convinced that some more development toward producing better homogeneous analyzer systems as well as formulating and programming a more complete resolution theory will make neutron Bragg optics a technique applicable to quite a number of problems. After all it took 2000 years from Archimedes to a modern zoom lens.

ACKNOWLEDGEMENTS

We have benefited from many discussion with Professor H. MAIER-LEIBNITZ. We express our gratitude to Mr. B. WANZEL, who constructed the Ge analyzer and assisted during the experiment.

REFERENCES

[1] RISTE, T., Nucl. Instrum. Meth. **86** (1970) 1.

[2] NUNES, A.C., SHIRANE, G., Nucl. Instrum. Meth. **95** (1971) 445.

[3] CURRAT, R., Nucl. Instrum. Meth. **107** (1973) 21.

[4] MAIER-LEIBNITZ, H., Ann. Acad. Scient. Fennicae, Phys. Ser. VI (1967) 267.

[5] MAIER-LEIBNITZ, H., in Some Lectures on Neutron Physics (Summer School, Alushta 1969) Dubna : JINR (1970) 183.

[6] MAIER-LEIBNITZ, H., in NEUTRON INELASTIC SCATTERING (Proc. Grenoble 1972) IAEA, Vienna (1972) 681.

[7] EGERT, G., DACHS, H., J. Appl. Cryst. **3** (1970) 214.

[8] KALUS, J., Z. Physik **254** (1972) 148

[9] KALUS, J., GOBERT, G., SCHEDLER, E., J. Phys. E. 6 (1973) 488.

[10] KALUS, J., J. Appl. Cryst. $\underline{8}$ (1975) 361.

[11] FREY, F., Nucl. Instrum. Meth. $\underline{115}$ (1974) 277.

[12] SCHERM, R., DOLLING, G., RITTER, R., SCHEDLER, E., TEUCHERT, W., WAGNER, V., Nucl. Instrum. Meth. $\underline{143}$ (1977) 77.

[13] POPOVICI, M., Acta Cryst. $\underline{A31}$ (1975) 507.

[14] KJEMS, J.K., REYNOLDS, P.A., in NEUTRON INELASTIC SCATTERING (Proc. Grenoble 1972) IAEA, Vienna (1972) 733.

[15] LAMBERT, B., SALIN, D., JOFFRIN, J., SCHERM, R., to be published in Journal de Physique Lettres.

[16] VODOPYANOV, L.K., KUTSCHERENKOV, I.V. SHOTOV, A.P., SCHERM, R. in "LATTICE DYNAMICS" (Proc. Paris 1977) to be published.

DISCUSSION

J.W. WHITE *(Chairman)*: Could the signal-to-noise ratio be degraded by using your ω-scan MARX system instead of, say, a normal 3-axis constant-E scan?

R. SCHERM: In our particular environment, i.e. in the guide hall, the fast background is extremely low. Moreover, the constant-E MARX arrangement illustrated in Fig.9 has a narrow entrance slit in front of the detector. The noise figure should therefore be better than in the standard MARX arrangement with a wide detector opening.

A NEW SPECTROMETER FOR THE STUDY
OF QUASI-ELASTIC NEUTRON SCATTERING

D. GLASENAPP, F. SCHMIDT, R. STOCKMEYER,
H. STORTNIK, R. WAGNER
Institut für Festkörperforschung der
   Kernforschungsanlage Jülich GmbH,
Jülich,
Federal Republic of Germany

Abstract

A NEW SPECTROMETER FOR THE STUDY OF QUASI-ELASTIC NEUTRON SCATTERING.
   The neutron spectrometer SV5-C at the FRJ-2 reactor of the KFA Jülich is a conventional time-of-flight machine, with additional equipment for studying quasi-elastic line broadening. We describe first the configuration for the time-of-flight measurement and then the alternative analysing device, which consists of thirty crystals, arranged for large Bragg angles. For elastic scattering with $E_0 = 3.41$ meV a resolution (FWHM) $\Delta E \approx 70$ μeV is achieved with time-of-flight and a resolution $\Delta E \approx 20$ μeV with crystal analysis.

1. INTRODUCTION

Quasi-elastic line broadening of the order of 10 μeV is often investigated with time-of-flight spectrometers. They are, however, not well suited for these problems, because on the one hand the range of measured energy transfer is much too large, while on the other hand the time exploitation is very poor. With a statistical chopper the duty cycle is much better than with a Fermi chopper. However, because of the less good signal/noise ratio it becomes difficult to measure accurately the shape of the wings of quasi-elastic distributions, which often are very important. In the following, we describe a modification of our time-of-flight spectrometer SV5-C at the FRJ-2 reactor in Jülich [1]. Alternatively to the usual time-of-flight mode of operation, it can be used as a multicrystal spectrometer, which is well adapted to the problems mentioned.

Besides this, there are many problems, where the temperature dependence of neutron scattering intensities is of interest. Such measurements are possible in practice with large temperature steps only, because of the long time needed for each time-of-flight experiment. Special difficulties appear with studies on absorbed molecules, because one cannot use two different spectrometers for inelastic and for quasi-elastic scattering: the sample cannot simply be degassed,

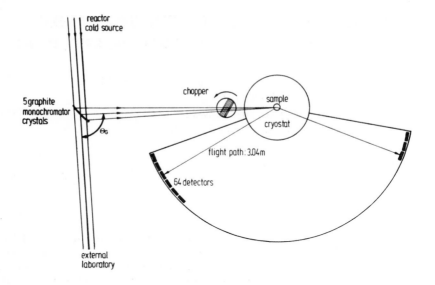

FIG.1.   The design of the time-of-flight spectrometer SV5-C.

and the intensity difference to the empty can run is usually so small that both
should be done immediately one after the other. Therefore, both types of
operation should be available at the same instrument. At the spectrometer
SV5-C, only few manipulations are necessary to change from the time-of-flight
to the multicrystal technique.

2.   CONFIGURATION OF THE TIME-OF-FLIGHT SPECTROMETER

The design of the spectrometer is shown in Fig.1. The neutrons from the
reactor are slowed down by a cold source; the number of neutrons with a wavelength of about 4.9 Å is enhanced in this way by a factor of 10.

In the evacuated neutron guide, which takes the neutrons to an external
laboratory [2], the monochromator for the spectrometer SV5-C is installed in
the reactor hall. A group of five ⟨200⟩-oriented graphite crystals reflects neutrons
of a wavelength of 4.9 Å under a Bragg angle of 91°. The primary neutron beam
has a cross-section of 10 cm × 10 cm and so the five plane graphite crystals
have a width of 3 cm to cover the whole incoming beam. With these crystals,
the monochromatic beam is focused on the sample area of 3 cm × 12 cm. In
order to change the incoming wavelength, the graphite crystals must be turned

and the whole spectrometer must be displaced. This can be done by hand with the help of an air-cushion, although the total weight of the spectrometer is 30 t.

On its way to the sample, the neutron beam passes the beam shutter and the chopper position. Different choppers can be mounted for different purposes. The sample is placed in a cryostat, which is integrated in the spectrometer so that the total flight path of the neutrons from the reactor to the detectors can be evacuated. The cryostat is a liquid N_2 (or He) continuous flow cryostat for temperatures from 10 to 300 K.

The scattered neutrons are detected over a range of scattering angles, between 20 and 160°, mounted in a half circle around the sample position at a distance of 3.04 m (flight path). Each detector consists of six ^{3}He tubes, each one 40 cm high and with a diameter of 1 cm. The detectors are shielded with a mixture of Na_2BO_3 and water or H_3BO_4 and polyethylene granulate against fast and slow background neutrons from the reactor hall.

This is an efficient arrangement for the study of problems, for which the scattering law $S(Q,\omega)$ depends only weakly on the momentum transfer $\hbar\vec{Q}$, that is in particular for incoherent scattering. The energy resolution of the spectro-meter is 70 μeV for elastic scattering. Some experiments carried out with this arrangement are presented in another paper presented at this conference [3].

The spectrometer is controlled by a PDP11/40 computer with a 96 K memory, two discs, two CAMAC crates [4] and a data display. The software system is a real time FORTRAN program with fast assembler routines for disc access, CAMAC access and display, using the overlay technique to have an almost unlimited volume for the FORTRAN programs [5]. Besides starting, stopping, supervising and interrupting the current run, there are 50 different programs for data handling. They can run simultaneously with the measurement and its supervision. In addition to small manipulations like changing experimental parameters (for instance the analysing channel width or the permissible tempera-ture variation for the sample), adding data from different scattering angles or channels etc., we can subtract empty can data, apply various data corrections (for instance detector properties, monitor ratios, neutron absorption) convert to $S(Q, \omega)$, extract density of state functions etc. Finally, there is a program with a free subroutine for any assumed scattering law, to be compared with experi-mental results on a time-of-flight scale, after folding the data with the experi-mental resolution function. Fitting procedures are also available, but they are rather slow.

In addition to this software system, there is a fast data path to the central IBM computer, where further calculations can be done, especially those calculations for which the PDP11/40 is too slow, for instance, if there are numerical integrals in the assumed scattering law, or if parameters of the scattering law shall be fitted.

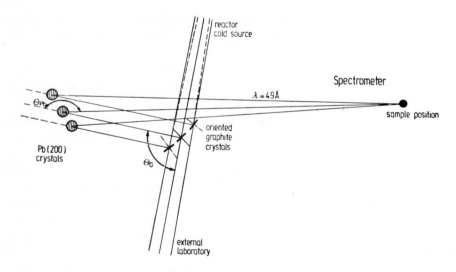

FIG.2.   *The asymmetric focussing double monochromator.*

3.   THE DOUBLE MONOCHROMATOR

In order to use the crystal analyser system we need an incoming beam, which is comparable in energy spread to the analyser resolution. There are two different possibilities to achieve this: As

$$\frac{\Delta\lambda}{\lambda} \equiv \frac{1}{2}\cot\left(\frac{\theta_M}{2}\right) \cdot \Delta\theta_M$$

with λ the neutron wavelength and θ_M the monochromator scattering angle, one can (a) diminish the angular divergence $\Delta\theta_M$, or (b) use scattering angles θ_M near 180°.

For (a), one needs a collimator before and behind the monochromator crystal. Because of the multi-use of the beam from the cold source (Fig.1) we have to work with a second reflection in the monochromatic beam. The intensity loss is governed by three factors: the reflectivity of the second crystal (≈ 0.7 for graphite), the remaining loss of the collimators for neutrons passing in its mean direction (≈ 0.6 for short collimators) and the square of the resolution gain, which is a consequence of not only reducing the transmitted wavelength width but also the transmitted solid angle. Installations are available for such a monochromator, if a moderate improvement of the resolution is needed.

For a large resolution gain, (b) is more advantageous, and we choose the asymmetric arrangement shown in Fig.2 [6], because the usual symmetric double monochromator is not possible at the neutron guide. Three of the graphite crystals reflect the incoming beam from the cold source to the opposite side of the spectrometer under a scattering angle of $\theta_G \approx 91°$. The beam is reflected again by three ⟨200⟩-oriented lead crystals under a large Bragg angle. Each of these crystals is a cylinder of 3 cm diameter and 10 cm height. The beam is focused on the sample position as shown in Fig.2.

In a first alignment of the asymmetric double monochromator, we have set it to a scattering angle $\theta_{Pb} = 166°$. This is an extreme position with respect to resolution and intensity: The resolution gain, compared to the graphite mono-chromator, is the ratio of the $\cot\theta_M$-factors (in our case $\cot(166°):\cot(90°) = 9:1$, for the angular divergence remains unchanged) and the resolution becomes $\approx 6 \mu eV$. The intensity loss is governed by two factors, the reflectivity of the lead crystals, which is 0.25 at best, and the resolution gain. Experimentally, we get 1.5%, and the remaining loss is due to the fact that we now only use three graphite crystals and the adjustment is not optimal. In case (a), using collimators, the remaining intensity would only be 0.5% for the same resolution gain at best, and the neutron flux at the sample position would be further more reduced because with collimators the 10 cm × 10 cm primary beam cannot be focused to the sample area.

As will be discussed in section 4, this resolution is too good, compared to our crystal analyser system. With the asymmetric monochromator at this position we can study the features of the analyser system. For usual experiments, the monochromator resolution will be adapted to the analyser resolution by reducing the scattering angle at the monochromator.

4.   ANALYSER CRYSTALS IN A TIME-OF-FLIGHT SPECTROMETER

On the analyser side, back-scattering crystals can be used in the same way as for our monochromator, in order to achieve good energy resolution. The large number of detectors installed for the time-of-flight measurement should be used too. We therefore choose an arrangement as shown in Fig.3. The sample is surrounded by 30 analyser crystals, mounted under the scattering angles $10° \leqslant \theta_S \leqslant 170°$ in a distance of 36 cm from the sample. We use the same ⟨200⟩ oriented lead crystals as for the asymmetric double monochromator.

These lead crystals reflect neutrons under their Bragg angle θ_A, and each lead crystal can aim at any detector. This means that there is a set of up to 64 measurable energy transfers which are defined by the geometrical arrangement of the detectors. Obviously, at a given time each analyser crystal must reflect unambiguously to a different detector.

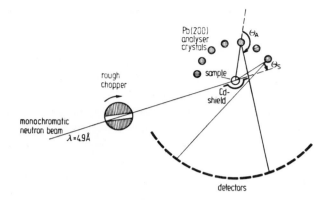

FIG.3.　The analyser crystal system in the time-of-flight spectrometer.

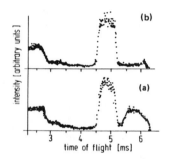

FIG.4.　Time-of-flight spectrum (a) with and (b) without an analyser crystal aiming at a detector. We used a rough chopper. The sample is polycrystalline nickel. The broad peak at 5 ms is due to the neutrons directly reflected by the sample. The peak at 5.8 ms in (a) represents the signal neutrons. The peak at 2.5 ms is from the higher order neutrons, which have twice the velocity.

As the detectors also see neutrons directly from the sample, those arriving after reflection from the lead crystals may be identified by the time-of-flight technique. Therefore, we use a rough chopper, which leads to time-of-flight spectra, one of which is shown in Fig.4. While the broad peak in the middle is due to the elastically scattered neutrons which directly reach the detectors, the smaller peak at later times is due to the neutrons reflected by the analyser lead crystal. The peak at the left side of the curve at shorter time-of-flight is due to the higher order neutrons which have twice the velocity. They can be suppressed by a beryllium filter.

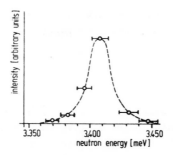

FIG.5. Resolution function of the analyser system for one back-scattering lead crystal. The sample is polycrystalline nickel. The open circles are the neutron intensities from the different detectors, when the lead crystal reflects the beam to it. The bars indicate the width of the detectors. The dashed line is a guide to the eye.

Alternatively to the time-of-flight technique it is possible to capture the direct neutrons by a cadmium shield as shown in Fig.3. According to experience, a combination of both methods brings the best results to reduce the background scattering.

The resolution of the crystal arrangement is limited by the vertical divergence of the beam from the sample to the analyser crystals via the lead crystals. The analyser resolution is limited therefore to 15 μeV. The resolution function of the system, measured with a polycrystalline Ni sample, is shown in Fig.5. As discussed in section 3, the contribution of the monochromator is small.

5.   FURTHER DEVELOPMENT OF THE SPECTROMETER

Now we will describe the spectrometer, which is designed but not yet tested.

First, the ⟨111⟩ plains of the analyser lead crystals can be used instead of the ⟨200⟩ plane. So, neutrons of $\lambda = 4.9$ Å are scattered under 120°. The resolution gain is rather small and the monochromator will consist of two graphite crystals and two collimators as discussed in section 3. This arrangement is useful if only the elastic line is interesting and the line broadening is more than 20 μeV, or if a phase transition is observed. With this arrangement the incoming neutron wavelength can easily be changed by displacing one graphite crystal and a collimator.

In the other case, using the asymmetric double monochromator (Fig.2), it is more complicated to change the incoming energy. Displacing the whole spectrometer cannot be done by the computer, and therefore we must either heat the monochromator lead crystals or use the Doppler effect. This gives us more experimental points at the elastic line.

The whole system of the analyser crystals is controlled by the PDP 11/40 computer. This needs an elaborate software which is designed for the following operations:

(a)   Analyser variation

The computer gets a matrix which assigns each analyser crystal to every detector. Each matrix element means an energy transfer in a diagram like Fig.5, for a certain scattering angle. Only those matrix elements are kept, for which the energy transfer is in the interesting quasi-elastic range. The initial position, where the measurement is started, is the first line of this matrix. Then one crystal after the other is turned to the next detector in a rigid sequence, with the first detector counting until the last crystal has reached its new position. The number of neutron counts gets all necessary corrections and the data are recorded on the disc. Then the crystal is turned to the next detector and the next point is started. Because of the rigid sequence, the next detector is not used by any other crystal.

(b)   Monochromator variation

Here the monochromator energy is changed by the computer, while the analyser crystals do not move. If the lead crystal monochromator (section 2) is used, its temperature must be varied, while, when we use the graphite crystals and collimators, the graphite crystals and a collimator must be displaced. This leads to points in between those from the analyser variation.

(c)   Parameter variation

For this type of experiment monochromator as well as analyser crystals remain unchanged. The analyser crystals can reflect elastically or inelastically scattered neutrons and the sample temperature or another parameter is varied.

6.   SUMMARY

The neutron spectrometer described can be used either as a time-of-flight or as a crystal instrument.

For conventional time-of-flight runs we use a graphite monochromator, fully evacuated beam guides, an integrated cryostat with an elaborate temperature control system, and 64 detector groups after a flight path of 3.04 m to measure at many scattering angles simultaneously.

Instead of the energy analysis with the time-of-flight technique, 30 back-scattering analyser lead crystals can be used to get a resolution of 20 μeV. The arrangement is similar to a triple-axis-spectrometer. The differences are that because of the large analyser angles it is possible to get a good energy resolution, that the time-of-flight technique allows to distinguish between the signal neutrons and background neutrons, and that thirty scattering angles can be measured at a time.

The idea of an optimized spectrometer for quasi-elastic, incoherent neutron scattering is not best realized by adding the components described to the existing time-of-flight spectrometer. However, the experiments with these components show that a new spectrometer could be designed with good quality crystals and a position sensitive detector, which then could very successfully operate in the gap between the existing back-scattering spectrometers on the one hand and high resolution triple axis and time-of-flight spectrometers on the other hand.

ACKNOWLEDGEMENT

The authors wish to express their gratitude to Prof. Stiller for helpful discussions and critical reading of the manuscript.

REFERENCES

[1]   STOCKMEYER, R., Jül-Rep.-1162 (1975).
[2]   BAUER, G., JOSWIG, G., SCHELTEN, J., SCHMATZ, W., Kerntechnik **14** 9 (1972).
[3]   STOCKMEYER, R., STORTNIK, H., these Proceedings, Vol.2, IAEA-SM-219/31.
[4]   DURCANSKY, G., GLASENAPP, D., CAMAC Bulletin (7 July 1973).
[5]   GLASENAPP, D., STORTNIK, H., Jül-Rep., to be published.
[6]   WANKA, T., Ing.-Arbeit FHS Aachen Abt. Jülich (1976);
      KAISER, T., Ing.-Arbeit FHS Aachen Abt. Jülich (1977);
      WESTERHAUSEN, W., Ing.-Arbeit FHS Aachen Abt. Jülich (1977).

DISCUSSION

J.W. WHITE *(Chairman)*: What was the intensity penalty incurred through installing the backscattering geometry in your spectrometer? In other words, what did it cost you to go to a resolution of about 40 μeV?

R. STOCKMEYER: The monochromatic beam from the graphite crystals is reflected a second time by the lead crystals at a scattering angle of 166°. The resulting intensity loss factor is given by the product (reflectivity) $\times$ (reduction in wavelength interval) $\times$ (reduction in the number of crystals in the focusing

multicrystal arrangement). The loss factor is thus $0.25 \times 0.1 \times 0.6 = 1.5\%$.
Compared with the time-of-flight analyser the intensity gain factor of the
crystal analyser at the elastic line is given by the product (duty cycle gain)
$\times$ (reflectivity of analyser crystals) $\cong 500 \times 0.25 = 1.25$.

THERMAL DIFFUSE SCATTERING
IN MOVING SINGLE CRYSTALS

W. MINOR, I. SOSNOWSKA, H. KĘPA
Institute of Experimental Physics,
University of Warsaw,
Warsaw,
Poland

Abstract

THERMAL DIFFUSE SCATTERING IN MOVING SINGLE CRYSTALS.
The thermal diffuse-scattering contribution to Bragg peaks in moving single crystals is discussed. A simple reciprocal-lattice construction is presented in the case of neutrons scattered inelastically by moving lattices. The theoretical calculations concerning the energy distribution of thermal diffuse-scattering intensity in a rotating single crystal yield results which seem to be in good agreement with experiment. The experimental results are independent of extinction effects.

INTRODUCTION

Achievement of high accuracy in neutron diffraction requires detailed consideration of all effects affecting the intensity of the diffraction maxima. One of the effects which should be taken into account is thermal diffuse scattering (TDS). TDS gives peaks beneath the Bragg peaks and can contribute substantially to the observed intensity (see, e.g. Ref.[1]). As has been discussed in a number of recent papers [1−5], correction of measured intensities for TDS is necessary; however, this is difficult, in practice. The effect of ignoring the TDS correction is generally equivalent to an artificial decrease in the Debye-Waller factor (see, e.g. Ref.[5]).

The theoretical estimation of thermal diffuse scattering requires knowledge of the elastic constants and use of a theory involving numerous approximations. Moreover, this estimate requires numerical integration over the respective volume in the reciprocal space.

Since diffuse scattering and Bragg scattering are maximized simultaneously, it is difficult to separate these effects experimentally. In the X-ray case, a direct test of theory has been provided by measurements involving the Mössbauer effect [6−7]. In neutron diffraction, only few experiments have been devised for testing the validity of numerous assumptions made by the theory [8]. The use of the crystal in motion makes it possible to shift the TDS peak from the elastic-scattering position; moreover, the results are independent of extinction.

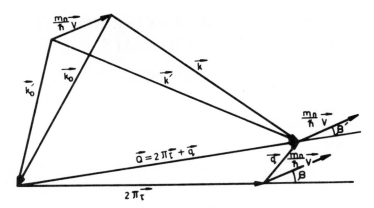

FIG.1.   *Reciprocal-lattice construction for the case of inelastic scattering in a moving lattice.*
$\vec{k}_0$ *and* $\vec{k}$ *are the incident and scattered neutron wavevectors in the moving crystal frame,* $\vec{k}_0'$
and $\vec{k}'$ *are the incident and scattered neutron wavevectors in the laboratory frame,* $\vec{V}$ *is the*
velocity of the crystal, β' *is the angle between the scattering vector* $\vec{Q}$ *and the velocity vector* $\vec{V}$.
The other symbols have their usual meaning.

THEORY

Coherent one-phonon scattering of neutrons is governed by the momentum
and energy conservation laws. The momentum conservation and energy conservation laws have different forms in the laboratory frame and the moving-crystal
frame [9].

Figure 1 illustrates the reciprocal-lattice construction for the case of inelastic
scattering in a moving lattice. In Fig.1, $\vec{k}_0$ and $\vec{k}$ represent the wavevectors of the
incident and the scattered neutron in the moving crystal frame, $\vec{k}_0'$ and $\vec{k}'$ are
the wavevectors of the incident and the scattered neutron in the laboratory frame,
β' is the angle between the scattering vector $\vec{Q} = 2\pi\vec{\tau} + \vec{q}$ and the crystal velocity
$\vec{V}$, where $\vec{\tau}$ is the reciprocal lattice vector and $\vec{q}$ is the wavevector of the lattice
mode of vibration. The wavevector of the incident neutron in the crystal frame
is described by the equation:

$$\vec{k}_0 = \vec{k}_0' - V \frac{m_n}{\hbar} \tag{1}$$

where m_n is the neutron mass and $\hbar = h/2\pi$, h being the Planck constant. The
wavevector of the scattered neutron in the laboratory frame (see Fig.1) is given
by the equation

$$\vec{k}' = \vec{k} + \vec{V} \frac{m_n}{\hbar} \tag{2}$$

These equations and the trigonometrical calculations based on Fig.1 lead to the equations

$$\vec{k}' - \vec{k}_0' = 2\pi\vec{\tau} + \vec{q} = \vec{Q}$$

$$\vec{k}'^2 - \vec{k}_0'^2 = \pm \frac{2\,m_n\,\omega_j\,(\vec{q})}{\hbar} + \frac{2\,m_n\,VQ\cos\beta'}{\hbar} \qquad (3)$$

which represent the momentum and energy conservation laws in the laboratory frame, respectively. In equations (3) "+" corresponds to phonon annihilation and "−" corresponds to phonon creation.

For a stationary crystal ($\vec{k} = \vec{k}'$, $\vec{k}_0 = \vec{k}_0'$ when $\vec{V} = 0$), Eqs (3) can be transformed into the well-known form

$$\vec{k} - \vec{k}_0 = 2\,\pi\vec{\tau} + \vec{q}$$

$$\frac{\hbar^2 k^2}{2\,m_n} - \frac{\hbar^2 k_0^2}{2\,m_n} = \pm\hbar\omega_j\,(\vec{q}) \qquad (4)$$

For elastic scattering in moving lattices ($\beta' = \beta$, $\vec{Q} = 2\pi\vec{\tau}$ when $\vec{q} = 0$), Eqs (3) can be rewritten as

$$\vec{k}' - \vec{k}_0' = 2\pi\vec{\tau}$$

$$k'^2 - k_0'^2 = \frac{4\pi m_n\,V\,\tau\cos\beta}{\hbar} \qquad (5)$$

where β is the angle between the reciprocal-lattice vector $\vec{\tau}$ and the crystal velocity $\vec{V}$. Substituting in Eqs (5) neutron velocity vectors for the neutron wave-vectors we obtain these equations in the form as given in Ref.[10].

METHOD AND NUMERICAL CALCULATIONS

The principle of the experimental set-up is shown in Fig.2. A collimated monochromatic neutron beam is scattered by a spinning single crystal with the zone axis parallel to the axis of rotation and perpendicular to the experimental plane. The intensities of the neutrons scattered by the crystal are measured by means of a neutron counter connected to a multichannel time analyser. The counter was placed in the Bragg position for the reflection under investigation. The time distributions of the diffracted neutrons were investigated by the time-of-flight technique. The neutrons scattered elastically are recorded by the multichannel

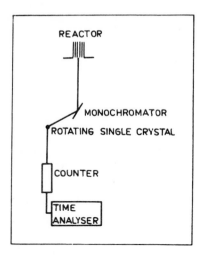

FIG.2. Principle of experiment.

time analyser in the channel

$$N = \frac{\lambda m_n \ell}{h \Delta t} \tag{6}$$

where λ is the neutron wavelength, ℓ the distance between the sample and the counter (flight path), and Δt is the time width of the channel. It was assumed that the time analyser was triggered when the crystallographic plane under investigation is in the reflecting position. Scattering with change of the neutron energy can take place not only in the Bragg position but also in the position which deviates from the Bragg position by an angle ϵ. The shift ΔN in the channel number, which corresponds to the change ΔE of the neutron energy, is given by

$$\Delta N = \frac{\lambda m_n \ell}{h \Delta t} \left(\frac{A}{\sqrt{A^2 + \Delta E \lambda^2}} - 1 \right) + \frac{\epsilon}{\omega \Delta t} \tag{7}$$

where ω is the angular velocity of the crystal and A is a constant relating the neutron wavelength in ångströms to the energy in milli-electron-volts

$$\lambda = \frac{A}{\sqrt{E}} = \frac{9.044}{\sqrt{E}} \tag{8}$$

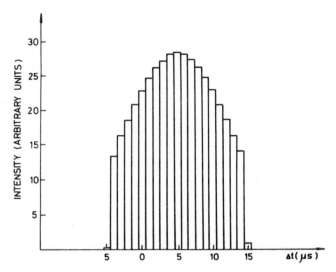

FIG.3. Typical profile of thermal diffuse scattering maximum obtained numerically for the CaF$_2$ crystal (reflection $2\bar{2}0$).

The profile of the thermal diffuse scattering maximum in the time scale was obtained theoretically by using a computer program. The TDS contribution to the neutron intensity measured at a fixed orientation of the crystal can be calculated by summing the scattering cross-sections for all the modes lying on the scattering surfaces of the rotating crystal (Eqs (3)). The procedure has to be repeated for a set of different positions of the crystal because the angle between $\vec{k}_0$ and the reflecting plane also varies continuously as a result of the crystal rotation. This approach is analogous to integration over the respective volume in the reciprocal space. Since the crystal velocity $\vec{V}$ "seen" by the neutron on its path is varying continuously, the crystal was divided into a number of squares with dimensions small enough to allow neglecting the variation of $\vec{V}$ within each square and assuming its constancy. The scattering process occurred in the centre of a square. It was also assumed that the elastic properties of the crystal are approximately isotropic, only the low frequencies of the acoustic modes are important, and the dispersion effects can be ignored. Mosaic spread and divergence of the incident beam were ignored. As a result of these calculations (the ϵ-step was 0.02° and the crystal was divided into 400 squares), a profile of the maximum of the thermal diffuse scattering was obtained. Such a profile for a $2\bar{2}0$ reflection from CaF$_2$ is shown in Fig.3 as an example of numerically obtained results.

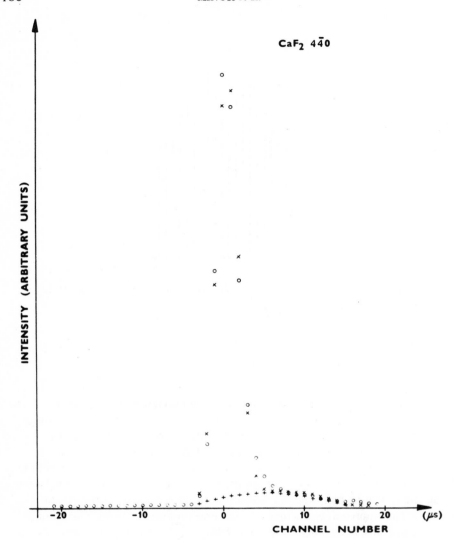

FIG.4. *Typical neutron diffraction pattern obtained with the set-up in Fig.2 for CaF_2 single crystal (reflection $4\bar{4}0$). X − observed intensity, ○ − calculated thermal diffuse scattering, + − calculated intensity (TDS + Bragg scattering).*

EXPERIMENT AND RESULTS

The measurements were performed by using the TKSN-420 neutron spectrometer at the EWA reactor in Świerk. A pyrolitic graphite monochromator was used and the collimation of the incident beam was 30′ of arc. A scintillation

counter with a circular (diameter 2 cm) ZnS (Ag) boron-loaded scintillator was
used. The counter was connected to a 1024-channel time analyser. The flight
path ℓ could be varied by shifting the counter within the shielding. The rotation
speed of the motor driving the crystal could be varied continuously from
1200 rev/min to 18 000 rev/min and it could be stabilized within this range with
a high accuracy controlled by a RC generator. Single crystals of calcium fluoride
7−12 mm in dia. and bismuth 8−10 mm in dia. are used as samples. The [111]
and [001] crystallographic axes were parallel to the axis of rotation and perpendicular to the experimental plane for bismuth and calcium fluoride, respectively.

In the preliminary measurements, the integrated intensity of neutrons
scattered on the spinning single crystal as a function of the speed of rotation was
measured. The intensity of neutrons reflected from a rotating single crystal
increases with the speed of rotation [11]. By increasing the angular velocity of
the crystal, "saturation" of the measured integrated intensity may be obtained and
the saturation value can then be used as the extinction-free integrated Bragg
intensity [11, 12].

Further measurements were made for the range of rotation speeds where
the integrated intensity was independent of the angular velocity of the crystal.
A typical result of the experiment is presented in Fig.4, which shows the $4\bar{4}0$
reflection from the calcium fluoride crystal. The speed of rotation was
15 000 rev/min, and $\lambda = 1.36$ Å. In the same figure, the TDS profile obtained from
the computer program described above and the Bragg intensity calculated by the
least-square fit to the experimental points are shown. The input data corresponded
to the experimental conditions. The results of measurements made for other
crystals and wavelengths show a similar agreement with calculations.

CONCLUSIONS

The theoretical calculations of the energy distribution of TDS intensity in
a rotating single crystal yield results which seem to be in good agreement with
the experiments. Although the resolution in the method presented is worse than
that in Ref.[8], the method can be used for standard neutron spectrometers.
Moreover, the results presented are independent of extinction effects.

ACKNOWLEDGEMENTS

We wish to express our gratitude to Drs T. Giebułtowicz and A. Rajca for
helpful and stimulating discussions. We are also grateful to A. Barcz and S. Kulisz
for technical assistance.

REFERENCES

[1] WILLIS, B.T.M., PRYOR, W.W., Thermal Vibrations in Crystallography, Cambridge University Press (1975).

[2] COCHRAN, W., Acta Crystallogr. **A25** (1969) 95.

[3] ROUSE, K.D., COOPER, M.J., Acta Crystallogr. **A25** (1969) 615.

[4] WILLIS, B.T.M., Acta Crystallogr. **A26** (1970) 396.

[5] HARADA, J., SAKATA, M., Acta Crystallogr. **A30** (1974) 77.

[6] BUTT, N.M., O'CONNOR, D.A., Proc. Phys. Soc. **90** (1967) 247.

[7] WÖLFEL, E.R., BÄRNINGHAUSEN, E., Acta Crystallogr. **A31** (1975) 5180.

[8] STEICHELE, E., Acta Crystallogr. **A31** (1975) S180.

[9] LOWDE, R.D., in Use of Slow Neutrons to Investigate the Solid State (Proc. Meeting Stockholm, 1957) 112.

[10] BURAS, B., GIEBUŁTOWICZ, T., Acta Crystallogr. **A28** (1975) 15.

[11] BURAS, B., GIEBUŁTOWICZ, T., MINOR, W., RAJCA, A., Nucl. Instrum. Methods **77** (1970) 13.

[12] GIEBUŁTOWICZ, T., MINOR, W., SOSNOWSKA, I., Institute of Experimental Physics, Warsaw University Report No IFD/1/1976.

DISCUSSION

E. STEICHELE: Can you confirm that the relative shift $\Delta\tau/\tau$ between TDS-peak and Bragg-peak is of the same order as the ratio of the Doppler velocity of the crystal to the velocity of sound?

I. SOSNOWSKA: The relative shift $\Delta\tau/\tau$ is a function of this ratio, but the relationship is not proportional.

C.G. WINDSOR: It would be a great help to diffraction experimenters if thermal diffuse scattering could be removed. Can it be completely separated from the Bragg scattering?

I. SOSNOWSKA: Separation should be possible with a moving single crystal at a sufficiently high constant velocity $\vec{V}$.

THE MULTIPLANE ANALYSER

P.P. CHANDRA, B.A. DASANNACHARYA
Nuclear Physics Division,
Bhabha Atomic Research Centre,
Trombay, Bombay,
India

Abstract

THE MULTIPLANE ANALYSER.
 A new method of using a single crystal as an energy analyser or a filter is suggested. This requires the beam to be incident along a high-symmetry direction and utilizes all the planes of a given set (hkl) for reflecting the neutrons. Expressions for the reflectivity of such a system are derived, and numerical calculations are made for several crystals. It is found that in the transmission geometry it is possible to obtain a peak reflectivity higher than 50%, the theoretical maximum for the normal case. An experiment is done to verify this result. It is shown that often gains in reflectivity of 1.5 to 2.5 times can be achieved. Some applications are suggested.

1. INTRODUCTION

The most common method of neutron monochromatization and energy analysis makes use of single-crystal Bragg reflection. Considerable effort has therefore been spent in recent years on improving the reflectivity of crystals like Ge, Cu, etc. [1−5]. The aim is, in general, to achieve the reflectivity of an "ideally imperfect" crystal. Here, we suggest a scheme by which, in principle, one should be able to achieve an 'effective' reflectivity better than that of an "ideally imperfect" crystal. The idea is to utilize all the planes of a set (hkl) by a proper choice of direction and wavelength of the incident neutrons. For example, if a beam of neutrons of wavelength λ is incident on a single crystal along a high-symmetry direction, like an n-fold rotation axis, several independent equivalent (hkl) planes will reflect simultaneously when the Bragg condition is satisfied. The effective reflectivity would, therefore, be enhanced. Since this scheme entails the use of more than one crystal plane at a time (and several detectors) we call it a multiplane reflector or a multiplane analyser[1]. As an illustration, Fig. 1 shows a typical multiplane geometry when the incident beam is along a 6-fold rotation axis of a hexagonal crystal. The reflected neutrons are detected in six detectors.

---

[1] A preliminary account of this work has been reported earlier. See CHANDRA, P.P., DASANNACHARYA, B.A., Nucl. Phys. and Solid State Physics (India) 17C (1974). There are some errors in this paper.

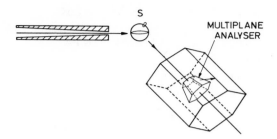

FIG.1. A conceptual assembly for diffraction with multiplane analyser.

In the next section, expressions for the effective peak and integrated reflectivities of the multiplane reflector will be derived. Subsequently, numerical calculations are given in order to examine the usefulness of this scheme in practice. Then, some experimental results will be presented to verify the ideas presented earlier in a qualitative way. Finally, some possible applications will be mentioned.

2.   MULTIPLANE REFLECTIVITY

The expressions for the peak and integrated reflectivities in reflection and transmission geometries will be derived following the procedure of Bacon and Lowde [6] and Zachariasen [7] for the single-plane case.

Let neutrons of wavelength λ be incident on an infinitely wide, ideally imperfect crystal along an n-fold rotation axis. Let r dt $\equiv$ QW(Δ)dt be the reflectivity of a (hkl) plane for a crystal thickness dt. Here $Q = \lambda^3 N_c^2 F^2 \exp(-2W)/\sin 2\theta_B$ with the usual crystallographic notations, and $W(\Delta) = (1/\sqrt{2\pi}\eta) \exp(-\Delta^2/2\eta^2)$ is the distribution function of the mosaic blocks of the crystal with η being the mosaic spread and Δ the deviation from the mean Bragg angle [6].

Following Zachariasen and Bacon and Lowde, we denote by $P_i(t)$ and $P_d(t)$ the powers of the incident and *one* of the n reflected beams at a depth t inside the crystal. The power equations, giving the rate of change of power with depth, can now be written as

$$d\,P_i(t) = \left[-P_i(t)\,\frac{(\mu+\gamma n)}{\Gamma_i}\,dt + P_d(t)\,\frac{\gamma n}{\Gamma_d}\,dt \right] \tag{1}$$

and

$$d\,P_d(t) = \pm \left[-P_i(t)\,\frac{\gamma}{\Gamma_i}\,dt + P_d(t)\,\frac{(\mu+\gamma)}{\Gamma_d}\,dt \right] \tag{2}$$

Γ_i and Γ_d are direction cosines of the incident and outgoing beams with respect to the inward normal to the crystal face, μ is the linear attenuation coefficient and the $+$ or $-$ signs apply to the reflection and transmission geometries, respectively. Differentiating and eliminating $P_i(t)$, we find for the case of *reflection geometry*

$$\frac{d^2 P_d(t)}{dt^2} + 2\,b\,\frac{d\,P_d(t)}{dt} - \delta^2 P_d(t) = 0 \tag{3}$$

where

$$2\,b = \left[\frac{(\mu + \gamma n)}{\Gamma_i} - \frac{(\mu + \gamma)}{\Gamma_d} \right] \tag{4}$$

and

$$\delta^2 = \left[\frac{(\mu + \gamma)(\mu + \gamma n) - n\gamma^2}{\Gamma_i \Gamma_d} \right] \tag{5}$$

For this geometry, the boundary conditions $P_i(0) = P_0$ and $P_d(t_0) = 0$, where t_0 is the thickness of the crystal, apply. The reflectivity defined as $R_R(\Delta) \equiv n\,P_d(0)/P_0$ turns out to be given by

$$R_R(\Delta) = \frac{n\,(\gamma/\Gamma_i)\,(1-K)}{[b + (\mu + \gamma)/\Gamma_d]\,(1-K) + \sqrt{b^2 + \delta^2}\,(1+K)} \tag{6}$$

where

$$K = \exp[(-2\sqrt{b^2 + \delta^2})\,t_0] \tag{7}$$

It is instructive to examine some special cases. When $n \neq 1$ and $\mu = 0$, i.e. for non-absorbing crystals, $\delta \to 0$, and we find the simple expression:

$$R_R(\Delta) = \frac{n\,\Gamma_d\,(1-K)}{n\,\Gamma_d - K\,\Gamma_i} \tag{8}$$

which can easily be seen to reduce to the Bacon and Lowde expression

$$R_R(\Delta) = \frac{\gamma\,t_0/\Gamma}{1 + \gamma\,t_0/\Gamma} \tag{9}$$

when $n = 1$ and symmetric reflection ($\Gamma_i = \Gamma_d = \Gamma$) is considered. (Bacon and Lowde use $\check{r}$ for our r/Γ). For absorbing crystals in symmetric reflection position,

TABLE I. REFLECTION GEOMETRY

	(hkl)	$2\theta_B$	$\lambda(\text{Å})$	$R^{max}\%$ Multi	$R^{max}\%$ Single	R^λ Multi	R^λ Single
1.	Zn(013)	108.9	2.18	89.5	45.7	52.2	21.3
	Mg(013)	116.0	2.50	83.8	31.4	43.5	13.6
	Ge(113)	129.5	3.08	91.3	57.7	53.4	27.5
	Ge(115)	148.4	2.09	84.0	39.0	17.0	6.7
	Al(113)	129.5	2.20	66.7	26.7	21.1	7.6
	Pb(113)	129.5	2.69	96.7	57.8	47.9	23.3
2.	Ge(113)	121.0	2.96	79.0	53.8	48.1	28.8
	Al(113)	121.0	2.12	47.7	23.3	16.5	7.6
	Pb(113)	121.0	2.59	83.9	53.4	43.2	24.2
	Pb(133)	136.0	2.10	70.4	35.6	18.6	8.6
	Pb(022)	109.5	2.85	79.4	61.7	60.2	40.4
3.	Pb(131)	117.0	2.54	62.1	51.4	32.1	24.4

1. Incident beam along (001); n = 6 for hcp and 4 for cubic crystals
2. Incident beam along (111); n = 3
3. Incident beam along (110); n = 2

we can regain the standard expression for the conventional Bragg reflection condition, i.e.

$$R_R(\Delta) = \frac{\gamma/\mu}{(1 + \gamma/\mu) + (1 + 2\gamma/\mu)^{1/2} \coth\left[\dfrac{\mu t_0}{\sin\theta_B}(1 + 2\gamma/\mu)\right]^{1/2}} \tag{10}$$

Integrated reflectivities R_R^θ and R_R^λ are given by [6]:

$$R_R^\theta = \int_{-\infty}^{\infty} R_R(\Delta)\, d\Delta \equiv R_R^\lambda/(2\, d_{hkl} \cos\theta_B) \tag{11}$$

It is relevant to remark here that in the multiplane case symmetric reflection is not possible for all planes and the more relevant case will be the one where the beam is incident perpendicular to the crystal surface, i.e. $\Gamma_i = 1$. Reflection geometry will then correspond to cases with a scattering angle larger than 90°, and transmission geometry to that with a scattering angle smaller than 90°.

For transmission geometry, the boundary conditions $P_i(0) = P_0$ and $P_d(0) = 0$ apply. The reflectivity defined as $R_T(\Delta) \equiv n\, P_d(t_0)/P_0$ now works out to be

$$R_T(\Delta) = \frac{n\,\gamma}{\Gamma_i\,(\sqrt{b^2 - \delta^2})}\, \sinh(\sqrt{b^2 - \delta^2}\; t_0)\, \exp(-b t_0) \tag{12}$$

with

$$2b = \left[\frac{(\mu + \gamma n)}{\Gamma_i} + \frac{(\mu + \gamma)}{\Gamma_d} \right] \tag{13}$$

Again, it is easy to deduce special cases. For $\mu = 0$ we find

$$R_T(\Delta) = \frac{n}{2}\, \frac{\gamma}{b\,\Gamma_i}\, [1 - \exp(-2\, b\, t_0) \tag{14}$$

which gives the maximum reflectivity in the transmission geometry as

$$R_T^{max} = \frac{n\,\gamma}{b\,\Gamma_i} \tag{15}$$

For normal incidence,

$$R_T^{max} = \frac{n}{n + (1/\Gamma_d)} \tag{16}$$

This can be much larger than the maximum value of 0.5 attainable with the conventional geometry. For $n = 6$ and when the outgoing beam is at 60° to the inward normal, $R_T^{max} = 0.75$. This property may be utilized in using the crystal as a single-crystal filter for certain specific wavelengths.

For $\mu = 0$ and $n = 1$, the transmitted reflectivity reduces to the standard expression

$$\frac{1}{2}\, [1 - \exp(-2\,\gamma\, t_0/\Gamma)] \tag{17}$$

when symmetric reflection is considered.

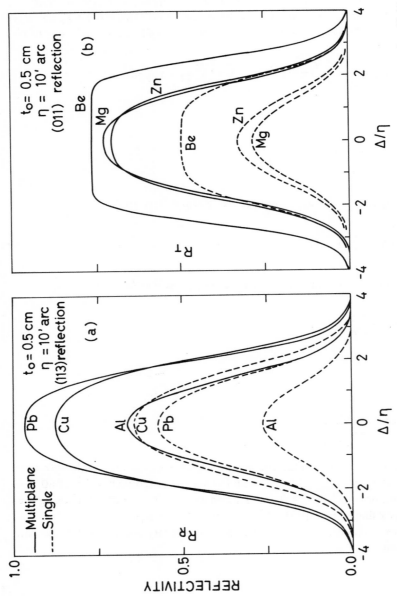

FIG. 2. Calculated diffraction curves for conventional and multiplane geometries in (a) reflection, and (b) transmission modes. Multiplicities for fcc and hcp crystals are 4 and 6, respectively. The incident beam is along the (001) direction.

TABLE II. REFLECTION GEOMETRY

(hkl*)	$2\theta_B$	λ(Å)	R^{max}%		R^{λ}	
			Multi	Single	Multi	Single
Zn(015)	133.6	1.67	82.8	27.7	19.4	5.4
Mg(015)	138.9	1.83	58.3	14.4	11.5	2.6
Be(013)	117.8	1.75	99.9	74.2	51.8	27.8
Be(015)	140.2	1.27	99.4	53.2	19.1	7.5
Be(114)	114.8	1.19	97.1	50.2	28.9	11.6
Be(016)	146.4	1.09	72.0	19.6	7.2	1.7
Be(018)	154.5	0.85	44.1	9.4	2.3	0.5
Be(027)	125.3	0.80	54.7	14.1	6.5	1.5
Cu(113)	129.5	1.97	92.9	63.8	37.1	20.6

*n = 6 for hcp and 4 for fcc crystals; incident beam along (001).

3.   CALCULATIONS

The reflectivities have been computed by using Eqs (6) and (12) for the multiplane and the conventional cases. The incident beam for the multiplane reflector is always normal to the crystal surface, i.e. $\Gamma_i = 1$, whereas for the single-plane cases the symmetric geometry $\Gamma_i = \Gamma_d = \Gamma$ is used, this being the usual mode of its utilization.

Calculations have been carried out for $t_0 = 0.5$ and 1.0 cm with $\eta = 5'$, 10' and 30' arc. The incident beam was assumed to be along (001), (111) or (110) directions giving n = (6, 4), 3 and 2, respectively. Some selected results of interest are listed in the tables.

(a)   Reflection geometry

Table I gives the peak and integrated reflectivities for some typical planes in the reflection geometry for $t_0 = 0.5$ cm and $\eta = 10'$.

The multiplane analyser in the reflection geometry is a high-resolution device since the scattering angle is by definition larger than 90°. Most of the reflections given in Table I are in the region of a scattering angle of 125° ± 10° giving cot $\theta_B \sim 0.5$ and hence high resolution. There are a number of reflections with quite high peak as well as integrated reflectivities even for a crystal thickness as small as 0.5 cm. Compared to conventional geometry the peak reflectivity

TABLE III. EFFECT OF t AND η VARIATION

(hkl*)	$2\theta_B$	λ(Å)		0.5 cm; 10'		1.0 cm; 10'		1.0 cm; 5'		0.5 cm; 5'	
				$R^{max}\%$	R^λ	$R^{max}\%$	R^λ	$R^{max}\%$	R^λ	$R^{max}\%$	R^λ
Zn(013)	108.9	2.18	Multi	89.5	52.2	93.0	61.5	96.5	36.0	96.0	32.2
			Single	45.7	21.3	59.9	30.6	73.2	21.0	62.1	15.9
Mg(112)	74.1	1.65	Multi	45.0	29.2	57.1	42.6	61.5	27.2	57.3	21.3
			Single	14.2	8.1	24.3	14.6	36.8	12.0	24.4	7.3
Be(034)	72.7	0.63	Multi	37.9	9.2	53.3	14.4	62.2	9.8	53.4	7.2
			Single	10.6	2.3	18.9	4.3	30.7	3.7	18.9	2.2
Pb(024)	126.8	1.97	Multi	69.1	21.0	87.6	30.0	97.5	19.3	87.9	15.1
			Single	28.6	7.8	44.3	12.9	61.3	9.8	44.5	6.5
Ge(115)	148.4	2.09	Multi	84.0	17.0	89.8	20.6	94.8	12.5	94.0	11.0
			Single	39.0	6.7	50.9	9.5	64.7	6.7	55.0	5.2
Ge(111)	70.5	3.76	Multi	38.6	107.9	26.0	80.9	25.9	43.6	38.5	59.2
			Single	39.8	90.7	31.7	83.1	31.7	46.2	39.8	52.1

*n = 6 for hcp and 4 for cubic crystals; incident beam along (001)

TABLE IV.   TRANSMISSION GEOMETRY

(hkl*)	$2\theta_B$	$\lambda(\overset{\circ}{A})$	$R^{max}\%$		R^{λ}	
			Multi	Single	Multi	Single
Mg(011)	56.1	2.31	72.8	28.8	111.2	35.3
Zn(011)	50.0	1.77	74.6	33.2	107.4	36.9
Zn(112)	66.8	1.29	55.2	18.6	33.8	9.8
Be(011)	57.8	1.68	76.1	49.8	121.1	62.6
Be(022)	57.8	0.84	38.3	9.2	16.0	3.6
Be(021)	30.9	0.51	43.2	9.5	22.0	4.5
Pb(111)	70.5	3.29	56.4	49.5	134.8	96.4**
Al(111)	70.5	2.69	55.1	48.0	80.7	44.0

*n   =   6 for hcp and 4 for cubic crystals; beam along (001).

**Some of these peaks can give much better reflectivities in the
conventional single-plane reflection geometry.   This has to be
individually examined.

R^{max} is larger by 1.5 to 3 times and the integrated reflectivity R^{λ} is larger by
1.5 to 2.5 times, for the reflections with n = 6, 4 or 3 in Table I. Not all reflections
show such gains, but examining the table it seems that the multiplane reflector
shows larger gains for metals like aluminium which are normally poor monochromators. These gains can be best made use of when the background is low. Since
an increase in the number of counters would linearly increase the background, a
guide-tube laboratory would be ideally suited for this application.

Figures 2a and 2b show the reflectivity $R(\Delta)$ against Δ/η both for
conventional and multiplane cases, for hcp and fcc crystals, respectively, for
n = 6 and 4.

Since multiplane configuration requires the scattering angle to be greater
than 90°, for reflection geometry wavelengths around 2 Å or more are usually
obtained. However, shorter wavelengths can also be obtained easily, particularly
with beryllium. These reflections are listed in Table II along with their
reflectivities, for t_0 = 0.5 cm and η = 10'. Wavelengths from 0.8 to 2.0 Å are
shown. Reflectivity as high as 99.9% is obtained even for a crystal of only
0.5 cm thickness for (013) reflection. Other reflections also show high peak
reflectivities and gains over the conventional geometry.

Finally, we have also examined the effect of varying t and η. Some of the
results are tabulated in Table III. One finds that when both t and η are doubled

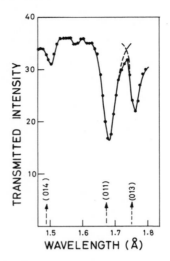

FIG.3.   *Transmitted intensity through a beryllium single crystal adjusted such that the incident beam was along the c-direction.*

from 0.5 cm and 5' arc to 1.0 cm and 10' arc the integrated intensity roughly doubles in reflection geometry. Calculations have also been done for $\eta = 30'$ for the same two values of thickness. The general result of this calculation suggests that, by increasing η, the loss in peak intensity is usually more than compensated for by the gain in integrated intensity. This is not usual with the conventional geometry. The most favourable example of this is Be(013) reflection, where R^{max} was reduced from 99.9% to 97.1% for η going from 5' to 30' arc but R^{λ} was increased from 28.8 to 120' Å. Other cases were far from so dramatic.

(b) Transmission geometry

Table IV gives the results of calculations for the transmission geometry. The most important point to note here is that it is possible, in principle, to achieve $R^{max} > 0.5$ which is the maximum for single-plane transmission. The theoretical maximum now (Eq. 16) becomes $n/(n + 1/\Gamma_d)$. That this is true, will be shown by experiments described in the next section for the Be(011) plane. Be(021) and Pb(111) are examples of other interesting planes. For Be(021) the transmission geometry can give better R^{max} and R^{λ} even than its reflecting geometry counterpart in the single-plane case.

4.   EXPERIMENTAL RESULTS

Some measurements have been performed on a beryllium single crystal
with its surface parallel to the basal plane. The crystal was aligned on a
diffractometer such that the incident beam was along the c-axis of the crystal.
The diffractometer had a Cu(111) monochromator and the incident wavelength
could be varied continuously. The transmitted beam was measured in a BF_3
counter. Figure 3 shows the transmitted intensity as a function of wavelength in
the range of 1.45 to 1.85 Å. Dips in the transmitted beam due to (014), (011)
and (013) reflections can be identified easily. A meaningful comparison is
possible only in the case of (011) reflection since it is only for this reflection
that the Bragg angle is nearly matched with the monochromator Bragg angle.
In other words, this gives parallel geometry with Be being aligned for transmission
geometry. The measured dip in the transmitted beam is not less than 53%,
demonstrating, in principle, that a reflectivity larger than 50% is possible. The
calculated peak reflectivity is $\sim$ 76%. The fact that the large dip is due to the
multiplane effect was further checked by rotating the Be-crystal so that the
incident beam was not along the c-direction. A drastic reduction in the dip was
observed.

Be(013) and (014) give much smaller dips since these planes reflect at much
larger angles than the Cu-monochromator. Be(013) with a calculated reflectivity
of 99.9% reflects λ = 1.75 Å at 117° 48' whereas Cu(111) reflects at 49° 37',
giving a ratio of cot θ_B of about 3.6. Furthermore, second-order contamination
has to be considered.

5.   SUMMARY AND POSSIBLE APPLICATIONS

A new geometry for the use of crystals has been proposed. This is called
the multiplane geometry since it utilizes several planes of a given set of (hkl)
planes. Expressions for peak and integrated reflectivities have been derived and
detailed calculations have been performed on several crystals. It is shown that
by utilizing this geometry it is possible to obtain considerable gains in peak as
well as integrated reflectivities, typical gains being 1.5 to 2.5 for multiplicities
of 4 and 6. It is possible to achieve high reflectivities even with rather thin
crystals. In reflection geometry it is a high-resolution device with good
reflectivities. The number of planes available in transmission proves to be rather
limited. However, a very interesting feature of the transmission geometry is that
one can obtain peak reflectivities larger than 50% which is the theoretical
maximum for the conventional case.

An experiment done to demonstrate the multiplane effect on Be(011) plane shows that it is possible to get reflectivities larger than 50% in the transmission geometry.

There are several potential applications for this device. It could be particularly useful as a high-resolution energy analyser, typically for cases shown in Table I. Since neutrons of these wavelengths can be guided out of the reactor hall, the background may not be a serious problem.

In principle, it can also be used for diffractometry if an inverted geometry is utilized for the experiment. The positions of monochromator and sample are now replaced by the sample and multiplane reflector. Different planes of the sample are then tuned to give Bragg reflection for the wavelength accepted by the analyser. Examples cited in Table II may be considered useful for this.

Finally, it is also possible to use this arrangement as an efficient single-crystal filter for eliminating higher-order neutrons. The demonstration experiment is one example of this for $\lambda = 3.35$ Å. Similarly, Be(013) and Be(015) planes may be used for $\lambda = 3.5$ and 2.54 Å neutrons, under favourable conditions.

ACKNOWLEDGEMENTS

The idea of utilizing several planes together for energy analysis arose during discussions on effective utilization of low- and medium-flux reactors. One of the authors (BAD) is grateful to Dr. N.S. Satya Murthy for several discussions on this point. The authors are grateful to Dr. P.K. Iyengar for inspiration provided by his innovative approach to experiments. We thank Dr. K.R. Rao for valuable comments on an earlier version of the manuscript.

REFERENCES

[1]   DOLLING, G., NIEMAN, H., Nucl. Instrum. Methods **49** (1967) 117.
[2]   TURBERFIELD, K.C., UKAEA Report AERE-R 5647 (1968).
[3]   DYMOND, R.R., BROCKHOUSE, B.N., in Instrumentation for Neutron Inelastic Scattering (Proc. Panel, Vienna, 1969), IAEA, Vienna (1970) 105.
[4]   ANTONINI, M., CORCHIA, M., NICOTERA, E., RUSTICHELLI, F., Nucl. Instrum. Methods **104** (1972) 147.
[5]   THAPER, C.L., DASANNACHARYA, B.A., DESHPANDE, A.S., IYENGAR, P.K., Nucl. Phys. Solid State Phys. (India) **17C** (1974) 446.
[6]   BACON, G.E., LOWDE, R.D., Acta Crystallogr. **1** (1948) 303.
[7]   ZACHARIASEN, W.H., X-Ray Diffraction in Crystals, Wiley, New York (1945).

DISCUSSION

T. RISTE: Have you considered the difficulty you may have through double Bragg scattering, especially in the inverted geometry?

B.A. DASANNACHARYA: We have not considered this problem in detail. However, a priori, I do not see why it should be worse than in the standard geometry.

R. SCHERM: You showed that the crystal reflectivity might be increased by the use of a multiplane analyser, but I suspect that a number of difficulties would be involved in this method:

First, angular resolution is usually very relaxed perpendicular to the scattering plane, but your method requires cylindrical symmetry around the beam;

Second, as you already mentioned, there is the difference between the focused and the defocused side in the scattering plane; and, finally,

Third, the greater number of detectors will certainly increase the background.

B.A. DASANNACHARYA: Your first observation is quite relevant. The multiplane system can be used in circumstances where cylindrical symmetry is acceptable. At large Bragg angles ($2\theta_B > 120°$) relaxing horizontal collimation need not be a big problem since $\cos \theta$ is small. As to the second point, this difference will in fact lead to difficulties in calculating the resolution function. However, there is no difficulty in experimentally measuring the incoherent elastic resolution. The background question is considered in the paper. One can think of several situations where an improved signal would make a poorer signal-to-background ratio acceptable.

OBSERVATION OF PHONON SCATTERING
SURFACES BY NEUTRON FILM METHODS*

D. HOHLWEIN
Institut für Kristallographie der
    Universität Tübingen,
Tübingen,
Federal Republic of Germany

Abstract

OBSERVATION OF PHONON SCATTERING SURFACES BY NEUTRON FILM METHODS.
    The scattering surfaces of acoustic phonons are, in a first approximation, ellipsoids or hyperboloids for thermal neutrons travelling slower or faster than sound velocity. The projections of ellipsoids onto a film have been observed under the experimental conditions: stationary Al and $BaTiO_3$ crystals, some mm^3 large, $\lambda = 1.7$ Å and 2 to 24 hours of exposure time. The projected ellipsoids appearing on the film as rings have sharp boundaries. Their diameters can be determined precisely and are a measure of the energy of the excited phonons. The accuracy of the derived sound velocity of transverse phonons in aluminium is of the order of 1%. Transverse and longitudinal phonon rings can be distinguished. The intensity distribution on the rings is explained. In $BaTiO_3$, the diffuse planes known from X-ray scattering experiments could be observed.

1. INTRODUCTION

In the last few years, film methods for neutron diffraction were developed [1]. It was shown that the classical X-ray film techniques like rotating crystal, Weissenberg and precession can be used for neutrons with similar properties and exposure times [2]. A new technique, a modified Laue method conceived by Maier-Leibnitz [3], was developed for neutron structure determination to reduce the data collection time. Here, a bent monochromator focuses a relatively long-wavelength band onto the crystal, giving rise to many simultanous reflections that are recorded by a cylindrical film camera. Our insight into the structure of an organic molecule of 25 atoms has been refined with data (4000 reflections) collected by this method in only 30 hours [4].

In this contribution, we shall show that also very weak intensities — until about 10^5 times weaker than Bragg scattering — can be recorded on films. This opens an opportunity to observe different kinds of diffuse scattering. Here, mostly scattering by acoustic phonons will be discussed.

---

* Work partly performed at the Institut Laue-Langevin, Grenoble, France.

TABLE I. SCINTILLATOR-FILM SYSTEM

Composition:	LiF (96% ^{6}LiF) + ZnS(Ag) in a plastic binder [5]
Reaction:	^{6}Li + n → α + t + 4.8 MeV → ZnS → 10^4 photons of λ = 4400 Å
Thickness:	0.4 mm (optimal thickness = 0.25 mm [6])
Absorption:	20% at 1 Å and 27% at 1.7 Å for one screen
Film:	'KODAK REGULIX' pressed between two screens

2. SCINTILLATOR-FILM DETECTION SYSTEM

Some characteristics of the detection system are presented in Table I. Figure 1 shows a calibration curve. The influence of the intensity on the optical density (log I_0/I) is discussed elsewhere [1]. We see that an intensity of about 2000 n·mm^{-2} already produces an optical density of 1.0 which corresponds to medium spot blackness. In the X-ray case, one needs 10^6 quanta·mm^{-2} to produce the same optical density of 1.0 [7]. This factor of about 10^3 in speed enables us to use also the conventional X-ray film techniques with neutrons in comparable exposure times as was mentioned in the introduction. The — about 10^4 times lower — flux at the sample position can be further compensated for by a larger crystal volume because of, the normally, much lesser absorption. Crystals a few mm^3 in volume will often produce more intense diffuse scattering than the crystals one has to use in X-ray scattering experiments ($\sim 10^{-3}$ mm^3).

3. SCATTERING SURFACES OF ACOUSTIC PHONONS

Let us first compare scattering of X-rays and neutrons by acoustic phonons. In both cases (one-phonon process), momentum and energy have to be conserved:

$$\vec{Q} = \vec{k}_0 - \vec{k}_1 = \vec{\tau} + \vec{q} \tag{1}$$

$$E(k_0) - E(k_1) = \hbar\omega(q) \tag{2}$$

where $\vec{k}_0$, $\vec{k}_1$ are the wavevectors of the incoming and the scattered X-rays or neutrons, E their energies, $\vec{\tau}$ is a reciprocal lattice vector, $\vec{q}$ a phonon vector and $\hbar\omega(q)$ the energy of the phonon. In the X-ray case, the energy E (k_0) is of the order of keV and much greater than the energy of the phonon which is of the order of 10 meV. This means that $|k_0|$ and $|k_1|$ are nearly identical. A reciprocal-lattice point near the Bragg position gives rise to phonon scattering with phonon vectors

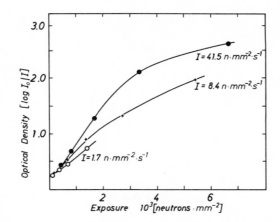

FIG.1. *Optical density on the film versus exposure for different incoming neutron intensities.*

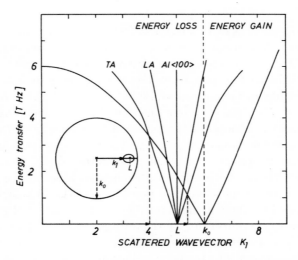

FIG.2. *Energy transfer as a function of scattered wavevector k_1 together with phonon dispersion curves of aluminium along $\langle 100 \rangle$; incoming beam k_0 ($\lambda = 1.79$ Å), L = reciprocal-lattice point.*

terminating on the so-called scattering surface which is in this case the Ewald sphere. The resulting diffuse spot on an X-ray film has no sharp boundaries. The intensity in the spot decreases with $1/q^2$ for the linear part of a phonon branch.

Thermal neutrons have similar energies as phonons so that the wavelength of the scattered neutrons is appreciably different from the incoming one. The scattering surfaces are, in a first approximation, ellipsoids or hyperboloids if the sound velocity is greater or less than the velocity of the incoming neutrons [8,9].

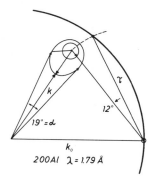

FIG. 3. *Transverse and longitudinal phonons terminating on the outer and inner 'ellipse', respectively; calculated for the 200 reflection of aluminium, 12° away from Bragg position, λ = 1.79 Å and isotropic sound velocities of 3.23 and 6.29 km·s⁻¹.*

Figure 2 explains this fact: a reciprocal-lattice point not lying on the Ewald sphere gives rise to scattering of phonons with well defined energies and vectors. Let us consider the direction from the centre of the Ewald sphere to the reciprocal-lattice point L. If one of the phonon vectors terminated on the Ewald sphere the corresponding energy of the phonon would be zero. The diagram shows the energy transfer $(\hbar^2/2m)\cdot(k_0^2 - k_1^2)$ as a function of the scattered wavevector k_1. As the end point of a phonovector originating at L coincides with the end point of k_1, the energy of the phonon must be equal to the energy transfer drawn at k_1. So, if we draw the phonon dispersion curve, at the point L, the intersection with the energy transfer parabola defines the phonons which can be excited. There are only two phonons in one direction of k_1 for a given branch. In two dimensions the excited phonons are defined by the intersection of a paraboloid with a conical dispersion curve (for a given isotropic branch). This is an ellipse for slower-than-sound neutrons because then the slope of the linear part of the dispersion curve is greater than the slope of the paraboloid at k_0. In three dimensions, the ellipse has to be rotated about the axis joining the centre of the Ewald sphere with the reciprocal-lattice point: the scattering surface is an ellipsoid with the lattice point in one focus.

Figure 3 shows, as examples, ellipses in the horizontal plane for the 200 reflection of Al, a wavelength of 1.79 Å and a deviation from the Bragg position D(θ) of 12°. The outer ellipse corresponds to transverse phonons travelling along ⟨0$\bar{1}$1⟩ and the inner ring to longitudinal phonons travelling along ⟨100⟩.

The scattering surfaces can be calculated by a computer program (Eqs (1) and (2)) or can be constructed graphically with the help of Fig. 2. In the latter case, one has to make the following construction in a reciprocal plane: First, we draw a circle around the reciprocal-lattice point with radius q (a given phonon vector length). Figure 2 provides the length of k_1 for the corresponding energy transfer. Then, we draw a circle with radius k_1 about the centre of the Ewald sphere. The intersection of the two circles defines the scattered phonons for the given q. This has to be repeated for different values of q.

The case of ellipsoids is especially interesting because in this case the diffuse spot seen on a film will have sharp boundaries. The diameter will be a function of the dispersion relation. If we move the lattice point away from the Bragg position, the ellipsoid expands; we are following the dispersion curve, Fig.2. For the linear part of the dispersion curve we have, to a good approximation, a linear relation between the projection angle α (Fig.3), which defines the spot diameter and the deviation from the Bragg position D (θ):

$$\alpha/2 = (C_S^2/V_N^2 - 1)^{-1/2}\ \sin(2\theta)\cdot D(\theta) \tag{3}$$

where C_S, V_N are the velocities of sound and the incoming neutrons, respectively, and θ is the Bragg angle. The nearly linear behaviour of the exactly calculated relationship is shown in Fig.9.

4.   EXPERIMENTAL CONDITIONS

The experiments were performed at the D 12 instrument of the ILL High Flux Reactor in Grenoble [1]. The instrument is situated at the end of a thermal neutron guide. Wavelengths in the range of 1.6 to 1.8 Å are reflected by a graphite monochromator. The divergence seen by the sample in a distance of 65 cm is 1°. The divergence of the neutrons in the neutron guide is 10 arc minutes times the wavelength in Å. Thus, the beam impinging on the sample can be characterized by a wavelength variation of 3.5% across the beam directions (1 degree) and a wavelength spread in beam direction of 0.9%. The flux at the specimen is about $10^7\ n\cdot cm^{-2}\cdot s^{-1}$.

A vertical cylindrical camera with a radius of 31 mm surrounds the specimen. The diameter of the circular beam is 2 mm. A single crystal of aluminium with the dimensions 2 X 2 X 2 mm is oriented with the 011-axis vertical on a turn-table; the crystal volume in the beam is about 6 mm³.

Measurements are done with the crystal in a fixed position and exposure times of up to 24 hours (monochromatic Laue technique). The background on the film without crystal and open beam is still negligible for these exposure times.

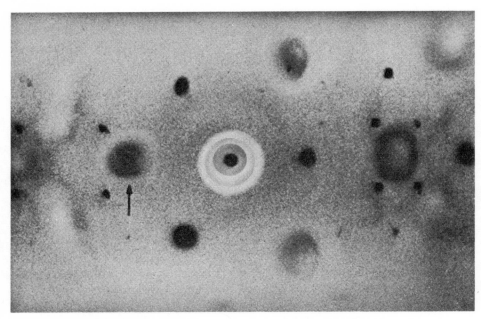

FIG.4.   Neutron photograph of aluminium, stationary crystal of 6 mm³, λ = 1.79 Å, exposure time 12 hours.   In the centre the primary beam, ⟨011⟩ vertical. (↑) Phonon rings of the 200 reflection with D(θ) = 12°.

5.   RESULTS AND DISCUSSION

The projection of the phonon ellipsoid described in Section 3 can clearly be observed in the photographs, Figs 4, 5. Some rectangular shaped small spots are Bragg reflections of the λ/2 contamination. They facilitate the identification of the layer lines: the horizontal or 0-layer and the first layers (⟨011⟩ vertical).

Intensity distribution on the ellipsoids

Let us study in more detail the diffuse scattering around the position of the 200 reflection in the horizontal layer for a deviation from the Bragg angle of 12°, Fig.4. We can clearly distinguish an outer and inner ring which are the projected scattering surfaces of transverse and longitudinal phonons, respectively. The intensity distribution on the outer ring is not uniform: in the vertical direction the boundaries are clearly visible, to the left we can just see them and to the right no boundary is detectable.

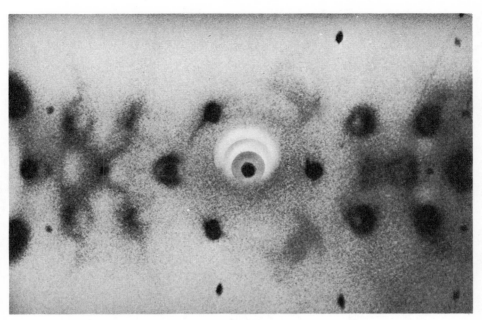

FIG.5.   Neutron photograph of aluminium, stationary crystal of 6 mm³, λ = 1.60 Å, exposure
time 15 hours. ⟨011⟩ vertical, D (θ) = 10° for 200.

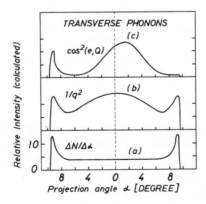

FIG.6.   Calculated intensity along the horizontal line for transverse phonons belonging to the
200 reflection of aluminium, 12° away from Bragg position, λ = 1.79 Å, C_s = 3.23 km·s⁻¹
(as in Figs 3, 4).

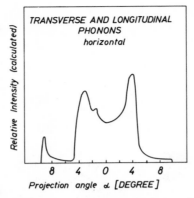

FIG. 7. *Calculated intensity along the horizontal line for longitudinal and transverse phonons belonging to the 200 lattice point, other data as in Fig. 3.*

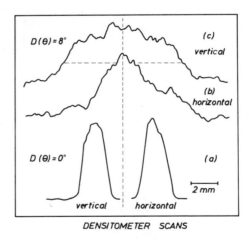

DENSITOMETER SCANS

FIG. 8. *Densitometer scans with a slit aperture of 0.2×1.6 mm^2, in vertical and horizontal direction of the Al 200 reflection in (a) Bragg position and (b,c) $D(\theta)$ $8°$ away.*

The intensity at the boundaries is determined mainly by three factors: (1) the number of phonons ΔN seen in a certain solid angle $\Delta\Omega$ ($\Delta\alpha$ for the linear problem of Fig. 4), the intensity in the photograph will be proportional to $\Delta N/\Delta\Omega$, (2) the q-dependence of the cross-section, which is, for the linear part of a given dispersion branch, proportional to $1/q^2$ and (3) the angle between the polarization vector $\vec{e}$ of the phonon and the momentum transfer Q; the intensity is proportional to $(\vec{e}\cdot\vec{Q})^2$ (only modes in special symmetry directions will have just one polarization vector).

The influence of these three factors for pure transverse phonons on the intensity distribution of the diffuse spot along the horizontal line is shown in Fig.6. The relative number of phonon vectors per projection angle was calculated for a $\Delta\alpha$ of $0.5°$ and a sound velocity of $3.23 \ km \cdot s^{-1}$. This factor is responsible for the enhancement of the intensity at the border of the spot giving it the appearance of a ring. The diagram above shows the influence of the factor $1/q^2$ giving more intensity in the centre. The direction of the polarization vector is the main reason for the different intensities on the left- and right-hand sides, Fig.7c.

The same calculations were done for longitudinal phonons (with the sound velocity in the $\langle 100 \rangle$ direction).

The final calculated intensity distribution for longitudinal and transverse phonons is shown by Fig.8. The details are smeared out in the densitometer scan by the resolution curve to be discussed below.

The sharp boundaries in the vertical direction of the transverse phonon ring are explained by the fact that $(\vec{e} \cdot \vec{Q})^2$ has its maximum here.

Resolution

The resolution is determined by the crystal size (direct space) and the characteristics of the monochromatic beam (reciprocal space).

The direct space resolution will be contained in a densitometer scan of the 200 spot in the Bragg position, Fig.8.

The resolution in reciprocal space, i.e. the thickness of the ellipsoid can be estimated by formula (3) of Section 3 and the characteristics of the monochromatic beam described above. For the focusing side and the reciprocal-lattice point inside the Ewald sphere, we have

$$\Delta\alpha/\alpha = \left\{ (\Delta\alpha/\alpha)_{WL}^2 - (\Delta\alpha/\alpha)_{DIV}^2 \right\}^{1/2} \tag{4}$$

with

$$(\Delta\alpha/\alpha)_{WL} = \left\{ \left(\frac{c_s^2/v_N^2}{c_s^2/v_N^2 - 1} \right)^2 + (2 \tan\theta \cot 2\theta)^2 + \left(\frac{\tan\theta}{D(\theta)} \right)^2 \right\}^{1/2} \Delta\lambda/\lambda \tag{5}$$

which is the relative change of the width of the phonon ring for a given wavelength spread $\Delta\lambda$ in the beam direction (parallel beam);

$$(\Delta\alpha/\alpha)_{DIV} = \gamma/D(\theta) \tag{6}$$

is the relative change of the width for a constant wavelength with divergence γ.

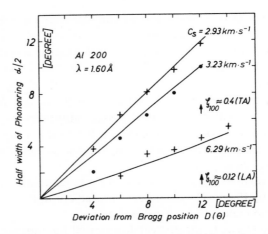

FIG.9.   *Widths at half height (+) of the phonon rings of Al 200 as a function of D(θ) together with the theoretical curves for sound velocities of 2.93 km·s⁻¹ (TA along ⟨111⟩), 3.23 km·s⁻¹ (TA along ⟨100⟩) and 6.29 km·s⁻¹ (LA along ⟨100⟩). For the points (●) we have subtracted the width of the 200 reflection in Bragg position.*

In our case, $\Delta\lambda/\lambda$ is 3.5% and $\gamma = 1°$; for $\lambda = 1.60$ Å and the 200 reflection we have $(\Delta\alpha/\alpha)_{WL} = 0.13$ and $(\Delta\alpha/\alpha)_{DIV} = 0.10$ for a $D(\theta)$ of 10°, i.e.

$$\Delta\alpha/\alpha = 8\%$$

This is only a rough estimate (we have also neglected the wavelength spread of 0.9% in the beam direction).

Determination of sound velocity

At the wavelength of 1.60 Å, we measured the diameters of the transverse phonon rings in vertical direction as a function of the deviation from the Bragg position $D(\theta)$. The diameter of the inner ring belonging to longitudinal phonons was determind along the horizontal line.

Typical densitometer scans are shown by Fig.8. We simply measured the width at the half heights of the boundaries. The results can be seen in Fig.9. The values of the outer ring lie nearly exactly on the theoretical curve for a sound velocity of 2.93 km·s⁻¹. This is the velocity of transverse phonons in the ⟨111⟩ direction. Tangential to the vertical ellipse we see, however, phonons travelling about in ⟨001⟩ direction (45° away from the vertical (011)-axis); they have a 10% higher velocity: 3.23 km·s⁻¹ (lower curve). If we subtract the

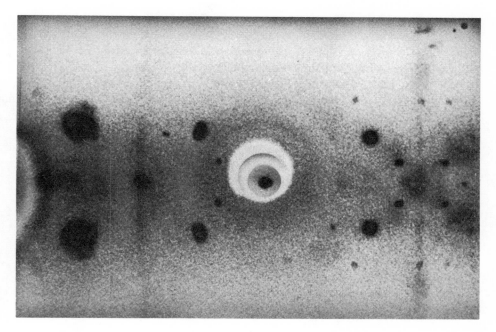

FIG.10.   Neutron photograph of BaTiO₃, stationary crystal of 2.5 × 2.5 × 2.5 mm³, λ = 1.79 Å, exposure time 15 hours.   Primary beam in the centre, ⟨010⟩ and diffuse planes vertical.

half width of the 200 spot in the Bragg position from the raw data we obtain the correct sound velocity for the spots with large diameters, Fig.9. For smaller diameters the de-convolution of the resolution function will not be so simple.

As can be seen in Fig.9, the accuracy of the sound velocity derived from the larger rings in vertical direction is of the order of 1 per cent. Relative changes of the sound velocity should be measurable with a precision of the order of a promille.

6.   CONCLUSIONS

One of the advantages of the method presented is that all diffuse scattering (of dynamic or static origin) for a given crystal orientation can be detected and located. In certain cases, as demonstrated for acoustic phonons, also the energy of the diffuse scattering can be analysed by simple geometric considerations and measurements of distances on the film (and not of intensities as in the X-ray case). The experiments can be done with rather small crystals of a volume of some mm^3. The aluminium crystal of 6 mm^3 reflects 8000 c·s^{-1} in the peak of the 200 reflection. This reflection can be recorded on the film with an optical density of 1.0 in one second, i.e. during exposure times of 24 hours, we record 10^5 lower intensities with a similar optical density.

Not only crystals with very good diffraction properties as those of aluminium can be studied. Figure 10 shows a photograph of a BaTiO$_3$ crystal, 2.5 X 2.5 X 2.5 mm^3. We also see the ellipsoids of the acoustic phonons. Furthermore, we see the diffuse planes already detected with X-rays. The observations are possible despite the strong incoherent scattering of Ba (b$_{coh}$ = 3.4 b, b$_{inc}$ = 2.6 b) and Ti (b$_{coh}$ = 1.4 b, b$_{incoh}$ = 3 b).

The measurements of the phonon ring widths described correspond to the so-called diffraction technique [9] where the film is replaced by a scanning counter with small aperture. The high accuracy of this method in the region of moderately small q-vectors for the determination of the spin wave dispersion relation has been demonstrated [10]. There will be advantages of the film method also in this field.

The appearance of the ellipsoids or rings on the films are also a relative direct illustration of the vibration of the atoms in the crystal if one remembers that the diameter of such rings will be smaller if the atoms are more tightly bound and vice versa.

ACKNOWLEDGEMENTS

The author thanks Professor W. Prandl for helpful discussions and Professor K. Fischer of the University of Saarbrücken for the loan of the BaTiO$_3$ crystal. The technical assistance of M. Berneron at the ILL is gratefully acknowledged.

REFERENCES

[1] HOHLWEIN, D., Proc. Neutron Diffraction Conf. Petten, **234** (1975) 410.

[2] HOHLWEIN, D., JOSWIG, W., J. Appl. Crystallogr. **9** (1976) 130.

[3] MAIER-LEIBNITZ, H., Ann. Acad. Sci. Fenn. **A VI** 267 (1976).

[4] HOHLWEIN, D., Acta Crystallogr. **A 33** (1977) 649.

[5] THOMAS, P., J. Appl. Crystallogr. **5** (1972) 373.

[6] SPOWART, A.R., Br. J. Non-Destr. Test. **11** (1969) 2.

[7] MORIMOTO, H., UYEDA, R., Acta Crystallogr. **16** (1963) 1107.

[8] SEEGER, R.J., TELLER, E., Phys. Rev. **62** (1942) 37.

[9] LOWDE, R.D., Prov. R. Soc. **A 221** (1954) 206.

[10] ALPERIN, H.A., STEINSVOLL, O., NATHANS, R., SHIRANE, G., Phys. Rev. **154** (1967) 508.

DISCUSSION

P.E. HIISMÄKI: Are your techniques limited to the very low backgrounds obtained with guide tubes and high flux reactors?

D. HOHLWEIN: I don't think so. I have just tried some preliminary measurements with the Karlsruhe FR-2 reactor. The diffuse scattering can also be observed with acoustical phonons, and the background does not appear to be an important problem.

M. LAMBERT: Your photograph for $BaTiO_3$ shows inelastic diffuse ellipsoids and diffuse planes. These diffuse planes are very similar to those which are visible in the case of X-ray photographs. Do you interpret this result in terms of elastic, or slightly inelastic, scattering?

D. HOHLWEIN: I cannot say at the moment. I am just studying the problem of how one can determine the energy of the diffuse planes and with what precision. At first sight, it seems that the planes are located at the same position as in the X-ray case.

M. LAMBERT: It would be interesting to perform the same experiment with $KNbO_3$ to check whether it gives similar results.

W. SCHMATZ: The dependence of dynamic neutron scattering on the energy of the incoming neutrons is different from that of static scattering. Can one use this difference to separate the two phenomena in the photographic technique?

D. HOHLWEIN: Yes. At constant wavelength, too, a change of crystal orientation will modify the intensity distributions for static and dynamic disorder effects in different ways.

B.A. DASANNACHARYA: How would the photographic method work in the presence of low-lying optical modes?

D. HOHLWEIN: If the optical mode is isotropic and flat, one will have 4π diffuse scattering without structure. However, any strong anisotropy or dips in the optical branches should be observable. A more detailed study is necessary.

E. STEICHELE: The determination of sound velocity with your technique depends on the assumption of an ellipsoidal scattering surface. Can you also get correct sound velocities when these are not isotropic and you have no ellipsoidal scattering surface?

D. HOHLWEIN: This is a difficult question. Probably you will easily see the anisotropy but, as you invariably have the projection of a surface on the film, it will not always be possible to determine the surface quantitatively. The influence of the polarization vector on the intensity will facilitate the task, however.

EXPERIMENTAL CAPABILITY STUDY OF NON-CONVENTIONAL METHODS IN NEUTRON TIME-OF-FLIGHT ANALYSIS

G. BADUREK, H. RAUCH
Institut für Experimentelle Kernphysik und
    Atominstitut der Österreichischen Universitäten,
Vienna,
Austria

Abstract

EXPERIMENTAL CAPABILITY STUDY OF NON-CONVENTIONAL METHODS IN
NEUTRON TIME-OF-FLIGHT ANALYSIS.
   The pseudostatistical correlation method and the so-called Fourier method of neutron
time-of-flight analysis are critically discussed with respect to their applicability to different
types of choppers. Results of experimental test measurements with a mechanical Fourier
chopper system and an electronic spin-flip chopper spectrometer for polarized neutrons are
presented, where special attention is drawn to the occurrence of systematic errors in the time-of-
flight patterns obtained by means of a Fourier synthesis or decorrelation procedure, respectively.

1. Introduction

Nearly a decade ago, already, two techniques - the pseudostatistical correlation method [1,2] and the so-called Fourier method [3,4] - have been proposed
to increase the efficiency of neutron time-of-flight (TOF) experiments. In
contrast to the standard single-pulse TOF method, where the necessary conditions of nonoverlapping of neutrons of subsequent bursts leads to a very low
time utilization of the available neutrons of typically 0.1%, these 'nonconventional'[1] methods allow to use up to 50% of the primary intensity. This
high duty cycle - i.e. the ratio of the 'open' and 'closed' times of the beam
chopping device - is achieved by modulating the beam intensity either according to a binary pseudo-random sequence (correlation method) or - in combination with a Fourier analysis of the detector output - with a series of
discrete frequencies by means of a periodic signal that contains the frequency in question as basic frequency (Fourier method). The TOF spectrum then
can be computed either by cross correlation of the detector signal with the
pseudo random modulation sequence or by Fourier inversion of the directly
measured data, respectively.

As a consequence of the increased time utilization an application of these
high efficiency TOF methods should - at least in principle - allow to obtain

---

[1] In this context we refer to the novel spin-echo technique [6], which may also be regarded as
'nonconventional' TOF analysis but is not content of this paper.

a higher statistical precision than with a conventionally performed experiment of equal running time. But, although many authors [7-30] - though predominantly theoretically - have been engaged in deriving their individual advantages compared to the conventional TOF analysis, neither the correlation nor the Fourier method actually could achieve large scale application in experimental neutron spectroscopy until now. This fact might be due to two main reasons.

At first, because of the indirectness of both methods the theoretical gain in statistical accuracy is not governed by the increase of the duty factors alone and reaches therefore for experimental situations only a significantly high value to justify their increased expense concerning the experimental setup and the more complicated data processing, where an appreciably high background count rate unmodulated by the chopper ist present. Secondly, deviations of the actual chopper modulation function from its theoretically ideal value lead to systematic errors in the computed TOF distributions, which may hinder a correct evaluation of the latter or seriously limit their accuracy.

In this paper we discuss both methods with respect to their applicability to mechanical and electronic types of neutron choppers and we present results of experimental tests which were performed at our 250 kW TRIGA Mark II reactor facility with a mechanical Fourier chopper system and an electronic spin-flip chopper spectrometer for polarized neutrons.

2. Critical comparison of the Fourier and the correlation method for different chopper types

To obtain a basis for this comparison we will shortly review the functional principles of both techniques and mention their most important features, yet without going too far into details. Generally, for any TOF arrangement, where the beam intensity is modulated in time by a chopper according to a function $M(t)$ $(0 \leq M(t) \leq 1)$, the time-dependent count rate at the detector is given as

$$z(t) = \int_o^T f(\tau)M(t-\tau)d\tau + b \equiv f*M + b \qquad (1)$$

b ... time independent background count rate

which is the convolution of the neutron TOF distribution $f(t)$ and the chopper function. This TOF distribution, which is assumed to include the primary intensity already and to be nonzero within the finite time interval $0 \leq t \leq T$ only, represents the response function of the system chopper-sample-detector and is closely related to the sample double differential cross section, being the main quantity of interest. It is evident that, for a conventional single-burst chopper with deltafunction-type modulation function, the recorded intensity would directly be proportional to the TOF distribution of the scattered neutrons, though yet with the above mentioned disadvantage of low neutron economy.

With a Fourier chopper the modulation function as well as the detected intensity signal are essentially periodic and may be evaluated into their harmonic components by Fourier series expansion

$$M(t) = \sum_{r=-\infty}^{\infty} P_1(r\omega) \exp(-i\omega t) \tag{2a}$$

$$z(t) = \sum_{r=-\infty}^{\infty} P_2(r\omega) \exp(-i\omega t) \quad , \tag{2b}$$

where the complex contributions of each harmonic frequency are defined by their respective amplitudes and phases as

$$P_{1,2}(r\omega) = A_{1,2}(r\omega) \exp[-i\phi_{1,2}(r\omega)] \tag{3}$$

and the extension to the unphysical negative frequency range is accomplished by the definition $P(-\omega) \equiv P*(\omega)$. Insertion of eqs.2 into eq.1 immediately yields the result

$$F(0) = P_2(0) - b/P_1(0) \tag{4a}$$

$$F_{r\neq0}(r\omega) = P_2(r\omega)/P_1(r\omega) = A(r\omega) \exp[-i\phi(r\omega)] \quad , \tag{4b}$$

$$(A = A_2/A_1, \ \phi = \phi_2 - \phi_1)$$

i.e. the Fourier transform $F(\omega)$ of the TOF spectrum $f(t)$ can be measured if the amplitude and phase shift of the count rate oscillations relative to the originally impressed modulation signal are determined by means of a phase sensitive neutron detection system. After this measurement has been performed for a series of equidistant frequencies ω_k (ω_k: 0, $\Delta\omega$, $2\Delta\omega$, ... $N\Delta\omega = \omega_{max}$), the TOF spectrum finally can be synthesized by Fourier inversion as

$$f(t) = \frac{\Delta\omega}{2\pi} \sum_{k=-N}^{N} C_k F(\omega_k) \exp(i\,\omega_k\,t) \tag{5}$$

where the weighting factors C_k of the individual Fourier components are necessary to avoid the occurence of systematic side lobes of the resolution function because of the non infinite upper frequency of a real chopper [4,7]. The TOF pattern constructed in this way is represented definitely within the periodicity interval $T = 2\pi(\Delta\omega)^{-1}$ with a time uncertainty Δt of approximately $2\pi(\omega_{max})^{-1}$ and has a statistical accuracy, that is constant for each point of time and is governed by the total sum of neutrons detected only. Simultaneously the signal to background ratio is increased compared to a conventionally measured spectrum by the ratio of the chopper duty cycles. This result, which implies that there is no actual gain of accuracy if no background is present, is exactly the same with a correlation chopper of duty cycle 50% as we will see later.

The basic idea of the correlation technique in turn is to deconvolute $f(t)$ and $M(t)$ by a suitable function $D(t)$, which is 'inverse' to the modulation sequence in the sense that it fulfils the integral equation

$$\int_0^T M(t') D(t-t') dt' = \Phi(t) \tag{6}$$

where the 'resolution function' $\Phi(t)$ is peaked around $t = 0$ with a certain small halfwidth Δt and is constant elsewhere within the periodicity intervall $0 \le t \le T$. Since then, obviously, the cross correlation of the detected count rate and this deconvolution sequence yields the TOF distribution convoluted with the resolution function as it would be obtained in a conventional experiment with the same resolution:

$$K(\tau) = \int_0^T Z(t)\, D(t-\tau)\, dt = \int_0^T f(t') \int_0^T M(t-t')\, D(t-\tau)\, dt\, dt' + \text{const} =$$

$$= \int_0^T f(t')\, \Phi(t'-\tau)\, dt' + \text{const} \equiv f*\Phi + \text{const} \tag{7}$$

From Eq. (6) there would be complete freedom for the choice of the modulation function but the latter also must fulfil the condition that the variance of the TOF spectrum obtained after decorrelation achieves its minimum. To solve this minimization problem it proofed to be necessary to consider the modulation function as linear superposition of pulses of equal shape $\phi(t)$, which are generated at equidistant times $t_i = i\theta$ $(i = 0, 1, \ldots N-1)$ with a probability amplitude a_i $(a_i \in \{0, 1\})$:

$$M(t) = \sum_{i=0}^{N-1} a_i\, \phi(t-t_i) \tag{8}$$

$$M(t+T) = M(t+N\cdot\theta) = M(t)$$

To write the modulation according to Eq. (8) automatically implies a symmetric pulse shape, i.e.

$$\sum_i \phi(t-t_i) = 1 \tag{9}$$

since otherwise it would not be possible to describe correctly the 'plateau' occurring between two pulses with amplitude 1. As we will see in our experimental results, it is just the not exact symmetry of the pulses of a real correlation chopper that may cause serious systematic errors in the determination of the TOF distribution.

Within this formalism it was found that the smallest variance of the results can be obtained when the a_i are chosen according to so called pseudo-random binary sequences (PRBS), whose autocorrelation function is given as [16]

$$A(k) \equiv \sum_{i=0}^{N-1} a_i\, a_{i+k} = m(1-c)\delta(k) + mc \tag{10}$$

$$(k = 0, 1 \ldots N-1;\; a_{i+N} \equiv a_i)$$

where m is the number of 'ones' and $c = \frac{m-1}{N-1}$ is approximately the duty cycle of the sequence, and the decorrelation is performed with a rectangularly shaped function based on the same PRBS. The optimum duty cycle changes from $c = 0$ (conventional method) for no background to $c = 0.5$ for high background and

also the theoretical gain in statistical accuracy becomes more pronounced as
the signal-to-background ratio decreases. At c = 0.5 the statistical variance - as in the Fourier method - is equal for all peaks of the spectrum and
proportional to the total number of detected neutrons.

Since the Fourier as well as the correlation method give about the same statistical precision for equal number of detected neutrons and need approximately the same experimental expense it should be rather easy to decide, which
method would be more appropriate for a given type of chopping system. This
clearly would be that method, which - on the one hand - would allow for a
better utilization of the available beam for equal resolution and - on the
other hand - would make less troubles concerning systematical errors in the
determination of the TOF spectra.

The mechanical Fourier chopper, usually consisting of a disk rotor with
equally spaced radial absorption stripes and a corresponding stator, offers
the distinct advantage to its correlation counterpart that the usable beam
cross section is independent of the resolution, whereas for the correlation
chopper both of these quantities are determined by the width of the smallest
slot of the absorption pattern. This fact by far overcompensates the smaller
average transmission of 25% compared to up to 50% of a pseudo-random modulation. A further advantage of the mechanical Fourier chopper is its greater
flexibility. Whereas for a mechanical correlation chopper the periodicity
interval,   which determines the maximum possible length of the TOF distribution, cannot be increased without decreasing the rotational speed of the
chopper (and hence the resolution) it can be chosen freely with a Fourier
chopper simply by varying the frequency step $\Delta\omega$, thus avoiding overlapping
problems in any case and maintaining the resolution desired.

The main source of systematic errors of the Fourier method is the phase sensitive neutron detection system that can be realized by synchronized sub-
division of the chopper modulation period into n time-sequenced counting
channels [5]. From the contents of these channels estimates of the Fourier
components of the DC-term (r = 0, Eq.(4a)) the basic frequency (r = 1) and
all higher harmonics up to the order $r_{max} \leq n/2$ (r integer) can be calculated. These estimates were derived by Virjo [4] according to a least square
error criterion. They are exactly identical to the real Fourier components
only for the case of a purely sinusoidal modulation without any content of
higher harmonics or for an infinite number of counting channels (n = ∞). In
any other case the measurement of the component corresponding to a certain
harmonic frequency is disturbed by all remaining harmonics. We have shown
recently [31] that for the triangular modulation of a usual mechanical Fourier
chopper the systematic errors arising from the presence of the odd higher harmonics in pratice are even then negligible, if the comfortably small number
of only four synchronized counting intervals is applied and that it is by
no means necessary to modulate the beam purely sinusoidally. The latter would
be to achieve only with a stator of complicated and intensity wasting shape,
as proposed in [32]. In the same context we could further verify that the use
of only three detector channels would give even more accurate results than
those obtained with n = 4.

Other possible sources of systematic errors, as inaccuracy in the preparation of the absorption pattern, speed variations of the rotor etc. are similarly existing also with the correlation chopper but should be kept at an
insignificant level by careful construction and maintenance of the whole system.

As mentioned earlier there may occur anomalous structures within the TOF spectra measured by the correlation technique if the shape of the elementary

pulses is not symmetrical. As shown very recently by Pelizzari and Postol [33]
it is yet possible - at least for a mechanical correlation chopper - to cancel
these effects of imperfect beam modulation by means of an 'effective' decorre-
lating sequence that can be found from a numerical solution of Eq.(6) if M(t)
is analytically known from a separate measurement of extremely long duration.

For electronic choppers the situation is totally different. With the exception
of the novel magnetic chopper of Weise et al. [34], but which is impractical
because of its low modulation depth, all existing types of electronic choppers
have a common feature: the modulation starts to be rectangular at low frequencies and changes continuously to more or less sinusoidal shape at their upper
maximum frequency. It is self-evident that the problem of the large higher-
harmonic disturbances in the low frequency range practically excludes the
Fourier method to be applied with electronic choppers. Moreover, since there
is - in first order - no connection between the beam area and the time resolution for electronic choppers also the main advantage of the Fourier method
over the correlation technique no longer would be valid. On the other hand,
it would be necessary with electronic correlation choppers to achieve highly
symmetric pulses, since it would not be meaningful to try to find a similar
effective decorrelation sequence as mentioned above for the mechanical chopper
systems. The latter is true because the modulation function is not uniquely
fixed forever as in the case of the mechanical rotor but may be slightly
different from measurement to measurement by not exactly reproduced adjustment or electronic instability effects.

3. Experimental test measurements

According to the previous arguments we have realized a mechanical Fourier
chopper and an electronical spin-flip chopper for polarized neutrons. The
Fourier chopper essentially consists of a rotor-stator arrangement with identical radial slit pattern and triangular transmission characteristic, allowing
for a maximum beam cross section of 10×8 cm^2 and an upper modulation frequency of about 100 kHz. Control of the chopper is achieved via CAMAC stan-
dardized interfaces by means of a 24 kbyte PDP11/05 mini-computer which also
performs the Fourier inversion of the raw data according to Eq.(5). To test
the performance of the spectrometer and to see wether systematical errors can
be avoided we have measured the TOF distribution of neutrons scattered at an
Al-single crystal. The chopper was run according to a Tukey coefficient window [4] with a maximum frequency of 75 kHz. The result of this measurement
is shown in Fig.1. Obviously the Fourier chopper functions properly, no significant anomalous structure is present in the TOF pattern. The statistical
variance and the width of the peaks were found to be in complete agreement
with their theoretically expected values. We aim to use this chopper in a
white beam diffractometer for structural investigations of powdered or polycrystalline materials. Preliminary tests on Be and Al polycrystal samples
showed promising results, but the setup as a whole is not yet optimal and
should be further improved for doing the real experiments.

For the spin-flip chopper we developed a new system of rapid polarisation inversion, consisting of only a thin DC-flipping coil, which is driven by an
advanced electronic switching system [35]. It allows a periodical or pseudostatistical beam modulation with a minimum elementary pulse width of about
5 μs. For the correlational mode of operation a pseudo-random binary sequence
of length $N = 258$ and duty cycle $c = 0.5$ was used as chopper control signal,
which was generated by proper feedbacking of a 8-bit shift register. Each
elementary interval (width θ) of the modulation sequence was subdivided into

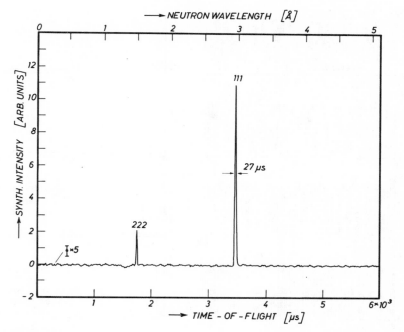

FIG.1. Time-of-flight distribution of neutrons reflected from an Al single crystal as measured with a mechanical Fourier spectrometer.

four time channels of a multichannel analyzing system that consists of a NOVA 1200 mini-computer in connection with a special TOF interface [36]. Figure 2b shows the TOF distribution of the neutrons reflected from the Fe-Co analyser as determined with the correlation technique for elementary intervals of θ = 8, 12, 36 and 100 µs and the corresponding channel widths of 2, 3, 9 and 25 µs, respectively. The directly measured raw data are plotted in Fig.2a. Whereas for θ = 8 and 12 µs some anomalous systematical structure is obviously seen, a comparison of the theoretically calculated and experimentally achieved variance of the off-peak part of the TOF distribution shows that for θ = 36 and 100 µs also the variance may not arise from purely statistical deviations but contains systematical contributions as well.

We have done a series of conventional and correlation measurements at various heights of relative background, which were simulated simply by variation of the flipping efficiency of the polarization inverter. The results are shown in Fig.3 for θ = 36 µs and Fig.4 for θ = 100 µs. The variances again were determined for the off-peak part of the spectrum, which, of course, should be zero and superimposed on a constant background throughout this region. The parameter s_r denotes the relative signal height and is given by the ratio of the sum of signal height (zero for this case) and background to the integrated spectrum. By splitting the observed variance into a time-dependent statistical and a time-independent part

$$\sigma^2(t) = \sigma^2_{stat}(t) + \sigma^2_{sys} \tag{11}$$

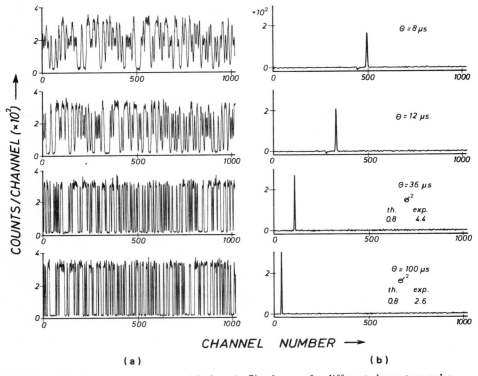

FIG.2. *Correlation measurements with the spin-flip chopper for different elementary pulse widths θ. (a) Directly measured detector signal and (b) TOF distributions obtained by cross-correlation of these signals with the pseudo-random modulation sequence.*

and assuming Poisson distribution of the count rates, i.e.

$$\sigma^2_{stat}(t_1) \, / \, \sigma^2_{stat}(t_2) = t_2 \, / \, t_1 \; , \tag{12}$$

we could determine both σ^2_{stat} and σ^2_{sys} from measurements of different durations t_1 and t_2 and derive an effective gain factor

$$g^2_{eff} = \sigma^2_{conv} \, / \, \sigma^2_{corr} \tag{13}$$

of the correlation method over the conventional one as function of I·t (I ... average neutron intensity of the detector, t ... measuring time), the total sum of detected neutrons. From Eq.(5) where the functional dependence of g^2_{eff} versus I·t is plotted for θ = 36 and 100 µs, one can see how long for given signal/background ratio and average scattered intensity a conventional measurement has to last to be at least as accurate (g^2_{eff} = 1) as the corresponding correlation experiment. It follows that the correlation technique,

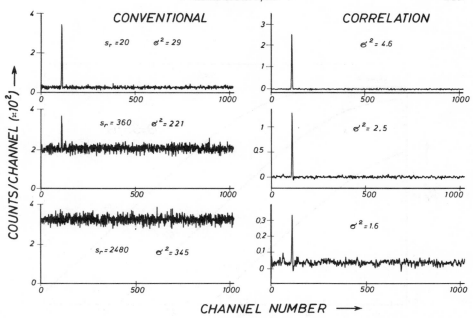

FIG.3. *Comparison of conventional and correlation method for different modulation depths of the chopper (corresponding to different signal/background ratios) and pulse width θ = 36 μs.*

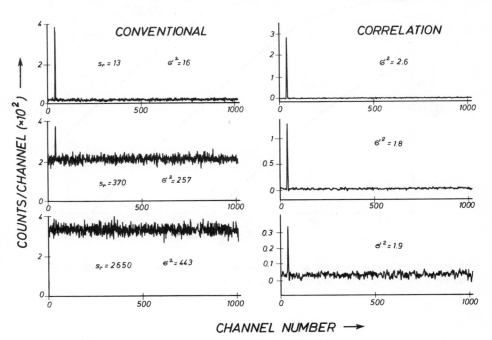

FIG.4. *Similar measurements as in Fig.3 for θ = 100 μs.*

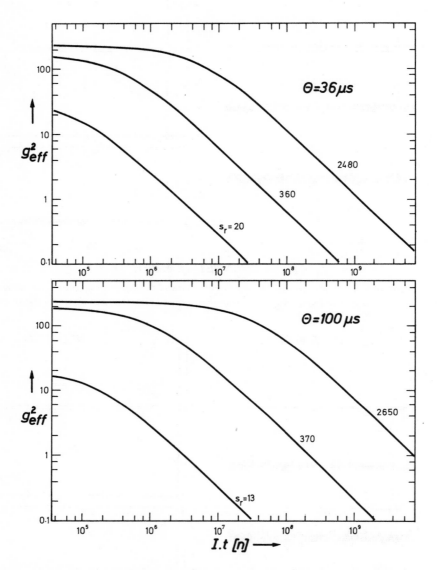

FIG.5.   Effective gain factor of the correlation method over the conventional single-pulse
technique for the electronic spin-flip chopper system.

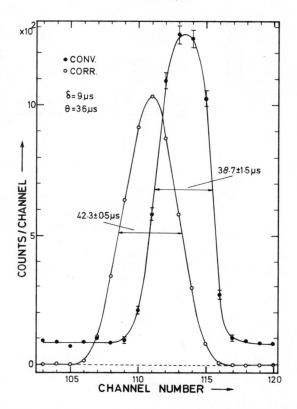

*FIG.6.   TOF peaks as measured conventionally and by the correlation method (the error bars
of the correlation peak are below point size).*

in spite of its systematical error sources with an electronic chopper of
such   type, may yield considerable saving of measuring time, if either the
modulation depth is small (as in the case of investigations of spin-dependent
scattering only without the use of an analyser) or the scattered intensity is
very low (implying automatically a high s_r value) and one is further content
to know the TOF spectrum with a total variance corresponding to about 1.5 -
2 times the value of the systematic variance. The latter just corresponds to
the region where the gain factor of Fig.5 starts to decrease linearly.

In Fig.6 for $\theta = 36$ µs and a channel width of $\delta = 9$ µs the peak region is displayed on an enlarged scale for both methods. The resolution is only slightly less for the correlation measurement than for the conventional one but the
width of the peak is more precisely determined because of the smaller error
bars of the individual channel contents. The mutual shift of the peak positions is simply due to the different definition of the time-of-flight, as
one can easily verify.

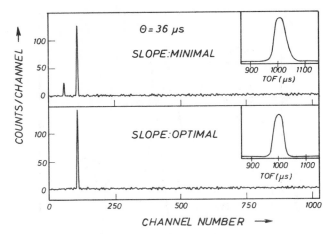

FIG. 7. Correlation measurements with symmetrically ('OPTIMAL') and asymmetrically ('MINIMAL') adjusted slopes of the elementary pulses of the modulation function (see insert).

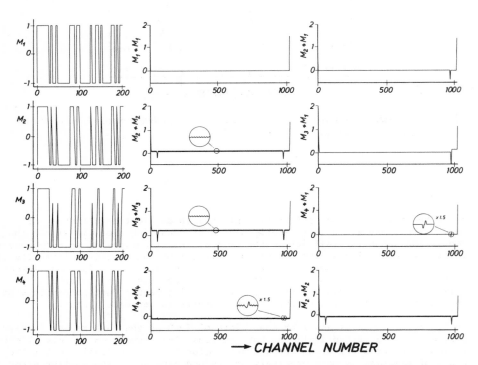

FIG. 8. Ideal modulation sequence M_1 and 'imperfect' sequences M_2, M_3, M_4 (left), their autocorrelation functions M_i *M_i (middle) and the cross-correlations $M_{2,3,4}$ *M_1 of the imperfect sequences with the ideal one (right). $\overline{M}_2$ is a sequence with inverted asymmetry compared to M_2.

To get a better understanding of the possible systematic errors that are
induced by imperfect beam modulation, Fig.7 shows two correlational measurements with different adjustments of the 'slope' potentiometer of the chopper
control unit, that allows to symmetrize the slopes of the chopper modulation
function. In the inserts the shape of an isolated elementary pulse is displayed for these two different adjustments. Obviously, the pulse asymmetry
only causes the occurence of a second unphysical peak, but does not affect
the other 'spurious' systematic deviations which we have treated in our
gain factor derivation as if they were statistically distributed. The latter
is of course essential in the correct interpretation of data, since then
one can be sure that any observed 'peak' is really of physical origin.

This experimentally observed systematic error peak agrees well with theoretical computer simulations shown in Fig.8. Besides the ideal rectangular
modulation sequence M_1 three other 'imperfect' sequences M_2, M_3, M_4 were
generated, which are partially plotted on the left side of this figure.
The autocorrelation functions M_i*M_i of all sequences and the cross-correlations $M_{2,3,4}*M_1$ of the imperfect sequences with the ideal one were calculated and are displayed in the middle and right columns, respectively, of
Fig.8. It is further shown that the convolution of the asymmetric function
M_2 with its counterpart $\overline{M}_2$, that has an inverted asymmetry, does not lead
to an elimination of the systematic errors.

We finally mention, without figuring these results explicitely, that filtering of the dominant peak by means of a second asynchronous sequence, as
proposed in [27,37], in any case would lead to a deterioriation of the
accuracy of the residual parts of the spectrum.

4. Conclusion

It was be shown that with mechanical choppers the Fourier TOF method
can be managed properly and that for electronical chopper systems the pseudo-random correlation technique, in spite of some problems arising from imperfect beam modulation, may be favourably applied.

REFERENCES

[1]   GOMPF, F., et al., Neutron Inelastic Scattering (Proc.Int.Conf. Copen-
      hagen, 1968) 2, IAEA, Vienna (1968) 417.
[2]   PAL, L., ibid. p. 407.
[3]   COLWELL, J.F., MILLER, P.H., WHITTEMORE, W.L., ibid. p. 429.
[4]   VIRJO, A., Nucl.Instr.Meth. 76 (1969) 189.
[5]   COLWELL, J.F., et al., Nucl.Instr.Meth. 76 (1969) 135.
[6]   MEZEI, F., Z.Physik, 255 (1972) 146.
[7]   COLWELL, J.F., et al., Nucl.Instr.Meth. 77 (1970) 29.
[8]   HIISMAEKI, P., POEYRY, H., VIRJO, A., Acta Poly. Scand. Ph 96 (1973).
[9]   POEYRY, H., HIISMAEKI, P., VIRJO, A., Nucl.Instr.Meth. 126 (1975) 421.
[10] HIISMAEKI, P., JUNTILLA, J., PIIRTO, A., Nucl.Instr.Meth. 126 (1975)
      435.
[11] VIRJO, A., Nucl.Instr.Meth. 63 (1968) 351.
[12] SKOELD, K., Nucl.Instr.Meth. 63 (1968) 114.
[13] QUITTNER, G., Nucl.Instr.Meth. 68 (1969) 290.
[14] VIRJO, A., Nucl.Instr.Meth. 75 (1969) 77.
[15] WILHEMI, G., GOMPF, F., Nucl.Instr.Meth. 81 (1970) 36.
[16] JAN, R., SCHERM, R., Nucl.Instr.Meth. 80 (1970) 69.

[17] HOSSFELD, F., AMADORI, R., SCHERM, R., Instrumentation for Neutron Inelastic Scattering Research (Proc.Int.Conf. Vienna, 1970), IAEA, Vienna (1970) 117.
[18] PRICE D.L., SKOELD, K., Nucl.Instr.Meth. **82** (1970) 208.
[19] REICHHARDT, W., et al., ibid. p. 147.
[20] PELLIONISZ, P., Nucl.Instr.Meth. **92** (1971) 125.
[21] WEISE, K., Nucl.Instr.Meth. **98** (1972) 119.
[22] GRAFFSTEIN, A., Nucl.Instr.Meth. **119** (1974) 101.
[23] GLAESER, W., GOMPF, F., Nukleonik **12** (1969) 153.
[24] MATHES, W., Neutron Inelastic Scattering (Proc.Int.Conf. Grenoble,1972), IAEA, Vienna (1972) 773.
[25] AMADORI, R., HOSSFELD, F., ibid. p. 747.
[26] KROO, N., et al., ibid. p. 763.
[27] PELLIONISZ, P., KROO, N., MEZEI, F., ibid. p. 787.
[28] MEZEI, F., PELLIONISZ, P., ibid. p. 797.
[29] AMADORI, R., Report of the Kernforschungsanlage Juelich, JUEL-1050-FF (1974).
[30] ROULT, G., BUEVOZ, J.L., CENG Grenoble Report, 76B65 (1976).
[31] ZIEGLER, P., BADUREK, G., WESTPHAL, G.P., Nucl.Instr.Meth. **137** (1976) 59.
[32] MC. CARTHY Jr., J.P., DANNER, H., Nucl.Instr.Meth. **121** (1974) 609.
[33] PELIZZARI, C.A., POSTOL, T.A., Nucl. Instr.Meth. **143** (1977) 139.
[34] WEISE, K., et al., Nucl.Instr.Meth. **140** (1977) 269.
[35] BADUREK, G., to be published.
[36] BADUREK, G., WESTPHAL, G.P., Nucl.Instr.Meth. **128** (1975) 315.
[37] AMADORI, R., HOSSFELD, F., Nucl.Instr.Meth. **124** (1975) 429.

DISCUSSION

F. MEZEI: An alternative method of Fourier TOF analysis is the use of Larmor precession modulation. This technique has the advantage that the modulation has no spurious frequency components, and it can easily be pushed to very high resolutions or frequencies.

G. BADUREK: This would, of course, be a nice technique but the Fourier method would still have no great advantage over the correlation method for electronic choppers.

F. MEZEI: Yes, I agree that in most cases the statistical method seems to be superior to the Fourier method.

P.E. HIISMÄKI: Can you state any requirements as regards the stability of the chopper drive system?

G. BADUREK: In our case the rotational speed of the chopper was held constant to within about 0.1% and this was entirely adequate.

P.E. HIISMÄKI: I quite agree with what you said regarding the efficiency of the mechanical Fourier chopper in your presentation and in this connection I would like to show Fig.A, illustrating a time-of-flight spectrum for iron powder which was measured at Otaniemi ten days ago. None of the unwanted interference or ghost peaks observed in the first experimental results published in this field can be seen. Clearly, the Fourier technique is not limited to fitting

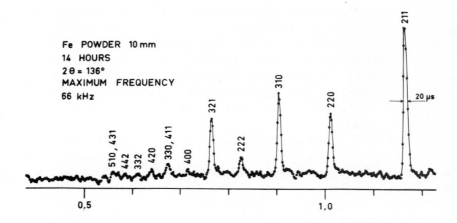

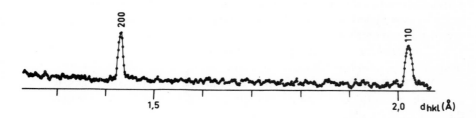

FIG.A.   Time-of-flight spectrum for iron powder.

a small number of parameters; it can also be used to reproduce fairly complex spectra. The spectrum shown here was measured with a reverse time-of-flight spectrometer characterized by a thin scintillation detector and by the absence of angular collimators; in addition there are special focusing arrangements for the chopper, sample and detector.

T. SPRINGER: With a statistical chopper, one of the problems is that it is difficult to study weak peaks in the presence of strong peaks. Do you have the same difficulty in the case of the Fourier chopper?

G. BADUREK: If you are interested in the whole spectrum, yes. If, however, you are interested only in, say, the width of small, narrow peaks superimposed on a broad residual distribution, then the Fourier method may be advantageous, because these widths can be found easily from the Fourier amplitudes at higher frequencies without performing the whole Fourier inversion procedure.

R. STOCKMEYER: You have pointed out various reasons why the statistical chopper has so far not been very much used. From my experience I would say that the statistical chopper gives a resolution similar to that of the conventional chopper, but much more intensity. Nevertheless, I cannot use the statistical chopper to study the quasielastic peak from adsorbed molecules, for instance, because the elastic peak has a heavy background, which is due to the method, not to the lack of shielding. Has this situation now been improved by new developments?

G. BADUREK: Not at all, but it should be mentioned that for quasi-elastic scattering it would often be possible to have the duty cycle close to 0.5, thus making any indirect method unnecessary from the start. Of course, the same argument as in my answer to Mr. Springer's question is valid here, too.

N. KROÓ: You mentioned in your presentation that you had made a comparison between the correlation and Fourier methods, but you did not mention the possibility of two-dimensional analysis in connection with the correlation method. A nice example of two-dimensional analysis is to be found in the case of pulsed sources. This possibility might shift the balance towards the correlation method.

G. BADUREK: I omitted it because in the literature I could find only theoretical work in this field and no corresponding experiments.

N. KROÓ: You did not mention the filtering out of elastic peaks, which is very simple in the correlation technique. Can it be done in the same way in the Fourier method?

G. BADUREK: Filtering is also possible, of course, with the Fourier method, especially in the so-called 'inverted' mode. However, I did not explicitly mention it because in the case of low background one would hardly need one of the indirect methods and therefore the gain in accuracy by filtering is rather marginal. As mentioned in our paper, however, we have tested it experimentally with the electronic correlation chopper.

N. KROÓ: Filtering out of the elastic peaks was tried with the two-dimensional correlation spectrometer on the Dubna pulsed reactor and proved to be useful. This correlation spectrometer is to be used with the new IBR-2 pulsed reactor at Dubna.

G. BADUREK: For pulsed sources the situation might be different. Were your results published? This is the first time I have heard about this experiment.

N. KROÓ: Yes. The first test experiments — without filtering — were described in the Proceedings of the IAEA Symposium on Neutron Inelastic Scattering, held in Grenoble in 1972, and later on in several JINR (Dubna) Reports.

A.P. MURANI: I would like to make a comment. When one uses the correlation technique to study small inelastic scattering intensities, the 'artificial' background due to elastic incoherent scattering can be quite important. This artificial background is simply the probability of mistaking elastic scattering for inelastic. In such a situation filtering of the elastic scattering intensity can be quite useful.

G. BADUREK: Your arguments are correct, but remember that filtering is advantageous only if the elastic peak is concentrated in just a few (1–2) channels. Otherwise, you have no gain in accuracy because of peak reduction; instead, you have a large loss of accuracy due to the intensity loss inherent in the filtering technique.

Sessions III and IV

MOLECULAR SPECTROSCOPY

Invited Review Paper

ROTATIONAL EXCITATIONS AND TUNNELLING

A. HÜLLER, W. PRESS
Institut für Festkörperforschung
    der Kernforschungsanlage Jülich GmbH,
Jülich,
Federal Republic of Germany

Abstract

ROTATIONAL EXCITATIONS AND TUNNELLING.

In a molecular crystal each molecule experiences an orientational potential as it rotates in the field of its neighbours. The orientational potential reflects both the symmetry of the molecule itself and the symmetry of its lattice site. Depending on the potential strength the rotational energy level scheme may be characterized as (almost) free rotation (weak potential) or as librational oscillation in one of the potential pockets (strong potential). For an intermediate potential strength the tunnelling between different pockets leads to a splitting of the librational ground state multiplet. The tunnelling transitions are single particle excitations. Almost free rotations and librations may or may not have single particle character. Particle exchange symmetry relates the tunnelling sub-levels in the librational states with spin states of definite symmetry. In neutron scattering experiments from samples containing NH_4^+ or CH_4 tetrahedra these proton spin correlations lead to interference effects. Experiments to test the predicted $\vec{Q}$-dependence of the neutron scattering intensities are suggested. At high temperatures each molecule in the crystal feels a time dependent potential that acts like a random force on its angular degrees of freedom. The resulting rotational motion is rotational diffusion which is either continuous or stepwise. Neutron scattering from this type of motion leads to several quasi-elastic lines in addition to an elastic component.

I   Introduction

In molecular crystals we distinguish between the following elementary excitations: Excitons, internal vibrations of the molecules, and external modes which may be grouped into translational and rotational modes |1|. Excitons are coupled electronic excitations of the molecules which typically have an energy of 10 eV. For small molecules the energy of the internal vibrations is of the order of 100 meV, whereas external modes normally range below 10 meV. A clearcut separation of the external modes from internal vibrations and electronic excitations is then possible. Larger molecules may, however, show internal modes of relatively low energy. A discrimination between internal and external modes then is no longer possible and the concept of a molecular crystal and the external mode approach

become less useful. Methods which have been developed for the
calculation of phonons in atomic crystals are more effective.
Naphtalene is an example where internal and external modes are
in the same frequency range |2|.

This paper is concerned with the external mode approach to
the rotational excitations in systems consisting of small molecules with high energy internal modes. The molecules may then
be considered as rigid units characterized by their centre of
mass position $\vec{r}_i$ and by a set of angular coordinates ω_i describing their orientation in space. The external mode treatment
for molecular rotations (and translations) is appropriate and
successful. The concept may readily be extended from proper
molecular crystals (consisting of neutral molecules) to ionic
crystals containing molecular ions (e.g. NH_4^+ in $NH_4^+Cl^-$) and,
as far as rotations are concerned, to rigid radicals (e.g. CH_3-
groups).

Energetically rotations and translations fall into the same
regime. In the region of an accidental degeneracy of a rotational and a translational excitation branch there is a transfer of the mode character and the degeneracy is lifted by level
repulsion. A distinction between rotational and translational
modes is not possible. If the coupling between the rotational
and translational degrees of freedom is weak, the regions of
character transfer are small and the different excitations may
be treated separately. The main object of this article are
systems where the separation is possible. The effect of trans-
lation-rotation coupling has been studied in a few systems,
e.g. in context with deviations from the Cauchy relations |3-6|.

The rotational excitations of molecules in a crystal differ
markedly from gas phase spectra. In the gas the molecules rotate
freely during the time intervals between the rather infrequent
collisions with each other. In the solid the molecules remain
always at distances where their mutual interactions are important.

The angle dependent terms of the interaction may be divided into
two different contributions. $V_1^{ij}(\omega_i;\vec{r}_i,\vec{r}_j)$ is the interaction
of the i-th molecule with the j-th particle which does not
possess angular degrees of freedom (atom, monoatomic ion). V_1
also includes the monopole-multipole interation of two molecules which depends on the angular coordinates of only one of
the two partners. $V_2^{ij}(\omega_i,\omega_j;\vec{r}_i,\vec{r}_j)$ represents the interaction
which depends on the orientation of both molecules.

The orientational potential seen by the i-th molecule is
given by a sum of V_1 and V_2 over all the neighbours of the i-th
molecule:

$$w^i(\omega_i;\{\omega_j',\vec{r}_j\}) = \sum_{j=1}^{N+M}{}' \; V_1^{ij}(\omega_i;\vec{r}_i,\vec{r}_j) + \sum_{j=1}^{M}{}' \; V_2^{ij}(\omega_i,\omega_j;\vec{r}_i,\vec{r}_j) \qquad (1.1)$$

M is the number of molecules, N the number of other particles in the crystal. W^i depends on $\{\omega'_j, \vec{r}_j\}$, the set of centre of mass coordinates and angular coordinates of all particles in the crystal (with ω_i omitted). W^i is time dependent. (1) From the classical point of view this is due to the time dependence of $\vec{r}_j$ (due to lattice vibrations) and of ω_j (due to rotational excitations). (2) Quantum mechanically $W^i(\vec{\omega}_i;\{\omega'_j, \vec{r}_j\})$ has to be integrated over the states of the neighbours of the i-th molecule:

$$V^i(\omega_i, t) = \prod_{j=1}^{N+M} d\vec{r}_j \prod_{j=1}^{N}{}' d\omega_j \, P(\{\omega_j, \vec{r}_j\}, \{\omega_j, \vec{r}_j\}; t) \, W^i(\omega_i; \{\omega'_j, \vec{r}_j\})$$

(1.2)

$P(\{\omega_j, \vec{r}_j\}, \{\omega'_j, \vec{r}'_j\}; t)$ is the density matrix of the system under consideration. The prime at the product denotes the omission of the integration over ω_j for j=i. A simple approximation to Eq. (1.2) is the replacement of the full density matrix by a product of single particle density matrices. This is the Hartree approximation or molecular field theory. The excitations then are single particle excitations without q-dependence. The time dependent Hartree approximation or random field approximation (RPA) corresponds to the Ornstein-Zernike approach to order parameter fluctuations at continuous phase transitions. It includes the q-dependence of rotational excitations |7,8|, but becomes inadequate when a rotational mode softens close to an orientational phase transition. Orientational correlations then become very important and are not properly accounted for by the above theory. More powerful methods have been developed for strongly fluctuating systems |9,10|.

The time dependence of $V^i(\omega_i, t)$ stems from transitions between the phonon states and the rotational states of the system. In general the time average $V^i_{st}(\omega_i)$ of $V^i(\omega_i, t)$ is different from zero, but it may be very small. Candidates for this case are orientationally disordered phases where rapid rotational diffusion of the neighbours smears out the average potential for each molecule. There also exist molecular crystals with partial orientational order: the orientational field at certain sublattices vanishes due to a cancellation of the contributions from symmetry related neighbours (e.g. CH_4 II, O_2).

The fluctuating part of the potential $V^i_{fl}(\omega_i, t) = V^i(\omega_i, t) - V^i_{st}(\omega_i)$ is of the order of kT. $V^i_{fl}(\omega_i, t)$ is responsible for the rotational diffusion of the molecules at high temperatures. The diffusion is continuous over the angular degrees of freedom of the molecule, if $V^i_{st}(\omega_i)$ is small. For large static potentials $V^i_{st}(\omega_i)$ the molecules have a discrete number of equilibrium orientations which they take on in a random sequence. The term used for this kind of motions is jump diffusion or molecular reorientation.

At low temperatures the fluctuating part of the potential dies out. The translational phonon modes are no longer populated

and the system approaches its rotational ground state which is
stationary. The density matrix then simplifies to the absolute
square of the ground state wave function which in the Hartree
approximation is a product of single particle wave functions.
To develop a picture that is as simple as possible, we will
always start with the Hartree approximation at zero temperature
and consider its deficiencies at a later stage.

II   The Orientational Potential

     The orientational potential a molecule experiences in the
crystal is of multifold origin.

(1)   In ionic crystals the overwhelming contribution stems from
the interaction between the electrostatic multipoles of a molecule and the charges in its neighbourhood. The multipole-mono-
pole interaction between i-th molecule and the k-th ion is of
the form $V_1^{ij}(\omega_i; \vec{r}_i, \vec{r}_j)$.

(2)   In proper molecular crystals the interactions of the
permanent multipole moments of the molecules are dominating:
$V_2^{ij}(\omega_i, \omega_j; \vec{r}_i, \vec{r}_j)$.

(3)   A further and normally less important contribution is due
to the interaction of the molecule under consideration with its
polarizable neighbours (atoms or ions). For methane molecules
in a rare gas matrix |11| this may be an important term.

     The electrostatic contributions which have been mentioned
so far, are expanded into a multipole series with wellknown
analytical expressions for each term. (4) Anisotropic dispersion forces and (5) valence forces are also important. Analytical expressions for them are, however, not easily obtained.
One thus depends on phenomenological expressions as e.g. the
Kihara core potential |12| or atom-atom potentials |13|. The
phenomenological potential parameters are adjusted to fit experimental data.

     The sum over all these interactions, averaged selfconsis-
tently over the ground state of the neighbours of one molecule
yields the single particle potential $V_{st}(\omega)$ at zero temperature.
It is useful to expand $V_{st}(\omega)$ into a set of orthonormal functions. The coefficients of such an expansion can be calculated
from the pair potential if the latter is known. Otherwise the
coefficients may be considered as adjustable parameters.

     For the expansion of the potential any complete set of
orthonormal functions may be used. The number of nonzero coefficients will, however, be greatly reduced if one takes advantage
of symmetry adapted harmonics.

(1) In the simple case of a molecule that rotates around a single axis, the potential can be expanded into a series of trigonometric functions:

$$V_{st}(\alpha) = \sum_{n=o}^{\infty} (a_n \cos n\alpha + b_n \sin n\alpha) \qquad (2.1)$$

α is the rotation angle. A very interesting example for one-dimensional rotation are CH_3-groups or NH_3-groups rotating around the threefold molecular axis. Molecular symmetry reduces the expansion (2.1) to the terms with n=0,3,6.... An additional symmetry of the lattice may further reduce the number of non-zero coefficients. A mirror plane e.g. makes all coefficients b_n vanish. In $Ni(NH_3)_6I_2$ the rotation axis of the NH_3-group is a fourfold symmetry axis of the crystal. Only $a_{12}, a_{24}, \ldots$ are different from zero |14|. In order to relate the case of one-dimensional rotation with the following examples, it is remarked that for some applications it is useful to express $V_{st}(\alpha)$ in terms of $\tau_1 = \cos \alpha$ and $\tau_2 = \sin \alpha$.

(2) For linear molecules with two rotational degrees of freedom ($\omega = \Theta, \phi$) the potential may be expanded into a series of spherical harmonics:

$$V_{st}(\Theta, \phi) = \sum_{\ell=o}^{\infty} \sum_{m=-\ell}^{+\ell} A_{\ell m} Y_{\ell m}(\Theta, \phi) \qquad (2.2)$$

$V_{st}(\Theta, \phi)$ contains only terms of even order in ℓ if the linear molecule possesses inversion symmetry. Examples are H_2 |15|, N_2 |16| or N_3 in sodium azide |17|. For high site symmetry an expansion into the corresponding symmetry adapted harmonics may be profitable. Na^+CN^- |18| is an example where the symmetry of the CN^- site is cubic. An expansion into cubic harmonics

$$V_{st}(\Theta, \phi) = \sum_{\ell=o}^{\infty} \sum_{\mu=1}^{2\ell+1} B_{\ell m} K_{\ell m}(\Theta, \phi) \qquad (2.3)$$

contains only the nonvanishing coefficients B_{01}, B_{41}, $B_{61}, \ldots$ The corresponding cubic harmonics become particularly simple if expressed in carthesian coordinates: $\tau_1 = \sin\Theta \cos\phi$, $\tau_2 = \sin\Theta \sin\phi$, and $\tau_3 = \cos\Theta$. In terms of τ the forth order function K_{41} reads: $K_{41} = |\tau_1^4 + \tau_2^4 + \tau_3^4 - 3/5| 5\sqrt{21}/4\sqrt{4\pi}$. The minima of V_{st} are also called the pockets of the potential. If in the cubic case the series (2.3) is restricted to the first nonvanishing term $B_{41} K_{41}(\Theta, \phi)$, then V_{st} is the Devonshire potential |19| with six pockets in the (100) directions for negative B_{41} or eight pockets in the (111) directions for positive B_{41}.

(3) The orientational potential for three dimensional molecules and polyatomic ions like CH_4, SF_6, and NH_4^+ depends on three angular degrees of freedom, e.g. the Euler angles

$\omega=(\xi,\eta,\zeta)$. The potential may again be expanded into a series of orthonormal functions. The Wigner D-functions are a possible choice.

$$V_{st}(\xi,\eta,\zeta) = \sum_{\ell=0}^{\infty} \sum_{m,n=-\ell}^{+\ell} A_{mn}^{(\ell)} D_{mn}^{(\ell)} (\xi,\eta,\zeta) \qquad . \qquad (2.4)$$

As in the twodimensional case an expansion into symmetry adapted functions may be useful. In terms of cubic rotator functions the expansion reads:

$$V_{st}(\xi,\eta,\zeta) = \sum_{\ell=0}^{\infty} \sum_{\mu,\nu=1}^{2\ell+1} B_{\mu\nu}^{(\ell)} U_{\mu\nu}^{(\ell)} (\xi,\eta,\zeta) \qquad (2.5)$$

For a tetrahedral molecule at a site of tetrahedral symmetry most of the coefficients $B_{\mu\nu}^{(\ell)}$ vanish (which would not be the case with the coefficients $A_{mn}^{(\ell)}$ in Eq. (2.4)). Different from zero are: $B_{11}^{(0)}$, $B_{11}^{(3)}$, $B_{11}^{(4)}$, $B_{11}^{(6)}$,... A transformation from the Euler angles to carthesian coordinates converts $U_{\mu\nu}^{(\ell)}$ into a polynomial of order 2ℓ. The transformation is:

$$\begin{aligned}
\tau_1 &= \sin \tfrac{1}{2} \eta \ \sin \tfrac{1}{2} (\xi-\zeta) \\[4pt]
\tau_2 &= \sin \tfrac{1}{2} \eta \ \cos \tfrac{1}{2} (\xi-\zeta) \\[4pt]
\tau_3 &= \cos \tfrac{1}{2} \eta \ \sin \tfrac{1}{2} (\xi+\zeta) \\[4pt]
\tau_4 &= \cos \tfrac{1}{2} \eta \ \cos \tfrac{1}{2} (\xi+\zeta)
\end{aligned} \qquad (2.6)$$

The coordinates τ which are called quaternious fulfil the condition: $\tau_1^2+\tau_2^2+\tau_3^2+\tau_4^2=1$. With the definition $H_{\mu\nu}^{(\ell)}(\tau)=U_{\mu\nu}^{(\ell)}(\xi(\tau),\eta(\tau),\zeta(\tau))$ one obtains $|20,21|$:

$$H_{11}^{(3)}(\tau) = 16(\tau_1^6+\tau_2^6+\tau_3^6+\tau_4^6) - 20(\tau_1^4+\tau_2^4+\tau_3^4+\tau_4^4) + 5 \qquad (2.7)$$

$H_{11}^{(3)}(\tau)$ is invariant under the combined group of the twelve proper rotations that leave a tetrahedral molecule invariant and the twelve proper rotations that leave the crystal invariant $H_{11}^{(3)}(\tau)$ thus is invariant under the 144 proper symmetry operations of the product group. The potential $B_{11}^{(3)}H_{11}^{(3)}(\tau)$ has 12 pockets at positions $\tau=(1,0,0,0)$ and $\tau=(1/2,1/2,1/2,1/2)$ for negative $B_{11}^{(3)}$, there are the same number of pockets at positions $(1/\sqrt{2}, 1/\sqrt{2}, 0,0)$ if $B_{11}^{(3)}$ is positive. For a tetrahedron in a cubic crystal field (examples are the ammonium halides in their disordered cubic phase or methane in a rare gas matrix) $B_{11}^{(3)}$ vanishes. $H_{11}^{(4)}(\tau)$ then is the lowest order cubic rotatior function that contributes to $V_{st}(\tau)$.

III   Rotational Excitations at Low Temperatures

To calculate the rotational excitation spectrum of molecules in the crystal we shall, for the moment, restrict ourselves to the single particle picture. The problem then is to
calculate the eigenstates of the Hamiltonian

$$H = T + V_{st}(\tau) \tag{3.1}$$

where T is the kinetic energy. In terms of the carthesian coor-
dinates τ the kinetic energy operator reads |20,22|:

$$T = -\kappa \frac{\hbar^2}{2\Theta} \left[\sum_{\mu=1}^{d+1} \frac{\partial^2}{\partial\tau_\mu^2} -d \sum_{\mu=1}^{d+1} \tau_\mu \frac{\partial}{\partial\tau_\mu} - \sum_{\mu,\nu=1}^{d+1} \tau_\mu\tau_\nu \frac{\partial^2}{\partial\tau_\mu\partial\tau_\nu} \right] \tag{3.2}$$

where for the cases of one, two, and three dimensional rotation
d is equal to 1, 2, and 3. κ is equal to 1 for the one and two
dimensional case, but equal to 1/4 for 3 dimensions.

The limits of very strong and of vanishing potential $V_{st}(\tau)$
are well known:

a) For strong potentials the molecule sits in one of the pockets
and performs small oscillations. The excitation spectrum is that
of a harmonic oscillator with equally spaced energy levels.

b) For vanishing V_{st} the molecule is a free rotor. The magnitude
of the level spacing is determined by the rotational constant
$B=\hbar^2/2\Theta$, where Θ is the moment of inertia.

c) The intermediate regime where the splitting of an individual
oscillator state into several sublevels is still observable, is
the so-called tunneling regime.

Fig. 1 is a sketch of the rotational energy levels as a
function of the potential strength. The figure covers all three
regimes. It is clear from the above discussion that the potential has a strong influence on the energy levels if it is strong
in comparison with the rotational constant. B thus is the natural
unit in which the potential strength should be measured.

The rotational constant of H_2 is extremely large: B=85 K.
In addition to that, the molecular field in solid H_2 is small.
It can be estimated from the phase transition temperature of
2.8 K. In contrast to that typical crystal fields are large in
terms of the rotational constant of a heavy molecule (e.g.
$B(CCl_4)=0.08$ K). CH_4, $-CH_3$, NH_4^+, and $-NH_3^+$ with a rotational
constant B=8 K are intermediate cases. Choosing different
chemical environments the potential strength may be varied such
that all three regimes are covered.

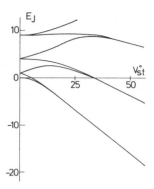

FIG.1.   *The energy level scheme of a rotor in an orientational potential. Shown is the transition from free rotations to librations with increasing potential strength* V_{st}^0 . *The splitting of the librational multiplets is the tunnel splitting.* V_{st}^0 *and* E_J *are given in units of* $B = h^2/2\Theta$.

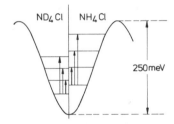

FIG.2.   *The librational energy levels of the* NH_4^+ *and* ND_4^+-*ions in one of the potential pockets in ammonium chloride. The indicated transitions have been observed in infra-red* [23] *and Raman spectroscopy* [24] *and the transition from the ground state to the first excited state also in neutron scattering* [25, 26].

In the following we shall treat the three cases: a) oscillations, b) (almost) free rotation, and c) tunneling, in detail. Special attention will be paid to the rotational tunneling.

a)   Oscillation in a strong orientational potential

The ammonium halides represent excellent examples for the strong potential limit. The halide ions in the neighbourhood of a NH_4^+ tetrahedron create a strong single particle potential of the form:

$$V_{st}(\tau) = B_{11}^{(4)} H_{11}^{(4)}(\tau) + \ldots \tag{3.3}$$

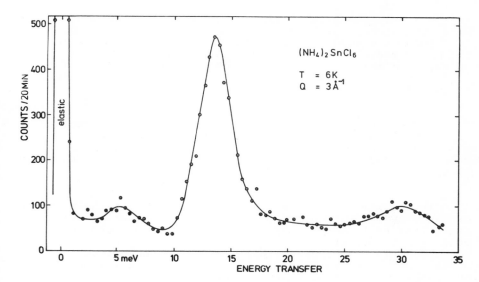

FIG.3. Inelastic neutron spectrum of $(NH_4^+)_2 SnCl_6^{--}$. *The inelastic lines at 13.4 meV and 30 meV are interpreted as transitions from the librational ground state to the first and second librational level, respectively. An additional peak at about 6 meV probably is due to acoustic zone boundary phonons* [28].

In $NH_4^+Cl^-$ e.g. the potential strength is $B_{11}^{(4)}$ = 360 B |21|. At 243 K there is a phase transition which reduces the NH_4^+ site symmetry from cubic to tetrahedral. $V_{st}(\tau)$ then contains a small admixture of $H_{11}^{(3)}(\tau)$. Fig. 2 is a schematic drawing of the potential around one of the twelve equilibrium orientations. The energy levels are also given. The deviation from an equally spaced oscillator level scheme is due to anharmonicities. The indicated transitions from the ground state to three excited states have been found in IR-absorption spectroscopy |23| and in Raman scattering |24|. The excitation to the first excited state has also been found in neutron scattering |25,26|. The librational branch is flat (within the experimental accuracy of 3%) showing the adequacy of the single particle picture.

     This is different in proper molecular crystals where the dominating two body forces $V_2^{ij}(\omega_i,\omega_j;\vec{r}_i,\vec{r}_j)$ depend on the orientation of both partners. Hexamethylenetetramine (HMT) is an extremely well studied example |27| where the librations are collective modes; the librational excitation branches show considerable dispersion.

For relatively small librational amplitudes a conventional Born-von Kármán type calculation, with the rotational degrees of freedom included |1|, provides an adequate description of the experimental results. If anharmonic effects are important, on may do a calculation in time dependent Hartree approximation |7,8|, in self consistent phonon theory |9| or using other techniques |10|.

$(NH_4^+)_2$ $SnCl_6^{--}$ is an example where the single particle approach to the NH_4^+-rotation should give an excellent description. Anharmonicities, however, seem to be important. Fig. 3 shows the neutron scattering from the librational excitations in this substance |28|.

In the limit of strong rotational potentials the particle exchange symmetry is not important. If the tunneling sublevels (splitting ΔE_t) in one oscillator state are not resolved in the experiment, then the interaction time of the probe with the rotating object is shorter than the "tunneling period" $t = \hbar / \Delta E_t$. During the measuring process the probe "sees" the molecule in one pocket. The tunneling particles do not exchange their positions and thus identical particles can be considered distinguishable. Consequently spin correlations cannot be observed in such an experiment.

b)   Quantum mechanical free rotation

A situation close to quantum mechnical free rotation in the crystal is exceptional. Solid H_2 with the unusually big rotational constant B = 85 K almost ideally fulfils the conditions for free rotation. A less clearcut example is CH_4 in its partially ordered phase II which exists below 20.4 K. In phase II three quarters of the methane molecules are orientationally ordered. The order closely resembles that of an antiferromagnet. Each of the remaining molecules is surrounded by a cage of 12 nearest neighbours which are all (anti-) ordered. The octupole field in the centre of the cage vanishes due to compensation. The next order crystal field term (hexadecapole) is relatively weak. One quarter of the molecules thus rotates almost freely |29,30|. The rotational potential seen by these molecules is similar to the potential experienced by matrix isolated CH_4 in Ar, Kr, and Xe |11,31|.
The onedimensional rotation of $-CH_3$ groups in γ-picoline |32| is another borderline case. The potential has a strength of 8B. The measured transition frequencies differ from the free case by 15%.

Theoretically the situation of free rotation is simple. (In this limit there is of course no coupling between neighbouring molecules and the single particle picture holds). The Schrödinger equation with H=T (Eq. (3.2)) is readily solved for the three cases of practical importance, namely the rotation around a fixed axis, rotation of a linear molecule, and the

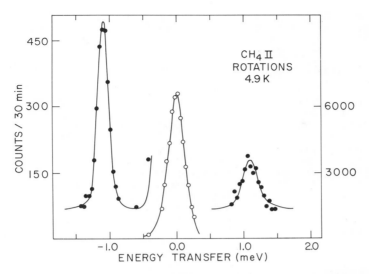

FIG.4.   One quarter of the molecules in CH₄II *experiences a weak orientational potential of octahedral symmetry.   The transition at 1.09 meV is attributed to the J = 0 and J = 1 transition, which in zero potential would occur at 1.3 meV* [30].

rotation of a spherical top, with 1, 2 and, 3 rotational degrees of freedom. The corresponding energy levels are: $E_1 = BJ^2$, $E_2 = BJ(J+1)$, and $E_3 = BJ(J+1)$ where $\hbar J$ is the total angular momentum. J assumes the values: J=0,1,2,... In the onedimensional case the ground state is single and all excited states are doubly degenerate. For linear molecules the degeneracy of the different levels is 2J+1 and for the spherical top it is $(2J+1)^2$.

Particle exchange symmetry plays an important role for freely rotating molecules. The total wave function of the H_2 molecule e.g. has to be antisymmetric under the exchange of two protons. The total wave function ψ is a product of a rotational part ϕ and a spin part χ. Therefore symmetric rotational wave functions (J=0,2,4,...) combine with the antisymmetric proton spin function $\chi_a=(|\alpha\beta\rangle-|\beta\alpha\rangle)/\sqrt{2}$ (para H_2) whereas the antisymmetric rotational wave functions (J=1,3,5,...) combine with one of the three symmetric spin functions: $\chi_s^+ = |\alpha\alpha\rangle$, $\chi_s^0 = (|\alpha\beta\rangle+|\beta\alpha\rangle)/\sqrt{2}$ and $\chi_s^- = |\beta\beta\rangle$ (ortho H_2). $|\alpha\rangle$ and $|\beta\rangle$ denote the z component of the nuclear spin $\langle I_z\rangle=+1/2$ and $-1/2$. In the unperturbed crystal spin conversion is very slow and therefore para and ortho H_2 behave like distinct species with separate excitation spectra. Neutrons can flip the proton spins and neutron scattering has been used to observe the J=1 to J=0 transition. The energy difference is 14.6 meV in the orientationally disordered phase and 13.7 meV in the ordered fcc structure |33-36|. A wave vector dependence of the excitation is not observed.

The ordered fcc structure exists only at high ortho concentrations (c > 0.55). The J=1 (ortho-) ground state in the molecular field splits into a m=o singlet and a m=±1 doublet. The m=o to m=±1 excitations at different molecules interact. The energy therefore depends on the polarization |37| and the wave vector |38,39| of the excitation.

For CH_3 and CH_4 the group of proper rotations which transform the molecule into itself is isomorphous with the group of even permutations of three and four protons respectively. Consequently the total wave function has to be symmetric under these operations. Rotational wave functions and spin wave functions have to be combined such that their product is totally symmetric. This again relates separate level schemes to the different spin species. Fig. 4 shows neutron intensities for the O →1 and 1 → 2 transition in CH_4 II |30|. There is no wave-vector dependence of these transitions as expected. The rotating molecules are well separated from each other by their cages of ordered molecules.

c)   Rotational tunneling

Neutron scattering results exist for the tunneling motion of CH_4 |30|, NH_4^+ |40,41,28|, CH_3 |42,43,44,45|, and NH_3 |14| in various environments. Fig. 5 shows the tunneling lines of Ref. |28|. In all examples the number of pockets in the potential is determined by the symmetry of the rotating group, i.e.: three potential pockets for the onedimensional rotors CH_3 and NH_3 and twelve pockets for the threedimensional rotors CH_4 and NH_4^+. If the proton spin is neglected we cannot distinguish the protons and consequently also the molecular orientations belonging to the different pockets are indistinguishable too (see Fig. 6). The tunneling between these equivalent potential minima therefore differs in an important detail from the tunneling between inequivalent minima. If, for example, a proton in a host lattice is tunneling between different interstitial sites, the proton is dressed by a phonon cloud |46| (polaron effect) which tends to deepen the potential at the actual proton position. Such a polaron effect does not exist for the rotational tunneling of molecules between equivalent minima. The threefold or twelvefold symmetry of the potential cannot be removed by a lattice distortion. Tunneling between equivalent orientations thus is not a combined effect of molecular rotation and lattice relaxation. Consequently the "mass" of the tunneling object is just the bare moment of inertia.

If the orientational potential is extremely strong, then the molecule is confined to one pocket where it performs zero point librations. The molecule is in one of its pocket states, which in the limit of infinitely high barriers are exact eigenstates of the Hamiltonian (3.1). For a finite potential $V_{st}(\tau)$ the tails of the pocket state wave function extend into the neighbouring pockets and there is a finite probability for a tunneling process into a neighbouring pocket. The pocket states then are not stationary - they are no eigenstates of the problem.

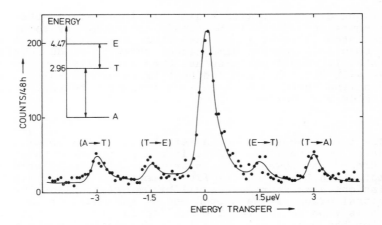

FIG.5. *The tunnelling lines in* $(NH_4^+)_2SnCl_6^{--}$ [28]. *The tunnelling frequencies differ by three orders of magnitude from the librations shown in Fig. 3.*

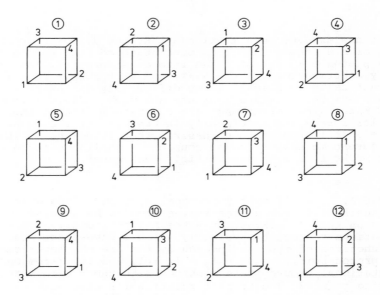

FIG.6. *The twelve equivalent orientations of a tetrahedron in a crystal field. If one of the orientations is an equilibrium orientation, then all twelve orientations are equilibrium orientations, independent of site symmetry or lattice relaxation.*

In one dimension, with a sinusoidal potential, the Schrödinger equation reduces to Mathieu's equation. Its solutions
are tabulated |47,48|. In two and three dimensions there is no
closed solution. The two dimensional rotation of dumb-bells or
off center lithium impurities has been carefully reviewed in
context with specific heat and heat transport anomalies |49|.
The tunneling there is between inequivalent potential minima.
The problem will not be touched here.

The tunneling states of a tetrahedral H_4 group will be
considered in detail |22,50,51|. If one of the orientations of
the tetrahedron shown in Fig. 6 represents an equilibrium
orientation in the molecular field, then the other eleven
orientations also represent equilibrium orientations. The
librational ground state around one of the equilibrium orientations is a pocket state. The Hamiltonian (3.1) is not diagonal for the pocket states. All off diagonal elements are
different from zero and there are seven different values for
them, corresponding to the four threefold and the three twofold rotation axes which relate the twelve states to each other.
A diagonalization of the Hamiltonian matrix leads to a singlet
ground state (A), three triply (T) and one doubly (E) degenerate
excited states. For a particular site symmetry some of the overlap matrix elements may be equal and as a consequence the degeneracy of the levels may be increased. The rotational wave
functions are linear combinations of pocket states with A, T,
and E type symmetry under the symmetry operations of the tetrahedron.

It has already been mentioned that the different pocket
states of a H_4-group cannot be distinguished from each other
if the proton spin is not taken into consideration. The proton
density distributions in the A, T, and E type wave functions
are practically identical. (They differ only in the overlap
region where the wavefunctions are not much different from
zero). Within the librational ground state multiplet the intermolecular forces are practically independent of the tunneling
sublevel. It is therefore emphasized that tunneling excitations
on different molecules do not couple - tunneling between equivalent pockets is a single particle phenomenon.

The A, T, and E-type rotational wave functions which have
been constructed from pocket states have to be combined with
the proton spin functions. Only the A-type (totally symmetric)
combinations represent physically allowed wave-functions. The
spin functions of the four proton system are characterized by the
total proton spin $I^t = I_1 + I_2 + I_3 + I_4$ and its z-component I_z^t.
The rotational ground state combines with the 5 spin functions
belonging to $I^t=2$. The triplet rotational states combine with
the $I^t=1$ spin functions and the doublet with the $I^t=0$ spin
functions. Out of the 192 products of 12 rotational wave functions and 16 spin wave functions 16 eigenfunctions ψ_α
($\alpha=1,2,...16$) can be formed which are totally symmetric.

With the known wavefunctions for the tunneling system the doubly differential scattering cross section can be directly calculated from

$$\frac{d^2\sigma}{d\Omega d\omega} = \frac{k'}{k} \sum_{\mu,\mu'=-1/2}^{+1/2} \sum_{\alpha,\alpha'=1}^{16} P_\mu P_\alpha |<\psi_{\alpha'}\mu'\vec{k}'|W|\psi_\alpha\mu\vec{k}>|^2 \delta(\hbar\omega - E_\alpha + E_{\alpha'})$$

(3.4)

Unprimed symbols refer to quantities before the scattering event, primed symbols to the same quantity after scattering. μ and $\vec{k}$ denote the neutron spin and wavevector, E_α is the energy of the molecule in the state ψ_α, $\hbar\omega$ the transferred energy. P_α is the initial probability for the state ψ_α. In a typical tunneling experiment the energy differences are of the order of 10 $\mu eV = 1.2 \times 10^{-2}$ K and the temperature is above 4.2 K. All P_α then are equal to 1/16. For an unpolarized beam $P_\mu = 1/2$. W is the interaction of the scattered neutron with the four protons in a molecule.

$$W = \sum_{\gamma=1}^{4} [a_{coh} + \frac{2a_{inc}}{\sqrt{I(I+1)}} \vec{S}\cdot\vec{I}_\gamma \delta(\vec{r}-\vec{R}_\gamma)]$$

(3.5)

$\vec{R}_\gamma$ is the position of the γth proton, $\vec{I}_\gamma$ its spin operator, $\vec{r}$ and $\vec{S}$ denote position and spin of the neutron. The spin independent scattering length a_{coh} is very small for protons.

Usually the nuclear spins in a sample are uncorrelated and therefore the spin dependent scattering length a_{inc} leads to incoherent scattering. If, however, in a tunneling experiment the different transition lines are resolved, then the spin state of the four protons is known before and after the scattering event, and in contrast to the usual situation, there are interference effects for the protons within one molecule. The scattering intensity of each tunneling line depends on the momentum transfer $\vec{Q}=\vec{k}-\vec{k}'$. $NH_4^+ClO_4^-$ and $(NH_4^+)_2SnCl_6^-$ are good candidates for a measurement of the $\vec{Q}$ dependence of the scattering intensity in a single crystal experiment. Such an experiment has not yet been performed. Powder experiments yield only information on the $|\vec{Q}|$-dependence of the scattering. Angular averages over the intensities of the tunneling lines |50| are in excellent agreement with intensity ratios at a fixed $|\vec{Q}|$. Powder data exist for $NH_4^+ClO_4^-$ |41| and $(NH_4^+)SnCl_6^-$ |28|. Another test is the $|\vec{Q}|$ dependence of the scattering intensity. For each inelastic line theory |50| yields an intensity proportional to $(1-j_0(Qd))$ where d is the proton-proton distance in the molecule and $j_0(x)$ a spherical Bessel function. All lines (elastic and inelastic) add up to a scattering cross section of $4a_{inc}^2$ if the spin independent part is neglected.

The pressure dependence of the tunnel splitting is an interesting but experimentally unexplored field. A change in the lattice constant affects the angle dependent forces and the orientational potential. The overlap matrix elements which directly determine the tunnel splitting depend exponentially

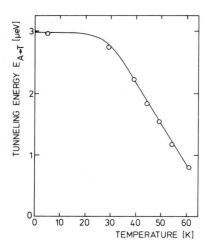

FIG.7.   The temperature dependence of the tunnel splitting in $(NH_4^+)_2SnCl_6^{--}$.

on the potential. Technically attainable pressures can change
the tunneling frequencies by as much as an order of magnitude.
This has to be compared with phonon frequency shifts under
pressure which amount to a few percent. Frequency shifts have
been extensively used to determine mode Grüneisen parameters
and to obtain information on interatomic potentials. From the
strong pressure dependence of tunneling frequencies it is clear
that the tunneling spectroscopy can be developed into a sensitive probe for intermolecular forces.

The temperature dependence of the energy and width of
tunneling lines is a fascinating and active field of research.
(See e.g. |44|). Fig. 7 shows an example for which detailed
experimental data are available |28|. Theory has so far. been
concentrating on the A-E transition of tunneling CH_3-groups.
The shift and broadening is attributed to rapid transitions
from the librational ground state into the first excited state.
Mechanisms of this kind are discussed in another article of
these proceedings |44|. A general theory of the rotational
tunneling in the presence of thermally excited phonons has not
yet been developed.

IV   Rotational Diffusion at High Temperatures

So far the presentation of rotational excitations has been
restricted to low temperatures. If the rotational states (and
the phonon modes) are not highly excited, the interactions between the elementary excitations can be neglected. The excited
rotational states then have a well defined energy and the width

is much smaller than their distance ΔE. A purely quantum mechanical calculation is valid, if kT << ΔE, in which case the transition rate 1/τ between the states is much smaller than h/ΔE. ΔE denotes the energy difference between free rotational or librational states.

The tunneling sublevels of a librational state represent an exception. They belong to different nuclear spin species and transitions between them are forbidden. (The spin-rotation coupling is of the order of 10^{-10} eV |52|.) For this reason neutron induced transitions between the tunneling states can be observed even for values of kT which are several orders of magnitude larger than ΔE_t.

In the following again a distinction will be made between (a) strong and (b) weak static potentials. If kT is comparable with the (a) librational or (b) free rotational energy levels, the purely quantum mechanical calculation has to be replaced by a statistical theory of the many body system. The following discussion will be restricted to sufficiently high temperatures, such that the classical approach is valid. Only a short survey of the rotational diffusion problems will be given here, a thorough discussion is found in Ref. |53| section 7.

a)   Strong static potentials $V_{st}(\omega)$

In strong static orientational potentials a molecule possesses several equilibrium orientations in the pockets of the potential. The molecule sits for a long time in one of the pockets. The time dependent part $V_{fl}(\omega,t)$ of the orientational potential acts on the molecule like a random force which from time to time causes the molecule to reorient from one pocket into another one.

The NH_4^+-ion in $NH_4^+Cl^-$ for example possesses 24 equilibrium orientations. They belong to two inequivalent groups, each with twelve equivalent orientations. Above the order-disorder phase transition at T = 243 K the two groups have the same energy, whereas they differ below. 90° reorientations around the four-fold rotation axes bring a molecule from one group into another, 120° reorientations around a threefold axis leave it in the same group. The respective jump rates are denoted by ν_3 and ν_4.

Looking at the incoherent scattering only, the intensity from the individual protons has to be added up. Each of the four protons of an ammonium ion may be found in eight different positions around its nitrogen atom. The probability of finding a proton in the position α (α = 1,2,...,8) at a time t is denoted by $p_\alpha(t)$. $p_\alpha(t)$ fulfils the following rate equation |54-56|:

$$\frac{d}{dt} p_\alpha(t) = \sum_{\beta=1}^{8} \gamma_{\alpha\beta} \, p_\beta(t) \qquad (4.1)$$

$\gamma_{\alpha\beta}$ (for $\alpha \neq \beta$) is the rate at which the proton jumps from
position β into position α. $\gamma_{\alpha\beta}$ is either equal to one of the
jump rates ν_3 and ν_4 or it is zero. $-\gamma_{\alpha\alpha}$ is the total probability for jumping away from the position α.

The solution of Eq. (4.1) yields the conditional probabil-
ity $P(\beta,t|\alpha,o)$ to find the proton in position β at a time t,
if it was in position α at time t = 0. The Fourier transform of
$P(\beta,t|\alpha,o)$ leads to the incoherent scattering law $S_{inc}(\vec{Q},\omega)$.
$S_{inc}(\vec{Q},\omega)$ consists of an elastic component and of three quasi-
elastic Lorentzians, the width of which depends on the jump
rates ν_3 and ν_4. The selection of several $\vec{Q}$ values allows a
separation of the different quasielastic components and a
determination of the rates ν_3 and ν_4. A characteristic temperature dependence of ν_3 and ν_4 has been observed in the vicinity
of the phase transition in NH_4Cl |55,56|.

b)   Weak static potentials $V_{st}(\omega)$

Some globular molecules form a solid phase with a weak
static potential $V_{st}(\omega)$. In a weak orientational potential the
orientational localization of a molecule cannot be pronounced.
All orientations of a molecule are almost equally probable –
the probability distribution $p_i(\omega_i)$ for molecular orientations
is almost constant (spherically symmetric). If the monopole-
multipole interaction $V_1^{ij}(\omega_i;\vec{r}_i,\vec{r}_j)$ is sufficiently small to
be neglected, the static part $V_{st}^i(\omega_i)$ of the orientational
potential at the i-th molecule is calculated from an average
of $\sum\limits_j V_2^{ij}(\omega_i,\omega_j;\vec{r}_i,\vec{r}_j)$ over the probability distributions $p_j(\omega_j)$
of the neighbours of the i-th molecule. If $p_j(\omega_j)$ is a constant,
$V_{st}^i(\omega_i)$ vanishes and therefore $p_i(\omega_i)$ is constant, self-consis-
tently.

The rotational motion of a heavy molecule (e.g. CCl_4 in an
orientationally disordered phase at temperatures which are
large in comparison with the rotational constant B is classical,
but it should not be called "free rotation". For classical free
rotation the rotational kinetic energy $K_{rot} = \Theta M^2/2$ and the
three components of the angular momentum $\vec{M}$ are conserved quantities. In the solid the fluctuating part $V_{fl}(\omega,t)$ of the
orientational potential and K_{rot} both are of the order of kT.
As a result K_{rot} and $\vec{M}$ are strongly fluctuating. Therefore, in
analogy with the translational diffusion of particles in a
liquid, the rotational motion of a molecule in a solid in which
$V_{st}(\omega)$ is weak, is called rotational diffusion.

The incoherent scattering function is obtained from a
Fourier transform of the orientational selfcorrelation function
$G(\omega,t | \omega_o,0)d\omega$, which is the probability of finding the molecule in the orientation ω at a time t, if it was in the orientation ω_o at t=0. In the absence of a static potential $V_{st}(\omega)$
the selfcorrelation function depends only on $\omega-\omega_o$. $G(\omega-\omega_o,t) =$

$G(\omega,t|\omega_0,0)$ is expanded into a set of spherical harmonics (or Wigner D-functions). With the exception of a_{00} which is constant, all coefficients $a_{\ell m}$ of such an expansion decay with time, and the decay constant depends on ℓ. S_{inc} consists of an elastic line (due to a_{00}) and an infinite series of Lorentzians for the different orders ℓ |57|. Their width increases proportional to $\ell(\ell+1)$. This distinguishes the continuous diffusion from the jump diffusion which leads to a finite number of Lorentzians.

The two particle interaction correlates the orientations of neighbouring molecules. Close to a continuous or almost continuous phase transition correlations become particularly important. The coherent structure factor $S_{coh}(\bar{Q})$ may then be calculated from the orientational pair correlation function |58|

$$< \sum_{ij} U_{\tau\mu}^{(\ell)} (\omega_i) \ U_{\tau'\mu'}^{(\ell')} (\omega_j') >$$

which leads to critical scattering near T_c. The critical slowing down of the fluctuations leads to a quasielastic line which becomes increasingly narrow as the phase transition temperature is approached |59,60|.

REFERENCES

|1| VENKATARAMAN, G., SAHNI, V.C., Rev. Mod. Phys. 42
      (1970) 409.

|2| BOKHENKOV, E.L., DORNER, B., NATKANIEC, I., SHEKA, E.F.,
      Solid State Comm. to be published.

|3| PRESS, W., DORNER, B., STILLER, H.H., Solid State Comm.
      9 (1971) 1113.

|4| STIRLING, W., PRESS, W., STILLER, H.H., J. Phys. C,
      to be published (1977).

|5| HAUSSÜHL, S., Solid State Comm. 13 (1973) 147.

|6| KRASSER, W., BUCHENAU, U., HAUSSÜHL, S., Solid State
      Comm. 18 (1976) 287.

|7| HÜLLER, A., Phys. Rev. B10 (1974) 4403.

|8| DUNMORE, P.V., Can. J. Phys. 55 (1977) 554.

|9| RAICH, J.C., GILLIS, N.S., KOEHLER, T.R., J. Chem.
      Phys. 61 (1974) 1411.

|10| KROLL, D.M., MICHEL, K.H., Phys. Rev. B15 (1977) 1136.

|11| KATAOKA, Y., PRESS, W., BUCHENAU, U., SPITZER, H., These Proceedings, Vol. 1, IAEA-SM-219/26.

|12| MACRURY, T.B., STEELE, W.A., BERNE, B.J., J. Chem. Phys. 64 (1976) 1288 and references therein.

|13| KITAIGORODSKY, A.I., "Molecular Crystals and Molecules", Academic Press, New York (1973).

|14| PRESS, W., PRAGER, M., J. Chem. Phys., to be published (1977).

|15| JAMES, H.M., RAICH, J.C., Phys. Rev. 162 (1967) 649.

|16| MANDELL, M.J., J. Low Temp. Phys. 18 (1975) 273.

|17| RAICH, J.C., GILLIS, N.S., J. Chem. Phys. 65 (1976) 2088.

|18| ROWE, J.M., RUSH, J.J., PRINCE, E., J. Chem. Phys. 66 (1977) 5147.

|19| DEVONSHIRE, A.F., Proc. Roy. Soc. (London) A153 (1936) 601.

|20| FOREMAN, J.W., Jr., thesis, Purdue University (1964) unpublished.

|21| HÜLLER, A., KANE, J.W., J. Chem. Phys. 61 (1974) 3599.

|22| HÜLLER, A., KROLL, D., J. Chem. Phys. 63 (1975) 4495.

|23| SCHUMAKER, N.E., GARLAND, C.W., J. Chem. Phys. 53 (1970) 392.

|24| FREDERICKSON, L.R., DECIUS, J.C., J. Chem. Phys. 66 (1977) 2297.

|25| TEH, H.C., BROCKHOUSE, B.N., Phys. Rev. B3 (1971) 2733.

|26| KIM. C.H., RAFIZADEH, H.A., YIP, S., J. Chem. Phys. 57 (1972) 2291.

|27| DOLLING, G., POWELL, B., Proc. Roy. Soc. A319 (1970) 209.

|28| PRAGER, M., PRESS, W., ALEFELD, B., HÜLLER, A., J. Chem. Phys., to be published (1977).

|29| KAPULLA, H., GLÄSER, W., Inelastic Scattering of Neutrons in Solids and Liquids, p. 841, IAEA, Vienna (1973).

|30| PRESS, W., KOLLMAR, A., Solid State Comm. 17 (1975)
        405.

|31| NISHIYAMA, K., YAMAMOTO, T., J. Chem. Phys. 58 (1973)
        1001.

|32| ALEFELD, B., KOLLMAR, A., DASANNACHARIA, B., J. Chem.
        Phys. 63 (1975) 4415.

|33| EGELSTAFF, P., HAYWOOD, B., WEBB, F., Proc. Phys. Soc.
        90 (1967) 681.

|34| SCHOTT, W., RIETSCHEL, H., GLÄSER, W., Phys. Letts.
        A27 (1968) 566.

|35| NIELSEN, M., Phys. Rev. B7 (1973) 1626.

|36| STEIN, H., STILLER, H., STOCKMEYER, R., J. Chem. Phys.
        57 (1972) 1726.

|37 | HARDY, W., SILVERA, J., MCTAGUE, J., Phys. Rev. Letts.
        22 (1969) 297.

|38 | RAICH, J.C., ETTERS, R.D., Phys. Rev. 168 (1968) 425.

|39 | MERTENS, F.G., BIEM, W., HAHN, H., Z. Phys. 213 (1968)
        33.

|40 | PRAGER, M., ALEFELD, B., J. Chem. Phys. 65 (1976)
        4927.

|41 | PRAGER, M., ALEFELD, B., HEIDEMANN, A., Colloque
        Ampère, Heidelberg (1976).

|42 | ALEFELD, B., KOLLMAR, A., Phys. Letts. 57A (1976)
        289.

|43 | KOLLMAR, A., ALEFELD, B., Proceedings of the Conference
        on Neutron Scattering, Gatlinburg (1976) 330.

|44 | CLOUGH, S., HEIDEMANN, A., These proceedings, Vol. 1,
        IAEA-SM-219/76.

|45 | CLOUGH, S., HOBSON, T., NUGENT, S.M., J. Phys. C8
        (1975 L95.

|46| FLYNN, C.P., STONEHAM, A.M., Phys. Rev. B1 (1970)
        3966.

|47| TAMIR, T., Math. Comp. 16 (1962) 100.

| 48 | GLODEN, R.F., Euratom Report EUR 4349f (1970).

| 49 | NARAYANAMURTI, V., POHL, R.O., Rev. Mod. Phys. 42 (1970) 201.

| 50 | HÜLLER, A., Phys. Rev., to be published.

| 51 | SMITH, D., J. Chem. Phys. 66 (1977) 4587.

| 52 | PINTAR, M., NMR, Basic Principles and Progress 13 (19) 125.

| 53 | SPRINGER, T., Springer Tracts in Modern Physics Vol. 64 (1972).

| 54 | MICHEL, K.H., J. Chem. Phys. 58 (1973) 1143.

| 55 | TÖPLER, J.M., Dissertation, Techn. Hochschule Aachen (1977) unpublished.

| 56 | TÖPLER, J.M., RICHTER, D., SPRINGER, T., to be published.

| 57 | SEARS, V.F., Can. J. Phys. 45 (1967) 237.

| 58 | HÜLLER, A., PRESS, W., Phys. Rev. Letts. 29 (1972) 266.

| 59 | PRESS, W., HÜLLER, A., STILLER, H., STIRLING, W., CURRAT, R., Phys. Rev. Letts. 32 (1974) 1354.

| 60 | KROLL, D.M., MICHEL, K.H., Phys. Rev. B15 (1977) 1136.

DISCUSSION

J.W. WHITE: Did I understand you to say that you do not expect dispersion of tunnelling excitations? Is this only within the limit where one neglects the nuclear magnetic dipole-dipole Hamiltonian?

A. HÜLLER: Yes. The nuclear magnetic dipole-dipole interaction is several orders of magnitude smaller than the observed tunnelling energies.

T. SPRINGER: My question is related to Mr. White's question concerning the dispersion of tunnelling transitions. Could there be dispersion in the case of tunnelling transitions related to non-equivalent orientations?

A. HÜLLER: Yes. One expects dispersion for the tunnelling between non-equivalent orientations. However, it is doubtful whether tunnelling between non-equivalent orientations could be seen at very low energy transfers, say in the μeV regime. Lattice imperfections lead to different well depths for non-equivalent potential pockets, and rapid transitions between the tunnelling states will smear out the energy levels. Moreover, there exists a polaron effect for the tunnelling between non-equivalent orientations. The tunnelling co-ordinate is a collective co-ordinate which contains the rotation angle of the molecule and lattice displacements.

K.H. MICHEL: Could you comment on the way the shape of the spectra changes with temperature? Have you observed the transition to a quasi-elastic line experimentally?

A. HÜLLER: The transition from tunnelling at low temperatures to rotational diffusion at high temperatures has been studied experimentally in a few cases. $(NH_4^+)_2 SnCl_6^{--}$ is an example where detailed information has been gathered. No general theory to account for the width of the tunnelling lines due to interactions with lattice phonons is available yet. Clough's paper, IAEA-SM-219/76, is concerned with the temperature dependence of tunnelling of methyl groups, and I think he will review the state of the art for one-dimensional rotational tunnelling.

R.M. PICK: In the normal temperature regime where the experiments performed there are lots of phonons available. How is it that one can still see tunnelling states which are only a few μeV apart?

A. HÜLLER: The phonons cannot flip the proton spins, so they cannot cause transitions between the tunnelling levels which belong to different spin species of the four-proton system in CH_4 or NH_4^+.

T. SPRINGER: I would like to draw attention to the spin echo method presented in paper IAEA-SM-219/56 by Mezei. The sign of the Fourier components in the spectrum will depend on whether a tunnelling transition is connected with spin flip or not. Consequently, combining conventional spectrum measurements with spin echo Fourier spectra may yield information on the spin assignment of the tunnelling states.

A. HÜLLER: The use of the spin echo method for determining tunnelling spectra is something that should be tried. As you mention, the spin-flip and non-spin-flip scattering events can be separated. Transition matrix elements have been calculated and they should be compared with experimentally determined intensities. The spin echo method could also be used to get more precise information on the width of tunnelling lines.

L.A. DE GRAAF: With regard to the equivalence of pocket states for distorted molecules, I would like you to comment on recent results we obtained with QENS on $NH_4 ZnF_3$ where the ammonium ion is heavily distorted. This is shown clearly from the elastic intensity, which indicates that four quasi-equilibrium sites exist for the protons on the time-scale of our observations.

A. HÜLLER: Of course, a crystal field of low symmetry distorts an ammonium tetrahedron. However, this does not destroy the equivalence of the potential pockets as the distortion is the same in each of the equivalent orientations.

TEMPERATURE DEPENDENCE OF INELASTIC AND QUASI-ELASTIC NEUTRON SCATTERING OF A TUNNELLING METHYL GROUP

S. CLOUGH
Department of Physics,
University of Nottingham,
United Kingdom

A. HEIDEMANN
Institut Laue-Langevin,
Grenoble

Abstract

TEMPERATURE DEPENDENCE OF INELASTIC AND QUASI-ELASTIC NEUTRON SCATTERING OF A TUNNELLING METHYL GROUP.

The inelastic neutron scattering peak associated with the tunnelling rotation of the 4-methyl group in MDBP (4-methyl-2, 6-ditertiarybutylphenol) has been studied over the temperature range 4-28 K using the high resolution back-scattering spectrometer IN10 at ILL. A few measurements of the width of the quasi-elastic scattering peak have also been made. The inelastic peak occurs at low temperatures at an energy transfer of 35 μeV, shifting towards lower energies with increasing temperature. The temperature dependent widths of both inelastic and quasi-elastic peaks can be deduced from two previous magnetic resonance experiments, namely the temperature dependence of the proton spin lattice relaxation time and of the time constant for conversion between the A and E proton spin permutation symmetry species. The agreement between neutron scattering and magnetic resonance results is excellent. The ratio width/shift for the inelastic peak and the ratio of the width of inelastic and quasi-elastic peaks are connected with two angles x and y which characterize the orientational changes occurring to the methyl group as a result of thermal excitations. At temperatures above 16 K the dominant process has an activation energy of 130 K and x and y are both of the order 0.6 radian. Below 16 K the dominant process has a much lower activation energy and x and y are both small. It is suggested that the former process is the torional excitation of the methyl group and the latter process involves excitation of strongly coupled lattice modes.

1. INTRODUCTION

The classical model of the thermally activated rotation of methyl groups in solids is of sudden random rotations through an angle of $\pm 2\pi/3$ to equivalent orientations favoured by the hindering barrier. With this model, the angle $\phi(t)$ which defines the orientation of the group fluctuates between three values, and the correlation function $F(\tau) = \langle \exp(i\phi(t))\exp(-i\phi(t + \tau))\rangle$ is then easily shown to be equal to $\exp(-\lambda_\tau)$ where $\lambda/3$ is the probability per unit time for a rotation through $2\pi/3$. The spectral density function of

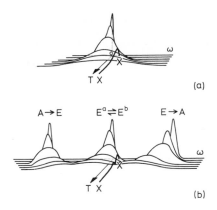

FIG.1.   The motional spectrum associated with CH_3 rotation (a) for the simple classical model (b) for the quantum model.   The line XX is a section through the spectrum at the proton Larmor frequency and is effectively what is measured by proton spin lattice relaxation measurements.

the operator $\exp(i\phi)$ is the Fourier transform of $F(\tau)$ and is therefore expected to be a Lorentzian function $G(\omega)$ where

$$G(\omega) = \pi^{-1}\lambda(\lambda^2 + \omega^2)^{-1} \tag{1}$$

From a classical point of view the sudden rotations require excitation of the methyl group to the top of the hindering barrier E_0 so that one anticipates a temperature dependence

$$\lambda = \lambda_0 \exp(- E_0/kT) \tag{2}$$

The classical model therefore has $G(\omega)$ as a single peak as in figure 1(a), always centred at $\omega = 0$ and broadening with increasing temperature.
      The quantum theory involves a considerable modification of this simple picture. The spectral density function which corresponds to (1) exhibits structure (see figure 1(b), and requires more parameters to describe it, so that the temperature dependence is more complex than (2). At sufficiently high temperatures though, the structure is not resolved because of line broadening and the spectral density function probably approaches a Lorentzian form centred near $\omega = 0$. This accounts for the success of the classical theory at relatively high temperatures, a success which only reflects the loss of detailed information from the spectral density function. To understand on a microscopic level the phonon scattering events which lead to molecular rotations, it is necessary to study the spectral density function at those low temperatures where the information contained in its structure can be extracted. Figure 1(b) illustrates a rotational spectral density function whose study is described in this paper. In addition to a peak centred at $\omega = 0$, peaks also occur at $\omega = \pm \omega_t$ where ω_t is often referred to as the frequency of tunnelling rotation. At least three temperature dependent parameters emerge, namely ω_t and the widths of the central and flanking peaks.

Two experimental techniques are ideally suited to study CH_3 rotation because of their sensitivity to large amplitude proton motion, namely magnetic resonance and neutron scattering. The strength of the magnetic resonance techniques, of which a large number have been applied to this purpose, is in their ability to handle spectral density functions with small splittings ω_t. At present neutron scattering is limited to those cases where $\hbar\omega_t > 1$ μeV which means relatively weakly hindered methyl groups. The strength of neutron scattering is in the ability to study the changes of the spectral density function with increasing temperature [8,9]. This paper describes measurements made on MDBP (4-methyl-2,6-ditertiarybutylphenol), a system which has already been extensively studied by magnetic resonance methods at low temperatures [1-6]. The neutron scattering experiments provide new information which throws new light on the dynamical processes responsible for the 4-methyl group rotation.

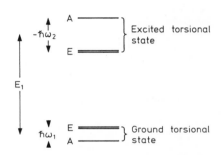

FIG.2.   The lower energy levels of the tunnelling CH_3 group in MDBP. The motional spectrum of Fig.1 is explained in terms of these levels and the phonon induced transitions which occur between them.

2.   THE MOTIONAL SPECTRUM OF A TUNNELLING METHYL GROUP

The lower levels of a CH_3 group moving about its symmetry axis in a hindering potential of the form $\frac{1}{2}E_o(1 - \cos3\phi)$ are shown in figure 2. We shall account for the general form of the motional spectrum of figure 1(b) in terms of these levels and the transitions which occur between them due to phonon scattering. A more complete discussion would need to include levels associated with strongly coupled lattice modes. In the absence of tunnelling rotation the levels of figure 2 could be simply classified as torsional levels, and each would be three-fold degenerate. In fact this degeneracy of each torsional state is lifted to leave a singlet A and a doublet E. This is frequently referred to as a tunnelling splitting of the torsional levels. Figure 2 shows the two lowest torsional levels, the most important at low temperatures. Because rotation involves the interchange of indistinguishable particles, the exclusion principle enters in, with the consequence that the torsion-rotation states A, E^a, E^b have proton spin states belonging to different representations of the permutation group. Conversion between these three spin species requires proton spin flips, and occurs rather slowly in general, due to the modulation of proton dipole-dipole interactions by thermal vibrations. Conversion between spin species is also caused in neutron scattering, those scattering events involving conversion between the A

and the E species giving rise to inelastic scattering (i.e. the outer peaks
of figure 1(b) and conversion between the two E species giving rise to quasi-
elastic scattering (the central peak of figure 1(b)).

The scattering law may thus be expressed in the following form

$$S(q,\omega) = A(q)\delta(\omega) + B(q)L(\omega) + C(q)(I(\omega) + I(-\omega)) \qquad (3)$$

The delta function $\delta(\omega)$ corresponds to $A \to A$, $E^a \to E^a$ and $E^b \to E^b$ transitions.
$L(\omega)$ is a Lorentzian function arising from transitions between the two E
states while $I(\omega)$ and $I(-\omega)$ are the spectral functions for $A \to E$ and $E \to A$
transitions, respectively.

To understand the form of the spectrum in figure 1(b), it is necessary
to add to the energy levels of figure 2 the effect of rapid transitions
between torsional levels caused by phonon scattering processes [6]. Such
transitions are spin independent and involve no change in the spin symmetry.
One result is that the inelastic neutron scattering experiments do not in
general reflect directly the energy splittings between A and E species of
figure 2, but rather a dynamically averaged spectrum $I'(\omega)$ [7].

$$I'(\omega) = \frac{\lambda(\omega_2-\omega_1)^2\exp(-E_1/kT)(1+\exp(-E_1/kT))^{-1}}{(\omega-\omega_1)^2(\omega-\omega_2)^2+\lambda^2((\omega-\omega_1)+(\omega-\omega_2)\exp(-E_1/kT))^2} \qquad (4)$$

This is just the spectrum of a frequency modulated oscillator switching randomly between two states in which its frequencies are ω_1 and ω_2, respectively,
though spending a smaller time (smaller by the factor $\exp(-E_1/kT)$) in the
second state than the first. It describes the dynamic averaging of the
energy splittings of figure 2 due to transitions between ground and first
excited torsional states. λ^{-1} is the lifetime of the excited torsional state
while ω_1, ω_2 and E_1 are defined in figure 2. It is easy to see that if λ is
small, then (4) exhibits two peaks with Boltzmann weighted intensities at
$\omega = \omega_1$ and $\omega = \omega_2$ while if λ is large there is a single peak near
$\omega = (\omega_1+\omega_2\exp(-E_1/kT))(1+\exp(-E_1/kT))^{-1}$. At fairly low temperatures when
$\exp(-E_1/kT) \ll 1$, $I'(\omega)$ is small except for $\omega \sim \omega_1$ and the denominator of (4)
can be approximated by replacing $(\omega - \omega_2)$ by $(\omega_1 - \omega_2)$ when the denominator
assumes the form $((\omega_1 - \omega_2)^2 + \lambda^2)((\omega - \omega_1 - \delta)^2 + a^2)$ with

$$\delta = (\omega_2 - \omega_1)(1 + x^2)^{-1}\exp(-E_1/kT) \qquad (5)$$

$$a = \lambda x^2(1 + x^2)^{-1}\exp(-E_1/kT) \qquad (6)$$

$$x = (\omega_2 - \omega_1)\lambda^{-1} \qquad (7)$$

Thus at temperatures less than about $\frac{1}{2}E_1/k$, $I'(\omega)$ has a Lorentzian shape,
centred at $\omega = \omega_1 + \delta$ and with a width (FWHM) equal to $2a$. At low temperatures a narrow line at $\omega = \omega_1$ is expected, shifting to lower energy (because
$\omega_2 - \omega_1$ is negative due to the inversion of the levels in the excited torsional state compared with the ground state) and broadening, with increasing
temperature. This is one of the outer peaks (A to E) of figure 1(b); the
other outer peak (E to A) is $I'(-\omega)$. These peaks are subject to further
broadening due to a second motional process to be described shortly. For
this reason we distinguish between $I'(\omega)$ and $I(\omega)$, the latter including the
additional broadening.

The line width $2a$ of $I'(\omega)$ can be understood in terms of the change of
the tunnel frequency $(\omega_2 - \omega_1)$ which accompanies an excursion of the methyl
group to the excited torsional state. Because of the random occurrence of
these excursions, the phase coherence of the tunnelling motion is lost, and

this manifests itself in the frequency domain by a broadening of the order
of the reciprocal of the time constant for loss of phase coherence. The
parameter $x = (\omega_2 - \omega_1)\lambda^{-1}$ is the mean additional phase angle acquired as a
result of an excursion to the excited state. If x is much less than 1 radian,
then an average of x^{-2} excursions are necessary before the resulting random
walk process leads to an accumulated phase angle of 1 radian and substantial
loss of phase coherence. If $x \gg 1$ a single excitation is enough. In this
latter case, the broadening parameter a is $\lambda\exp(-E_1/kT)$, the reciprocal of
the ground state lifetime. In the former case it is $x^2\lambda\exp(-E_1/kT)$, as may
be confirmed from the more exact expression (6).

Although x is a phase angle associated with CH_3 motion it cannot be
identified with the classical concept of rotation, since no direction, clockwise or anticlockwise is involved. The character of quantum mechanics, with
states describing a mixture of configurations, enables us to visualise rotational motion which is both clockwise and anticlockwise. The name flip-flop
motion has been used [5] to distinguish this from rotation as ordinarily
understood. Flip-flop motion may be regarded as a consequence of the different time evolution of A and E states, rotation as a consequence of the
different time evolution of E^a and E^b states. The frequencies ω_1 and ω_2
therefore refer to the frequency of flip-flop motion in the ground and
excited states. Rotation may also occur during the transitions between
torsional levels and shows up as a phase factor $\exp(i\eta)$ for E^a states and
$\exp(-i\eta)$ for E^b states where η can be identified with a rotation angle
(though not restricted to $\pm 2\pi/3$ as often assumed in classical models).
Since random rotation leads to a loss of memory of the methyl group orientation, it also contributes to the broadening of the motional spectrum. For
reasons which closely parallel those outlined in our discussion of $I'(\omega)$,
the broadening parameter b due to rotation has a similar temperature dependence to that of a

$$b = \lambda y^2(1 + y^2)^{-1}\exp(-E_1/kT) \qquad (8)$$

where y^2 is the mean value of η^2. If the two types of motion are uncorrelated, the total width of each of the outer lines $I(\omega)$ and $I(-\omega)$ of the
motional spectrum is $2(a + b)$.

While two types of motional process contribute to the width of the
outer peaks of the motional spectrum, only one (rotation) affects the width
of the central line. This is because the pairs of E levels are degenerate
in both ground and excited torsional state, so matrix elements connecting
the E states are not subject to frequency modulation as are the AE matrix
elements as a result of thermal excitation. On the other hand, the effects
of rotation on $E^a E^b$ matrix elements is double that on AE matrix elements
since rotation has no effect on the phase of A states. Consequently the
function $L(\omega)$ has a width 2b' where

$$b' = 4\lambda y^2(1 + 4y^2)^{-1}\exp(-E_1/kT) \qquad (9)$$

Thus a study of the widths of the inelastic and quasi-elastic lines provides
information about the orientational changes x and y associated with phonon
scattering processes characterised by the activation energy E_1.

3. EXPERIMENTAL RESULTS

Measurements were made at the HFR in Grenoble using the high resolution
back scattering spectrometer IN10. The sample consisted of 1.5 g of polycrystalline MDBP, deuterated so that all hydrogen atoms other than those of the
4-methyl group were replaced. At low temperatures the inelastic neutron peak

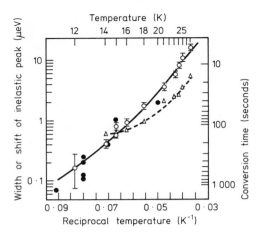

FIG.3.   *The open circles show the width (FWHM) of the inelastic neutron scattering peak which is located at an energy transfer of 35 µeV at low temperatures. The triangles show the temperature dependent shift of the centre of the peak to lower energy transfer. The closed circles show the width inferred from magnetic resonance experiments which measure the time constant for spin symmetry conversions between A and E species (right-hand scale). The continuous line is 1450 exp(−130/T) + 13 exp(−55/T).*

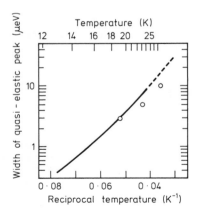

FIG.4.   *The circles are measurements of the width (FWHM) of the quasi-elastic scattering peak. The line shows the width as deduced from n.m.r. (proton spin lattice relaxation measurements).*

occurs at an energy transfer of 35 µeV, a value known from the magnetic resonance measurements. To accommodate this relatively large energy transfer, a
calcium fluoride monochromator was used in conjunction with silicon analysers.
Doppler scanning of the monochromator gave an energy window of 25 ± 15 µeV
which contained the inelastic peak at all temperatures up to 28K when the
width of the peak was comparable with the width of the window. The experiments were performed at a momentum transfer q of 1.85 Å^{-1}.

In order to study the quasi-elastic peak, both monochromator and
analyser crystals were of silicon to give an energy transfer window centred
on the elastic peak. Time allowed only very preliminary measurements of the
quasi-elastic peak, the main object having been to demonstrate that its width
can be measured accurately notwithstanding the interference from the elastic
peak.

The results are shown in figures 3 and 4. The resolution of the
instrument was such that a line width of 1 µeV was obtained at low temperatures (∿ 4K). This instrumental broadening was unfolded from the data
obtained at higher temperatures to give the width data of figures 3 and 4.

4.   COMPARISON WITH MAGNETIC RESONANCE RESULTS

Two types of magnetic resonance measurements have been made in the
temperature range from 4 to 60K. The proton spin lattice relaxation time
has been measured over this range [4,6], and this effectively gives a
section through the motional spectrum at a frequency equal to the nuclear
Larmor frequency. It provides evidence of the broadening of the central
peak of the motional spectrum up to a temperature of about 30K and is mainly
sensitive to the outer peaks above this temperature. A second type of experiment measures the rate of conversion between the A and E spin species
using paramagnetic impurities as resonant sensors of the ratio of A to E
populations [5]. What is measured by this experiment is a section through
the outer peaks only, at $\omega = 0$. This latter result is most relevant to the
neutron scattering measurements on the inelastic peak.

The connection between the conversion rate T_c^{-1} between A and E species
and the motional spectrum is that T_c^{-1} is 5.6×10^{10} times the amplitude of the
outer peaks of the motional spectrum at $\omega = 0$, the constant being obtained
from the magnitude of the intra-methyl group dipole-dipole interactions. At
low temperatures the Lorentzian approximation for $I(\omega)$ is valid and $I(0)$ is
just the width of the outer peaks of the motional spectrum divided by
$2\omega_1^2 = 7.2 \times 10^{21}$ sec^{-2} so that the width of the outer peaks as expressed in µeV
is related to the conversion time T_c expressed in seconds by the relation
width = 84 T_c^{-1}. The width deduced from the T_c measurements according to this
simple relationship is plotted in figure 3 and agrees well with the neutron
scattering results.

The width of the central line of the motional spectrum may be deduced
from proton spin lattice relaxation measurements [6] in the range 6-30K, to
be 1305 exp(-130/T) + 48 exp(-65/T) µeV. This data is much more accurate
than the conversion time measurements since the experimental technique is
much simpler. The quasi-elastic neutron scattering measurements of figure 4
are rather preliminary but are entirely consistent with the nmr results.

5.   DISCUSSION

The most important new data is the temperature dependence of the shift
δ of the outer peaks of the motional spectrum since this is not accessible
by any alternative technique. This temperature dependence shows an interesting and significant feature. At temperatures above about 16K the shift is

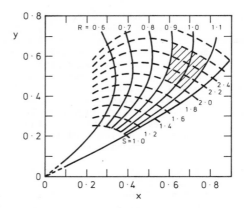

FIG.5.   *Contours of R and S on the x y plane. R is the ratio of the widths of inelastic and quasi-elastic peaks; S is the ratio of the width to the shift of the inelastic peak. The shaded portion corresponds to experimental results between 16 and 28 K. The contours are obtained from equations in the text.*

less than the width, and increases with temperature with the same activation energy ($E/k \sim 130K$) as shown by the widths of both central and outer peaks. On the other hand, it appears that below 16K the shift may exceed the width.

The measurements provide two dimensionless parameters which characterise the dominant type of motional excitation involved. These parameters are (a) the ratio R of the widths of inelastic and quasi-elastic lines, and (b) the ratio S of the width of the inelastic line to the shift δ. Above 16K the data gives $R \sim 1.0 \pm 0.1$ and $S \sim 2.3 \pm 0.3$. At temperatures below 16K $R \sim 0.6$ and $S \ll 1$. From these values it can be inferred from figure 5 in the higher temperature range x and y are roughly equal and of order 0.6 radian. In the lower temperature range they remain roughly equal but are much less than 0.2 radian.

The nmr relaxation measurements between 4 and 60K show clearly that the temperature dependence of the motional spectrum reflects two types of thermally activated process with activation energies E such that E/k is given by 130K and about 65K, the latter process becoming dominant below 16K. The neutron scattering results confirm this feature. The important question concerns the nature of these thermally activated processes as described within a simple extension of the energy level scheme of figure 2. This allows only a single process, namely activation from the ground to the first excited torsional state with $E = E_1$, but it can be extended by including higher torsional levels, or by including lattice modes to which the torsional motion of the methyl group is strongly coupled (for example molecular torsional modes of short wavelength). The question may then be posed: are the two observed activation energies associated with different torsional levels of the methyl group, or is one identifiable with the frequency of strongly coupled lattice modes?

The measurement of the shift of the inelastic line is crucial to a resolution of this question. Since the sign of the splittings between A and E states alternates in the successive torsional levels, it follows that excitation to the first excited state leads to a reduction in ω_t, but the

second excited state leads to an increase. The experimental data leaves no
doubt that both terms have the same sign. Furthermore it is possible to
calculate E_1 from the known value of ω_1 assuming a simple three-fold cosine
hindering potential and one finds E_1/k = 120K. It is natural therefore to
identify the larger of the two activation energies observed with E_1. There
is then no alternative but to identify the lower activation energy with the
excitation of strongly coupled lattice modes. Such excitations result in a
small reduction of ω_1 so that although the methyl group remains nominally in
its ground torsional state, matrix elements between A and E states experience
a frequency modulation leading to both shift and broadening of the inelastic
line. Because the change in ω_1 is small, the resulting phase angle x, associated with a brief excitation of a coupled lattice oscillator, is also expected to be small, and the same should apply to the parameter y associated with
rotation. It is therefore entirely consistent with this model for the methyl
group motion that the values of x and y are found to be much smaller for the
process of lower activation energy than the 0.6 radian found for the higher
activation energy process. This illustrates that the temperature dependence
of δ is the key to an understanding of the thermal processes responsible for
methyl group motion.

REFERENCES

[1]   CLOUGH, S., MULADY, B.J., Phys. Rev. Lett. 30 (1973) 161.
[2]   CLOUGH, S., HOBSON, T., J. Phys. C: Solid St. Phys. 7 (1974) 3387.
[3]   CLOUGH, S., HILL, J. R., J. Phys. C: Solid St. Phys. 8 (1975) 2274.
[4]   CLOUGH, S., HENNEL, J.W., J. Phys C: Solid St. Phys. 8 (1975) 3115.
[5]   CLOUGH, S., HILL, J. R., J. Phys C: Solid St. Phys. 9 (1976) L645.
[6]   BECKMANN, P., CLOUGH, S., J. Phys C: Solid St. Phys. 10 (1977) L231.
[7]   ALLEN, P.S., J. Phys C: Solid St. Phys. 7 (1974) L22.
[8]   PRAGER, M. ALEFELD, B., Magnetic Resonance and Related Phenomena (Proc XIX
       Congress Ampere, Heidelberg 1976) 389.
[9]   MULLER-WARMUTH, W., SCHULER, R., Magnetic Resonance and Related Phenomena
       (Proc XIX Congress Ampere, Heidelberg 1976) 345.

DISCUSSION

T. SPRINGER: The observed large shifts of tunnelling frequencies with
temperature was interpreted in terms of a mixing of ground state and excited
state splittings. Qualitatively, it is difficult to see why such mixing should be
produced by a *random* disturbance of these states, without a significant broadening
of the observed energies. Could you comment on this?

S. CLOUGH: The broadening exists but may not always be detected because
of limited resolution. Especially when excitations occur very rapidly, the predicted
broadening is small, being inversely proportional to the excitation rate. An
expression is given for the width in the full text of my paper (Eq.(6)).

W. PRESS: I believe you have reported the first observation of a quasi-elastic
component in rotational tunnelling. Can you say a bit more about the origin of
this quasi-elastic peak?

S. CLOUGH: This peak is due to the existence of thermally activated rotation, as in the old classical models. It is disguised because we have to use the wave-like states E^a and E^b, rather than localized pocket states, owing to the tunnelling splitting. A neutron cannot convert a methyl group from E^a to E^b without also scattering phonons to carry away angular momentum. The transition is not elastic, though E^a and E^b levels are shown as degenerate in Fig.2. Rotation freezes out at low temperature. The motion which persists at low temperature is the flip-flop motion associated with the tunnelling splitting. This dies out at high temperature, and the description can then be made in terms of the pocket states to obtain the usual classical model.

A COMPARATIVE STUDY OF THE ROTATIONAL POTENTIAL OF CH$_3$ GROUPS IN METHYL-SUBSTITUTED PYRIDINES BY NMR-T1 AND INS

M. PRAGER, A. KOLLMAR
Institut für Festkörperforschung der
    Kernforschungsanlage Jülich GmbH,
Jülich

W. MÜLLER-WARMUTH, R. SCHÜLER
Institut für Physikalische Chemie der
    Universität Münster,
Münster,
Federal Republic of Germany

Abstract

A COMPARATIVE STUDY OF THE ROTATIONAL POTENTIAL OF CH$_3$ GROUPS IN METHYL-SUBSTITUTED PYRIDINES BY NMR-T1 AND INS.
    The proton-spin-lattice relaxation behaviour of 2,6-methyl-pyridine, 3-methyl-pyridine and 3,5-methyl-pyridine has been studied in the temperature range 8 K ≤ T ≤ 200 K at 15 MHz and 30 MHz. Tunnelling of the methyl groups has manifested itself in an anomalous relaxation. The results are interpreted on the basis of an extended relaxation theory which includes the quantum-mechanical aspects of the molecular rotation. Inelastic neutron scattering experiments with the same substances have revealed tunnel splitting and yielded the transition energies to excited librational states of the hindered CH$_3$ group. Furthermore, for 3,5-methyl-pyridine the temperature dependence of the tunnel splitting and of the width of the tunnel lines has been measured. For 2,6- and 3,5-methyl-pyridine, the interpretation of the NMR-T1 curves is in complete agreement with the rotational potentials derived from the INS data. This consistency confirms the applied model of spin-lattice relaxation in substances with tunnelling methyl groups. A small discrepancy for 3-methyl-pyridine may be due to higher-order terms in the rotational potential.

Introduction

Nuclear magnetic resonance experiments on molecular substances containing CH$_3$ or NH$_4$ groups cannot be described by the classical BPP-theory /1,2/. To understand the relaxation mechanism in such materials an extended theory has been developed taking into account the quantum nature of the molecular rotation /1/. With this theory an evaluation of NMR-T1-curves with respect to the rotational potential is possible. Inelastic (INS) and

quasielastic neutron scattering allows direct measurement of some
essential parameters of the rotational potential as the tunnel
splitting, librational energies and the activation energy.
NMR, and INS experiments on the same materials have been
carried out in this work to test the theoretical model of the
NMR spin-lattice relaxation and to derive the rotational potentials.

The theory of spin-lattice relaxation in molecular substances

NMR T1-curves from molecular substances show sometimes significant deviations from classical behaviour such as different
absolute values of the spin-lattice relaxation time T1, different slopes of the high and low temperature sides of the
maximum of 1/ T1 (if plotted against 1/ T) and/or additional
Larmor-frequency - independent maxima. These anomalies can be explained by the tunnelling rotation of molecular groups like CH_3 or
NH_4. By treating quantummechanically the spins of the protons
of the methyl group and the rotational motion of the molecule
the semiclassical BPP-formula for the relaxation rate is extended to /1/

$$\frac{1}{T1} = C_1 \frac{\tau_c}{1 + \omega_t^2 \tau_c^2} + C_2 \left(\frac{\tau_c}{1 + \omega_o^2 \tau_c^2} + \frac{2 \tau_c}{1 + 4 \omega_o^2 \tau_c^2} \right) \qquad (1)$$

where

ω_o Larmor frequency

ω_t tunnelling frequency $(\omega_t \gg \omega_o)$

τ_c correlation time

The first term describes one part of the intramolecular contribution to the relaxation rate, the second term contains additionally the relaxation due to the interaction with other protons and has therefore a somewhat different meaning as in the
classical BPP-theory.

In the two cases $\omega_o \tau_c \gtrless 1$ the correlation time τ_c can often be
described by Arrhenius laws with apparent activation energies
E_A' and E_A''. In the high-temperature limit the activation energy E_A' is assumed to be the distance E_A from the librational
groundstate to the barrier height of the hindering potential

as in a classical relaxation mechanism (correspondence principle).In the low-temperature limit τ_c arises from nonmagnetic
transitions between the tunnelling sublevels of
different librational states. Since only the librational ground
state is populated significantly at the lowest temperatures E_A'
reaches the value E_{o1} which is the distance to the first excited librational state. Depending on the absolute scale of Tl in
the temperature range where only the librational groundstate is
populated, however, this limit cannot be observed experimentally
in each case. Formerly such a temperature dependence can be described by

$$\tau_c - \tau_{Ao} \exp (E_A/k\,T) \quad \text{in the high-temperature region}$$
$$\tau_c = \tau_{2o} \exp (E_{o1}/k\,T) \quad \text{in the low-temperature region} \tag{2}$$

Energy levels of the hindered rotator

The tunnelling frequency as well as the librational energies E_i
and the activation energy E_A of the hindered rotator are given
by the eigenvalues of the Schrödinger equation

$$(H_R - E)\,\psi = 0 \tag{3}$$

with the rotational Hamiltonian

$$H_R = \frac{\hbar^2}{2I}\frac{\partial^2}{\partial\varphi^2} - V(\varphi)$$

I   momentum of inertia of the molecular group
φ rotational angle
V   rotational potential

To solve this equation for a static potential $V(\varphi)$ as given
at low temperatures the rotational potential has been expanded
in functions of suitable symmetry, which in the case of
CH_3 groups are sin- and cos-functions with 3n-fold periodicity

$$V(\varphi) = \sum_{\substack{m=1 \\ N\to\infty}}^{N} \frac{V_{3m}}{2}(1 + (-1)^k \cos 3n\varphi) \tag{4}$$

For N = 2 the eigenvalues are tabulated as functions of V_3 and
V_6 for k = 1 and k = o /3/. The expansion   of $V(\varphi)$ up to

N = 2 covers a wide variety of potential shapes and allows a comparison with experimental results. For a given k the coefficients of the potential can be obtained if two eigenvalues of
(3) are known.

With increasing temperature the static potential $V(\varphi)$ becomes
time-dependent, due to the coupling of the molecular rotations
to the lattice vibrations. The energy levels of the molecule
in the fluctuating hindering potential now are given by the
solutions of the time-dependent Schrödinger equation with the
static Hamiltonian (3) and a time-dependent perturbation. Whereas the influence of the time-dependent part of the Hamiltonian
on the librational energies is small, the tunnel splitting becomes strongly temperature-dependent, since a modulation of
the rotational potential changes considerably the overlap of
the wave functions. The temperature-dependent tunnel splitting
can be expressed in this model /7/ (and other models /4-6/) as
a coherent mixture of the tunnel splittings of all librational
states in the unperturbed potential, each weighted with its
proper Boltzmann factor /5/:

$$\omega_t(T) = \sum_{\substack{i=1 \\ N \to \infty}}^{N} \omega_t^i(0) \exp(-E_{0i}/kT) \bigg/ \sum_{\substack{i=1 \\ N \to \infty}}^{N} \exp(-E_{0i}/kT) \qquad (5)$$

This formula has already been used succesfully to describe temperature-dependent tunnel splittings /7-9/. It has to be applied
implicitly in (1) to interpret the NMR-T1 data.

With increasing temperature transitions to higher librational
levels give rise to a broadening of the tunnel lines and to
quasielastic neutron scattering. From the temperature dependence of the linewidths an apparent activation energy of the
rotational potential can be derived on the basis of the Arrhenius laws (2).

NMR-T1: experimental results

Proton spin-lattice relaxation rates of 3-methyl-pyridine,
2,6-methyl-pyridine /1o/ and 3,5-methyl-pyridine have been measured over the temperature range 8 - 2oo K at 15MHz and 3oMHz.

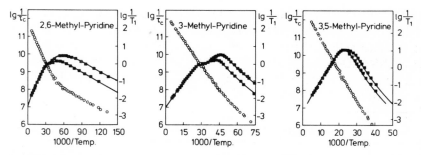

FIG.1.   Spin-lattice relaxation times (full squares) and correlation times (open circles) derived
therefrom on the basis of Eq. (1) for some methyl-substituted pyridines.

All these substances exhibit anomalous relaxation (fig. 1, full
squares). The evaluation of a NMR-T1 curve is usually performed
in the following way: With parameters C1, C2 and ω_t which are
kept constant for all temperatures a correlation time τ_c is deduced for each point of the curve 1/T1 (fig. 1, open circles).
A fit of this τ_c (1/T) with formula (2) gives reasonable values
τ_{A0}, τ_{20}, E_A' and E_A'' if ln (τ_c (T^{-1})) is linear over a significant temperature range at low and high temperatures. The
application of a constant ω_t for simplicity despite of (5)
gives only a negligible fault since in the low-temperature
region ω_t is really constant and in the high-temperature range
$\omega_t \tau_c \ll 1$.

2,6-methyl-pyridine is a material well-suited to prove the
above-developed theory, since the high- and the low-temperature limit is reached, giving values E_A' and E_A'' which are
unambiguous with respect to their experimental determination.
3-methyl-pyridine seems to be another rather favourable example.
However, the low-temperature limit has been reached only approximately: So the derived low-temperature activation energy
is affected by a large error.   - If the high- or low-
temperature limit is not at all reached as in the case of 3,5-
methyl-pyridine, in the low-temperature range we get only one
parameter of the rotational potential from the spin-lattice
relaxation. - For all substances a tunnel splitting at the
temperature of the tunnel maximum of $T1^{-1}$ has been obtained

TABLE I. EXPERIMENTAL RESULTS ON ROTATIONAL POTENTIALS OF HINDERED CH_3 ROTATORS IN 2,6- (1.), 3- (2.) AND 3,5-METHYL-PYRIDINE (3.) OBTAINED BY NMR-T1 (COLUMNS 1 TO 3) AND BY INS (COLUMNS 4 TO 6) EXPERIMENTS. COLUMNS 7 TO 9: POTENTIAL PARAMETERS $V_S = V_3 + V_6$ AND $\delta = V_3/V_S$ DERIVED FROM INS DATA. ALL VALUES ARE IN meV.

	E'_A	E''_A	$10^3 \hbar\omega_t(T)$	$10^3 \hbar\omega_t(0)$	E_{01}	$E''_A{}'$	k	V_S	δ
1.	15.6	3.7	2 (36 K)	190	3.6	—	0	25	0.52[a]
							1	20	0.23
2.	19.7	10.4	4.4 (37 K)	10	8.9	—	0	49	0.77
							1	47	0.22[a]
3.	36.3	31.1	1 (48 K)	1.5	12.8	38.7	0	59	0.87
							1	62	0.24
					16.6		1	58	0.34[a]
								50	0.80

[a] Best suited potential.

from the condition $\omega_t(T_{max}) \, \tau_c(T_{max}) = 1$. These values, however, are not very useful, since, first, their accuracy is rather poor and secondly a derivation of the wanted splitting at T→0 K needs already the knowledge of the rotational potential. The experimental results are represented in Table I, columns 1 to 3.

INS: experimental results

Inelastic neutron scattering has already succesfully been used to determine the rotational potential of methyl groups /11/. The calculation of the rotational potential starts with two eigenvalues of the Schrödinger equation (3). Usually the tunnel splitting of the librational groundstate $\hbar\omega_t(0)$ and the energy of the first excited librational state are measured.

The tunnel splitting of a CH_3 group in weak static rotational potentials is of the order $\hbar\omega_t \lesssim \hbar^2/2I \sim 0.5$ meV and can undoubtedly be identified since usually no other excitations occur in this energy range. The experiments concerning the

tunnel splitting have been performed at a triple axis spectrometer of high energy resolution (ΔE_{res} = 38 μeV) in Jülich
in the case of 2,6-methyl-pyridine and at two backscattering
spectrometers (ΔE_{res}= o.3/ueV) in Jülich (3,5-methyl-pyridine)
and Grenoble (3,5- and 3-methyl-pyridine), respectively.

The librational energies are of the order of a few meV and may
coincide with soft acoustic phonons. No phonon dispersion curves
of the investigated substances are available. So we have tried
to distinguish librational peaks from phonons by applying different temperatures to the samples. At low temperatures librational peaks should be of higher intensity than phonon peaks
of the same energy due to the different mass dependence of
their inelastic structure factors $F(Q,\omega)$ /1o/. At higher temperatures, however, the librations should strongly be damped
because of lifetime effects while the phonon peaks are only
little affected. If a identification of the librations was not
unambiguously possible with this method we looked also for consistency of other experimental data as higher librational levels (2,6-methyl-pyridine) or the temperature dependence of the
tunnel frequency (3,5-methyl-pyridine) with the derived rotational potential (see discussion). The librational energies
have been determined with a high-resolution triple axis spectrometer in Jülich (2,6-methyl-pyridine (fig. 2)) and a TOF-
spectrometer for thermal neutrons in Grenoble (3,5- and 3-me-
thyl-pyridine).

In an intermediate temperature range the tunnel splitting decreases with increasing temperature /7-9/. This behaviour has
been confirmed for 3,5-methyl-pyridine. Taking a constant intensity relation between elastic and inelastic peaks from the
low-temperature spectrum (T=5K) we get from a 3-Lorentzian fit
the results shown in fig. 3 (open points). - In the case of
2,6-methyl-pyridine the tunnel lines broadened and disappeared
with increasing temperature before showing a shift.

Quasielastic measurements have not been performed in this work.
The temperature-dependent width of the tunnel lines, however,

has been evaluated for 3,5-methyl-pyridine by an Arrhenius fit giving an activation energy E_A''' (fig. 4).

The experimental results are represented in Table I, columns 4 to 6.

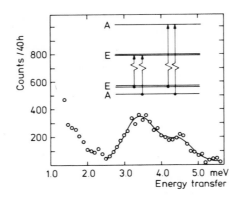

FIG.2.   *Inelastic neutron spectrum of 2,6-methyl-pyridine in the energy range 1 meV ≤ E ≤ 5.5 meV. The doublet line is attributed to the transitions between the librational ground state and the first excited librational state (insert).   The distance of the two lines is given by the tunnel splitting in the first excited librational state.*

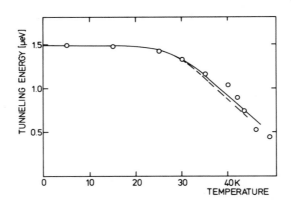

FIG.3.   *Temperature dependence of the tunnel splitting in 3,5-methyl-pyridine in the range 5 K ≤ T ≤ 49 K:*
Open points: experimental data;
Lines: tunnel splitting calculated with Eq. (5) by using 12 librational levels.
Full line: k = 0, E_{01} = 12.8 meV, k = 1, E_{01} = 16.6 meV, δ = 0.34
Dashed line: k = 1, E_{01} = 12.8 meV.

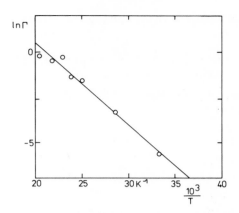

FIG.4. *Temperature dependence of the width of tunnel lines in 3,5-methyl-pyridine:*
Open points: experimental data;
solid line: A fit by an Arrhenius law gives $E_A''' \approx 450\ K$

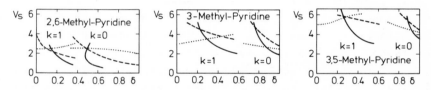

FIG.5. *Curves of constant tunnel splitting (– – – –), constant first excited librational*
energy (————) and constant activation energy (- - - - - - - - - - -) as functions of the height
of the rotational potential (4), $V_S = V_3 + V_6$, and of the potential shape characterized by
$\delta = V_3/(V_3 + V_6)$ and k = 0, 1 for 2,6-methyl-pyridine, 3-methyl-pyridine and 3,5-methyl-
pyridine. V_S in kJ/mol.

Discussion

To prove the NMR-theory with the help of the INS-data and to
derive from the experimental data compiled in the table the coefficients of the rotational potential (4) we construct for each
substance on the basis of the Schrödinger equation (3) with (4)
the curves of constant tunnel splitting, constant librational
energy and constant activation energy E_A in dependence of the
potential parameters k, $V_S = V_3 + V_6$ and $\delta = V_3/(V_3+V_6)$ (fig. 5).

All these curves should intersect each other in one point
$(V_S, \delta)_k$ if
1) all measured values ($\hbar \omega_t(o)$, E_{01}, E_A) are really eigenvalues of the Schrödinger equation.
2) the potential can be described by (4): Terms of higher order
   are negligible.

Point 1) is fulfilled from the spectroscopical INS-values.
Some uncertainty of the NMR data is caused by the model-dependent interpretation of the spin-lattice relaxation and by
some possible experimental difficulties (see above). Point 2)
is a necessary mathematical simplification because the Schrödinger equation (3) has been solved only for rotational potentials of the form (4).
2,6-methyl-pyridine which experimentally and in the framework
of the relaxation theory in the NMR experiment gives unambiguous activation energies $E_A' = E_A$ and $E_A'' = E_{01}$ does not show
any discrepancies to the INS measurements. So we can conclude
that the model-dependent description of the nuclear relaxation
and the interpretation of E_A' and E_A'' as suggested can really
be employed. From the coordinates of the intersection point in
fig. 5 we obtain the potential parameters represented in the
table and therewith the energy level scheme of the hindered
molecular rotator. With these energy levels the shape of the
doublet line in fig. 2 can nearly quantitatively be explained
by the transitions between the tunnelling sublevels of the two
lowest librational states as shown in the insert of fig. 2.
Assuming equal transition probabilities between all sublevels
we would expect a intensity relation I(3.6 meV)/I(4.3 meV) = 2
which approximately is observed. The difference between the
two level schemes of $V(\varphi)$ with k=o and k=1 is to small to
decide from fig. 2 on the phasefactor k. Fig. 5, however,
shows that there is a better agreement of the potential parameters for k=o.

For 3-methyl-pyridine we do not get such a good consistency
between NMR and INS data. That is partly caused because the
low-temperature limit has not fully been reached (fig. 1)
leading to $E_A'' > E_{01}$, which is confirmed by the INS measurements.

Additionally, however, the activation energy derived
from the spin-lattice relaxation is not consistent with the tunnel splitting and the first excited librational energy. This
means that the suppositions 1)and 2) postulated above may not be
fulfilled both in this material. Since NMR-T1 experiments have
often shown that the high-temperature activation energy is not
very different from E_A we believe that higher-order terms for
the rotational potential have to be involved. Structural data
on 3-methyl-pyridine are required to prove such a suggestion.
In spite of these open questions parameters of a rotational potential (4) has been derived from the tunnel splitting and the
energy of the first excited librational state as measured by
INS. They are represented in the table. Earlier results /12/
could not be confirmed by our experiment.

In 3,5-methyl-pyridine the relaxation at high temperatures has
reached a clear Arrhenius dependence giving, in the framework of
the relaxation theory, E_A. No low-temperature activation energy,
however, could be derived. With the measured E_A all combinations
$(V_S, \delta)_K$ along the iso-activation-energy curves (fig. 5) are
compatible. A determination of $V(\varphi)$ is only possible with the
help of the INS-data. Whereas no doubt exists on the tunnel
splitting the interpretation of the TOF-spectrum containing
three peaks of nearly the same intensity was not clear ab initio.
The peak at the lowest energy is interpreted as phonon peak because of the small temperature dependence. Both upper peaks are
strongly damped with temperature and could be attributed to librations. Using alternatively both values we calculated the
temperature-dependent tunnel splitting (5) including twelve
energy levels. Within the experimental errors suitable rotational potentials which fit the temperature behaviour of the tunnel splitting can be constructed for both values of E_{01}. The
best agreement with the activation energy of the NMR experiments, however, is obtained for $E_{01} = 16.6$ meV and $k = 1$. The activation energy from the spin-lattice relaxation time has been
confirmed by an Arrhenius fit of the temperature-dependent width
of the tunnel lines (fig. 4, solid line) which is in agreement
with the course of the correlation time τ_c in the same temperature interval   (fig. 1).

Conclusion

The rotational potentials of the hindered methyl groups in 2,6-
3- and 3,5-methyl-pyridine have been derived from the tunnel
splitting and the energy of the first excited librational level as measured by inelastic neutron scattering (see Table I).
The results confirm the interpretation of the spin-lattice relaxation in substances with tunnelling methyl groups given by
Haupt. A determination of rotational potentials (4) except for K
from NMR data alone on the basis of this theory is only possible,
if the high- and low-temperature limit of the relaxation is
clearly reached as in 2,6-methyl-pyridine. An understanding
of the rotational potentials and of some observed discrepancies
in 3-methyl-pyridine needs the knowledge of the structures of
the investigated substances which, however, have not been clarified, as yet

Acknowledgement

We want to thank Dr. A. Heidemann and Dr. J. Suck for the
performance of the experiments at the ILL Grenoble.

REFERENCES

[1]   HAUPT, J., Z. Naturforsch. **26a** (1971) 1578.
[2]   HAUPT, J., MÜLLER-WARMUTH, W., Z. Naturforsch. **23a** (1968) 208;
      Z. Naturforsch. **24a** (1969) 1066.
[3]   GLODEN, R.F., Euratom Report EUR 4349 f (1970).
[4]   ALLEN, P.S., J. Phys. **C7** (1974) L 22.
[5]   EMID, S., WIND, R.A., Chem. Phys. Lett. **33** (1975) 269.
[6]   CLOUGH, S., J. Phys. **C9** (1976) L 523.
[7]   ROSCISZEWSKI, K., to be published.
[8]   PRAGER, M., ALEFELD, B., 19th Congress Ampère, Springer, Heidelberg (1976) 389.
[9]   PRAGER, M., PRESS, W., ALEFELD, B., HÜLLER, A., J. Chem. Phys., to be published.
[10] MÜLLER-WARMUTH, W., SCHÜLER, R., KOLLMAR, A., PRAGER, M., 19th Congress
      Ampère, Springer, Heidelberg (1976) 345.
[11] ALEFELD, B., KOLLMAR, A., Neutron Scattering (Proc. Conf. Gatlinburg, 1976),
      1 (1976) 330.
[12] BROM, H.B., ZWEERS, A.E., HUISCAMP, W.J., Thesis, Leiden (1976).

DISCUSSION

A.J. DIANOUX: I think one can easily discriminate between librational
peaks, coming from the torsional oscillations of the CH_3 group in its three-fold

potential, and phonon peaks, by comparing the neutron spectra for the normal sample and the deuterated sample. This has been illustrated in the case of methyl group rotation in the solid phase of the liquid crystal PAA (para-azoxyanisole)[1].

M. PRAGER: Thank you for this comment. I agree with you. Unfortunately we had no sample available for such an experiment.

K.H. MICHEL: When you mention librational energies, do you have in mind a local mode or a collective mode?

M. PRAGER: We think that the librational energies are single-particle excitations, so they will have local character.

---

[1] HERVET, H., DIANOUX, A.J., LECHNER, R.E., VOLINO, F., J. Phys. **37** (1976) 587.

TORSIONS AND METAL-METAL INTERACTIONS IN Pt AND Pd AMMINES STUDIED BY INELASTIC NEUTRON SCATTERING

J. HOWARD, T.C. WADDINGTON
Department of Chemistry,
University of Durham,
Durham,
United Kingdom

Abstract

TORSIONS AND METAL-METAL INTERACTIONS IN Pt AND Pd AMMINES STUDIED BY INELASTIC NEUTRON SCATTERING.

We have obtained the inelastic neutron scattering spectra of some transition metal ammines and from the observed torsional frequencies, barriers to the NH_3 torsions have been calculated. As expected these are low and they are in general agreement with values calculated from other techniques. We have not observed any interaction between NH_3 rotors in molecules with more than one rotor and this is compared with some previously published calculations and assignments. Evidence for significant metal-metal interactions in $[Pt(NH_3)_4][PtCl_4]$ and cis-$Pt(NH_3)_2Cl_2$ has also been obtained through the assignment of some lattice vibrations.

Introduction

We have obtained inelastic neutron scattering (INS) data on cis and trans Pt and Pd dichlorodiammines, Magnus's Green Salt $[Pt(NH_3)_4][PtCl_4]$, $Pt(NH_3)_4Cl_2 \cdot H_2O$ and $Pd(NH_3)_4Cl_2 \cdot H_2O$. There are three main aspects of this work:

1. the observation of NH_3 torsional and metal-nitrogen skeletal modes which are absent or very weak in the optical spectra of these complexes.

2. the investigation of the degree of coupling between the NH_3 ligands bonded to the same metal atom.

3. the assignment of lattice vibrations associated with extended metal-metal interactions.

The barriers to rotation of the NH_3 ligands in several complexes e.g. trans-$Pd(NH_3)_2Cl_2$, [1] trans-$Pd(NH_3)_2I_2$, [1] $[Pd(NH_3)_4Cl_2]Cl$, [2] $Co(NH_3)_6I_2$, [3] and $Ni(NH_3)_6I_2$ [3] have been previously determined by a variety of methods e.g. INS, i.r. bandshape analysis and thermodynamic and n.m.r. measurements. In all cases the barrier has been found to be very low ca.

TABLE I. POTENTIAL BARRIERS TO THE INTERNAL ROTATION
OF NH_3 LIGANDS

COMPLEX	BARRIER		Frequency of $\tau(NH_3)$ cm^{-1}	Ref.
	$kJ \cdot mole^{-1}$	cm^{-1}		
trans-Pd(NH$_3$)$_2$Cl$_2$	7.9	661	-	5
trans-Pd(NH$_3$)$_2$Cl$_2$	5.1	430	-	1
trans-Pd(NH$_3$)$_2$Cl$_2$	6.4	532	193	a
trans-Pd(NH$_3$)$_2$I$_2$	2.7	225	-	1
cis-Pd(NH$_3$)$_2$Cl$_2$	5.1	430	-	5
cis-Pd(NH$_3$)$_2$Cl$_2$	6.4	532	192	a
cis-Pt(NH$_3$)$_2$Cl$_2$	5.4	532	177	a
trans-Pt(NH$_3$)$_2$Cl$_2$	4.6	381	162	a
Pd(NH$_3$)$_4$Cl$_2$.H$_2$O	5.4	532	176	a
Pd(NH$_3$)$_4$Cl$_2$	4.2	350	-	29
Pt(NH$_3$)$_4$Cl$_2$.H$_2$O	5.4	532	178	a
(Pt(NH$_3$)$_4$)(PtCl$_4$)	6.8	566	201	a,14

a) this work.

2-8 $kJ \cdot mol^{-1}$ (table I). Even with barriers as low as these the torsional
frequency will be comparatively high because the moment of inertia of the NH_3
ligand, about the axis joining the nitrogen atom to the metal atom , is very
small (ca. $2.816 \times 10^{-40} g \cdot cm^2$) [4].

An n.m.r. study of cis and trans-Pd(NH$_3$)$_2$Cl$_2$ [5] has been interpreted in
terms of two inequivalent ammine ligands in the trans form and the second
moments of the n.m.r. signals for both cis and trans complexes are consistent
with ammine reorientation which is occurring at a sufficient rate (above 77K)
to narrow the n.m.r. line. Ulrich and Dunell [5] also concluded that whole-
molecule rotation does not take place in either complex but that libration
probably does. The presence of the two inequivalent groups in the trans
complex can be explained because this complex exists in two crystalline forms
which occur together unless special care is taken during the preparation [6].
The activation energy for the cis is lower than for the trans complex;
Ulrich and Dunell ascribed this to the presence of greater intermolecular
interactions in the trans-form [5]. From measurements of the band contours
of the perpendicular (E) vibration of the NH_3 ligand in the i.r. Leech et al.
[1] have determined the barriers in trans-Pd(NH$_3$)$_2$Cl$_2$ and trans-Pd(NH$_3$)$_2$I$_2$
(see table I).

The concept of coupling between NH_3 ligands, in the cis and trans complexes, via the metal d orbitals has been used by Nakamoto et al. [7] to explain the splitting of the i.r. bands in the NH_3 deformation region (ca. 1580 cm^{-1}). The smaller splittings in the cis complexes were said to result from the ligands sharing only one d orbital compared with two in the trans form. Smaller splittings were also expected for the Pd ammines because the spatial extent of the d orbitals is less in Pd than in Pt. Nakamoto et al. were able, by introducing ligand-ligand coupling into a normal co-ordinate analysis, to predict two bands in the NH_3 deformation region. In fact between two and four bands are observed [7] so that their work cannot be regarded as complete. Coupling of ligands bound to the same atom has previously been observed, using INS spectroscopy, through splitting of the torsional modes [8,9]. Observation of such splitting in the Pt and Pd ammines would confirm, at least in part, the model of Nakamoto et al.

The existence of extended Pt-Pt interactions [10] in $[Pt(NH_3)_4][PtCl_4]$ (MGS) is indicated by some spectral properties [11] and its anisotropic electrical conductivity [12]; doubt however arises from conflicting i.r. and Raman assignments. Hiraishi et al. [13] have assigned a temperature dependent i.r. band at ca. 200 cm^{-1}, in the spectrum of MGS, to the A_{2u} translational lattice mode. Although it would normally be expected to occur below 100 cm^{-1} they claim this mode is increased in frequency by Pt-Pt interactions. Adams et al. [14] while agreeing that this mode has A_{2u} symmetry, have assigned it to the NH_3 torsion and have assigned the A_{2u} lattice mode to a band at 81 cm^{-1} thus casting doubt on the extent of the Pt-Pt interactions. The i.r. work of Hiraishi did not extend below 200 cm^{-1}.

Experimental

Cis and trans $Pd(NH_3)_2Cl_2$ and $Pt(NH_3)_2Cl_2$ were prepared by literature methods [6,15]. $[Pt(NH_3)_4][PtCl_4]$, $Pt(NH_3)_4Cl_2 \cdot H_2O$ and $Pd(NH_3)_2Cl_2 \cdot H_2O$ were purchased from Johnson Matthey Ltd.

Neutron energy loss spectra were obtained (at 4.5K) using the IN4 rotating crystal time-of-flight spectrometer at the Institut Laue Langevin in Grenoble [16] with an incident energy of 298 cm^{-1} and (at 77K) on the beryllium filter detector spectrometer (BFD) at AERE Harwell [17]. The transition frequencies have been obtained from the peak maxima of the BFD spectra by using the correction factors of Gamlen et al. [17]. Neutron energy gain spectra were obtained (at 295K) using the 6H time-of-flight spectrometer at AERE Harwell [18]. Standard programs [19] have been used to calculate $P(\alpha, \beta)$ defined by

$$P(\alpha, \beta) = 2\beta \sinh(\beta/2) \frac{S(\alpha, \beta)}{\alpha}$$

where $\qquad \alpha = \dfrac{\hbar Q^2}{2MT} \qquad \beta = \dfrac{\hbar \omega}{KT}$

$S(\alpha, \beta)$ is the incoherent scattering law
$Q \qquad$ is the momentum change of the neutron
$M \qquad$ is the mass of the scattering atom
$\hbar \qquad$ is Plank's constant
$K \qquad$ is Boltzmann's constant
$\hbar \omega \qquad$ is the energy transfer
$T \qquad$ is the absolute temperature

from the time-of-flight data.

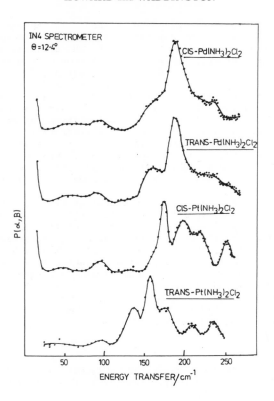

FIG.1.   Time-of-flight (IN4 spectrometer) spectra of the Pt and Pd dichlorodiammines.

The far-infrared spectra were obtained as nujol mulls supported on a polythene disc using a Beckman-RIIC FS 720 Fourier Transform spectrophotometer.

<u>Results and Discussion</u>

Figs. 1 and 2 show our INS data for the complexes listed in table I. A 6H spectrum is shown for comparison with the data obtained using IN4 and it can be seen that the IN4 data is obviously far better resolved than that from 6H, however, it must be noted that the IN4 results (neutron downscattering) were obtained with the samples at 4.5K and the 6H (neutron upscattering) results with the samples at ambient (ca. 295K) temperatures. Narrower bands would be expected at lower temperatures.

a)   <u>NH_3 Torsions and Ligand-Ligand Interactions</u>

If the NH_3 ligands in the cis and/or trans complexes are coupled then it is easily shown that two torsional modes are expected. These are the in-phase (i.p.) and out-of-phase (o.p.) modes (fig. 3). The dynamical equations

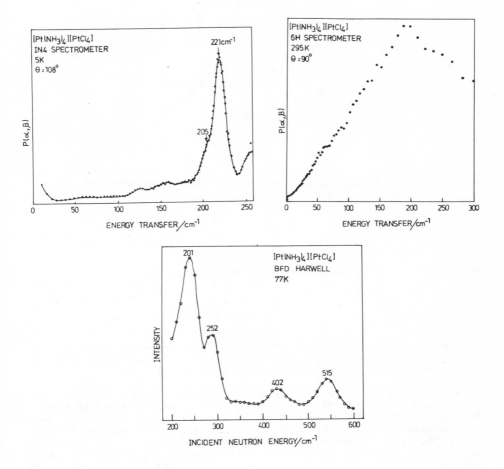

FIG.2. *Inelastic neutron scattering spectra of* $[Pt(NH_3)_4][PtCl_4]$.

for this system can be solved and the results are identical to those obtained for the bis-π-allyls [20] or for the hydrazinium salts [21] i.e. if we write the potential energy variation on rotation as

$$V_i = \frac{V_o}{2} (1 - \cos n\,\theta) \qquad i = 1, 2; \text{ for the external field}$$

$$V = \frac{V_{1,2}}{2} (1 - \cos p\,(\theta_1 + \theta_2)) \qquad \text{for the internal field}$$

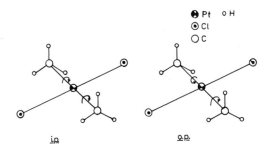

FIG.3.   *In-phase and out-of-phase torsions of $M(NH_3)_2 X_2$ compounds.*

then within the harmonic approximation we obtain

$$\omega_{o.p.}^2 = \frac{V_o n^2}{2I} \qquad\qquad \omega_{i.p.}^2 = \frac{V_o n^2 + 2V_{1,2} p^2}{2I}$$

where V_o is the barrier height for a single NH_3 torsion and n is the barrier multiplicity; $V_{1,2}$ is the barrier height for the interaction between the ligands and p is the barrier multiplicity.

These two modes are expected to be of approximately equal intensity in the INS spectra and because the moment of inertia of the NH_3 ligand is small and its incoherent cross-section is large we would expect the torsions to be the most intense bands.   Therefore, if the ligand-ligand interaction is great enough we expect to see two equally intense features in the INS spectrum of trans-$Pt(NH_3)_2Cl_2$ with perhaps two similar bands in the spectrum of the cis complex but being closer together in this case.   The INS spectra of the Pd complexes should show little or probably no splitting i.e. contain a single intense band.   Fig. 1 shows the relevant INS spectra and it can be seen that in each case one band is considerably more intense than the rest.   On the basis of its intensity we assign this band (150-200 cm^{-1}) in each spectrum (fig. 1) to the NH_3 torsion and we conclude that the NH_3 rotors are <u>at most</u> coupled very weakly.

The resolution of the IN4 spectrometer at 170 cm^{-1} is 5 cm^{-1} [22] (where by resolution we mean the full width at half height of the machine response to a delta function).   Using the Rayleigh criterion for the resolution of two bands this means that the separation of the torsional modes must be less than 6 cm^{-1}.   The interaction of the NH_3 ligands in these complexes is therefore significantly less than in e.g. $Co(NH_3)_6Cl_3$ where the three predicted torsional modes have been resolved (using IN4) [23].

As stated earlier, if we had observed splitting of the torsions in the Pd and Pt ammines this would have confirmed, in part, the model of Nakamoto et al.   The absence of observed splitting, however, does not invalidate their model.   Their explanation must however be treated with care since only

TABLE II. SUMMARY OF SPECTROSCOPIC DATA AND ASSIGNMENTS
FOR CIS AND TRANS-Pt(NH$_3$)$_2$Cl$_2$ (cm^{-1})

cis-Pt(NH$_3$)$_2$Cl$_2$			trans-Pt(NH$_3$)$_2$Cl$_2$		
I.R. + R.[a]	INS	ASSIGNMENTS	I.R. + R.[c]	INS	ASSIGNMENTS
248	254	δ(N-Pt-N)	248		δ(N-Pt-N)
210	221	δ(N-Pt-Cl)	235	239	out-of-plane Pt-N bend
			207[a]	213	
198	201	Pt-N out-of-plane bend		181[b]	δ(N-Pt-Cl)
	177	Torsion		162	Torsion
156	165	δ(Cl-Pt-Cl)	156		δ(Cl-Pt-Cl)
127		Lattice vibrations	136	140	out-of-plane Pt-Cl bend
85	97			95	
	50			50	

a) from ref. [13].   b) predicted in ref. [7].   c) from ref. [27].

two NH$_3$ deformations were predicted but up to four were observed. At the
time of their work the crystal structures were not available. Since then
the structures of the cis and trans Pt complexes have been published [24]
and for both there are two molecules per unit cell. For the cis complex for
instance from a factor group analysis four infrared active NH$_3$ deformation
bands are predicted. Only two are observed. This indicates the complexity
of the problem and it appears that the i.r. spectra of these complexes must
therefore await a more detailed explanation.

From the observed torsional frequencies (tables II and III) we have
calculated the height of the torsional barriers (table I) using the tables
of the solution of the Mathieu equation due to Herschbach [25]. The barrier
heights that we have calculated using our INS data are in general in
reasonable agreement with those calculated by other methods (table I). The
barriers for the cis and trans Pd complexes are higher than for the
corresponding Pt complexes. From the crystal structures of cis and trans-
Pt(NH$_3$)$_2$Cl$_2$ [24] there appears to be only one possible hydrogen bond in
each case. As far as we are aware there are no crystal structures available
for cis and trans-Pd(NH$_3$)$_2$Cl$_2$.

TABLE III. SUMMARY OF SPECTROSCOPIC DATA AND ASSIGNMENTS FOR CIS AND TRANS $Pd(NH_3)_2Cl_2$ (cm^{-1})

cis-$Pd(NH_3)_2Cl_2$			trans-$Pd(NH_3)_2Cl_2$		
I.R.[a]	INS	ASSIGNMENTS	I.R.[a]	INS	ASSIGNMENTS
	270			255?	
245	238	δ(Pd-N)	245	240	δ(Pd-N)
218	220?	δ(Pd-N)	220		δ(Pd-N)
	192	Torsion		193	Torsion
160	165	δ(Pd-Cl)	162	165	δ(Pd-Cl)
135		δ(Pd-Cl)	137		
109	97 ⎫	Lattice		93 ⎫	Lattice
	57 ⎭	modes		60 ⎭	modes

a) from ref. [28]. Perry et al. took an oversimplified description of the normal modes so that one of the δ(Pd-Cl) modes is in fact better described as δ(N-Pd-Cl).

The INS data for the cis and trans complexes together with i.r. and Raman assignments is given in tables II and III. Nakamoto et al. [7] have predicted a band at 181 cm^{-1} (δ(N-Pt-Cl)) for trans-$Pt(NH_3)_2Cl_2$ and we are able to confirm (fig. I) that an INS band occurs in this region.

The BFD spectra of the Pt and Pd tetrammines contain bonds at 178 and 176 cm^{-1}, respectively, which we assign to the NH_3 torsions and once again there is no indication of splitting due to ligand-ligand interactions (fig. 4).

b) Metal-Metal Interactions

There have been two detailed assignments of the vibrational spectra of $[Pt(NH_3)_4][PtCl_4]$ based upon i.r. and Raman studies. Hiraishi et al. [13] assigned a temperature dependent i.r. band at ca. 200 cm^{-1} to the A_{2u} (In D_{4h} symmetry) translational lattice mode (involving anti-phase motion of anion and cation) which, although it would normally be expected to occur below 100 cm^{-1}, had been increased in frequency as a result of metal/metal interactions. Magnus' Green Salt consists of columnar stacks in which anions and cations alternate. The Pt-Pt distance is 3.25Å [26]. Adams et al. [14] (table IV) obtained single crystal i.r. and Raman spectra of $[Pt(NH_3)_4][PtCl_4]$ and although they agreed that the mode at 200 cm^{-1} had A_{2u} symmetry they assigned it to the NH_3 torsion. They have eliminated the possibility of a phase change (to $-100°C$) by showing that there was no

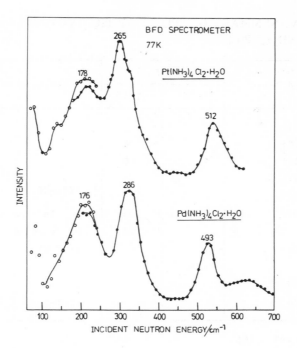

FIG.4. Beryllium filter detector (BFD) spectra of $M(NH_3)_4 Cl_2 \cdot H_2 O$ (M = Pt, Pd).

specific heat anomaly. By comparing the force constant for the metal/metal interaction, implied by the assignment of 200 cm^{-1} to the lattice mode, with known metal-metal force constants they deduced that the frequency was too high for it to be attributed to this mode. Instead the lattice vibration was assigned to a band at 81 cm^{-1}.

If the NH$_3$ rotors in Pt(NH$_3$)$_4$$^{2+}$ were coupled then using methods previously described [21] we have shown that there are three distinct torsional modes (one being doubly degenerate). Our BFD spectrum of MGS contains an intense feature at 201 cm^{-1}. The results described above for the Pt(NH$_3$)$_2$Cl$_2$ systems indicate that the torsional coupling is at most weak and the splittings are not observable. We therefore assign this band at 201 cm^{-1} to the NH$_3$ torsion thereby agreeing, thus far, with the assignments of Adams et al.

Fig. 2a, however, shows the higher resolution spectrum of MGS (IN4 spectrometer) and in this case there is an intense band at 220 cm^{-1} with a shoulder at 205 cm^{-1}. We consider that we have partially resolved the A$_{2u}$ lattice mode (205 cm^{-1}) from the NH$_3$ torsion (220 cm^{-1}) and that they are in fact co-incident in the BFD spectrum. Furthermore there is no INS band in the region of 80 cm^{-1} where Adams et al. assign the A$_{2u}$ lattice vibration.

TABLE IV. SUMMARY OF SPECTROSCPIC DATA AND ASSIGNMENTS
FOR [Pt(NH$_3$)$_4$][PtCl$_4$]

| I.R. and Raman[a] | INS | | Assignments |
	BFD	IN4	
71			
81		126	
141		160	
171			} δ(Pt-Cl)
173		178	
201	201	205 }	A$_{2u}$ lattice mode
		220	NH$_3$ torsion
241	} 252		π(Pt-N)
263			δ(Pt-N)
267			δ(Pt-N)

a) from ref. [14]

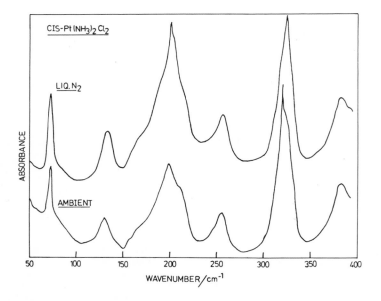

FIG.5.   Far infra-red spectra of cis-Pt(NH$_3$)$_2$Cl$_2$ at liquid nitrogen and ambient temperatures.

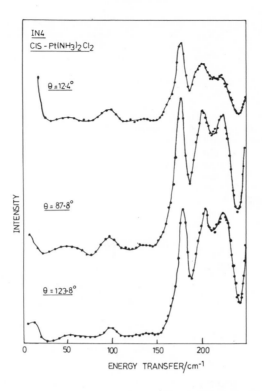

FIG.6.   Time-of-flight (IN4 spectrometer) spectra of cis-Pt(NH₃)₂Cl₂.

The position of the INS band at ca. 200 cm^{-1} varies with temperature. It occurs at 195 cm^{-1} (295K), 201 cm^{-1} (77K) and ∼ 220 cm^{-1} (4.5K). This trend is in agreement with the i.r. results [14]. It can be explained as being due to changes in the external field, on the torsion and lattice modes, as the lattice contracts.

In support of their assignment of the 200 cm^{-1} band to $\tau(NH_3)$, Adams et al. point out that there is no temperature dependent band in the i.r. spectrum of trans-Pt(NH$_3$)$_2$Cl$_2$. If the band at 200 cm^{-1} (in MGS) were the A$_{2u}$ lattice mode raised in energy as a result of Pt-Pt interaction then this is just what one would expect because the Pt-Pt distance [24] in the trans Pt complex is ca. 5Å compared to 3.25 in MGS [26]. We have, however, observed a temperature dependent i.r. band (fig. 5) at 195-210 cm^{-1} for cis-Pt(NH$_3$)$_2$Cl$_2$ and in this complex the Pt-Pt distance [24] is 3.37Å i.e. comparable with that found for MGS. Furthermore in this case the torsion occurs at lower frequency than in MGS (162 cm^{-1} (INS)) therefore the temperature dependent band cannot be the torsion. The reduced mass of two Pt(NH$_3$)$_2$Cl$_2$ molecules is almost identical to that of the Pt(NH$_3$)$_4^{2+}$ PtCl$_4^{2-}$ ions so perhaps it is not too surprising that the lattice mode should occur at a similar frequency if the Pt-Pt distances are very similar.

Further evidence that the i.r. and INS bands close to 200 cm^{-1}, in the spectra of cis-Pt(NH_3)$_2Cl_2$, are due to a lattice mode is obtained from the momentum transfer (Q) dependence of the INS spectrum (fig. 6). It can be seen that at high angles this mode is as intense as the torsion. This does not occur for any of the other complexes and such "Q" dependence is very difficult to explain on any other basis than that it is associated with a lattice vibration.

In view of these results it appears that for MGS the band at 200 cm^{-1} in its BFD spectrum contains the unresolved lattice and torsional modes. These are, however, separated in cis-Pt(NH_3)$_2Cl_2$. This also explains the very high intensity of the 200 cm^{-1} band in MGS relative to the skeletal modes. The relative intensity is very much greater than that found in the other complexes, where the torsion and lattice vibrations are well resolved. These results therefore confirm the existence of strong metal-metal interactions in MGS.

REFERENCES

[1]   LEECH, R.C., POWELL, D.B., SHEPPARD, N., Spectrochim. Acta., 21A (1944) 559.
[2]   ULRICH, S.E., DUNELL, B.A., J.C.S. Faraday II, 69 (1973) 1609.
[3]   JANIK, J.M., JANIK, J.A., MIGDAL, A., PYTASZ, G., Acta. Phys. Pol., A40 (1970) 741.
[4]   HERZBERG, G., "Infrared and Raman Spectra of Polyatomic Molecules", D. Van Nostrand Co. Inc., New York (1945).
[5]   ULRICH, S.E., DUNELL, B.A., Can. J. Chem., 52 19 (1974) 3378.
[6]   LAYTON, R., SINK, D.W., DURIG, J.R., J. Inorg. Nucl. Chem., 28 (1966) 1965.
[7]   NAKAMOTO, K., McCARTHY, P.J., FUJITA, F., CONRATE, R.A., BEHNKE, G.T., Inorg. Chem., 4 1 (1965) 36.
[8]   HOWARD, J., WADDINGTON, T.C., WRIGHT, C.J., J. Chem. Soc., Faraday II, 72 (1975) 513.
[9]   RATCLIFFE, C.I., WADDINGTON, T.C., J. Chem. Soc., Faraday II, 72, (1976) 1935.
[10]   INTERRANTE, L.V., "Extended Interactions Between Metal Ions" A.C.S. Symposium Number 5, Washington D.C. (1974).
[11]   DAY, P., Inorg. Chim. Acta. Rev., 3 (1969) 81.
[12]   INTERRANTE, L.V., J.C.S. Chem. Comm., (1972) 302.
[13]   HIRAISHI, J., NAKAGAWA, I., SHIMANOUCHI, T., Spectrochim. Acta., 24A (1968) 819.
[14]   ADAMS, D.M., HALL, J.R., J.C.S. Dalton, (1973) 1450.
[15]   KAUFFMAN, G.B., COWAN, D.O., Inorganic Syntheses, 7 (1963) 239.
[16]   DREXEL, W., "IN4 Manual", Report 74D187T of the Institut Laue Langevin, Grenoble (1974).
[17]   GAMLEN, P.H., HALL, N.F., TAYLOR, A.D., Unpublished AERE Harwell Report (1974).
[18]   BUNCE, L.J., HARRIS, D.H.C., STIRLING, G.C., AERE Harwell Report R6246 H.M.S.O. (1970).
[19]   BASTON, A.H., AERE Harwell Report M2570 H.M.S.O. (1972).
[20]   HOWARD, J., Ph.D. Thesis, University of Durham (1976).
[21]   LUDMAN, C.J., RATCLIFFE, C.I., WADDINGTON, T.C., J. Chem. Soc., Faraday II, 72 (1976) 1741.
[22]   SUCH, J.B., Personal Communication.
[23]   HOWARD, J., WADDINGTON, T.C., Unpublished Work.
[24]   MILBURN, G.H.W., TRUTER, M.R., J. Chem. Soc. A., (1966) 1609.

[25]   HERSCHBACH, D.R., "Tables for the Internal Rotation Problem",
       Department of Chemistry, Harvard University.
[26]   ATOJI, M., RICHARDSON, J.W., RUNDLE, R.E., J. Amer. Chem. Soc., 79
       (1957) 3017.
[27]   HENDRA, P.J., Spectrochim. Acta., 23A (1967) 1275.
[28]   PERRY, C.H., ATHANS, D.P., YOUNG, E.F., DURIG, J.R., MITCHELL, B.R.,
       Spectrochim. Acta. 23A (1967) 1137.
[29]   SOKOLOV, V.A., SHARPATAYA, G.A., Zh. Fiz. Khim., 44 3 (1970) 603.

DISCUSSION

K.E. LARSSON *(Chairman)*: Your data are presented on a linear energy
scale. How were the data collected?

J. HOWARD: Except for Fig.3(c) the data were collected by time-of-flight
techniques. Conversion to a linear energy scale was carried out during data
analysis. We believe it is very important to present data in this way for molecular
spectroscopic studies and also to use the function $P(\alpha,\beta)$, defined in the paper,
for the ordinate.

A. FURRER: I notice that none of the papers in the two sessions on
molecular spectroscopy cover the subject of exchange interactions between
metal atoms embedded in molecular complexes. I would like to point out that
the neutron inelastic scattering technique is a powerful method of studying
exchange splittings in the electronic ground state of molecular complexes. This
has recently been demonstrated for a series of polynuclear transition-metal
complexes[1]. Direct information has been obtained on the temperature
dependence of the exchange integrals, on the nature of the exchange interaction,
on the magnetic form factor, and on the geometrical configuration of the metal
ions, through the interference term in the cross-section formula. This type of
experiment will be most valuable for studying the electronic excitation of
proteins containing transition-metal ions.

J. HOWARD: This is very interesting information. However, I would point
out that when we started this particular piece of work the basic aim was not to
study metal-metal interactions. We were interested in obtaining some INS spectra
which would assist us in interpreting the INS spectra of ammonia adsorbed on
metal powders or in ion-exchanged zeolites. As the work progressed we found
that we could correct and amplify assignments previously made by means of
optical spectroscopy.

---

[1]   FURRER, A., GÜDEL, H.U., Phys. Rev. Lett. 39 (1977) 657.

Nakamoto and co-workers[2] also pointed out that, although the effect they were postulating was electronic in origin, it was likely to be small in magnitude and perhaps its effects would be more easily observed in optical spectroscopy where very subtle changes can have pronounced effects on the activity and number of fundamentals.

---

[2] Inorg. Chem. 4 1 (1965) 36.

ЭКСПЕРИМЕНТАЛЬНОЕ ИЗУЧЕНИЕ НЕПАРНОГО МЕЖИОННОГО ВЗАИМОДЕЙСТВИЯ ЧЕРЕЗ ЭЛЕКТРОНЫ ПРОВОДИМОСТИ В АЛЮМИНИИ

А.Ю.РУМЯНЦЕВ, В.В.ПУШКАРЕВ,
М.Г.ЗЕМЛЯНОВ, П.П.ПАРШИН,
Н.А.ЧЕРНОПЛЕКОВ
Институт атомной энергии им.И.В.Курчатова,
Москва,
Союз Советских Социалистических Республик

Abstract—Аннотация

EXPERIMENTAL STUDY OF A NON-PAIR INTER-ION INTERACTION THROUGH CONDUCTION ELECTRONS IN ALUMINIUM.

The method of neutron inelastic scattering in a triple-axis spectrometer was used to study an isolated singularity on the transverse phonon branch in the (100) direction of an Al single crystal in the neighbourhood of wave vector $q/q_{max} \approx 0.42$. The purpose of the study was to identify the singularity as being three-particle in nature, i.e. associated with the occurrence of unpaired inter-ion interaction, unlike the Kohn anomaly ($q/q_{max} \approx 0.76$) observed on the same branch. Phonon measurements ($\partial\omega/\partial\vec{q}$) were carried out both in the (100) and in the (10ξ) direction (ξ = 0.176, which corresponds to an inclination of 10° to the (100) direction), while in the non-symmetrical direction $\partial\omega/\partial\vec{q}$ was measured for phonons of different polarization. It was found that in the (10ξ) direction there is a 'splitting' of the singularities, the character and polarization dependence of which process indicate that for $q/q_{max} \approx 0.42$ the singularity is a three-particle one.

ЭКСПЕРИМЕНТАЛЬНОЕ ИЗУЧЕНИЕ НЕПАРНОГО МЕЖИОННОГО ВЗАИМОДЕЙСТВИЯ ЧЕРЕЗ ЭЛЕКТРОНЫ ПРОВОДИМОСТИ В АЛЮМИНИИ.

Методом неупругого рассеяния нейтронов на трехосном спектрометре изучена изолированная особенность на поперечной фононной ветви в направлении /100/ монокристалла Al в окрестности значения волнового вектора $q/q_{max} \approx 0,42$ с целью ее идентификации как трехчастичной, то есть связанной с проявлением непарного межионного взаимодействия, в отличие от наблюдавшейся на той же ветви аномалии Кона ($q/q_{max} \approx 0,76$). Для этого были выполнены измерения $\langle \partial\omega/\partial\vec{q} \rangle$ фононов как в направлении /100/, так и в направлении /10ξ/ (ξ=0,176, что соответствует отклонению на 10° от направления /100/), причем в несимметричном направлении $\partial\omega/\partial\vec{q}$ измерялась для фононов с различной поляризацией. Установлено, что в направлении /10ξ/ происходит "расщепление" особенностей, причем его характер и поляризационная зависимость свидетельствуют о том, что особенность при $q/q_{max} \approx 0,42$ является трехчастичной.

1. ВВЕДЕНИЕ

Начиная с работы Кона [1], в которой впервые было указано на существование особенностей в поляризуемости электронного газа, связанных со свойствами Ферми-поверхности металла и проявляющихся на кривых дисперсии фононов, эти аномалии постоянно привлекают внимание как с экспериментальной, так и теоретической точек зрения. Указанные особенности обусловлены резкой границей в распределении электронов проводимости в фазовом пространстве, что приводит к логарифмической расходимости групповой скорости фононов $\partial\omega/\partial\vec{q}$ при значении волнового вектора $\vec{q}$, соответствующем переходу электрона из одной точки поверхности Ферми в другую с противоположным направлением скорости. Аналогичные особенности были предсказаны и для спиновых волн [2].

Экспериментально аномалии Кона были впервые наблюдены Брокхаузом и др. в свинце [3] методом неупругого рассеяния тепловых нейтронов. В дальнейшем особенности Кона изучались в непереходных (Zn [4], Al [5]) и переходных (Nb [6], Cu [7]) металлах. В работе Веймута и Стедмана [5] впервые была продемонстрирована возможность измерять групповую скорость фононов с высокой точностью. Таким образом удается не только регистрировать сам факт существования особенности при том или ином значении волнового вектора фонона, что, конечно, интересно само по себе с точки зрения изучения поверхности Ферми, но, и это особенно важно, оценивать относительную величину наблюдаемой аномалии Кона. Последняя, как было показано в ряде теоретических работ [8-10], в существенной степени зависит от таких важнейших характеристик металла, как кривизна поверхности Ферми, величина энергетических щелей в зонной структуре, характер электрон-ионного взаимодействия.

Развитие Бровманом и Каганом [11] последовательной теории для непереходных металлов позволило предсказать существование на кривых дисперсии фононов аномалий нового типа: так называемых "трехчастичных" особенностей [12], отражающих непарный характер межионного взаимодействия. В работе [11] показано, что в многоэлектронной теории непереходных металлов динамическая матрица колебаний может быть представлена в виде ряда по степеням потенциала электрон-ионного взаимодействия ($V_{\vec{G}}/\epsilon_F$)

$$D_{\alpha\beta}(\vec{q}) = D_{\alpha\beta}^{(i)}(\vec{q}) + D_{\alpha\beta}^{(2)}(\vec{q}) + D_{\alpha\beta}^{(3)}(\vec{q}) + \ldots \qquad (1)$$

Здесь и далее для простоты рассматривается одноатомная решетка. $D_{\alpha\beta}^{(i)}$ – динамическая матрица колебаний ионной решетки в поле однородного невзаимодействующего электронного газа, $D_{\alpha\beta}^{(n)}$ – поправки от n-го порядка теории возмущений.

Вклады в квадрат частоты фонона от $D^{(2)}$ и $D^{(3)}$ выражаются в виде

$$\left[\omega_j^{(2)}(\vec{q})\right]^2 = \frac{\Omega_0}{M}\left\{\sum_{\vec{G}} \xi_j^2(\vec{q}+\vec{G})\, V_{\vec{q}+\vec{G}}^2\, \Gamma^{(2)}(\vec{q}+\vec{G},\ -\vec{q}-\vec{G})\right.$$

$$\left. -\sum_{\vec{G}}{}' \ (\vec{q}=0)\right\} \tag{2}$$

$$\left[\omega_j^{(3)}(\vec{q})\right]^2 = \frac{\Omega_0}{M}\left\{\sum_{\vec{G}_1\vec{G}_2} \xi_j(\vec{q}+\vec{G}_1)\,\xi_j(\vec{q}+\vec{G}_2)\, V_{\vec{q}+\vec{G}_1}\, V_{-\vec{q}-\vec{G}_2}\, V_{\vec{G}_2-\vec{G}_1}\right.$$

$$\times \Gamma^{(3)}(\vec{q}+\vec{G}_1,\ -\vec{q}-\vec{G}_2,\ \vec{G}_2-\vec{G}_1) - \sum_{\vec{G}_1\vec{G}_2}{}'\ (\vec{q}=0)\left.\right\} \tag{3}$$

где $\quad \xi_j(\vec{q}+\vec{G}) = (\vec{q}+\vec{G})\,\vec{e}_j(\vec{q}) \tag{4}$

$\vec{q}$ – волновой вектор фонона, $\vec{G}$ – вектор обратной решетки, $\vec{e}_j(\vec{q})$ – вектор поляризации j-ой моды колебания, $V_{\vec{G}}$ – псевдопотенциал электрон-ионного взаимодействия, ϵ_F – энергия Ферми.

Так называемые многополюсники $\Gamma^{(2)}$ и $\Gamma^{(3)}$ [11] описывают свойства однородного электронного газа при данной плотности и существенным образом влияют на характер фононного спектра металлов. В частности, при некоторых значениях волнового вектора эти многополюсники становятся сингулярными, что приводит к аномалиям в фононном спектре, которые могут наблюдаться экспериментально. Например, хорошо изученные особенности Кона связаны с сингулярностью $\Gamma^{(2)}$.

Наличие в (1) члена $D^{(3)}$ фактически означает учет так называемого непарного взаимодействия между ионами через электроны проводимости. В этом случае электроны могут дополнительно рассеиваться на третьем ионе, осуществляя косвенное взаимодействие между парой ионов, которое приобретает характер трехчастичного, и его учет позволяет предсказать наличие качественно новых особенностей в колебательных спектрах металлов. Именно непарное взаимодействие ответственно за существенную ассиметрию расщепления частот в точке "К" зоны Бриллюэна гексагональных металлов, что и наблюдалось экспериментально в Be, Mg, Zn и Cd [13-16].

Другим примером проявления трехчастичного взаимодействия являются особенности в групповой скорости фононов $\partial\omega/\partial\vec{q}$, которые в отличие от локального проявления непарности межионных сил в точке "К", могут, как и аномалии Кона, существенно влиять на тонкую структуру фононного спектра в целом. Последнее обстоятельство вызвано тем, что, несмотря на наличие в выражении (3) для $[\omega_j^{(3)}(\vec{q})]^2$ дополнительного, по сравнению с $[\omega_j^{(2)}(\vec{q})]^2$, малого параметра $(V_{\vec{G}}/\epsilon_F)$, более сильный корневой характер особенности в $\Gamma^{(3)}$ [11] по сравнению с логарифмическим для особенности Кона (в $\Gamma^{(2)}$) позволяет наблюдать ее непосредственно в экспериментах по измерению групповой скорости фононов. В частности, выполненные в работе [11] расчеты $\partial\omega/\partial\vec{q}$ в Al показывают, что аномалии, связанные с трехчастичными и коновскими особенностями одного порядка величины. Это обстоятельство позволяет реально поставить задачу экспериментального обнаружения и исследования трехчастичных особенностей в групповой скорости фононов.

В работе [5], посвященной изучению особенностей Кона в Al, наблюдались по крайней мере две аномалии, проидентифицировать которые как коновские не удалось. Хотя в работе [11] и было показано, что положение этих особенностей хорошо воспроизводится, исходя из геометрических условий, вытекающих из теории непарных сил, прямых экспериментов, подтверждающих трехчастичный характер указанных аномалий в $\partial\omega/\partial\vec{q}$, выполнено не было.

В настоящей работе изучалась особенность на поперечной фононной ветви в направлении /100/ монокристалла Al в окрестности значения волнового вектора $q/q_{max} \approx 0{,}43$, с целью ее идентификации как трехчастичной, в отличие от наблюдавшейся на той же ветви аномалии Кона $(q/q_{max} \approx 0{,}76)$.

2. ПОЛОЖЕНИЕ ОСОБЕННОСТЕЙ НА ДИСПЕРСИОННЫХ КРИВЫХ

Как известно, положение диаметральных особенностей Кона в модели Ферми-сферы определяется из условия

$$|\vec{q} + \vec{G}| = 2k_F \qquad (5)$$

ТАБЛИЦА I. ГРУППЫ ВЕКТОРОВ ОБРАТНОЙ РЕШЕТКИ, УДОВЛЕТВОРЯЮЩИЕ УСЛОВИЮ НАБЛЮДЕНИЯ ТРЕХЧАСТИЧНОЙ ОСОБЕННОСТИ

N группы	$\vec{G}_1$			$\vec{G}_2$			$\vec{G}_3 = \vec{G}_2 - \vec{G}_1$			ξ_{1z}	ξ_{1y}	ξ_{2z}	ξ_{2y}	ξ_{3z}	ξ_{3y}
	x	y	z	x	y	z	x	y	z						
1	1	1	1	0	0	2	-1	-1	1	1	1	2	0	2	0
	1	-1	1	0	0	2	-1	1	1	1	-1	2	0	2	0
	0	0	2	1	1	1	1	1	-1	2	0	1	1	2	0
	0	0	2	1	-1	1	1	-1	-1	2	0	1	-1	2	0
2	1	1	1	0	2	0	-1	1	-1	1	1	0	2	0	2
	1	-1	1	0	-2	0	-1	-1	-1	1	-1	0	-2	0	2
	0	2	0	1	1	1	1	-1	1	0	2	1	1	0	2
	0	-2	0	1	-1	1	1	1	1	0	-2	1	-1	0	2
3	1	1	-1	0	2	0	-1	1	1	-1	1	0	2	0	2
	1	-1	-1	0	-2	0	-1	-1	1	-1	-1	0	-2	0	2
	0	2	0	1	1	-1	1	-1	-1	0	2	-1	1	0	2
	0	-2	0	1	-1	-1	1	1	-1	0	-2	-1	-1	0	2
4	1	1	-1	0	0	-2	-1	-1	-1	-1	1	-2	0	2	0
	1	-1	-1	0	0	-2	-1	1	-1	-1	-1	-2	0	2	0
	0	0	-2	1	1	-1	1	1	1	-2	0	-1	1	2	0
	0	0	-2	1	-1	-1	1	-1	1	-2	0	-1	-1	2	0

где k_F — радиус Ферми-сферы. Для поперечной фононной ветви в направлении /100/ Al положение особенности при $q/q_{max} \approx 0,76$ хорошо воспроизводится из условия (5) при $\vec{G} = (1, \pm 1, \pm 1)$[1]. В то же время в достаточно широкой окрестности $q/q_{max} \approx 0,43$ для любых $\vec{G}$ отсутствуют диаметральные переходы, определяющие особенность Кона.

Положение трехчастичных особенностей на дисперсионных кривых определяется из условия [11], что радиус окружности, описанной вокруг остроугольного треугольника со сторонами $(\vec{q} + \vec{G}_1)$, $(-\vec{q} - \vec{G}_2)$ и $(\vec{G}_2 - \vec{G}_1)$, равен k_F. В дальнейшем при анализе удобно использовать вектор $\vec{G}_3 = \vec{G}_2 - \vec{G}_1$. В табл.1 приведены все векторы обратной решетки, образующие эквивалентные треугольники с точки зрения симметрии

---

[1] В дальнейшем компоненты векторов обратной решетки приводятся в единицах $(2\pi/a)$, где a — постоянная решетки.

ГЦК структуры при данном направлении волнового вектора
$\vec{q} \parallel /100/$ и определяющие положение трехчастичной особенности при $q/q_{max} = 0,46$, если воспользоваться значением
$2k_F = 2,255 \, (2\pi/a)$, что соответствует модели свободных
электронов. Эквивалентность пар векторов $\vec{G}_1$ и $\vec{G}_2$ означает, что при $\vec{q} \parallel /100/$ изменение знака компонент G_y и G_z
не изменит длины ни одной из сторон треугольника и, следовательно, он по-прежнему останется вписанным в окружность радиуса k_F. В табл.I приведены также значения поляризационных факторов (см. (2)-(4))

$$\xi_{1T} = \xi_T(\vec{q} + \vec{G}_1), \quad \xi_{2T} = \xi_T(\vec{q} + \vec{G}_2) \quad \text{и} \quad \xi_{3T} = \xi_{1T} \times \xi_{2T} \tag{6}$$

которые определяют условия существования трехчастичных
особенностей в групповой скорости фононов на ветвях с
различной поперечной поляризацией ($\vec{e}_T \parallel z$ и $\vec{e}_T \parallel y$). Как
следует из табл.I, трехчастичная особенность будет наблю-
даться в обеих поляризациях, но при этом для $\vec{e}_T \parallel z$ вклад
в особенность дают первая и четвертая группы векторов $\vec{G}_i$,
а для $\vec{e}_T \parallel y$ – вторая и третья. Таким образом, если
$\vec{q} \parallel /100/$, на поперечной ветви, которая в этом случае является двухкратно вырожденной, должна наблюдаться трехчастичная особенность при $q/q_{max} = 0,46$ [11].

Однако, если волновой вектор $\vec{q}$ отклонить от направления высокой симметрии /100/, например, в плоскости xz на
угол φ ($\vec{q}\,^* = q^*(\cos\varphi, \, 0, \, \sin\varphi)$), то для $\vec{e}_T \parallel z$ первая груп-
па векторов обратной решетки $\vec{G}_i$ в табл.I уже не будет
эквивалентна четвертой группе. При этом произойдет "расщепление" особенности, что можно пояснить следующим образом. На рис.1 изображены плоскости обратной решетки Al,
выделенные на схеме ячейки обратной решетки жирными линиями (рис.2), и треугольники, построенные на аргумен-
тах $\Gamma^{(3)}$. $\vec{G}_2$ и $\vec{G}_3$ принадлежат четвертой группе векторов
табл.I, а $\vec{G}_2'$ и $\vec{G}_3'$ – первой. Из рисунка видно, что для фононов с $\vec{q} \parallel /100/$ треугольники со сторонами ($\vec{q} + \vec{G}_1$),
($-\vec{q} - \vec{G}_2$), $\vec{G}_3$ и ($\vec{q} + \vec{G}_1'$), ($-\vec{q} - \vec{G}_2'$), $\vec{G}_3'$ равны и дают эквивалентный вклад в особенность. При отклонении $\vec{q}$ на угол φ
в плоскости xz (на рис.1, $\vec{q}\,^*$) стороны треугольников изме-
няют свою длину различным образом, а удовлетворение условия их вписанности в окружность радиуса k_F приводит к не-
совпадающим значениям. q_1^* и q_2^*, при которых имеет место
особенность. Аналогичные рассуждения справедливы для

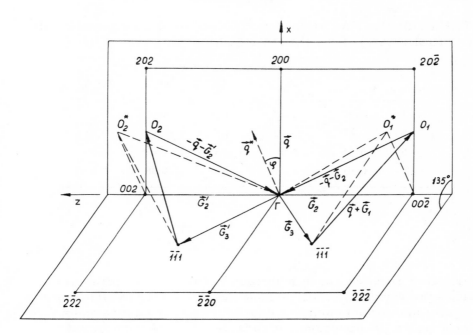

Рис.1. Расщепление трехчастичной особенности при отклонении волнового вектора фонона $\vec{q}$ от направления /100/ на угол φ.

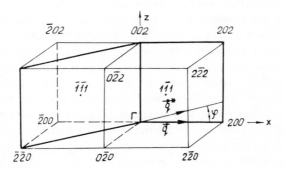

Рис.2. Схема ячейки обратной решетки Al. Жирными линиями выделены плоскости, приведенные на рис.1.

ТАБЛИЦА II. РАСЧЕТНЫЕ ПОЛОЖЕНИЯ ТРЕХЧАСТИЧНОЙ ОСОБЕННОСТИ ДЛЯ НАПРАВЛЕНИЯ /10ξ/

N группы	q^*/q^*_{max}	ξ_{3z}	ξ_{3y}	$N \times \xi_{3z}$	$N \times \xi_{3y}$
1	0,35	1,50	0,0	6,00	0,0
2	0,42	-0,12	2,0	-0,48	8,0
3	0,51	0,02	2,0	0,08	8,0
4	0,61	2,24	0,0	8,96	0,0

второй и третьей групп векторов табл.I. Рассчитанные положения трехчастичных особенностей в приближении Ферми-сферы при отклонении $\vec{q}$ в плоскости xz от направления /100/ на угол $\varphi = 10°$ приведены в табл.II. Кроме того в табл.II приведены значения поляризационных факторов ξ_{3T} (см.(6)), из анализа которых следует, что особенности, связанные с векторами первой и четвертой групп, будут наблюдаться при $\vec{e}_T \parallel z$, а второй и третьей групп — при $\vec{e}_T \parallel y$. Относительная величина особенностей будет пропорциональна произведению ξ_{3T} на число треугольников N, дающих эквивалентный вклад в данную особенность (величины этих произведений приведены в последних двух столбцах табл.II). В расчетах ξ_{3T} учитывалось, что при $\vec{q}$, смещенном от направления /100/, векторы поляризации могут быть непараллельны y и z.

    Рассмотрим теперь вопрос о поведении диаметральной особенности Кона с $q/q_{max} \approx 0,76$ при отклонении $\vec{q}$ от /100/. Эта особенность должна расщепиться на две, которые будут наблюдаться для поперечных ветвей с различной поляризацией при одинаковых значениях q^*_1 и q^*_2. Для $\varphi = 10°$ соответствующие расчетные положения особенностей Кона, поляризационные факторы и суммарные интенсивности приведены в табл.III. Как происходит расщепление особенности Кона в случае Ферми-сферы, показано на рис.3. Здесь $\vec{G}_1$ и $\vec{G}'_1$ — узлы обратной решетки типа $(1, \pm1, \pm1)$. При $\varphi = 0$ $q^*_1 = q^*_2$ и $\vec{G}_1$ и $\vec{G}'_1$ дают эквивалентные вклады в одну и ту же особенность. При $\varphi \neq 0$ очевидно, что $q^*_1 \neq q^*_2$ и $\vec{G}_1$ и $\vec{G}'_1$ определяют различные особенности Кона.

ТАБЛИЦА III. РАСЧЕТНЫЕ ПОЛОЖЕНИЯ ОСОБЕННОСТИ
КОНА ДЛЯ НАПРАВЛЕНИЯ /10ξ/

q^*/q^*_{max}	ξ_z^2	ξ_y^2	$N \times \xi_z^2$	$N \times \xi_y^2$
0,69	0,76	1,0	1,52	2,0
0,84	1,10	1,0	2,20	2,0

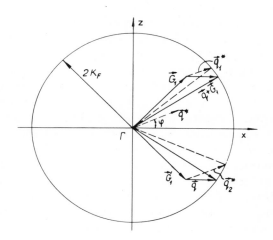

Рис.3. Расщепление особенности Кона при отклонении волнового вектора
фонона $\vec{q}$ от направления /100/ на угол φ.

3. ЭКСПЕРИМЕНТ

Таким образом, проведенный анализ показывает, что
при отклонении волнового вектора фонона $\vec{q}$ от направления /100/ трехчастичная особенность должна расщепиться
на четыре (табл.II), причем особенности с q_1^* и q_4^* будут
проявляться на ветви с $\vec{e}_T \parallel z$, а с q_2^* и q_3^* — с $\vec{e}_T \parallel y$. Особенность Кона при этом должна расщепиться на две, условия
наблюдения которых и положения не зависят от векторов поляризации $\vec{e}_T$ (табл.III).

Различное поляризационное поведение указанных особенностей открывает возможность экспериментального под-
тверждения трехчастичного характера особенности в окрестности $q/q_{max} \approx 0,43$ поперечной ветви в направлении /100/ Al .
Для этого нами были выполнены измерения $\partial \omega / \partial \vec{q}$ для фононов как в направлении /100/, так и в направлении /10ξ/
($\xi = 0,176$, что соответствует отклонению на угол $\varphi = 10°$ от
направления /100/). Снятие вырождения ветвей поперечных
колебаний в направлении /10ξ/ позволило измерить фононы
с $\vec{e}_T \parallel z$ и $\vec{e}_T \parallel y$, что обеспечивалось различной ориента-
цией образца[2].

Измерения проводились при комнатной температуре на
трехосном кристаллическом спектрометре нейтронов, уста-
новленном на реакторе ИРТ-М в Институте атомной энергии
им.И.В.Курчатова [17]. В качестве образца использовался
монокристалл Al с мозаичностью $\sim 20'$ цилиндрической формы (ось цилиндра параллельна кристаллографическому на-
правлению /010/). Расходимость нейтронного пучка, падающего на образец, составляла $\sim 25'$ и обеспечивалась за счет
естественной коллимации. Формирование рассеянного образцом пучка осуществлялось многощелевыми коллиматора-
ми, установленными перед кристаллом-анализатором и детектором, с расходимостью 30' и 20', соответственно. В
качестве монохроматора и анализатора спектрометра использовались монокристаллы меди с отражающими плоскостями
/111/ и мозаичностью $\sim 20'$. Расчетное импульсное разрешение составляло при этом 0,015 (в единицах q/q_{max}) и ха-
рактерные приращения волнового вектора фононов в измере-
ниях $\partial \omega / \partial \vec{q}$ выбирались равными 0,02. При измерении фононов в направлении /100/ и /10ξ/ с $\vec{e}_T \parallel z$ кристаллографи-
ческое направление /010/ образца было ортогонально плос-
кости рассеяния. Для $\vec{q} \parallel$ /10ξ/ и $\vec{e}_T \parallel y$ нормаль к плоскости рассеяния принадлежала плоскости xz и составляла
10° с направлением /001/. Все измерения проводились методом постоянного переданного импульса (постоянного $\vec{Q}$)
[18] при двух фиксированных значениях длин волн, падающих
на образец нейтронов 1,2 и 1,35$\overset{\circ}{A}$. Выбор такого метода оп-
равдан, поскольку при измерении низкоэнергетических поперечных ветвей удается выбрать широкие интервалы ска-
нирования фазового пространства, в которых изменение ус-

---

[2] В дальнейшем везде при анализе результатов для направления /10ξ/
подразумевается, что условия $\vec{e}_T \parallel z$ или $\vec{e}_T \parallel y$ выполняются не строго.

ловий фокусировки незначительно, а поправки, связанные с
изменением отражательной способности анализатора в пределах одного экспериментального максимума достаточно малы. Кроме того, мы сопоставляем групповые скорости фононов, отличающиеся направлением вектора поляризации, но
эквивалентные с точки зрения геометрии измерений, что
обеспечивает необходимую относительную точность.

Значения частот фононов ω_j определялись аппроксима-
цией экспериментальных максимумов гауссианом. Практически при всех значениях q/q_{max} такая подгонка была легко
осуществлена. Погрешности в определении частоты $\Delta\omega$,
определяемые статистической точностью измерений, вычис-
лялись по аналогии с [19]

$$\Delta\omega = \Delta\omega_{1/2}\,\frac{N_m^{1/2}}{N_m - N_\Phi}\cdot\frac{1}{n^{1/2}} \tag{7}$$

где $\Delta\omega_{1/2}$ — ширина измеренного максимума на полувысоте,
N_m — число отсчетов в максимуме, N_Φ — значение фона, n — количество экспериментальных точек на полной ширине измеренного максимума.

4. РЕЗУЛЬТАТЫ ИЗМЕРЕНИЙ И ИХ ОБСУЖДЕНИЕ

На измеренной зависимости групповой скорости фононов
от q/q_{max} для направления /100/ (рис.4) проявляются две
особенности — при $q/q_{max} = 0{,}42$ и $q/q_{max} = 0{,}77$, положения которых хорошо согласуются с результатами работы [5]. Как
уже отмечалось в разделе 2, анализ, проведенный в модели
Ферми-сферы, дает близкие положения особенностей, а
именно — при $q/q_{max} = 0{,}46$ должна наблюдаться трехчастичная
особенность, определяемая набором векторов обратной решетки, приведенных в табл.I, а при $q/q_{max} = 0{,}76$ — диаметральная особенность Кона с векторами типа $\vec{G} = (1,\,\pm1,\,\pm1)$.

На рис.5 представлены результаты измерений $\partial\omega/\partial\vec{q}$
для направления /10ξ/ при векторах поляризации фононов
$\vec{e}_T \parallel y$ и $\vec{e}_T \parallel z$. Видно, что произошло расщепление особенностей, причем характер расщепления второй особенности
качественно одинаков для $\vec{e}_T \parallel z$ и $\vec{e}_T \parallel y$. Напротив, характер расщепления первой особенности определяется направле-
нием вектора поляризации фононов. Для $\vec{e}_T \parallel z$ расщепление

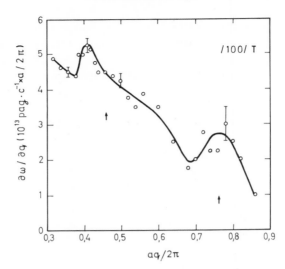

Рис.4. Групповая скорость поперечных фононов в направлении /100/.
Стрелками показаны положения трехчастичной и коновской особенностей,
вычисленные в приближении Ферми-сферы.

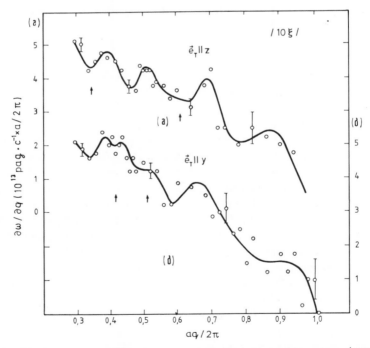

Рис.5. Групповая скорость поперечных фононов в направлении /10ξ/.
Стрелками показаны положения трехчастичных особенностей для ветвей с
различной поляризацией.

существенно больше, чем в случае $\vec{e}_T \parallel y$, когда недостаточ-
ное импульсное разрешение не позволило точно локализовать
положения особенностей. Стрелками на рис.5 показаны положения трехчастичных особенностей, вычисленные в приближении сферической поверхности Ферми.

Из сопоставления полученных результатов для $\partial \omega / \partial \vec{q}$ в
направлении $/10\xi/$ с расчетными следует, что характер расщепления и поляризационная зависимость первой особенности качественно согласуются со свойствами, предсказанными
для трехчастичной особенности, в то время как поведение
второй особенности соответствует аномалии Кона. Однако
существуют количественные расхождения экспериментальных
результатов с расчетными, которые заключаются в заметном
(10-15 %) несовпадении расчетных положений трехчастичных
особенностей и измеренных как в направлении $/100/$, так и
в направлении $/10\xi/$ и несколько меньшем ($\sim 5\,\%$) для особенности Кона в направлении $/10\xi/$ с $\vec{e}_T \parallel y$ (рис.5). Указанные расхождения могут быть связаны, с одной стороны,
с неучтенными возможными систематическими ошибками,
а, с другой стороны, некорректностью теоретических оценок,
основанных на приближении сферической поверхности Ферми.
При этом характер поверхности Ферми более существенно
влияет на положение трехчастичных особенностей. С учетом
последнего обстоятельства сдвиги положений особенностей
могут достигать величины порядка параметра энергетичес-
кой щели $\Delta \sim (V_{\vec{G}} / \epsilon_F)$, что и наблюдается в эксперименте для
особенностей с $q/q_{max} = 0{,}42$.

Однако учет реальной поверхности Ферми оказывает влияние не только на положения рассмотренных особенностей,
но и приводит к появлению в фононном спектре дополнитель-
ных, так называемых недиаметральных особенностей Кона.
Эти особенности связаны с электронными переходами между
точками поверхности Ферми, не переходящими друг в друга
при преобразовании инверсии. При этом, как обычно, тре-
буется антипараллельность скоростей электрона в этих
точках. Недиаметральные переходы показаны штриховыми
линиями на рис.6, на котором изображена простейшая поверхность Ферми в модели двух щелей в схеме приведенных зон.
Сплошными линиями на рис.6 показан треугольник, построенный на аргументах $\Gamma^{(3)}$ (см. раздел 2) и определяющий положение трехчастичной особенности при значении волнового
вектора фонона $\vec{q}_0^{(3)}$. Значения $\vec{q}_i^{(2)}$ (рис.7), при которых
имеют место недиаметральные особенности Кона, могут от-

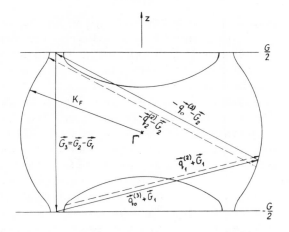

Рис.6. Схема упрощенной поверхности Ферми в модели двух щелей:
— — — —недиаметральные переходы Кона, ———— условия существования
трехчастичной особенности.

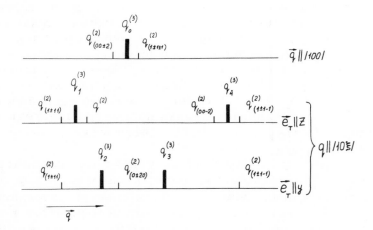

Рис.7. Диаграмма положения особенностей всех типов в окрестности
$q/q_{max} = 0,43$ с учетом реальной поверхности Ферми ($q_i^{(2)}$ – положение недиаметральной особенности Кона, определяемой узлом $\vec{G}$; $q_i^{(3)}$ – положение
трехчастичной особенности).

личаться от $\vec{q}_0^{(3)}$ на величину $\sim \Delta$. Однако в работе [20] показано, что величина особенностей, связанных с недиамет-
ральными переходами, определяется областью наиболее силь-
ной когерентной перестройки электронного спектра. Поскольку размеры этой области в простых металлах малы и

порядка параметра щели Δ, то и величина недиаметральных особенностей Кона также' мала. Действительно, эта величина связана с поправкой к $\Gamma^{(2)}$ или точнее к $\Pi_0(\vec{q})$ (Π_0—выражение для поляризационного оператора невзаимодействующего однородного электронного газа), учитывающей несферичность поверхности Ферми

$$\Pi(\vec{q}) = \Pi_0(\vec{q}) + \delta\Pi(\vec{q}) \tag{8}$$

Если $|\vec{q}|$ близко к положению недиаметральной особенности, то (см. [20])

$$\delta\Pi(\vec{q}) \sim \Delta^{3/2} \qquad \Delta \sim (V_{\vec{G}}/\epsilon_F) \tag{9}$$

а в остальных случаях — $\delta\Pi(\vec{q}) \sim \Delta^2$.

Учитывая, что

$$\Gamma^{(2)}(\vec{q}, -\vec{q}) = -\frac{1}{2} \cdot \frac{\Pi(\vec{q})}{\epsilon(\vec{q})} \tag{10}$$

где $\epsilon(\vec{q})$ — статическая диэлектрическая функция, легко показать, что поправка к квадрату частоты фонона (см. выражение (2)), связанная с учетом реальной поверхности Ферми

$$\delta\left[\omega_j^{(2)}(\vec{q})\right]^2 \sim \Delta^{3/2} \cdot \omega_p^2 \cdot \left(V_{\vec{q}+\vec{G}}/\epsilon_F\right)^2 \tag{11}$$

а весь вклад третьего порядка теории возмущений

$$\left[\omega_j^{(3)}(\vec{q})\right]^2 \sim \Delta \cdot \omega_p^2 \cdot \left(V_{\vec{q}+\vec{G}}/\epsilon_F\right)^2 \tag{12}$$

где ω_p^2 — квадрат плазменной частоты.

С точностью до членов третьего порядка теории возмущений

$$\omega^2(\vec{q}) = \omega_i^2(\vec{q}) + \left[\omega_0^{(2)}(\vec{q})\right]^2 + \delta\left[\omega^{(2)}(\vec{q})\right]^2 + \left[\omega^{(3)}(\vec{q})\right]^2 \tag{13}$$

а частота фонона

$$\omega(\vec{q}) = \omega_0(\vec{q}) + \frac{1}{2} \cdot \frac{\delta\left[\omega^{(2)}(\vec{q})\right]^2}{\omega_0(\vec{q})} + \frac{1}{2} \cdot \frac{\left[\omega^{(3)}(\vec{q})\right]^2}{\omega_0(\vec{q})} \tag{14}$$

где $\omega_0(\vec{q}) = \sqrt{\omega_i^2(\vec{q}) + \left[\omega_0^{(2)}(\vec{q})\right]^2}$

Подставив (11) и (12) в выражение (14), получим:

$$\omega(\vec{q}) \sim \omega_0(\vec{q}) + \frac{\omega_p^2 \Delta}{2\omega_0(\vec{q})} \left(\frac{V_{\vec{q}+\vec{G}}}{\epsilon_F} \right)^2 \left(\Delta^{1/2} + 1 \right) \tag{15}$$

Поскольку характерный размер области фазового пространства, где $\delta[\omega^{(2)}]^2$ и $[\omega^{(3)}]^2$ существенны, порядка параметра щели Δ, а изменение самих поправок к $\omega_0(\vec{q})$ порядка их величины $\delta\omega \sim \frac{1}{\omega_0} \left\{ \delta\left[\omega^{(2)}\right]^2 + \left[\omega^{(3)}\right]^2 \right\}$, то, учитывая гладкость функции $\omega_0(\vec{q})$ в указанной окрестности $\vec{q}$, получаем

$$\partial\omega / \partial\vec{q} \sim (\delta\omega / \Delta)$$

и

$$\frac{\partial\omega}{\partial\vec{q}} \sim \frac{\omega_p^2}{2\omega_0(\vec{q})} \left(\frac{V_{\vec{q}+\vec{G}}}{\epsilon_F} \right)^2 \left(\Delta^{1/2} + 1 \right) \tag{16}$$

Из полученного выражения следует, что отношение величин недиаметральной особенности Кона и трехчастичной пропорционально $\Delta^{1/2}$. В случае Al эта величина порядка 0,1-0,15 и влияние недиаметральной особенности на поведение $\partial\omega/\partial\vec{q}$ в окрестности трехчастичной незначительно. Однако наличие небольшого плеча в импульсной зависимости $\partial\omega/\partial\vec{q}$ при $q/\vec{q}_{max} = 0,51$ для направления $/10\xi/$ и $\vec{e}_T \parallel y$ (рис.5 б), расположенного под одной из расщепленных особенностей при $\vec{e}_T \parallel z$ (рис.5 а), возможно связано с проявлением недиаметральной особенности Кона, определяемой вектором $\vec{G} = (1, \pm 1, -1)$ (рис.7).

Таким образом, полученные экспериментальные результаты для групповой скорости поперечных фононов в направлениях $/100/$ и $/10\xi/$ решетки алюминия свидетельствуют о том, что особенность на дисперсионной ветви при $q/q_{max} = 0,42$ является трехчастичной, то есть связана с проявлением непарного межионного взаимодействия через электроны проводимости. Тот факт, что трехчастичная и диаметральная особенности Кона могут быть сопоставимы по величине, указывает на необходимость учета непарного взаимодействия для правильного понимания тонкой структуры дисперсионных кривых. Несомненно, что дальнейшее экспериментальное

и теоретическое изучение коновских и особенно трехчастичных особенностей с точки зрения влияния реальной поверхности Ферми помогут существенно расширить сведения об
электронных и фононных спектрах, а также специфике электрон-ионного взаимодействия в металлах.

В заключение авторы выражают благодарность Ю.Кага-
ну и А.Холасу за полезные обсуждения и постоянный интерес к работе, Е.Мельникову — за приготовление монокристалла алюминия.

ЛИТЕРАТУРА

[1]   KOHN, W., Phys. Rev. Lett. 2 (1959) 393.
[2]   WOLL, E.J., NETTEL, S.J., Phys. Rev. 123 (1961) 796.
[3]   BROCKHOUSE, B.N., RAO, K.R., WOODS, A.D.B., Phys. Rev. Lett.
       7 (1961) 93.
[4]   IYENGAR, P.K., VENKATARAMAN, G., GAMEEL, Y.H., RAO, K.R.,
       Neutron Inelastic Scattering (Proc. Symp. Copenhagen, 1968) IAEA,
       Vienna 1 (1968) 195.
[5]   WEYMOUTH, J.W., STEDMAN, R., Phys. Rev. B. 2 (1970) 4743.
[6]   POWELL, B.M., MARTEL, P., WOODS, A.D.B., Phys. Rev. 171 (1968) 727.
[7]   NILSSON, G., Neutron Inelastic Scattering (Proc. Symp. Copenhagen,
       1968) IAEA, Vienna 1 (1968) 187.
[8]   АФАНАСЬЕВ, А.М., КАГАН, Ю., ЖЭТФ 43 (1962) 1456.
[9]   TAYLOR, P.L., Phys. Rev. 131 (1963) 1995.
[10] ROTH, L.M., ZEIGER, H.J., KAPLAN, T.A., Phys. Rev. 149 (1969) 519.
[11] БРОВМАН, Е.Г., КАГАН, Ю., УФН 112 (1974) 369.
[12] БРОВМАН, Е.Г., КАГАН, Ю., ЖЭТФ 63 (1972) 1937.
[13] STEDMAN, R., AMYLYUS, Z., PAULI, R., SUNDYN, O., J. Phys. F,
       Metal Phys. 6 (1976) 157.
[14] PYNN, R., SQUIRES, G.L., Proc. R. Soc. Lond. A326 (1972) 347.
[15] ALMQVIST, L., STEDMAN, R., J. Phys. F, Metal Phys. 1 (1971) 785.
[16] ЧЕРНЫШОВ, А.А., ПАРШИН, П.П., РУМЯНЦЕВ, А.Ю., САДИКОВ,И.П.,
       СЕВЕРОВ, М.Н., ЖЭТФ 68 (1975) 347.
[17] ГОЛОВИН, А.Е., ЗАДОХИН, Г.И., ЗЕМЛЯНОВ, М.Г., КАРПОВ, И.И.,
       КРЕСНИКОВ, Ю.М., МОРЯКОВ, В.Н., НАУМОВ, И.В., ПАРШИН, П.П.,
       РУМЯНЦЕВ, А.Ю., СОМЕНКОВ, В.А., ЧЕРНОПЛЕКОВ, Н.А.,
       Препринт ИАЭ № 2445, 1974.
[18] BROCKHOUSE, B.N., Inelastic Scattering of Neutrons in Solids and Liquids
       (Proc. Symp. Vienna, 1960) IAEA, Vienna (1961) 113.
[19] STEDMAN, R., WEYMOUTH, J., Brit. J. Appl. Phys. D, 2 (1969) 903.
[20] КАГАН, Ю., ПУШКАРЕВ, В.В., ХОЛАС, А., ЖЭТФ 73 (1977) 507.

DISCUSSION

W.J.L. BUYERS: Was the line on your slide drawn by the experimenters
or is it a theoretical line?

M.G. ZEMLYANOV: The solid-line curves are based on experimental data and enable us to evaluate more clearly the behaviour of the group velocity as a function of the direction of the polarization vector. The arrows indicate the expected positions of the three-particle anomalies, calculated for the Fermi sphere.

W.J.L. BUYERS: Calculations of the self-energy (shift and width) arising from the three-particle interactions produced by the electron gas are notoriously difficult for all $\vec{q}$, ω. Have such numerical calculations been made for Al and by whom?

M.G. ZEMLYANOV: Dispersion relations were calculated for Al by Brovman and Kagan, on the assumption of a local pseudopotential and with allowance for three-particle interactions.

P. ZIESCHE: Do the theoretical predictions about phonon anomalies due to three-particle interaction depend on the pseudopotential and dielectric function used? And do anharmonic considerations influence these predictions?

M.G. ZEMLYANOV: The representation of three-particle interaction in the dispersion relations in the form of additional anomalies was based on the assumption of a local pseudopotential and the simplest form of dielectric function. This representation would not be substantially modified by assuming a non-local pseudopotential and a more complex dielectric function.

ROTATIONAL STATES OF CH₄ IMPURITIES IN SOLID RARE GAS MATRICES (Ar, Kr, Xe)

Y. KATAOKA[†], W. PRESS,
U. BUCHENAU, H. SPITZER
Institut für Festkörperforschung der
    Kernforschungsanlage Jülich GmbH,
Jülich,
Federal Republic of Germany

Abstract

ROTATIONAL STATES OF CH₄ IMPURITIES IN SOLID RARE GAS MATRICES (Ar, Kr, Xe).

With inelastic neutron scattering single particle rotations of methane molecules as substitutional impurities in solid rare gas matrices (Ar, Kr and Xe) are investigated. Observed line spectra at $T \cong 5$ K are interpreted as transitions between levels of a tetrahedral rotator in a crystalline field of octahedral symmetry. A numerical calculation is performed by expanding these eigenstates into symmetry adapted octahedral functions $F_J(\omega)$ with a restriction to the subspace spanned by $J \leqslant 15$. A systematic increase of the cubic crystalline field starting from CH₄-xenon to CH₄II, CH₄-krypton and CH₄-argon, finally, is found. In the system CH₄-argon the continuous transition from weakly hindered quantum mechanical rotation at low temperatures to a classical diffusive high temperature rotation is observed.

I.   Introduction

In the past few years several systems displaying rotational tunneling and almost free rotations have been investigated by inelastic neutron scattering |1|. While there is a considerable number of molecular crystals (consisting of small molecules or molecular groups) in the regime of rotational tunneling, only relatively few molecular crystals close to the limit of free rotation are known. The prime representative for quantum mechanical free rotation is solid hydrogen: there the rotational constant $B = h/2\Theta \approx 85$ K (Θ = moment of inertia) is much larger than any orientation dependent interaction in the solid |2|. All other systems are further away from the limit of free rotation, because of smaller rotational constants ($B \lesssim 8$ K) and larger rotational potentials ($V > 100$ K). γ-picoline |3| is a system with only one rotational degree of freedom for CH₃-groups, probably in a potential with a 6-fold symmetry axis |3,4|. The other known example is solid light methane (CH₄) in

---

[†] On leave from the Department of Chemistry, Faculty of Science, Kyoto University, Kyoto, Japan.

its phase II |5-7|. In CH$_4$II three out of four molecules are orientationally ordered. The remaining molecules are surrounded by a cage of ordered nearest neighbours, the octopole field of which cancels and does not contribute to the potential at the disordered sites |8,9|. Therefore the rotational excitations at these sites have been interpreted as perturbed free rotator states |10,11|, perturbed by the presence of a crystalline field with cubic symmetry.

This suggests a new class of systems close to the limit of free rotation, namely methane molecules diluted in solid rare gas matrices (Ar, Kr and Xe). We then have an example of single particle rotations of molecular impurities in an atomic crystal. In these systems the effect of the crystalline field is isolated and may be investigated in detail. The rotational states of matrix isolated methane have previously been studied with IR |12-14| and Raman |15| measurements of the vibration-rotation spectra. The analysis of combination modes |16-18|, however, is somewhat complicated due to the presence of a Coriolis coupling for motions in an accelerated framework. Therefore neutrons provide a more direct access to the study of single particle rotations.

Ideally the substitution of spherically symmetric rare gas atoms by orientationally anisotropic molecules occurs without perturbation of the centre-of-mass lattice. The potential parameters describing the centre-of-mass interaction of methane and the solid rare gases in fact are rather similar |19,20|.This holds in particular for CH$_4$-krypton. An obvious difference concerns the lattice constants of the pure crystals: In comparison with solid methane the nearest neighbour distances are about 9% smaller in argon, 3% smaller in krypton and 5% larger in xenon. This leads to a local lattice expansion around the CH$_4$ sites for CH$_4$-argon and CH$_4$-krypton, while there is a local lattice contraction in CH$_4$-xenon. We will ignore this effect in the following, as well as a dependence of the lattice relaxation on the rotational state of a molecule |21|.

The present investigation was started with the following aims:

(i)   Establish the rotational states of a molecular impurity (close to the limit of free rotation) in an atomic crystal.

(ii)   Investigate the role and magnitude of the crystalline field in bulk methane by a comparison with the rotational levels of matrix isolated methane.

(iii) Attempt to learn about the intermolecular interactions by relating pair potentials to the crystalline field.

(iv)   Study the continuous transition from weakly hindered quantum mechanical rotations at low temperatures to classical high temperature rotations, probably described by rotational diffusion. As the argon matrix only weakly

scatters neutrons ($\sigma_{inc}^{Ar} \cong 0.4$ barns, $\sigma_{inc}^{CH_4} \cong 320$ barns)
and hardly at all absorbs them, it is the best candidate
for such a study.

II. Theory

In this section we attempt to calculate the rotational
energy states of a methane tetrahedron in the rotational potential originating from the CH_4-rare gas interaction. The main
contribution to an angle dependent potential $V_c(\omega)$ (here ω
collectively denotes Euler angles) experienced by the methane
molecules stems from the anisotropic parts of the hard-core
repulsion and of the Van-der-Waals attraction. Both terms are
rather short-ranged and therefore only the twelve nearest neighbour rare gas atoms surrounding each methane molecule (in the
limit of low CH_4 concentrations) are important. $V_c(\omega)$ is called
the crystalline field, as it only depends on the orientation of
the molecule under consideration. $V_c(\omega)$ is important in bulk
methane, too |10|. In $CH_4 II$ a molecular field originating from
the ordered octopole moments of the methane molecules is present
at three quarters of sublattices only. There is a complete cancellation of this contribution from ordered molecules at the
sites of disordered molecules. The crystalline field is present
at all molecular sites in $CH_4 II$, but at the disordered sites it
is by far the dominant term.

In the following the effect of the crystalline field $V_c(\omega)$
will be treated as a perturbation of the free rotator states,
as has been done by other authors |22,12,13,16|. It will be
advantageous to expand $V_c(\omega)$ into an orthogonal set of symmetry-
adapted functions and as the symmetry at a CH_4 site is cubic
(m3m), octahedral functions $V_J(\omega)$ are used |22|. Only the two
lowest order terms of this expansion are retained:

$$V_c(\omega) = \beta_4 V_4(\omega) + \beta_6 V_6(\omega) \tag{1}$$

The functions $V_\ell(\omega)$ are normalized to $8\pi^2$. Higher order terms
($\ell \geq 8$) are neglected. This is justified by an estimate of β_8
assuming phenomenological pair interactions between the protons
in CH_4 and the rare gas atoms |23|. A similar estimate suggests
that a realistic potential should be searched for in the space
$\beta_4 > 0$ and $\beta_6 < 0$ |23|. Within this constraint rotational
energies are calculated as a function of β_4 and β_6, with the
intention of determining these coefficients by comparison of
calculated and measured rotational energies and without speci-
fying details of the interaction, initially. This scheme only
works if the potential parameters β_4 and β_6 do not depend or
only weakly depend on the rotational state of a molecule |21|.

The Hamiltonian

$$H = B\vec{J}^2 + V_c(\omega) \tag{2}$$

is used to calculate the rotational levels. $\vec{J}$ is the angular
momentum operator. In order to calculate eigenvalues following
the method outlined by King and Hornig |22|, the rotational
wave-functions are expanded into symmetry adapted octahedral
functions $F_J(\omega)$ (the completely symmetric function $F_J(\omega) \equiv V_J(\omega)$).
For reasons of computer time it is necessary to truncate the
space of eigenfunctions. In a previous calculation with a sub-
space $J \leq 9$ |16| (the J are the rotational quantum numbers of
a free molecule), the low-lying energy levels for CH_4-argon did
not converge satisfactorily. For this reason the present calculation was extended to a subspace $J \leq 15$. An extension to the
subspace $J \leq 15$ not only provides sufficient accuracy for the
present purpose but also seems to suffice for the analysis of
future experiments with matrix isolated methane under pressure.

    The energy levels $E(\bar{\Gamma}\Gamma)$ are labelled in terms of $\bar{\Gamma}\Gamma$, where
Γ stands for a representation of the octahedral group |22|. Two
labels are necessary to describe the symmetry within the crystalline frame (Γ) and within the molecular frame $(\bar{\Gamma})$. An example
of an energy level scheme is given in Fig. 1 and shows how the
free rotator states split into sublevels with different symmetry
labels in the crystalline field |22,12,13,16|. The rotational
constant B = 7.56 K = 0.157 THz of the free CH_4 molecule is used
as the natural energy unit.

    The results of the present calculation are shown in Fig. 2
in the form of contour maps of a few low-lying energy levels in
the (β_4, β_6)-space. For the aforementioned reasons we have concentrated on the region $0 \leq \beta_4 \leq 20$ B, $0 \geq \beta_6 \geq -35$ B. Meaningful solutions for the magnitude of the crystalline field are
expected to fall into that regime. The contour maps are obtained
by interpolating between values calculated for a discrete number
of (β_4, β_6) pairs with a mesh size $\Delta\beta_\ell = 2.5$ B. Interpolation
errors are estimated to be largest $(\delta\beta_\ell \leq 0.5$ B) around the
turning points in the $E(\bar{T}_1 T_1)$ and $E(\bar{T}_2 T_2)$ curves, even after
reducing the mesh size to $\Delta\beta_\ell = 1.25$ B in this regime. Everywhere
else the accuracy is much better and the subspace $J \leq 15$ is
sufficient to yield eigenvalues $E(\bar{T}_1 T_1)$-$E(\bar{A}_1 A_1)$ precise to
within three digits.

III.   Experimental

    (a) Sample preparation

    The methane-solid rare gas mixtures were prepared by
condensing the two components into the sample chamber of a
temperature variable helium cryostat. The desired methane
concentration was adjusted via the flow-rates of the methane
gas and the rare gas, respectively. In the case of CH_4-argon
(methane concentrations always will be given in at-%) the
mixture was vapour-deposited at about 20 K into a cylindrical
sample cell with thin Kapton walls. Polycrystalline samples

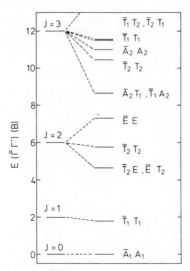

FIG.1.   Splitting of free tetrahedral rotator energy levels in a crystalline field of octahedral symmetry $(\beta_4 = 3 B, \beta_6 = -9 B)$; $B = h^2/2\theta = 0.157$ THz for CH_4.

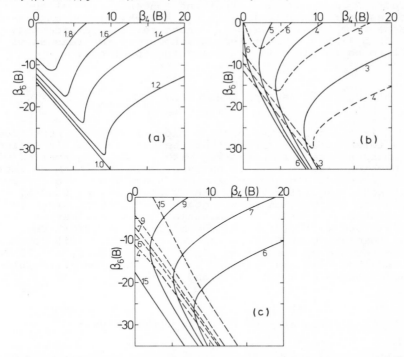

FIG.2.   Contour maps of low-lying rotational energy levels in the (β_4, β_6)-plane. The energy is measured from the lowest level $\bar{A}_1A_1$. The numbers at the curves give energies in units of B. (a) level $\bar{T}_1T_1$, (b) level $\bar{T}_2E$ (solid curves) and level $\bar{T}_2T_2$ (dashed curves), (c) level $\bar{A}_2T_1$ (solid curves) and level $\bar{A}_2A_2$ (dashed curves).

with 2.8 cm diameter and a height of about 5 cm were grown
by this technique. We believe that by vapour-deposition of the
mixtures a clustering of the methane molecules in the rare
gas matrices is ruled out.

The neutron absorption cross section of Kr and Xe (for
both systems: σ_{abs} = 18 barns, for a wavelength λ = 1.08 Å)
are rather high and demand a different sample geometry. A
flat aluminium cell with internal dimensions $5 \times 5 \times 0.25$ cm^3
was used. With this cell the mixture first had to be liquefied
and only afterwards was cooled to lower temperatures. Such a
procedure does not eliminate the possibility of clustering of
the component with low concentration. No evidence of clustering
has been observed, however.

Methane concentrations of 0.4% and 1.6% in argon (NB: at%),
1.5% CH_4 in krypton and 1.2% CH_4 in xenon have been used. For
the latter two systems the concentrations, adjusted via the
flow rates of the two components, were checked and confirmed
by a chemical analysis of the mixtures. With 1% CH_4 the probability of finding a CH_4 molecule as a first neighbour of
another CH_4 is about 10%. Further neighbours only weakly
interact. We may conclude, that the concentration of the CH_4
molecules is reasonably low, though somewhat lower concentrations seem to be desirable. Concentrations considerably
lower than 1% had to be ruled out, however, for reasons of
signal to noise ratio in the absorbing specimens.

(b) Inelastic neutron scattering

Inelastic neutron scattering experiments were performed
with a three axis spectrometer at the FRJ2 reactor in Jülich.
Most measurements were performed with pyrolytic graphite (OO2)
as monochromators as well as analyser with the incoming energy
E_i kept constant. In general two configurations were employed:
(i) In scans requiring larger energy transfers we used E_i =
14.7 meV in conjunction with a graphite filter in order to
remove the higher order contamination. With collimators
120,48,48 and 48^{min} (from monochromator to detector) the
energy resolution at E_i = E_f was ΔE_R = 0.3 THz. (ii) For somewhat better energy resolution ΔE_R = 0.07 THz at E_i = 1.25 THz
was used. The beam was filtered with a cooled beryllium block;
the collimators were 120,48,96 and 96^{min}.

(c) Experimental results at low temperatures

Fig. 3(a-c) shows scans performed with matrix isolated
CH_4 in three different solid rare gas matrices-argon, krypton
and xenon - at temperatures near the liquid helium temperature.
Due to the low incoming neutron energy E_i = 1.25 THz the scans

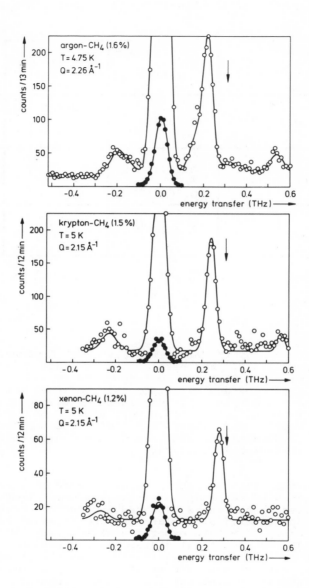

FIG.3.   Inelastic neutron scattering spectra at low temperatures for CH₄ in Ar, Kr and Xe.
The arrow marks the free rotator value for the J = 0 to 1 transition.   Solid lines refer to
computer fits; the elastic intensity (full points) is scaled down by a factor of ten.

TABLE I.   ROTATIONAL STATES OF METHANE MOLECULES IN Ar, Kr, CH
AND Xe

Matrix	Ar	Kr	CH_4	Xe
E_1 (THz)	$0.216(3)$ [a]	$0.237(3)$ [a]	$0.265(3)$ [c] 0.257 [d]	$0.275(4)$ [a]
E_2 (THz)	$0.53(1)$ [a]	$0.56(1)$ [a] $0.56(2)$ [b]	0.68 [d]	$0.63(2)$ [b]
E_3 (THz)	–	$1.24(3)$ [b]	1.33 [a]	$1.37(3)$ [b]

(a) this work: $k_i = 1.58 \text{ Å}^{-1}$.   (c) ref. $|7|$.

(b) this work: $k_i = 2.665 \text{ Å}^{-1}$.   (d) ref. $|5,6|$.

are limited to energy transfers $E \leq 0.66$ THz. A momentum transfer Q of about 2.15 Å^{-1} has been chosen in order to maximize
the intensity of the E_1 peak (corresponding to J=0 to 1 transitions
in the free molecule) and simultaneously to avoid powder peaks
from the rare gas matrices. It should be mentioned that the Q-
dependence of the E_1 intensity is very similar to the one
reported by Kapulla and Gläser $|5,6|$ for the disordered mole-
cules in CH_4 II. No detailed analysis of the Q-dependence $|24,
25|$ will be attempted in this paper, however.

    The low temperature spectra were recorded at least 12^h
after having cooled the samples to the measuring temperature.
The intensities of the peaks measured in neutron energy gain
and loss, respectively, are related by the detailed balance
factor exp(-E/kT) to within experimental accuracy. We may
conclude that the rotational states and hence also the nuclear
spin systems are in thermal equilibrium with the phonon bath.
A preliminary attempt was made to study the spin conversion
by fast cooling ($\simeq$ 10 minutes) the 1.6% CH_4 in argon sample
from 30 K to 4.7 K and monitoring the detailed balance factor.
The approach of thermal equilibrium is described by a relaxation time of about 1^h which, however, is felt to reflect the
thermal behaviour of the kapton cell rather than spin conversion. Nuclear spin conversion of "disordered" methane molecules
therefore seems to be fast, much faster than concluded in
previous neutron experiments $|6|$, but in agreement with recent
nmr experiments $|26,27|$ and a theoretical estimate $|28|$. More

careful experiments with matrix isolated methane or silane for
the study of spin conversion of these molecules in cubic sites
are suggested.

The spectra in the three systems look rather similar (Fig. 3):
apart from the elastic peak there is a fairly strong inelastic
peak at about 0.22 THz in the case of argon and at slightly
higher energy transfers for krypton and xenon. A second rotational excitation is observed for CH_4 in argon and krypton,
respectively. A scan with k_i = 1.58 $Å^{-1}$ does not show this
peak, for reasons of (i) intensity and (ii) maximal energy
transfer. The solid lines in Fig. 3 are the result of a least
squares fit. We may extract the peak positions listed in
table I. For comparison the corresponding values for the disordered molecules in CH_4 II are listed as well.

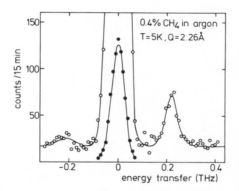

FIG.4. Neutron spectrum for 0.4% CH_4 in Ar. Solid lines refer to computer fits; the elastic
intensity (full points) is scaled down by a factor of ten.

No measurable energy width of the inelastic peaks was
observed. For CH_4 in argon the peak at E_1 = 0.216 THz has a
shoulder at lower energies, which has been included as an
additional feature into the fit (E_1'=0.16+0.01 THz). It's origin is
not entirely clear. The shoulder could be attributed to
transitions between rotational states of nearest neighbour
methane pairs, similar to the spectra of o-H_2 pairs in a p-H_2
matrix |29|. The intensity of pair spectra should strongly
depend on the CH_4 concentration. Therefore an additional
measurement with about 0.4% CH_4 in argon was performed (Fig. 4),
which confirms the peak position E_1 given in table I and does
not show a shoulder. On the other hand no significant shoulders
are found for the krypton and xenon matrices, where the CH_4
concentration was > 1%, too. This may be due to a less
favourable intensity situation, however.

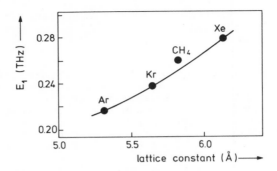

FIG.5.   Dependence of E_1 on the host lattice constant (for CH_4: average value of Refs [5, 7]).

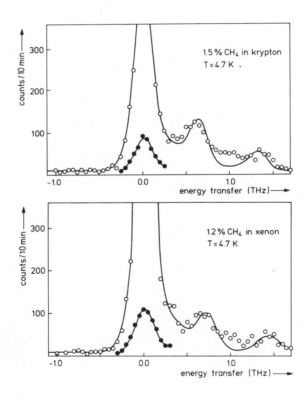

FIG.6.   Inelastic neutron scattering spectra at low temperatures with $Q = 3.05$ Å^{-1}, showing the rotational transitions E_2 and E_3 for CH_4 in Kr (top) and Xe (bottom). Solid lines refer to computer fits; the elastic intensity (full points) is scaled down by a factor of ten.

E_1 corresponds to transitions from the totally symmetric rotational ground state $(\bar{A}_1A_1)$ to the first excited state $(\bar{T}_1T_1)$. Fig. 5 shows E_1 for the three systems under consideration and for CH_4II as a function of the respective lattice constant. A smoothly varying function $E_1(a_0)$ confirms, that the potential experienced by the disordered molecules in CH_4II indeed is the crystalline field $V_c(\omega)$ and suggests, that the methane molecules approach the free rotator state $(E_1^{free} = 0.314$ THz) very closely, when the "cage" of surrounding atoms gets larger.

Additional measurements with the aim of finding transitions to the higher rotational levels have been performed for CH_4 in krypton and xenon with $E_i = 3.55$ THz. Spectra are shown in Fig. 6 together with least squares fits. Due to the more relaxed energy resolution the E_1-peak no longer is resolved. For reasons of the structure factors for the transitions the scans have been performed at $Q = 3.05$ Å^{-1}. The E_2 transition is now observed for xenon, too. Additionally a third relatively weak peak is found for both systems (Table I). The assignment of the rotational peaks will be discussed in section IV.

(d) Temperature dependence of the spectra (CH_4-argon)

So far we have been dealing with data around T = 5 K, only. Recently several investigations have been reported, which studied the continuous transition from the quantum mechanical low temperature situation to classical rotations at high temperatures |7,30-32|. In particular the transition from rotational tunneling at low temperatures to a thermally activated rotational motion has been investigated. A similar measurement for the transition from almost free rotations to rotational diffusion at high temperatures only has been published for CH_4II |6,7| so far. There, however, the situation is somewhat complicated by the presence of an orientational order-disorder transition at 20.4 K. CH_4 in argon, on the other hand, gives an opportunity to study the temperature dependence of rotations in a relatively weak potential in the absence of a phase transition. An argon matrix has been chosen for this experiment, because of the low absorption in this system.

Fluctuations of the rotational potential in CH_4-argon are due to phonons which become increasingly populated with rising temperature. This should lead to a broadening of the rotational states, which indeed can be seen in Fig. 7(a-d): Initially line spectra are observed (Fig. 7a), which broaden with increasing temperature (Fig. 7b,c) and ultimately merge into one quasi-elastic peak at T $\geq$ 30 K (Fig. 7d). The half-width-half-maximum (HWHM) Γ of the quasielastic contribution at high temperatures is a measure of the inverse lifetimes of the rotational states. To what extent the high temperature rotation can be described by rotational diffusion in the absence of a static rotational potential will be investigated in a separate paper.

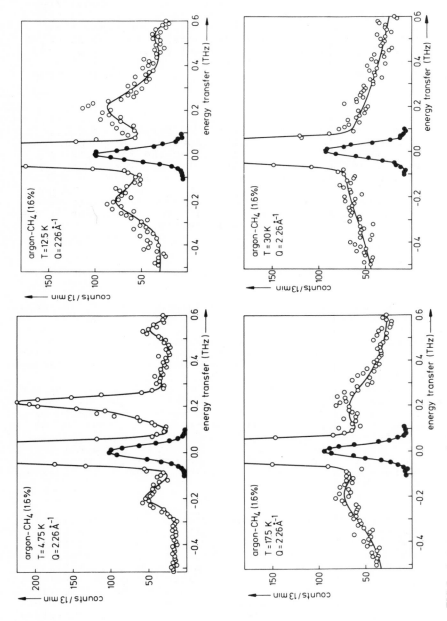

FIG. 7. Inelastic neutron scattering spectra for 1.6% CH₄ in Ar at four temperatures. Solid lines refer to computer fits; the elastic intensity (full points) is scaled down by a factor of ten.

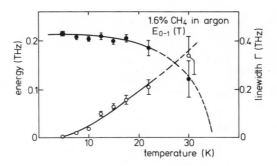

FIG.8. Temperature dependence of peak position E_1 (full points) and line width Γ (open points) for the lowest energy rotational excitation of CH_4 in Ar.

Peak positions $E_1(T)$ and line widths $\Gamma(T)$ are extracted from spectra in the transition region (assuming Lorentzians for the inelastic peaks) and are depicted in Fig. 8. The observed behaviour is very similar to the one of systems in the tunneling regime (at low temperatures). A quantitative analysis of the results has not been attempted at the present stage. In the case of tunneling CH_3 groups the frequency shift and broadening have been attributed to transitions to excited states which do not demand a change of the nuclear spin of the molecules |33,30|. In general a $\Gamma(T)$ has been found, which can be explained in terms of a single thermal activation energy $E^A \simeq E_{Lib}^{(1)}$, the energy of the first excited librational state. Due to the presence of many rotational levels (section IV) no simple picture emerges in the present case. If one nevertheless describes $\Gamma(T)$ with an Arrhenius behaviour and a single activation energy, $E^A \simeq 30$ K is found, which is of the expected order of magnitude.

(e) Localized mode

So far we have ignored the perturbation of the centre-of-mass system by the molecular impurities. Apart from local lattice relaxations a light impurity ($m_{CH_4} = 16$) in a matrix of relatively heavy atoms ($m_{Ar} = 40$) should give rise to a localized mode. There it is assumed that the interaction forces change but little. A broad peak observed at $E = 2.8$ THz in neutron energy loss ($E_f = 3.55$ THz fixed) for 1.6% CH_4 in argon seems to reflect this localized mode. Its linewidth (HWHM) is about 1 THz. The observed energy should be compared with typical zone boundary phonon energies in argon, which typically are about 2 THz.

IV. Assignment of the rotational peaks

The energies of the observed inelastic peaks are listed in Table I. In units of the rotational constant B, the energies E_1,

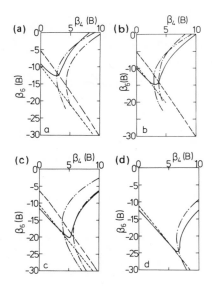

FIG.9.   Equi-energy-transfer curves in the (β_4, β_6)-plane. (a) CH_4 in Xe, (b) disordered sites in CH_4 II, (c) CH_4 in Kr, (d) CH_4 in Ar. Solid curve: $E(\overline{T}_1T_1)-E(\overline{A}_1A_1) = E_1$, dot dashed curve: $E(\overline{T}_2E)-E(\overline{A}_1A_1) = E_2$, dotted curve: $E(\overline{T}_2T_2)-E(\overline{A}_1A_1) = E_2$, two-dot dashed curve: $E(\overline{A}_2T_1)-E(\overline{A}_1A_1) = E_3$, dashed curve: $E(\overline{A}_2A_2)-E(\overline{A}_1A_1) = E_3$.

E_2 and E_3 correspond to ~ 1.5 B, ~ 4 B and ~ 8 B, respectively. For the free molecule, the transitions from J=0 to J=1,2,3 are at 2B, 6B and 12B. Since the J=1 level does not split in the octahedral field (see Fig. 1) we can unambiguously assign E_1 to the transition from $\overline{A}_1A_1$ to $\overline{T}_1T_1$. It should be noted that the thermal population of the lowest level $\overline{A}_1A_1$ at liquid-He temperature exceeds by far the one of the higher levels. Therefore any strong peak is likely to correspond to a transition from the $\overline{A}_1A_1$ level to some higher stationary state. In particular E_2 must be a transition from $\overline{A}_1A_1$ to one of the three levels originating from the crystal field splitting of the J=2 level. Since transitions from $\overline{A}$ to $\overline{E}$ are forbidden for reasons of nuclear spin conservation (this is the only selection rule |24, 25,7|), there are two possibilities:

(i) $E_2 = E(\overline{T}_2E) - E(\overline{A}_1A_1)$

(ii) $E_2 = E(\overline{T}_2T_2) - E(\overline{A}_1A_1)$

An unambiguous assignment could be based on the Q-dependent intensities of the rotational peaks. However, a calculation of the transition matrix elements as a function of β_4 and β_6 is not available at present.

In order to determine the two coefficients β_4 and β_6, at least two measured quantities are needed, for instance E_1 and E_2. For a given E_1, one can calculate all possible pairs (β_4, β_6) which yield the energy difference E_1 between the levels $\bar{A}_1A_1$ and $\bar{T}_1T_1$. The curves connecting these points are the solid lines in Fig. 9(a-d) for Xe, CH_4II, Kr and Ar, respectively. A second condition may be obtained by assuming possibility (i). This also gives a curve in the β_4-β_6 plane (the dot-dashed curves in Fig. 9). β_4 and β_6 are then determined by the intersection of the two curves. This intersection is well defined for Ar and CH_4II, while in Kr the two lines intersect at a small angle and in Xe they do not cross at all. Nevertheless, possibility (i) cannot be ruled out even in the case of Xe, because the minimum distance between the two curves is of the order of the uncertainty introduced by the limited accuracy of the measurements. For similar reasons there is a rather large region of possible β_4 and β_6 values in the other cases. The part of the solid curves in Fig. 3 fulfilling the condition $-3.7 \leq \beta_6/\beta_4 \leq 0$ will be called the first type of solutions.

A second possible set of values β_4 and β_6 for the four substances can be obtained by assuming possibility (ii) (dotted curves in Fig. 3). This assumption leads to comparatively small values of β_4 ($\beta_4 \simeq -0.2 \beta_6$). These will be called the second type of solutions.

Finally, one could try to include E_3 which generates a third curve in the β_4-β_6 plane. Unfortunately, the assignment is much more difficult than for E_2. Two curves for the assignments $E_3 = E(\bar{A}_2T_1) - E(\bar{A}_1A_1)$ (two dot-dashed) and $E_3=E(\bar{A}_2\bar{A}_2) - E(\bar{A}_1A_1)$ (dashed) are shown in Fig. 3.

V.   Discussion

Two types of solutions for the crystalline field have been suggested in the previous section. We now may start from empirical pair potentials for the interaction between a methane molecule and its rare gas neighbours |19,20| and estimate the magnitude of the crystalline field. The resultant β_4 and β_6 values yield a ratio $-1 \geq \beta_6/\beta_4 > -1.5$, in agreement with Yasuda's result |23|. This is in strong disagreement with the type two solutions, which do not seem to be realistic, therefore. Even if one attempts to reproduce $\beta_6/\beta_4 \simeq -3.7$ as obtained from the intersection of the lines for CH_4-argon and CH_4II, an extremely steep repulsive potential must be assumed. For a simple 6-exp potential, the constant α in the exponential term $A\exp(-\alpha r)$ must be taken twice as large as the commonly accepted value. This does not appear realistic either. Therefore, solutions on the E_1 line narrowed to a range $-1.5 \leq \beta_6/\beta_4 \leq -1$ seem to be most likely.

One may think of including into the crystalline field contributions other than the ones used in the above estimate.

For example we may include an octopole induced dipole moment in the rare gas atoms which acts back on the methane molecules in a way described by Hüller and Kane |34|. Their calculation has to be adapted to twelve nearest neighbours in an fcc lattice. This, however, mainly tends to reduce both $|\beta_6|$ and $|\beta_4|$, but affects their ratio only little.

The deuterium density distribution $\rho_0(\Omega)$ in the disordered phase of solid CD_4 |35|, determined by a structure analysis, may be used as a check for the reliability of the estimated crystalline field of pure CH_4. In an expansion of $\rho_D(\Omega)$ into cubic harmonics $K_{\ell m}(\Omega)$, contributions with $\ell \neq 0$ represent deviations from spherical symmetry. The leading term is $C_{41}K_{41}(\Omega)$. C_{41} can be related to β_4 and β_6, if a classical distribution function over the Euler angles is assumed |8|.

$$f(\omega) = G \exp(-V_c(\omega)/kT) \qquad\qquad (3)$$

G is a normalization constant. Experimental values for C_{41} are available for T = 77 K and 35 K and yield a further curve in the $(\beta_4; \beta_6)$ space. The ratio $\beta_6/\beta_4 = -2.4 \pm 0.5$ at its intersection with the $E_1(\beta_4, \beta_6)$ curve. No solution agrees well with these values, though there seems to be a clear preference for the first type, again.

We may summarize that the determination of crystalline field parameters from observed rotational transtions is not as straightforward as expected. As this first step is rather difficult already, it is not possible at present to extract reliable pair potential parameters from the experimental data. The second step may be accomplished with additional experimental results: The crystalline field in highly compressible solids depends very strongly on pressure. Therefore pressure experiments seem to be very promising. Also, an inclusion of the Q-dependence of the transition matrix elements should yield more detailed information.

Acknowledgement

The authors would like to thank Dr. A. Hüller, Prof. J. Raich and Prof. H. Stiller for many helpful discussions. The computational work was assisted by Mr. K. Wingerath and the chemical analyses were done by Mr. M. Thomé, whom we would like to thank for their help. One of us, Y.K., thankfully acknowledges the support by the Alexander von Humboldt Foundation.

REFERENCES

|1| HÜLLER, A., PRESS, W., these Proceedings, Vol. 1,
        IAEA-SM-219/129.

|2| SILVERA, I.F., Proc. 14th Int. Conf. on Low Temp. Phys., Helsinki 1975; KRUSINS, M., VUORI, M., (Eds), North-Holland Publishing Co., Amsterdam, (1975).

|3| ALEFELD, B., KOLLMAR, A., DASANNACHARYA, B.A., J. Chem. Phys. 63 (1975) 4415.

|4| HÜLLER, A., KROLL, D.M., J. Chem. Phys. 63 (1975) 4495.

|5| KAPULLA, H., GLÄSER, W., Phys. Lett. A31 (1970) 158.

|6| KAPULLA, H., GLÄSER, W., Proc. Symp. Neutron Inelastic Scattering IAEA, Grenoble, France, 1972 (1973) p. 841.

|7| PRESS, W., KOLLMAR, A., Solid State Commun. 17 (1975) 405.

|8| JAMES, H.M., KEENAN, T.A., J. Chem. Phys. 31 (1959) 12.

|9| PRESS, W., J. Chem. Phys. 56 (1972) 2597.

|10| KATAOKA, Y., OKADA, K., YAMAMOTO, T., Chem. Phys. Lett. 19 (1973) 365.

|11| YAMAMOTO, T., KATAOKA, Y., OKADA, K., J. Chem. Phys. 66 (1977) 2701.

|12| CABANA, A., SAVITSKY, G.B., HORNIG, D.F., J. Chem. Phys. 39 (1963) 2942.

|13| FRAYER, F.H., EWING, G.E., J. Chem. Phys. 46 (1967) 1994; 48 (1968) 781.

|14| CHAMBERLAND, A., BELZILE, R., CABANA, A., Can. J. Chem. 48 (1970) 1129.

|15| CABANA, A., ANDERSON, A., SAVOIE, R., J. Chem. Phys. 42 (1965) 1122.

|16| NISHIYAMA, K., YAMAMOTO, T., J. Chem. Phys. 58 (1973) 1001.

|17| KOBASHI, K., KATAOKA, Y., YAMAMOTO, T., Can. J. Chem. 54 (1976) 2154.

|18| KOBASHI, K., OKADA, K., YAMAMOTO, T., J. Chem. Phys. 66 (1977) 5568.

|19| HIRSCHFELDER, J.O., CURTISS, C.F., BIRD, R.B., Molecular Theory of Gases and Liquids, John Wiley & Sons Inc., New York (1954) pp 181, 1110.

|20| KLEIN, M.L. VENABLES, J.A., "Rare Gas Solids", Aca-
         demic Press, London (1976).

|21| RAICH, J.C. KANNEY, L.B., J. Low Temp. Phys. 28
         (1977) 95.

|22| KING, H.F., HORNIG   D.F., J. Chem. Phys. 44 (1966)
         4520.

|23| YASUDA, H., Prog. Theor. Phys. 45 (1971) 1361.

|24| HAMA, J., MIYAGI, H., Progr. Theor. Phys. 50 (1973)
         1142.

|25| HÜLLER, A., to be published in Phys. Rev. B.

|26| CODE, R.F., HIGGINBOTHAM, J., Can. J. Phys. 54,
         (1976) 1248.

|27| NIJMAN, A.J., TRAPPENIERS, N.J., to be published.

|28| NIJMAN, A.J., BERLINSKY, A.J., Phys. Rev. Lett. 38
         (1977) 408.

|29| HARDY, W.N., BERLINSKY, A.J., Phys. Rev. Lett. 34
         (1975) 1520.

|30| CLOUGH, S., HEIDEMANN, A., these Proceedings, Vol. 1,
         IAEA-SM-219/76.

|31| KOLLMAR, A., ALEFELD, B., Proc. of the Conf. on Neutron
         Scattering, Gatlinburg (USA) (1976) 330.

|32| PRAGER, M., PRESS, W., ALEFELD, B., Hüller, A.,
         J. Chem. Phys., to be published.

|33| ALLEN, P.S., J. Phys. C: Solid St. Phys. 7 (1974) L22

|34| HÜLLER, A., KANE, J.M., J. Chem. Phys. 61 (1974) 3599.

|35| PRESS, W., Acta Cryst. A29 (1973) 257.

DISCUSSION

S. YIP: In the case of the high-temperature measurements, do you think it would be possible to use computer molecular dynamics simulation — which is a classical calculation — to interpret your results? I am thinking, in particular, of the temperature dependence of the reorientational motions.

W. PRESS: Yes, I think such calculations would be very helpful and should accompany neutron scattering experiments. This was done recently for the hexagonal (disordered) phase of nitrogen by Klein at NRC in Ottawa, and very interesting results were obtained.

R.M. PICK: I understand that you have been dealing essentially with a quantum mechanics case. Is there any known way of making molecular dynamics calculations in such a case?

W. PRESS: If I am not mistaken, Mr. Yip's question referred to the high-temperature limit, where molecular dynamics calculations seem to be appropriate. To the best of my knowledge no such calculations have yet been performed in the quantum mechanical limit.

S. YIP: In this same connection I should like to say that one can consider quantum mechanical calculations using computer molecular dynamics techniques, but that would involve direct simulation of the wave function. Here, however, we are considering classical calculations only.

DYNAMIQUE DE $C_{10}D_{16}$ EN PHASE PLASTIQUE PAR DIFFUSION NEUTRONIQUE

J.C. DAMIEN*, R. CURRAT**,
J. LEFEBVRE*, B. HENNION+
* Laboratoire de dynamique des cristaux
  moléculaires (ERA n° 465),
  Villeneuve-d'Ascq
** Institut Laue-Langevin, Grenoble
+ Laboratoire Léon Brillouin,
  Gif-sur-Yvette,
  France

Abstract–Résumé

STUDY OF $C_{10}D_{16}$ DYNAMICS IN THE PLASTIC PHASE BY NEUTRON SCATTERING.
The paper describes the experimental conditions adopted in a neutron-scattering study
of the molecular crystal of adamantane in the plastic phase (T = 293 K), together with the
results of the study. The existence of librations was demonstrated, the main libration
frequency in the zone centre was measured and the phonon branches in the high-symmetry
directions were determined. Since the librations are very broad at whatever point of the
Brillouin zone the measurements may be made, the authors studied the evolution of certain
groups of neutrons as a function of temperature in order to determine the relative importance
of vibrational anharmonicity and of orientational disorder. The paper also presents a study
of the temperature dependence of neutron elastic scattering in adamantane around a Brillouin
zone selected for the intensity and interest of this scattering. On the basis of the work
performed, it should be possible to develop a dynamic model for this disordered crystal and
to study the role of the correlations between neighbouring molecules.

DYNAMIQUE DE $C_{10}D_{16}$ EN PHASE PLASTIQUE PAR DIFFUSION NEUTRONIQUE.
Les conditions expérimentales d'une étude en diffusion neutronique du cristal moléculaire
d'adamantane en phase plastique (T = 293 K) sont présentées ainsi que les résultats obtenus:
existence des librations, mesure de la fréquence principale de libration en centre de zone,
détermination des branches de phonons dans les directions de haute symétrie. Comme les
librations sont très larges quel que soit le point de la zone de Brillouin où est faite la mesure,
les auteurs ont cherché à préciser, par une étude de l'évolution de certains groupes de neutrons
avec la température, l'importance respective de l'anharmonicité des vibrations et du désordre
orientationnel. Les auteurs présentent également une étude de la variation avec T de la
diffusion élastique des neutrons dans l'adamantane autour d'une zone de Brillouin choisie pour
l'intensité et l'intérêt de cette diffusion. Ces résultats doivent permettre la mise au point d'un
modèle dynamique pour ce cristal désordonné ainsi que l'étude du rôle des corrélations entre
molécules voisines.

1.   INTRODUCTION

Ce mémoire présente les résultats expérimentaux obtenus en diffusion neutronique sur l'adamantane deutériée ($C_{10}D_{16}$) dans sa phase plastique. A notre connaissance il s'agit de la première étude de cette nature qui ait été menée à son terme sur un cristal moléculaire plastique.

Dans l'hypothèse des molécules rigides, la relative simplicité du cristal d'adamantane permettait a priori d'espérer que les résultats seraient plus complets que pour d'autres cristaux plastiques comme KCN [1]. Rien ne permettait cependant d'affirmer que les phonons de libration pouvaient être mesurés, ni même qu'ils existaient.

Nos mesures prouvent l'existence de ces librations et donnent leurs fréquences. Comme les phonons correspondants sont très larges dans toute la zone de Brillouin, il est apparu utile de chercher à compléter ces mesures à la température ambiante (T = 293 K) par une étude, en fonction de la température, de l'évolution de certaines fréquences de vibration dans l'adamantane. On pouvait en effet espérer obtenir de cette façon des renseignements sur l'importance de l'anharmonicité des librations et sur le rôle du désordre d'orientation permettant d'expliquer leur largeur.

L'adamantane franchit, à T_c = 208,6 K, une transition [2] entre une phase basse température quadratique ordonnée et une phase cubique désordonnée (groupe d'espace F m3m avec un paramètre a = 9,445 Å à T = 293 K) [3, 4]. La molécule ayant une symétrie tétraédrique ($\overline{4}3$ m), le désordre est dû à la possibilité pour ces molécules d'effectuer, dans le cristal, des sauts de réorientation entre 2 positions distinctes par des rotations de 90° autour de l'axe d'ordre 4 [5, 6].

Pour ce travail, nous n'avons bénéficié d'aucun renseignement sur les fréquences des modes externes puisqu'ils ne sont actifs ni en spectroscopie i.r. ni en Raman. Nous nous sommes donc appuyés au départ sur les calculs des facteurs de structure dynamiques pour réaliser une série de mesures préliminaires sur le spectromètre à 3 axes H4 du Centre d'études nucléaires de Saclay (Commissariat à l'énergie atomique). Nous avons ainsi pu déterminer les meilleures conditions expérimentales, mesurer une partie des phonons et vérifier que les librations existaient.

2.   ETUDE EXPERIMENTALE

2.1. Préparation de l'échantillon

Afin de réduire au maximum la diffusion incohérente de l'hydrogène, nous avons choisi un produit aussi deutérié que possible (98%). Le monocristal utilisé avait un volume de 5 cm³; il avait été fabriqué au Laboratoire de

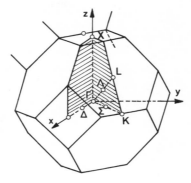

FIG.1. Zone de Brillouin — Plans de diffusion utilisés.

dynamique des cristaux moléculaires à partir du produit commercial fourni par
Merck-Canada en utilisant une méthode de transport en phase vapeur dans une
ampoule scellée. Des clichés de Laue effectués en transmission au travers de
tout le cristal ont permis de vérifier son caractère monocristallin et d'estimer
sa mosaïcité inférieure à 20′. Pour éviter la sublimation importante de l'adamantane,
cet échantillon a ensuite été placé dans un conteneur étanche en aluminium (AU3).

2.2. Conditions expérimentales

Les mesures ont été faites sur le spectromètre IN2 de l'Institut Laue-
Langevin de Grenoble. L'étude a porté sur les trois directions Δ, Σ, Λ du cube et
des vecteurs d'onde contenus dans deux plans de diffusion de type (001) et (0$\bar{1}$1)
(fig. 1). Ces deux plans ont été choisis de façon à permettre la détermination des
fréquences de vibration correspondant aux 2 modes transverses dans la direction
($\xi\xi$0). Il n'a toutefois pas été possible de mesurer l'une des librations dans la
direction d'ordre 3 puisqu'elle n'était active dans aucune des géométries possibles.

Sur IN2, le faisceau incident est obtenu après réflexions de Bragg sur un
double monochromateur en graphite pyrolytique travaillant sur la raie (002).
La majorité des groupes de neutrons a été obtenue en travaillant à longueur
d'onde incidente constante ($k_i = 2{,}662$ Å^{-1}, soit $\lambda_i = 2{,}360$ Å) avec une collimation favorisant l'observation des phonons en annihilation. Un filtre en graphite
pyrolytique placé sur le faisceau incident éliminait d'éventuelles réflexions d'ordre
supérieur sur les monochromateurs.

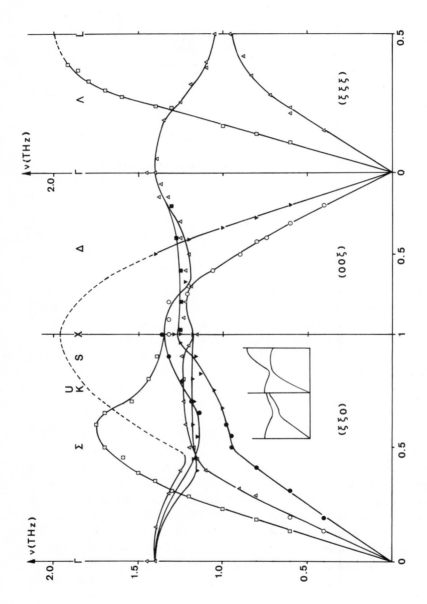

FIG. 2. *Courbes de dispersion de fréquences dans* $C_{10}D_{16}$. □ ■ *repère un groupe de neutrons à caractère longitudinal,* ○ ● *un groupe de neutrons à caractère transverse, et* △ ▼ *un groupe de neutrons à caractère mixte. (Sur cette figure, les lignes et le cartouche ne constituent que des guides pour l'œil.)*

2.3. Présentation et analyse des résultats à T = 293 K

Les géométries utilisées ont permis de mesurer les phonons relatifs aux branches suivantes:
— dans la direction de l'axe d'ordre 2 (Σ), les 6 branches prévues ont été suivies à l'exception d'une partie de Σ_4; cet échec, rare pour une branche longitudinale acoustique, est dû à la faiblesse particulière du facteur de forme sur la quasi-totalité des rayons de zone accessibles sur H4 ou sur IN2;
— dans la direction de l'axe d'ordre 4 (Δ), les 4 modes ont été suivis sauf une partie de Δ_1 pour la même raison que précédemment;
— dans la direction de l'axe d'ordre 3 (Λ), seul manque le mode de libration Λ_2 qui n'était actif dans aucune des photométries accessibles.

Les courbes expérimentales obtenues sont présentées sur la figure 2. Il est important de signaler que la mesure de la fréquence de libration ν_0 en centre de zone (représentation triplement dégénérée Γ'_{15}) est la première détermination directe de cette fréquence. La valeur trouvée ici: $\nu_0 = 1{,}40$ THz ($46{,}7$ cm^{-1}) est faible en comparaison de celle trouvée par Powell [7] pour l'hexaméthylène-tétramine HMT ($\nu_0 = 2{,}30$ THz, ou 77 cm^{-1}), mais cependant très supérieure à la valeur proposée par Luty [8] dans son modèle ($\nu_0 = 0{,}78$ THz, soit 26 cm^{-1}).

Les pentes des branches acoustiques sont liées directement aux constantes élastiques. Elles conduisent ici aux valeurs suivantes:

$$c_{11} = 7{,}73 \times 10^9 \ \text{N} \cdot \text{m}^{-2} \ (10^{10} \ \text{CGS})$$

$$c_{44} = 4{,}48 \times 10^9 \ \text{N} \cdot \text{m}^{-2} \ (10^{10} \ \text{CGS})$$

$$c_{12} = 3{,}36 \times 10^9 \ \text{N} \cdot \text{m}^{-2} \ (10^{10} \text{CGS})$$

qui sont en très bon accord avec les mesures ultrasonores [9] ou de diffusion Brillouin [10].

Quelle que soit la direction étudiée, nous avons toujours trouvé des librations très larges (largeur à mi-hauteur FWHM $\sim 1{,}0$ à $1{,}4$ THz; voir la figure 3), bien que parfaitement caractérisées et non suramorties. Si l'on estime à FWHM/10 l'incertitude de mesure, les fréquences sont alors connues à environ $0{,}1$ THz près et l'évolution des diverses branches est bien déterminée malgré la faible dispersion de certains modes.

Des estimations de la fonction de résolution ont été faites au moyen d'un programme de calcul inspiré de l'article de Cooper et Nathans [11]. On obtient par exemple les valeurs

$\Delta\nu = 0{,}24$ THz pour la libration Σ_4 en limite de zone ($\xi = 0{,}95$)
$\Delta\nu = 0{,}15$ THz pour la branche TA(111) au point L'_3
$\Delta\xi = 0{,}06$ pour la branche TA(001) au point $\xi = 0{,}32$ pour $\nu = 0{,}6$ THz.

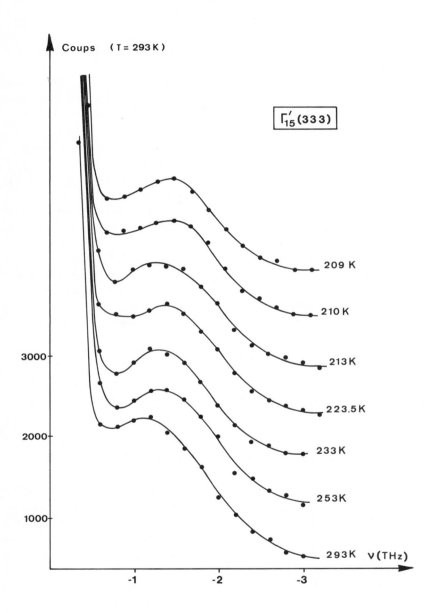

FIG. 3. Evolution avec la température du phonon de libration Γ'_{15}.

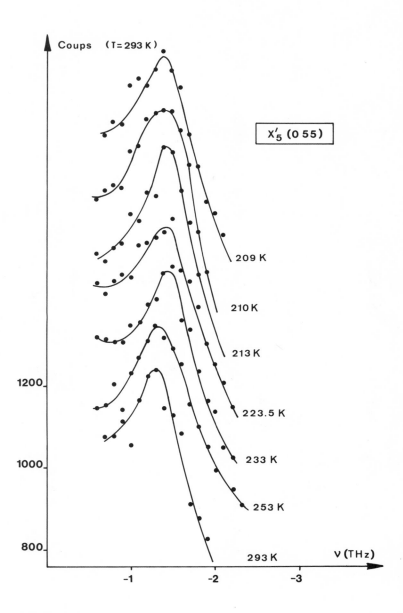

FIG.4.   Evolution avec la température du phonon TA(100) en bord de zone (X$'_5$).

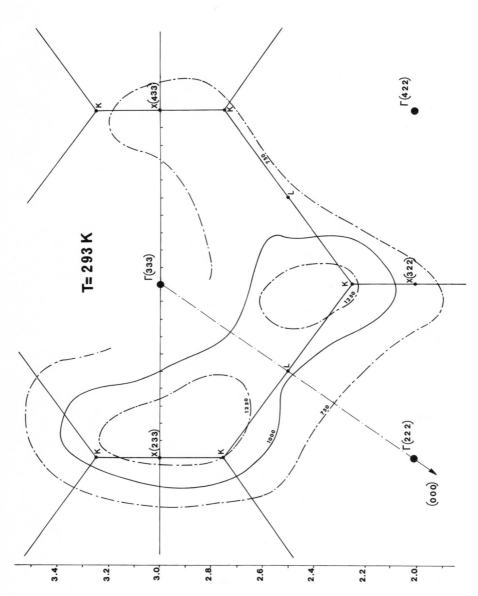

FIG.5. Diffusion élastique autour de la zone (333) à T = 293 K.

Ces valeurs modifient fort peu les largeurs à mi-hauteur des phonons mesurés.
Un calcul analogue mené pour le phonon transverse TA(00ξ) conduit à
$\Delta\xi = 0,09$ pour la largeur expérimentale, à $\Delta\xi = 0,06$ pour la fonction de
résolution, donc à une largeur propre environ 10 fois plus faible
($\text{FWHM}_{\text{propre}} \sim 0,13$ THz).

2.4. Mesures faites à température variable

Dans le souci d'apporter des informations supplémentaires sur le comportement dynamique de l'adamantane en phase plastique, nous avons ensuite effectué
sur le même cristal des mesures de groupes de neutrons en quelques points
particuliers de la zone de Brillouin à plusieurs températures T telles que
$T_c < T < 293$ K. Nous avons également étudié l'évolution avec T de la diffusion
élastique dans la région de l'espace réciproque où elle est apparue la plus intense
et la plus caractéristique.

Les figures 3 et 4 montrent l'évolution de la libration de centre de zone
Γ'_{15} et celle du phonon TA(100) de vibration transverse acoustique en bord de
zone X'_5. Cette variation pour ces 2 phonons reflète ce que nous avons obtenu
pour les 5 modes que nous avons suivis (Γ'_{15}, X'_5, L_3, L'_3 et Δ_5 en $\xi = 0,5$):
augmentation de l'ordre de 10% entre l'ambiante et 213 K, évolution indécise
ensuite. Pour tous ces phonons, nous n'avons pas noté, dans la limite de la
précision des mesures effectuées, de variation nette des largeurs à mi-hauteur.

Les points X sont les nœuds de surstructure où apparaissent de nouvelles
taches de Bragg en phase ordonnée; nous avons donc étudié également, dans
la zone de Brillouin centrée sur le nœud $\Gamma(333)$ et autour des points X voisins,
l'évolution de la diffusion élastique. Les résultats sont présentés aux figures 5,
6 et 7.

Cette évolution est caractéristique d'une transition de phase du 1.er ordre
où la température T_0 qui commande la variation de l'intensité diffusée diffère
sensiblement de T_c, température de transition. L'étude de cette variation au
voisinage des points X(233) et X(433) a permis de déterminer les paramètres
T_0 et β d'une loi du type

$$I = A(T - T_0)^{-\beta}$$

où $\beta = 0,525$ et $T_0 = 198$ K

La forme et l'intensité de cette diffusion élastique semblent bien s'inter-
préter dans le cadre d'une première étude théorique des corrélations [12].

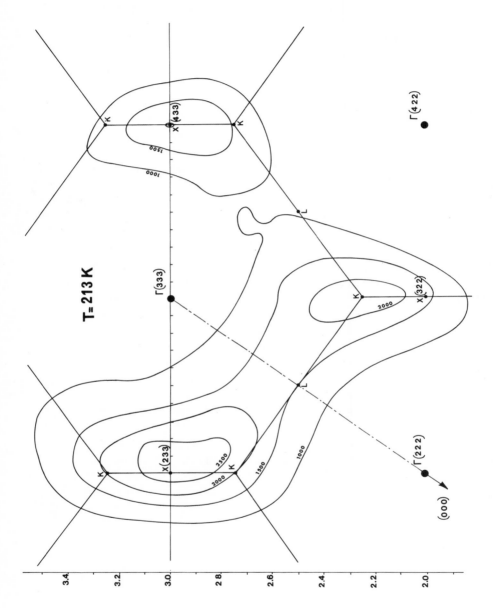

FIG. 6.   Diffusion élastique autour de la zone (333) à T = 213 K.

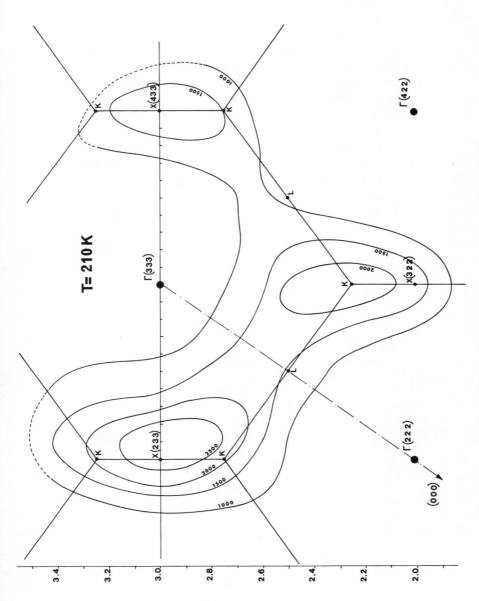

FIG.7. Diffusion élastique autour de la zone (333) à T = 210 K.

3.   CONCLUSION

L'étude de l'adamantane deutériée en diffusion neutronique a permis de mettre en évidence l'existence dans le cristal de mouvements collectifs de libration relativement bien définis. La quasi-totalité des branches de phonons a pu être mesurée. Ces résultats doivent fournir un excellent moyen de contrôle pour bâtir un modèle de ce cristal désordonné [13].

La fréquence principale de libration en centre de zone a, pour la première fois, été mesurée; sa valeur $\nu_0 \sim 1,40$ THz doit être comparée à la fréquence déduite du temps de réorientation mesuré en diffusion quasi-élastique: $\tau \sim 1,7 \times 10^{-11}$ s [6].

Une étude en fonction de la température fournit enfin des informations qui doivent permettre de mieux apprécier le rôle et la nature des corrélations entre molécules voisines. Pour estimer correctement l'importance de l'anharmonicité, il demeure très utile de pouvoir mesurer les phonons en phase ordonnée un peu en dessous de T_c, ce qui impose évidemment de disposer d'un monocristal dans cette phase. L'influence du désordre devrait en effet décroître rapidement en dessous de T_c et on devrait alors noter une rapide diminution des largeurs à mi-hauteur, en particulier des librations.

REFERENCES

[1]   DAUBERT, J., KNORR, K., DUTZ, W., JEX, H., CURRAT, R., J. Phys., C: Solid St. Phys. **9** (1976) L389.

[2]   CHANG, S.S., WESTRUM, E.F., J. Phys. Chem. **64** (1960) 1547.

[3]   NORDMAN, C.E., SCHMITKONS, D.L., Acta Crystallogr. **18** (1965) 764.

[4]   DONOHUE, J., GOODMAN, S.H., Acta Crystallogr. **22** (1967) 352.

[5]   STOCKMEYER, R., Discuss. Faraday Soc. (1969) 156.

[6]   LECHNER, R.E., HEIDEMANN, A., Commun. Phys. **1** (1976) 213.

[7]   POWELL, B.M., *in* Neutron Inelastic Scattering (Proc. Symp. Copenhagen, 1968) **2**, IAEA, Vienna (1968) 185.

[8]   LUTY, T., Acta Phys. Pol. Ser. A **40** (1971) 1.

[9]   DAMIEN, J.C., Solid State Commun. **16** (1975) 1271.

[10] DAMIEN, J.C., DEPREZ, G., Solid State Commun. **20** (1976) 161.

[11] COOPER, M.J., NATHANS, R., Acta Crystallogr. **23** (1967) 357.

[12] DESCAMPS, M., communication personnelle.

[13] DAMIEN, J.C., LEFEBVRE, J., MORE, M., HENNION, B., CURRAT, R., FOURET, R., à paraître.

DISCUSSION

C.G. WINDSOR: May I first congratulate you on resolving the librational modes in adamantane? Our results at Harwell (submitted to J. Phys. Chem.)

showed translational modes in excellent agreement with yours but failed to show distinct librational peaks. Instead we associated librational motion with a broad scattering law, $S(Q, \omega)$, analogous to that in a liquid or paramagnet, which we have measured by triple-axis and time-of-flight methods. I should like to ask how you were able to differentiate the librational modes from the other scattering?

J.C. DAMIEN: In addition to the usual phonon branches we clearly observed broad but well-defined modes. Their character and q-dependence, and their behaviour at crossing (or anti-crossing) points with phonon branches, indicate that the peaks observed definitely represent librational modes. We shall revert to the width later. For the experiments we used a big, well-deuterated single crystal with a very low mosaic spread. Despite this, we still had to make our measurements around the (333), (055) and (066) Brillouin zones and to work by energy annihilation. These conditions are severe but they are necessary for adamantane. We would have liked to work around (0010) in the four-fold direction but even on IN2 this was not possible.

P. SCHOFIELD: I would like to mention that, in collaboration with Pawley (Edinburgh) and Grout (Oxford), we are about to start a computer simulator study of adamantane using an atom-atom force model due to Pawley which gives the correct lattice spacing and fits many of the phonon branches observed at Harwell.

J.C. DAMIEN: It will certainly be very interesting to see the results of such a computer simulation. We have also made a few calculations to try to interpret our data; the work in question is described in the paper cited here as Ref. [13]. Our results will be published soon.

K.H. MICHEL: Is this librational mode a collective effect? If it is, then the existence of the mode is very puzzling because it occurs in the disordered phase. Should one perhaps look at possible analogies with sloppy spin waves in antiferromagnets?

H. HAHN: There seems to be a discrepancy of at least one order of magnitude between the width of the librational peak calculated from Stock-meyer's measured lifetime and your measured width. This indicates that other factors must be involved in the experimental width, presumably statistical inhomogeneities in the coupling between librating molecules.

J.C. DAMIEN: In the disordered crystal of adamantane, the reorientation time τ_R is large compared with the period of the libration. To study the dynamics, therefore, a good first approximation is to consider the different static configurations of the molecules in the crystal, given for instance by an Ising model. It is then possible to calculate the librational frequencies corresponding to the different neighbourhoods. When a neutron beam hits such a crystal, there is a random interaction with the different molecules. As the probabilities for establishment of the different configurations are obviously not equal, the response function $S(Q, \omega)$ will be broad but will have a maximum corresponding to the statistically more probable configuration. I think Mr. Hahn has clearly said that in his comment, and I agree with him. This is the basic hypothesis we have adopted for studying a model for adamantane in the plastic phase, and the results we have obtained clearly show that the idea was not wrong.

R.M. PICK: Measured data have been obtained for the lifetime of a molecule of adamantane in its potential well. Does this lifetime correspond to the measured width of the librations? If the time varies with temperature, why doesn't the measured width also vary?

W. PRESS: I think Mr. Pick's question is based on a misunderstanding concerning the single-particle jump rates. A measurement of the quasi-elastic scattering at $T = 214$ K by Alefeld and Stockmeyer (see Top. Curr. Phys. 3 (1977) 258) yields a half-width of about 4 μeV and hence jump rates much smaller than typical librational energies. This is probably enhanced in deuterated adamantane.

B.A. DASANNACHARYA: I should also like to comment on the question raised by Mr. Pick. If the width of the peak is governed by an exponential law with an effective potential V which is small compared with kT, then the temperature variation would not be expected to be large in the range 210–300 K.

C.G. WINDSOR: Surely, if a given molecule has 12 nearest neighbours and a jump frequency of order 10^{11} Hz, its librational motion will be interrupted by the jump of one neighbour with a frequency of 10^{12} Hz in agreement with the observed width of the librational modes?

J.C. DAMIEN: I will try to answer the last four speakers together. I believe that two different problems are involved in the questions raised. The time of residence does determine the lifetime of a libration. Stockmeyer (our Ref. [5]) gives a lifetime at least 10 times greater than the period of the libration for the most probable configuration.

If it were possible to observe the shape of the corresponding peak experimentally, it would no doubt vary with temperature according to an Arrhenius law, which is generally accepted as a good approach. However, the observed width in neutron scattering is mainly the effect of the orientational disorder which is established in the crystal after the transition and which will remain roughly the same up to the melting point.

The comment by Mr. Press, showing that the jump rate is far smaller at $T = 214$ K, leads to a lifetime of about 10^{-9} s. This value is consistent with the value given by the NMR experiments of MacCall and Douglass (J. Chem. Phys. 33 3 (1960) 777), namely a lifetime of a few times 10^{-8} s at 208 K, the transition temperature.

ANALYSIS OF NEUTRON INELASTIC SCATTERING SPECTRA OF NORMAL AND DEUTERATED FORMIC ACID*

C.V. BERNEY, S.-H. CHEN,
D.H. JOHNSON, S. YIP
Department of Nuclear Engineering,
Massachusetts Institute of Technology,
Cambridge, Massachusetts,
United States of America

Abstract

ANALYSIS OF NEUTRON INELASTIC SCATTERING SPECTRA OF NORMAL AND
DEUTERATED FORMIC ACID.

Calculations based on a planar single-chain model of solid formic acid have been carried out to interpret the observed neutron inelastic scattering spectra of HCOOH, HCOOD, and DCOOH, and to use the direct relationship between vibrational eigenvectors and neutron-scattering intensities to extract information concerning the dynamic modes of the system. Force constants similar to those used by previous investigators were refined (using a least-squares adjustment routine) to try to achieve agreement with observed zone-centre vibrational frequencies and with peak positions and intensities in the neutron-scattering spectra. The calculated neutron spectra were particularly sensitive to the out-of-plane force constants. The best calculation fits the HCOOH spectrum well, but results in a 30–40 cm^{-1} discrepancy for an out-of-plane mode in HCOOD and DCOOH. A two-phonon calculation has been carried out which accounts well for observed features around 515 cm^{-1} in HCOOH and HCOOD.

1. INTRODUCTION

Formic acid, HCOOH, is a clear liquid that boils at 100.7° and freezes at 8.4°C. Its liquid range is thus similar to that of water, which it also resembles in that many of its properties are due to its ability to form hydrogen bonds. The bonding in formic acid is simpler than that in water, however, since formic acid has only one donor and one receptor site per molecule. Thus, on freezing, formic acid molecules arrange themselves in essentially linear chains (Fig. 1),

* This work was carried out with support from the National Science Foundation under grant CHE-7616594.

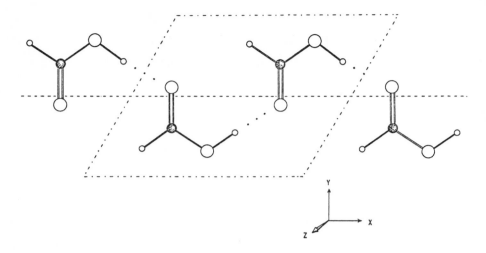

FIG.1. *Planar chain model for solid formic acid, HCOOH. Large circles represent oxygen atoms, small circles represent hydrogen atoms, and shaded circles are carbon atoms. Hydrogen bonds are schematically indicated (−OH . . . 0 = C−). The horizontal dashed line is the chain axis. The rhombus (− · − · −) encloses a representative catemer (unit cell).*

rather than forming a three-dimensional hexagonal lattice. This simplicity makes formic acid an attractive subject for the study of molecular dynamics of hydrogen-bonded solids.

In incoherent inelastic neutron scattering (INS) the contribution of a particular nucleus to a vibrational peak in the scattering spectrum is proportional to its incoherent-scattering cross section times the square of the vibrational amplitude. This direct relationship means that force-field models of vibrating systems can be used to predict INS intensities, and conversely, the intensities can be used to provide constraints on the specification of intermolecular and intramolecular forces. Further, the incoherent cross section of the light hydrogen (^{1}H) nucleus happens to be an order of magnitude larger than that of other common nuclei, including deuterium. The low mass of ^{1}H atoms results in relatively large vibrational amplitudes; this, combined with the high cross section, means that to a good approximation, the intensity of a vibrational peak in the INS spectrum of a hydrogen-containing

substance may be regarded as an indicator of hydrogen-atom involvement
in the corresponding vibration. If a given peak is due largely to the
motion of a certain ^{1}H atom, deuteration at that site will reduce the
intensity of the peak by an order of magnitude, providng a powerful
tool for confirming assignments.

    We have obtained neutron-scattering spectra of formic acid and
two deuterated derivatives (HCOOD and DCOOH). These spectra have been
published [1] with a qualitative discussion of their implications based
on the considerations outlined above. In the present report, we describe steps we have taken to extract more quantitative results from
these spectra.

2. SINGLE-CHAIN MODEL OF SOLID FORMIC ACID

    The only crystallographic study of formic acid thus far available
was reported in 1953 [2]. The lattice is orthorhombic, space group
Pna2$_1$ (C_{2v}^9). The unit cell contains four monomers, of which two belong
to a single hydrogen-bonded chain. Each monomer is planar; the planes
of adjacent molecules in a chain form a dihedral angle of $\sim 13^\circ$. Adjacent chains are within 16° of being orthogonal.

    Our initial attempts to simulate the INS spectrum of formic acid
involved a Born-von Kármán treatment of the full unit cell (20 atoms,
60 degrees of freedom) with nonbonded interactions supplied by potential
functions taken from the literature [3]. Completion of this type of
calculation remains our eventual goal; however, the manipulations are
too cumbersome and the number of parameters to be adjusted is too large
for this approach to be immediately successful. In an effort to bring
the problem down to tractable size, we have followed the example of
Mikawa, Brasch and Jakobsen [4] and of Tubino and Zerbi [5] and have
carried out calculations on a single planar chain. This simplification
reduces the repeating unit (the catemer) to two monomers (10 atoms,
30 degrees of freedom) and increases its factor-group symmetry from
C_s to C_{2v}.
    The single-chain model of HCOOH used in the present calculation
is shown in Fig. 1. The symmetry elements present are a screw axis, a
plane of reflection, and a glide plane. The vibrational representation

(including zero-frequency modes) at the center of the Brillouin zone is

$$\Gamma_{vib} = 10a_1 + 5a_2 + 10b_1 + 5b_2 \tag{1}$$

The a_1 and b_1 modes involve in-plane motions with the first and second monomers in-phase (a_1) and out-of-phase (b_1). In the a_2 modes, the out-of-plane motions of the two monomers are symmetric with respect to the operation of the screw axis (that is, when a given atom in the first monomer is coming out of the plane, the corresponding atom in the second monomer is going into the plane), and the b_2 modes involve out-of-plane motions which are antisymmetric with respect to the screw operation. Translations in the x, y, and z directions (Fig. 1) belong to the a_1, b_1, and b_2 irreducible representations, respectively. Rotation about the chain axis (the fourth zero-frequency mode) belongs to a_2.

We begin with an array of 32 internal coordinates R_i for the ith unit cell as defined in Table I. Let the array of 30 cartesian coordinates of the atoms in cell i be denoted by X_i. Then one has the transformation

$$R_i = B_o X_i + B_{-1} X_{i-1} + B_1 X_{i+1} \tag{2}$$

where the B matrices can be generated using standard programs [6]. The appearance of B_{-1} and B_1 stems from the fact that atoms in the neighboring cells to cell i may be needed to define the internal coordinates in cell i.

In terms of coordinates R_i the quadratic potential energy is

$$2V = \sum_{nn'} R_n^T F_{nn'}^R R_{n'} \tag{3}$$

where F^R is the force-constant matrix for internal coordinates. For our model we will take F as given in Table I. The dynamical matrix D can now be expressed in terms of F^R. One has [7]

$$D(\underline{q}) = M^{-\frac{1}{2}} F^X(\underline{q}) M^{-\frac{1}{2}} \tag{4}$$

Table I.   Internal Coordinates and Force Constants

Internal Coordinate Number	Description	Values of Corresponding Force Constant
1	O-H stretch	4.623
2	C-H stretch	4.616
3	C=O stretch	8.452
4	C-O stretch	7.345
5	COH bend	0.324
6	O=C-H bend	0.442
7	O-C-H bend	1.013
8	O=C-O bend	1.875
9	out-of-plane deformation	0.398
10	COH torsion	0.249
11	-H...O= stretch	0.275
12	-OH...O= in-plane bend	0.250
13	H...O=C bend	0.105
14	-OH...O= out-of-plane bend	0.068
15	OH...O=C torsion	0.009
16	H...O=C-H torsion	0.060

Interaction Force Constants:

$f(1,4) = 0.822$ $f(3,7) = -1.416$

$f(2,3) = 0.625$ $f(3,27) = 0.428$

$f(2,4) = 0.850$ $f(4,6) = 0.572$

$f(3,4) = 2.686$ $f(4,7) = 0.347$

$f(3,6) = -0.588$ $f(9,10) = 0.103$

A similar set of coordinates (numbered from 17 to 32) was used for the second molecule in the catemer. Coordinates 1-10 are intramolecular, while coordinates 11-16 are intermolecular. Stretching force constants are in mdy/Å, bending and torsion force constants are in mdy·Å/rad².

where M is the matrix of atomic masses, $\underline{q}$ is the wavevector, and

$$F^x(\underline{q}) = B^T(\underline{q}) \; F^R(\underline{q}) \; B(\underline{q}) \tag{5}$$

with

$$B(\underline{q}) = B_o + B_{-1} e^{-i\underline{q}\cdot\underline{r}_1} + B_1 e^{i\underline{q}\cdot\underline{r}_1} \tag{6}$$

and similarly for $F^x(\underline{q})$.

In Eqs. (5) and (6) $\underline{r}_1$ is the vector between adjacent unit cells. In our case $\underline{r}_1$ has magnitude 6.46 Å and is directed along the x-axis. Once $D(\underline{q})$ is formed, the eigenvalues $\omega_j(\underline{q})$ and polarization vectors $e(\underline{q}j)$ are obtained from

$$[D(\underline{q}) - \omega_j^2(q)I] \; e(qj) = 0 \tag{7}$$

where I is the unit matrix. Here $e(qj)$ is a column array of 10 atomic polarization vectors $\underline{e}(s|qj)$, where s is the atom index, s = 1, 2, ... , 10. The normalization condition is

$$\sum_s \underline{e}^*(s|qj) \cdot \underline{e}(s|qj') = \delta_{jj'} \tag{8}$$

$$\sum_j e_\alpha^*(s|qj) \; e_\beta(s'|qj) = \delta_{ss'}\delta_{\alpha\beta} \tag{9}$$

where subscripts α and β refer to Cartesian components.

The force constant values given in Table I have been used to obtain $\omega_j(q)$ and $\underline{e}(s|qj)$. These values were developed as explained in Section 4. A comparison of calculated and measured frequencies is shown in Table II. The dispersion curves calculated with this set of force constants are shown in Fig. 2. They are rather similar to the results of Tubino and Zerbi [5]. One can observe that the phonon branches involving motions of the hydrogen bond show the most dispersion.

3.   NEUTRON SCATTERING SPECTRA

To analyze the neutron inelastic scattering spectrum of poly-crystalline formic acid we use the expression for the one-phonon scattering cross section [8]

$$
\frac{d^2\sigma}{d\Omega d\omega} = A\left(\frac{E_f}{E_i}\right)^{\frac{1}{2}} \frac{Q^2\, e^{\displaystyle \hbar|\omega|/2k_BT}}{|\omega| \quad \sinh\left(\frac{\hbar|\omega|}{2k_BT}\right)} \sum_s \frac{\sigma_s}{m_s} e^{-2W_s} G_s(\omega) \tag{10}
$$

where A is a constant, $\hbar\omega = E_i - E_f$ is the energy transfer, Q is the
wavevector transfer, σ_s is the total scattering cross section of atom s,
$\exp(-2W_s)$ is the Debye-Waller factor, and the effective frequency distribution of atom s, $G_s(\omega)$, is defined by

$$
G_s(\omega) = \frac{1}{3nN} \sum_{qj} \delta(\omega-\omega_j(q))\ |\underline{e}(s|qj)|^2 \tag{11}
$$

In Eq. (11) N is the number of unit cells, n the number of atoms in a
unit cell (n=10), and the summation extends over N values of q in the
Brillouin zone and 3n number of branches j.

The basic quantity in the calculation is $G_s(\omega)$, which differs
from the thermodynamic frequency distribution in that the contribution
from each mode is weighted by the square of the vibrational amplitude
of a given atom. The Debye-Waller factor can be expressed in terms
of $G_s(\omega)$,

$$
2W_s = \frac{\hbar Q^2}{4m_s} \int d\omega\ \frac{G_s(\omega)}{\omega}\ \coth\left(\frac{\hbar\omega}{2k_BT}\right) \tag{12}
$$

We have computed $G_s(\omega)$ using the single-chain model of Section 2
for each of the 10 atoms in the unit cell, and the results were then
combined in Eq. (10) to obtain the spectrum of downscattered neutrons.
Figure 3 shows a comparison of the calculated cross section with the
measured spectrum for scattering from HCOOH at 77 K [1]. The measurement was carried out at a fixed final neutron energy of about 25 cm^{-1}
and variable incident neutron energy. The scattering angle was 81°.
Figures 4 and 5 show a similar comparison in the case of HCOOD and
DCOOH. The normalization between calculated and measured intensities
is arbitrary, but the same normalization was used for all three cases.

Table II. Observed and Calculated Zone-Center Frequencies (cm^{-1}) for
           Solid HCOOH.

a_1 Species	Target Frequency[a]	Calculated Frequency	Mode Description
ν_1	2960	2963	OH stretch
ν_2	2900	2898	CH stretch
ν_3	1620	1623	C=O stretch
ν_4	1370	1366	C-O stretch
ν_5	1324	1317	COH bend
ν_6	1248	1239	CH bend
ν_7	720	719	O=C-O bend
ν_8	---	220	libration
ν_9	88	78	libration
ν_{10}	---	0	x translation

a_2 Species			
ν_{11}	1090	1100	out-of-plane deformation
ν_{12}	960	961	COH torsion
ν_{13}	251	257	libration
ν_{14}	---	68	libration
ν_{15}	---	0	rotation about chain axis

b_1 Species			
ν_{16}	2960	2960	OH stretch
ν_{17}	2900	2896	CH stretch
ν_{18}	1620	1617	C=O stretch
ν_{19}	1378	1386	C-O stretch
ν_{20}	1324	1331	COH bend
ν_{21}	1210	1220	CH bend
ν_{22}	720	721	O=C-O bend
ν_{23}	---	173	libration
ν_{24}	---	155	out-of-phase x translation
ν_{25}	---	0	y translation

Table II (cont'd.)

b_2 Species	Target Frequency[a]	Calculated Frequency	Mode Description
ν_{26}	1050	1068	out-of-plane deformation
ν_{27}	991	995	COH torsion
ν_{28}	---	253	libration
ν_{29}	---	65	libration
ν_{30}	---	0	z translation

[a] Target frequencies were taken from the infrared observations of Mikawa, Brasch and Jakobsen [4], except for the a_2 and b_2 species, where the frequencies were estimated from the neutron-scattering data [1]. When no target frequency is indicated, the corresponding mode was not included in the least-squares adjustment. Note that our definition of a_2 and b_2 is opposite to that of Refs. 4 and 5, and that the mode numbering thus differs after the a_1 block.

4. FORCE-FIELD CALCULATIONS

The force field given in Table I was developed over several weeks of work in which a least-squares computer code was used to adjust a trial set of force constants for HCOOH to give agreement between the calculated (zone-center) frequencies and a set of target frequencies. Initially, the target frequencies were the infrared assignments of Mikawa, Brasch and Jakobsen [4]. After approximate agreement was obtained, simulated neutron spectra were calculated as described in the previous section, with intensities (summed over the Brillouin zone) stored in bins of 5 cm^{-1} width below 400 cm^{-1} and 20 cm^{-1} width above 400 cm^{-1} energy transfer (these bin widths were chosen to correspond roughly to the spectrometer resolution). The first few force fields obtained in this way gave poor agreement with the observed neutron spectra in the 1100-1000 cm^{-1} region, where the out-of-plane deformation

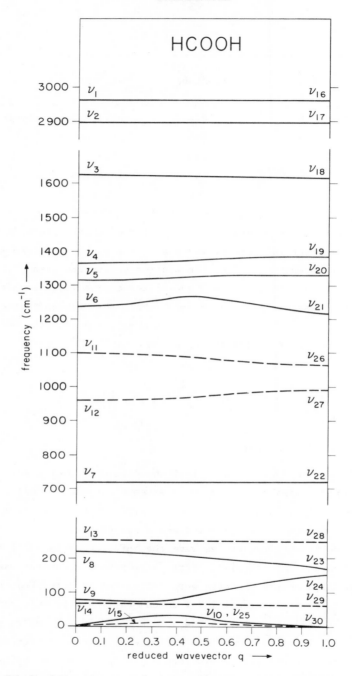

FIG.2. *Calculated dispersion curves (variation of frequency with reduced wavevector q, where q is parallel to the chain axis) for vibrations of the single-chain model for solid formic acid. Out-of-plane modes are indicated by dashed lines.*

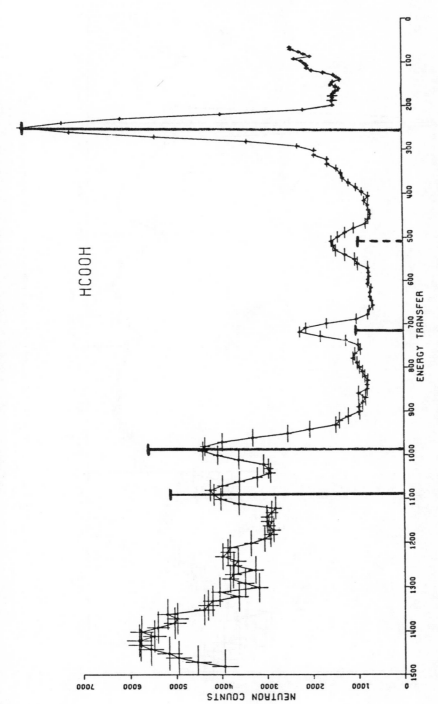

FIG.3. *Observed neutron-scattering spectrum of solid HCOOH at 77 K (horizontal lines represent spectrometer resolution; vertical lines attached to data points indicate one standard deviation above and below the observed count). Heavy vertical lines indicate frequencies and relative intensities obtained in the present calculation. The only normalization of calculated and observed intensities occurs at 250 cm⁻¹. The dashed vertical line represents the calculated intensity of the two-phonon peak.*

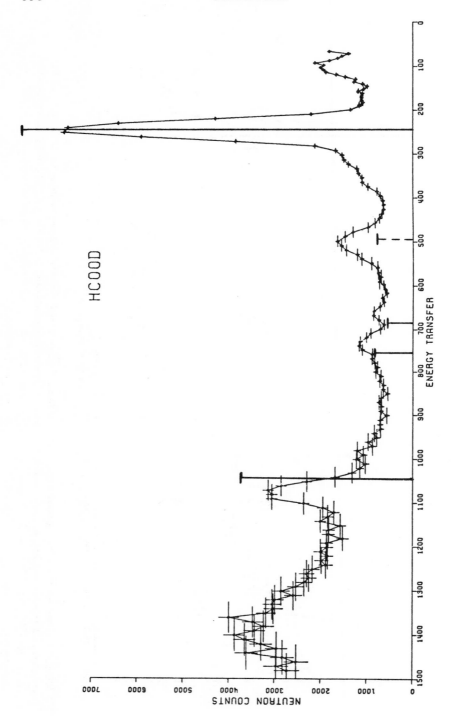

FIG. 4.   Same as Fig. 3 for solid HCOOD   Calculated intensities are shown on the same scale as those in Fig. 3.

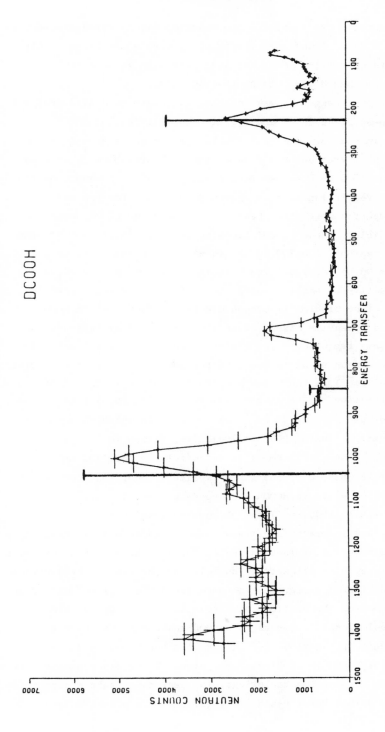

FIG.5.   Same as Fig. 4 for solid DCOOH.

and the OH torsion are located. The observed [4] infrared frequencies
(1078, 947, 910 cm^{-1}) were too low to allow the calculations to place
the INS peaks correctly, so we replaced them with zone-center target
frequencies estimated from the neutron spectra.

After this change, it was possible to secure good agreement with
respect to peak frequencies and relative intensities for HCOOH, as
illustrated in Fig. 3. (In this figure, the intensities were scaled
so that the histogram bar would match the peak at 250 cm^{-1}. The bars
at ∿ 1100 and 1000 cm^{-1} appear relatively too large; however, degraded
spectrometer resolution in this region may account for the effect.)
Calculated spectra were then obtained for HCOOD and DCOOH using the
same force field. These calculations again gave significant disagreement in the region (1100-700 cm^{-1}) containing the out-of-plane deformation and the OH(D) torsion. The calculated spectra proved to be extremely sensitive to small changes in the force constants affecting
these modes. The problem is compounded by the fact that in HCOOH
these modes are heavily mixed, since they are so close together and
are of the same frequency. The mixing is so complete, in fact, that
it may be more meaningful to describe the upper a_2, b_2 pair (calculated
at 1100, 1068 cm^{-1}) as the mode in which the acid H moves out of the
plane in opposition to the oxygen atom to which it is hydrogen-bonded,
and the lower pair (995, 961 cm^{-1}) as the mode in which these atoms
move in concert. In the DCOOH calculation, mixing is less severe --
the upper mode (1047, 1021 cm^{-1}) is definitely OH torsion, and the
lower mode (873, 839 cm^{-1}) has a D-C amplitude about 40% greater than
the OH motion -- while in HCOOD, the modes are nearly pure H-C
deformation (1048, 1040 cm^{-1}) and OD torsion (766, 756 cm^{-1}).

The strong interaction between these modes made it impossible to
secure perfect agreement in this region for all three isotopic species
(in spite of repeated attempts to do so), and the results presented in
Table II and Figs. 3-5 represent a force field which gives good agreement for HCOOH and the smallest discrepancies attainable within the
present calculational framework for HCOOD and DCOOH. We note that the
calculated peak in the 1100-1000 cm^{-1} region for HCOOD is 30 cm^{-1} too
low, while for DCOOH it is 37 cm^{-1} too high. These discrepancies may be
due to one or more of the following: (a) neglect of anharmonicity; (b)
neglect of possible Fermi resonances; (c) use of a planar molecular

chain when the monomers are actually tilted; (d) neglect of interactions
between molecules in neighboring chains (some atoms are as close as
3.3 Å); or (e) the assumption that all but 10 of the interaction force
constants are zero. Some of these deficiencies can be investigated
by further calculations, and we are planning to do this. In particular,
we are working on a computer code which will treat the full unit cell,
describing nonbonded interactions in terms of conventional atom–atom
potential functions.

5. DISCUSSION

In spite of the above-noted deficiencies, the force field given
in Table II performs, on the whole, remarkably well. The target frequencies (except for ν_{26}) are each reproduced to within 10 cm^{-1}, and
the effect of isotopic substitution on the 250-cm^{-1} peak is well reproduced. (Eigenvectors describing the modes contributing to this
peak confirm that they may be approximately described as librations
about the molecular A axis, as originally surmised [1].) In addition
we have performed a two-phonon calculation using Sjölander's expression [9]
which accounts well for the peak around 515 cm^{-1} in HCOOH and HCOOD, and
confirms the assignment previously made [1].

References

[1] Berney, C.V., White, J.W., J. Am. Chem. Soc. 99 (1977) 6878.

[2] Holtzberg, F., Post, B., Fankuchen, I., Acta Cryst. 6 (1953) 127.

[3] Berney, C.V., Johnson, D.H., Yip, S., Chen, S.-H., Proceedings
     of Conference on Neutron Scattering, Gatlinburg, 6–10 June 1976,
     CONF-760601-P1 (1976) 337.

[4] Mikawa, Y., Brasch, J.W., Jakobsen, R.J., J. Mol. Spectry. 24
     (1967) 314.

[5] Tubino, R., Zerbi, G., J. Chem. Phys. 53 (1970) 1428.

[6] Schachtschneider, J.H., Vibrational Analysis of Polyatomic
     Molecules, Technical Report 231-64, Shell Development Company
     (1964).

[7] Piseri, L., Zerbi, G., J. Mol. Spectry. <u>26</u> (1968) 254.

[8] Venkataraman, G., Feldkamp, L.A., Sahni, V.C., <u>Dynamics of Perfect</u>
<u>Crystals</u> (MIT Press, Cambridge, 1975) p. 284.

[9] Sjölander, A., Arkiv för Fysik <u>14</u> (1958) 315.

DISCUSSION

H. HAHN: Perhaps you might find it worthwhile using a different model for the intramolecular and some of the intermolecular force constants. You could use an adaptation of the 'bond charge' model employed by Weber for diamond-like group IV element crystals. We also adopted this model to describe polytetrafluoroethylene (Teflon).[1] In this model the homeopolar bond is simulated by introducing a 'bond charge' as an extra, massless, particle coupled to the other bond charges and to the other atoms by springs. The springs can be calculated from interatomic potentials for couplings between atoms without direct homeopolar bonds, while they are fitted to measured Raman and infra-red data — as are the charge magnitudes — for bond charges located either between or on the directly-bound atoms.

S. YIP: We would like to see your approach. I might add that we are in the process of doing the full lattice calculation using atom-atom potentials for the unbonded interactions and Coulomb interactions between effective charges. A preliminary report was published in the Gatlinburg Conference Proceedings 1976 (CONF-760601-PL, p. 337).

G. PEPY: At what temperature were the measurements performed? I am wondering whether any frequency corrections are necessary owing to temperature effects.

S. YIP: The temperature was 77 K. Whatever anharmonic effects are present in the spectrum of normal HCOOH, we think we have taken them into account in the force constants, which lead to quite good agreement with the data.

J.-B. SUCK: Your effective frequency distribution comes into your calculation twice. Did you try to extrapolate an effective frequency distribution from your measured data?

S. YIP: We have not done so yet, but we can certainly get an idea of what the effective frequency distribution should be from the data. In our case we feel it is sufficiently straightforward to go from the calculated effective frequency spectrum to the data since we are primarily concerned with only five distinct peaks in the spectrum.

---

[1] HAHN, H., KIELBLOCK, W., to be published in Kolloid-Z. Z. Polym.

B.A. DASANNACHARYA: Multiphonon contributions to intensity are important in the kind of experiments you are trying to compare your calculations with. These must be taken into account before a detailed intensity comparison is made.

S. YIP: I quite agree with you. We will take the multiphonon contributions into account in our final comparisons. For preliminary interpretation of the spectra we do not think that our conclusions concerning the mode assignment are influenced by multiphonon effects.

C.G. WINDSOR: The beryllium filter method implies relatively high values of the scattering vector Q and, hence, multiphonon correction. For quantitative measurements of line intensities I would recommend the use of a low-Q method involving high incident energies.

IAEA-SM-219/107

INCOHERENT NEUTRON SCATTERING STUDY OF MOLECULAR MOTIONS IN LIQUID CYCLOPROPANE

M.E. BESNARD, A.J. DIANOUX
Institut Laue-Langevin,
Grenoble

J. LASCOMBE, J.C. LASSEGUES
Laboratoire de spectroscopie infra-rouge,
Université de Bordeaux I,
Bordeaux

P. LALANNE
Centre de recherches Paul Pascal,
Université de Bordeaux I,
Bordeaux,
France

Abstract

INCOHERENT NEUTRON SCATTERING STUDY OF MOLECULAR MOTIONS IN LIQUID CYCLOPROPANE.

Liquid cyclopropane has been studied by incoherent neutron scattering at four temperatures: 155, 175, 194 and 250 K. Self-diffusion coefficients have been extracted from the analysis of the quasi-elastic profile at low momentum transfer and good resolution (1 and 37 μeV). They have been checked by n.m.r. spin-echo measurements between 182 and 297 K. The excellent agreement between the two kinds of results shows that in the investigated Q-range (0.12 to 0.39 Å^{-1}) the translational diffusion satisfies the conditions of a hydrodynamic regime. At higher momentum transfer the reorientational contributions to the quasi-elastic profile have been analysed with a time-of-flight spectrometer using resolutions of 37 and 225 μeV. To limit the number of parameters to be introduced in the rotational model, we have used the complementary information of Raman spectroscopy. A polarized line of A$_1$ symmetry (ν_{cc}) and a depolarized one of E" symmetry (ν_{CH}) have been analysed and have allowed the diffusion coefficients about the two main axes of the molecule to be evaluated. These values have been introduced in a model of rotational diffusion to interpret the quasi-elastic profile up to Q values of the order of 2.35 Å^{-1}. The authors present a critical analysis of the agreement between the experimental and calculated profiles, taking into account the uncertainty in the values of the various parameters used.

1. INTRODUCTION

It is now well established that incoherent neutron scattering is a
powerful tool to investigate the dynamical behaviour of hydrogenated
molecules in the condensed state [1].

Both the wavelength and the energy of thermal neutrons have the right
order of magnitude to follow the motion of the scattering centers on a
microscopic scale.

However, if the information given by a neutron experiment is numerous, it is also mixed together in the so-called quasielastic scattering profile. This makes the separation of the various vibrational, rotational and
translational contributions generally very difficult.

It appears more and more that a correct analysis of quasielastic scattering from molecular liquid needs the use of complementary information obtained
not only by neutron experiments under different conditions of resolution and
momentum transfer, but also by other techniques such as N.M.R. relaxation and
optical spectroscopy.

Furthermore, in the present state of the theory and of the experimental
possibilities, it is necessary to choose simple systems.

For example, the reorientational motions about the main symmetry axis
are better separated for highly symmetric molecules. Also the system to be
studied needs to satisfy the hypothesis of negligible molecular interactions.

For all these reasons we have chosen cyclopropane which is a highly
incoherent scatterer and D_3h symmetric top which can be rather easily studied
in the liquid state between the melting point at 145 K and room temperature
under a pressure of 5 bars.

The aim of the present work is to conjugate the information obtained by
different techniques in order to avoid, as much as possible, introducing
unknown parameters in the analysis of the neutron scattering data.

We present here incoherent neutron scattering experiments under different conditions of resolution, Raman scattering results for the reorientational motions and N.M.R. spin-echo measurements for the translational
diffusion.

2. THEORY

2.1. Incoherent Neutron Scattering

A neutron scattering experiment on a hydrogenated molecule such as
cyclopropane C_3H_6 allows to measure directly the incoherent differential
cross-section $\frac{d^2\sigma}{d\Omega d\omega}$ which is related by Fourier transform to the intermediate scattering law $I(\vec{Q}, t)$

$$\frac{\delta^2\sigma}{d\Omega d\omega} = N\, b_{inc}^2\, \frac{k}{k_o}\, \frac{1}{2\pi} \int_{-\infty}^{+\infty} I_S(\vec{Q}, t) \cdot e^{-i\omega t}\, dt \qquad (1)$$

where N is the number of protons in the sample, b_{inc}^2 their incoherent scattering length, $\vec{Q}$ is the momentum transfer related to the incident and scattered
neutron wavevectors $\vec{k_o}$ and $\vec{k}$ according to the vectorial relation :

$$Q = \vec{k} - \vec{k_o}$$

$\omega = \frac{\hbar}{2m} (k^2 - k_o^2)$ is the energy transfer, m being the mass of the neutron.

$$I_S(\vec{Q},t) = < e^{-i\vec{Q}\cdot\vec{r}(0)} e^{i\vec{Q}\cdot\vec{r}(t)} >$$ where the brackets denote a statistical average.

The protons change their position by translational, rotational and vibrational motions. One generally assumes, as a working hypothesis, that the intermediate scattering law is the product of these three contributions i.e. that the three kinds of motions are dynamically independent.

$$I_S(\vec{Q},t) = I_{trans}(\vec{Q},t) \cdot I_{rot}(\vec{Q},t) \cdot I_{vib}(\vec{Q},t) \qquad (2).$$

For an isotropic medium, the intermediate scattering law depends only upon the modulus of $\vec{Q}$ and we will be only concerned here with quasielastic neutron scattering, in such a way that we are allowed to write

$$I_S(Q,t) = I_{trans}(Q,t) \cdot I_{rot}(Q,t) \cdot I_{vib}(Q,\infty) \qquad (3)$$

Indeed molecular vibrations occur on a time scale much shorter than the diffusive processes. In particular for cyclopropane the first vibrational level is at 93.5 meV [2]. Furthermore, the coupling between translation and rotation is expected to be small for such a highly symmetric molecule [3]. Finally the Fourier transform of equation (3) gives :

$$S_{inc}(Q,\omega) = \exp(-<u^2>Q^2) \cdot \left\{ S_{trans}(Q,\omega) \otimes S_{rot}(q,\omega) \right\} \qquad (4)$$

where the vibrational contribution reduces to a Debye-Waller factor $\exp(-<u^2>Q^2)$ where $<u^2>$ is a mean-square amplitude of vibration. This factor is nearly 1 in the case of cyclopropane which is a rigid molecule with a mean-square amplitude of the order of 10^{-2} $\overset{\circ}{A}^2$ [4] . We will not further consider the vibrational contribution since it is only a multiplicative factor which does not affect the shape of the quasi-elastic profile.

The translational contribution for a simple diffusion model is characterized by the self-diffusion coefficient D and given by

$$I_{S\ trans}(Q,t) = \exp\{-DQ^2|t|\} \qquad (5)$$

The resulting scattering law is a Lorentzian :

$$S_{inc}(Q,\omega) = \frac{1}{\pi}\ \frac{DQ^2}{\omega^2 + (DQ^2)^2} \qquad (6)$$

The rotational contribution has been treated by Sears for spherical molecules [5] and extended by Zeidler for symmetric tops [6] in the rotational diffusion hypothesis.

In this latter case, the intermediate scattering law is given by

$$I_{S\ rot.}(Q,t) = j_0^2(Qd) + \sum_{\ell=1}^{\infty} (2\ell+1)\ j_\ell^2(Qd) e^{-\ell(\ell+1)D_\perp|t|}$$

$$\cdot \sum_{m=-\ell}^{+\ell} d_{m,0}^{(\ell)}(\theta)^2 e^{-m^2(D_{//}-D_\perp)|t|} \qquad (7)$$

where $j_\ell^2(Qd)$ are the spherical Bessel functions of order ℓ , d the radius of gyration i.e. the distance of the molecular center of mass to the scattering proton and θ the angle of this vector with the molecular axis. The $d_{m,0}^{(\ell)}(\theta)$ are related to the Wigner rotation matrices. $D_\perp$ and $D_{//}$ are the rotational diffusion coefficients for the motions perpendicular to and about the molecular axis.

The above models for vibrational, translational and rotational motions yield the following total scattering law :

$$S_{inc}(Q,\omega) = (\exp - <u^2> Q^2) \cdot \left[\frac{1}{\pi} \frac{DQ^2}{\omega^2 + (DQ^2)^2} \otimes \right.$$

$$\left. \left\{ j_o^2(Qd) \ \delta(\omega) + \text{Sum of Lorentzians} \right\} \right] \tag{8}$$

A special limiting case of great importance is given by the low Q limit of the above expression; the quasielastic profile reduces then to the translational Lorentzian since $j_o^2(Qd) \simeq 1$ and $j_\ell^2(Qd) \simeq 0$.

We will take advantage of this simple behaviour in the low Q limit to determine the diffusion coefficient D from the full-width at half maximum (F.W.H.M.) dependence over Q^2 : $\Delta E = 2\hbar D Q^2$.

Once D is known, it is possible to extract the so-called elastic incoherent structure factor (E.I.S.F.) of the rotational motion [7]). It corresponds to the fraction of the total quasielastic intensity contained in the purely translational contribution and is reached through the experimentally observable quantity :

$$R(\omega) \otimes \frac{1}{\pi} \frac{DQ^2}{\omega^2 + (DQ^2)} \cdot j_o^2(Qd) \tag{9}$$

where $R(\omega)$ is the resolution function of the spectrometer.

2.2. Raman Scattering

The scattered Raman intensity is given by [8] :

$$I(\omega) = \frac{1}{2\pi} \int_{-\infty}^{+\infty} dt \ \exp(-i\omega t) < (\vec{e}_{inc} \ \overset{\leftrightarrow}{\alpha}_{(0)} \vec{e}_{diff}) \ (\vec{e}_{inc} \ \overset{\leftrightarrow}{\alpha}_{(t)} \ \vec{e}_{diff}) > \tag{10}$$

where $\vec{e}_{inc}$ and $\vec{e}_{diff}$ are unit vectors along the direction of the electric field of the incident and scattered light. $\overset{\leftrightarrow}{\alpha}_{(0)}$, $\overset{\leftrightarrow}{\alpha}_{(t)}$ are the molecular polarizability tensors at times 0 and t.

With a linear polarized incident light and using a geometry such that the scattered unit vector can be made parallel or perpendicular to the incident one, it is usual to define the two components of the scattering as :

$$I_{iso}(\omega) = I_{//}(\omega) - \frac{4}{3} I_\perp(\omega) \propto \text{F.T.} \ < \overline{\alpha}_{(0)} \cdot \overline{\alpha}_{(t)} > \tag{11}$$

$$I_{aniso}(\omega) = I_\perp(\omega) \propto \text{F.T.} < \text{Tr.} \ \vec{\vec{\beta}}_{(0)} \ \vec{\vec{\beta}}_{(t)} > \tag{12}$$

The isotropic and anisotropic profiles are respectively the Fourier transform of the average polarizability $\overline{\alpha}$ and of the anisotropy of polarizability $\vec{\vec{\beta}}$.

Under the assumption of negligible vibrational rotational interaction and induced polarizability one shows that [9]

$$G_v(t) \propto < \overline{\alpha}_{(0)} \ \overline{\alpha}_{(t)} > \tag{13}$$

$$G_v(t) \cdot G_{2R}(t) \propto < T_r \ \vec{\vec{\beta}}_{(0)} \vec{\vec{\beta}}_{(t)} > \tag{14}$$

which means that the vibrational correlation function $G_V(t)$ is directly given by the isotropic profile. It is then possible to extract the orientational correlation function $G_{2R}(t)$ from the ratio of the Fourier transforms of the anisotropic profile and the isotropic one. This method implies however that the Raman band has an isotropic profile of non zero intensity i.e. that it corresponds to a totally symmetric vibration.

In the rotational diffusion limit [10]   [11], for a D_{3h} symmetric top molecule such as cyclopropane, the orientational correlation functions are [12][13].

For a Raman line of A_1 symmetry

$$G_{2R}^{A_1}(t) = \exp \{ - 6 D_\perp |t| \} \tag{15}$$

while for a Raman line of E" symmetry

$$G_{2R}^{E''}(t) = \exp \{ - (5 D_\perp + D_{//}) |t| \} \tag{16}$$

The corresponding correlation times $\tau = \int_0^\infty G_{2R}(t)dt$ are respectively $\tau_{2R}^{A_1} = 1/6D_\perp$ and $\tau_{2R}^{E''} = 1/(5D_\perp + D_{//})$.

3. EXPERIMENTAL PART

3.1. Quasielastic Neutron Scattering

The experiments were performed with the multichopper time-of-flight spectrometer IN5 [14] and the back-scattering spectrometer IN10 [15] at the Institute Laue-Langevin of Grenoble. The following experimental conditions were used.

SPECTROMETER	INCIDENT WAVELENGTH	MOMENTUM TRANSFER RANGE	ELASTIC RESOLUTION F.W.H.M.	INVESTIGATED TEMPERATURES
IN5	$\lambda_o = 9$ Å	$0.12 < Q < 1.28$ Å^{-1}	37 μeV	155 K 194 K
	$\lambda_o = 5$ Å	$0.22 < Q < 2.35$ Å^{-1}	225 μeV	251 K
IN10	$\lambda_o = 6.275$ Å	$0.15 < Q < 1.47$ Å^{-1}	1 μeV	155 K 174 K 194 K

In both experiments the sample was contained in an aluminium cell which scattered about 4 % of the incident intensity. The thickness of the cell is designed to give about 10 % of scattering by the cyclopropane itself. In fact, the measured percentage of scattering was of the order of 20 % because of wall deformation. This high value implies multiple scattering contamination of the experimental data that we shall discuss later.

The cyclopropane (MATHESON 99.5 %) was carefully deaerated in a vacuum line by successive trappings at liquid nitrogen temperature and then condensed in the container.

The raw data obtained on both spectrometers have been treated by the standard programs of data reduction available at Grenoble [16], [17]. These

programs perform mainly the container substraction, self-shielding correction, detector efficiency correction and normalize the scattered intensity
to that of a standard vanadium plate.

3.2. Raman Scattering

The Raman experiments have been performed with a double monochromator
CODERG PHO spectrometer equipped with an ionized argon laser SPECTRA-PHYSICS.
We used the exciting line at 4880 Å and typical spectral slit widths of the
order of 1.5 cm^{-1}. The cyclopropane was contained in a cylindrical glass
tube sealed under vacuum.

The spectra are recorded on magnetic tapes using a digital system
coupled with the spectrometer. Then numerical calculations are applied to
these data for base-line calculations, polynomial filtering of the fast
noise and normalization of the isotropic and anisotropic components to unit
area.

3.3. NMR Spin Echo Measurements

They have been performed using a spectrometer built by one of us
(P.L. [18]), on the proton resonance line at 60 MHz. We have applied the
method described by Hahn [19] and used Water as a reference at 297 K [20]
and Pentane at 219 and 182 K [21]. The details are given in ref. [22].

4.   RESULTS AND DISCUSSION

4.1.   Translational Motion

4.1.1. Quasielastic neutron scattering

It has already been pointed out that the translational diffusion can
be extracted from the quasielastic profile in the low Q limit of equation
(8). We discuss further the conditions to be fulfilled for a correct analysis
of the translational component [1], [7].
i) Qd < 1 which makes $j_0^2(qd)$ the dominant term in the Bessel expansion.
For cyclopropane the mean radius of gyration is 1.7 Å [23]. This leads to Q
values less than 0.5 Å.
ii) $DQ^2 < D_{rot}$ which permits a clear separation of the translational and
rotational contributions. In the most unfavourable case corresponding to
the tumbling motion of the threefold axis of cyclopropane $D_\perp$ = 0.22 ps^{-1}
(see Table II) at 251 K; the maximum DQ^2 value is 0.092 ps^{-1} (Tables I
and II).
iii) Finally, the amount of broadening has to exceed one fifth of the
resolution in order to minimize the errors in the convolution process. Indeed,
the principle of the measurement of D is to fit the experimental corrected
data with a simple Lorentzian folded by the resolution function.

This comparison is illustrated for some typical cases in fig. 1 for the
two spectrometers IN5 and IN10 used in the high resolution conditions and
low Q range.

In view of the very small energy transfers investigated, the momentum
transfer Q is assumed to be constant and equal to Q elastic for each angle
of observation. The F.W.H.M. of the best fitted Lorentzians are plotted
versus Q_{el} as shown on fig. 2 for two temperatures. The observed linear
dependence is also true for the other temperatures of the liquid and allows
one to determine the values of D reported in Table I.

As shown on fig. 2 a very good agreement exists between the results
obtained with the two spectrometers although the time-of-flight instrument
has much lower resolution than the back-scattering one. This shows the

TABLE I. TRANSLATIONAL DIFFUSION COEFFICIENTS IN UNITS OF
10^{-5} cm$^2 \cdot$s^{-1} AND ACTIVATION ENERGY FOR LIQUID CYCLOPROPANE
MEASURED BY QUASIELASTIC NEUTRON SCATTERING AND NMR SPIN-ECHO

Temperature (K)	Q N S	N M R
155	0.78 ± 0.05	
174	1.3 ± 0.15	
181.5		1.68 ± 0.09
194	2.26 ± 0.10	
219		3.55 ± 0.18
251	5.98 ± 0.24	
297		9.2 ± 0.5
Activation energy kcal/mol		1.60 ± 0.06

TABLE II. ROTATIONAL DIFFUSION COEFFICIENTS D$_\perp$ AND D$_\parallel$ OF LIQUID CYCLO-
PROPANE DERIVED FROM RAMAN MEASUREMENTS

$$\Delta_\perp = \left(\frac{2kT}{I_\perp} \right)^{1/2} \text{ with } I_\perp = 41.82 \times 10^{-40} \text{ g} \cdot \text{cm}^2 \quad \text{and}$$

$$\Delta_\parallel = \left(\frac{kT}{I_\parallel} \right)^{1/2} \text{ with } I_\parallel = 66.69 \times 10^{-40} \text{ g} \cdot \text{cm}^2$$

T(K)	D$_\perp$ (ps^{-1})	2D$_\perp$/$\Delta_\perp$	D$_\parallel$ (ps^{-1})	D$_\parallel$/$\Delta_\parallel$
298	0.33	0.15	2.4	0.97
253	0.22	0.11	2.2	0.96
223	0.17	0.09	1.9	0.88
194	0.14	0.08	1.4	0.70
155	0.08	0.05	0.9	0.50

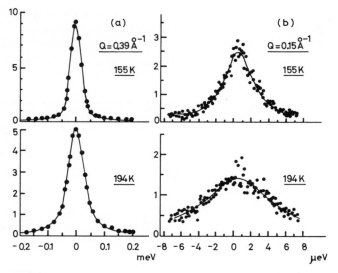

FIG.1. *Comparison of experimental (dots) and calculated (solid line) quasi-elastic profiles for liquid cyclopropane at 155 and 194 K in (a) time-of-flight and (b) back-scattering experiments.*

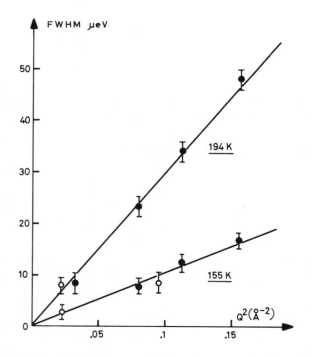

FIG.2. *FWHM of the fitted Lorentzians versus Q^2 for liquid cyclopropane at 155 and 194 K in the back-scattering ($\circ$) and time-of-flight experiment ($\bullet$).*

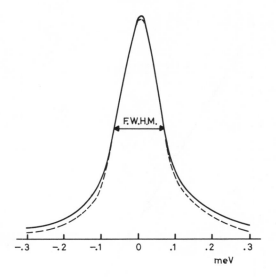

FIG.3. Comparison of the experimental quasi-elastic profile S(Q, ω) (solid line) with the profile corrected for multiple scattering (dashed line) for liquid cyclopropane at 251 K. The experiment was performed with the multichopper spectrometer IN5 at $\lambda_0 = 9$ Å and $Q_{el} = 0.39$ Å^{-1}.

reliability of the results which can be obtained with these two spectrometers in a continuous range of quasielastic broadenings from a few μeV up to more than 100 μeV.

As already pointed out , the percentage of scattering was relatively high in both cases (∿ 20 %) and an estimate of the multiple scattering contribution to the observed profiles is needed.

We have used a computer program,based on Monte-Carlo calculations [24], up to the third scattering order. Fig. 3 shows that multiple scattering induces only appreciable deviations in the wings of the quasielastic profile, but leaves the F.W.H.M. unchanged. Therefore we can conclude that our measurements of D are not affected by multiple scattering.

4.1.2. N.M.R. spin-echo measurements

A further check of the neutron results for translational diffusion is provided by N.M.R. spin-echo measurements in a field gradient which are summarized in Table I and reported on fig. 4 together with the Q.N.S. values.

In the whole temperature range one observes a very good agreement between the two sets of results. Since N.M.R. measures a truly macroscopic self-diffusion coefficient, one can say that in the Q range investigated by the neutron experiments the conditions for an hydrodynamic regime are satisfied.

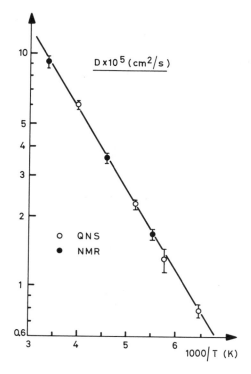

FIG.4.   QNS and NMR spin echo measurements of the self-diffusion coefficient of liquid cyclopropane as a function of reciprocal temperature.

4.2.   Rotational Diffusion Motion

4.2.1. Raman scattering

The reorientational motion of the threefold axis of cyclopropane was studied on the ν_{cc} stretching line of A_1 symmetry centered at 1188 cm^{-1} [2], [25]. The isotropic and anisotropic profiles are nearly Lorentzian. As a result the rotational correlation function derived as explained in 2.2 is found to be exponential. By using equ. (15) which corresponds to the rotational diffusion hypothesis one derives the values of $D_\perp$ reported in Table II. We have also given the values of the ratio $2D_\perp/\Delta_\perp$ where $\Delta_\perp = (2k\,T/I_\perp)^{1/2}$. One can see that in the whole temperature range $2D_\perp/\Delta_\perp$ is less than 1 as required by the rotational diffusion hypothesis [11]. The dependence of $D_\perp$ on the temperature allows to evaluate an activation energy of 1.0 ± 0.3 kcal/mol.

The reorientational motion of cyclopropane about its threefold axis was followed on the doubly degenerate ν_{CH} stretching vibration at 3080 cm^{-1}. This vibration was chosen because of its E'' symmetry but also because of the low value of the associated Coriolis constant $\xi \simeq -0.02$ [26] [27] which implies a negligible vibrational rotational interaction. Only the anisotropic profile can be studied for the ν_{CH}(E'') line. It was found to

be nearly Lorentzian giving again a nearly exponential correlation function. The correlation times were extracted at the same temperatures as
previously . In order to evaluate the rotational diffusion constant $D_{//}$
the following hypotheses were done :
i) The vibrational width of the E" line ($\Delta\nu_{1/2}$ vibr) was supposed to be
temperature independent and of the order of that of the $A_1^{'}$ line, i.e.
~ 5 cm^{-1}.
ii) Equation (16) corresponding to the rotational diffusion limit was used.
iii) The profiles are supposed Lorentzian to allow the following relation
to be applied :

$$\Delta\nu_{1/2}^{(E")} = \Delta\nu_{1/2} \text{ vibr} + \frac{5D_\perp + D_{//}}{\pi c}$$

where c is the velocity of the light.

Under these conditions, we have evaluated the values of $D_{//}$ given in
Table II. One can see that the ratio $D_{//}/D_\perp$ is of the order of 10, indicating that the reorientation about the molecular axis is much faster than
the reorientation of the axis itself.

However, it must be pointed out that the large number of hypotheses
needed for the evaluation of $D_{//}$ make its values rather uncertain. They can
only be considered as an order of magnitude . In particular, the values of
$D_{//}/\Delta_{//}$, where $\Delta_{//} = (kT/I_{//})^{1/2}$, are of the order of 0.9, i.e. no longer small
compared to 1. This implies that the rotational diffusion model may not
be very correct to describe this kind of motion.

4.2.2. Quasielastic neutron scattering

In principle the previous measurements provide all the necessary
information to analyze both the translational and rotational contributions
to the quasielastic profile.
However, the fact that we have now to analyze larger momentum and
energy transfers raises the following questions :
i) Is the translational process always describable by a simple diffusion
model in the investigated Q-range ?
ii) What is the consequence of the imprecision in the measurement of $D_{//}$
by Raman scattering ?
iii) Is the multiple scattering contamination always negligible at higher
ω and Q values ?
The two first questions have always been treated in the literature
[28], [29] by introducing more sophisticated models including in particular
residence times i.e. short time behaviour in the translational and rotational
motions. But the number of parameters becomes then important enough to ensure
a successful fit of the model to the experimental data. We prefer to analyze
our data following another direction : we start from the simplest hypothesis
i.e. applicability of Fick's law and of the $D_\perp$ and $D_{\parallel}$ determined
by Raman and neglect of multiple scattering and we compare the corresponding
calculated profiles convoluted by the resolution with the experimental data.
Only a flat background and an amplitude factor are fitted in this comparison.
The value of θ in equ. (7) is 57 degrees and we have limited the Bessel
expansion to $\ell = 5$. Some typical results obtained at 194 K in a Q range up
to 1.95 Å^{-1} are plotted in fig. 5. The background is also indicated.
The agreement between the calculated and experimental data is surprisingly good even at the higher Q values. It is also observed for all the
temperatures investigated.

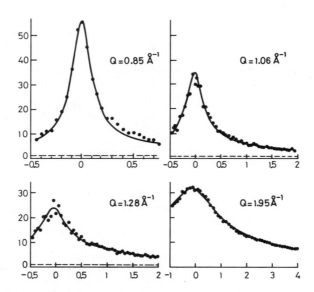

FIG.5.   Comparison of experimental (dots) quasi-elastic profiles for liquid cyclopropane at 194 K obtained in the time-of-flight experiments at $\lambda_0 = 9$ Å $(Q = 0.85$ Å^{-1} to $Q = 1.28$ Å$^{-1})$ and $\lambda_0 = 5$ Å with the calculated (solid line) profile using the translational diffusion coefficients given by NQS and NMR and the rotational coefficients derived from Raman measurements. The flat background is indicated by a dashed line.   The intensities are given in arbitrary units. Note that the ω scale (in meV) is different for each spectrum.

One can try to analyze the meaning of this agreement.
i) In view of the relatively high value of the self-diffusion coefficient of cyclopropane it is perhaps not surprising that the simple diffusion model holds up to rather large Q values. This seems to be true for other small organic molecules [30].
ii) We have seen that the $D_{//}$ values used could be rather imprecise. We have checked the influence of this parameter on the calculated profile by allowing the ratio $D_{//}/D_{\perp}$ to vary between 6 and 12, keeping $D_{\perp}$ the same as previously.
Fig. 6 shows that the agreement between the experimental and calculated values remains very good. This proves that the rotational components involving $D_{//}$ do not contribute significantly to the profile which is therefore mainly determined in the considered Q range by the translational diffusion and the slower rotational component.
iii) In view of the above agreement one is also led to conclude that the multiple scattering contribution is again negligible in the investigated Q and ω ranges.
A further information on a bound motion like the rotational process is contained in the EISF, i.e. on the long time limit of equation (7). In all the previous analyses this important aspect was implicit but we can try to evaluate it more specifically by using the known value of the diffusion coefficients and the method given in reference [7].
The results are reported on fig. 7 and show that the experimental data fit reasonably well the $j_0^2(Qd)$ function.

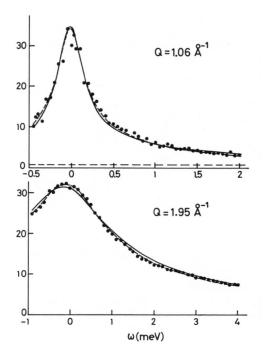

FIG.6. Influence on the quasi-elastic profile of the motion around the threefold axis of liquid cyclopropane at 194 K. The dots are experimental points. The dashed and solid lines represent the calculated profiles assuming a ratio of the diffusion coefficients $D_\parallel/D_\perp$ of 6 and 12, respectively. For clarity of presentation we include only two representative spectra from Fig. 5 covering a large Q range of the measurements. The intensities are given in arbitrary units.

This agreement was expected and in some way does not bring any new information. However it proves that the quasielastic profile can be reliably analyzed within the frame of the hypothesis given above, in particular that of negligible rotation-translation coupling. Furthermore it gives a self-consistent picture of the rotational motion in liquid cyclopropane.

CONCLUSION

It has been clearly shown that quasielastic neutron scattering from a hydrogenated molecule such as cyclopropane, gives at low Q values the same self-diffusion coefficient as the one measured by N.M.R., provided that a good enough resolution is used.

We have tried to take into account the rotational contribution at higher Q values by introducing the diffusion constants $D_\perp$ and $D_{//}$ determined by Raman scattering and assuming that the simple diffusion model for translation holds up to Q values of 2 Å^{-1}.

It happens that without introducing any other parameter one can correctly describe the experimental profiles even if the fit is not very sensitive to the $D_{//}$ value, i.e. to the faster rotational motion around the threefold axis. A correct evaluation of the elastic incoherent structure factor for the rotational motion adds weight to the previous analysis.

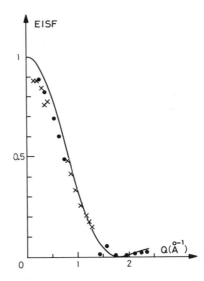

FIG.7.   Experimental EISF for liquid cyclopropane at 155 K.   The crosses and dots are obtained from the spectra at $\lambda_0 = 9$ Å and $\lambda_0 = 5$ Å.   The full line is the function $j_0^2(Qd)$.   The systematic deviation at low Q is explained by the contribution of multiple scattering to the spectra and is also inherent in the method used to extract the EISF.

One could conclude that the quasielastic neutron scattering experiments do not bring much more information than the N.M.R. and Raman experiments. We think, however, that it was necessary to prove the consistency of the three techniques in the study of molecular dynamics at long times, before looking at the more specific information contained in the inelastic part of the neutron scattering spectra. Work is in progress to take advantage of the unique capability of the neutron techniques to look at the short time behaviour in a large Q range.

Although the observed frequency distribution function is certainly rather strongly contaminated by multiple scattering, it appears to be a very severe test for all the existing dynamical models.

REFERENCES

[1] SPRINGER T., "Springer Tracts in Modern Physics" Vol. 64 Ed. G. HOHLER (Springer-Verlag, Berlin, Heidelberg, N.Y.) 1972.

[2] BESNARD M., Thesis 3e cycle, Bordeaux I (1974).

[3] YIP S., "Spectroscopy in biology and chemistry" Ed. CHEN S.H., YIP S., Academic Press, New York and London (1974) 91.

[4] CYVIN S.J., HAGEN G., Z. Naturforsch. <u>25b</u> (1970) 350.

[5]   SEARS V.F., Can. J. Phys. 45 (1967) 237.

[6]   ZEIDLER M.D., Ber. Bunsenges. physik. chem. 75 (1971) 769.

[7]   VOLINO F., DIANOUX A.J., Proceedings Euchem Conference, Schloss Elmau
       FRG (April 1976).

[8]   GORDON R.G., Advances in Magnetic Resonance 3 (1968) 1.

[9]   BRATOS S., MARECHAL E., Phys. Rev. A4 (1971) 1078.

[10]   KUBO R., J. Phys. Soc. Japan 17 (1962) 1100.

[11]   KUBO R., "Fluctuation, relaxation and resonance in magnetic systems",
       Ed. Ter Haar, Oliver and Boyd, Edinburgh (1962) 24.

[12]   BARTOLI F.J., LITOVITZ T.A., J. Chem. Phys. 56 (1972) 413.

[13]   LEICKNAM J.C., GUISSANI Y., "Molecular motions in liquids", Ed. J.
       LASCOMBE, D. REIDEL Publishing Company, Dordrecht-Holland (1974) 257.

[14]   LECHNER R.E., DOUCHIN F., "IN5 Multichopper user's manual" Internal
       Report 74L201T ILL, Grenoble (1974).

[15]   HEIDEMANN A., "User's Guide to the backscattering spectrometer IN10"
       Internal Report 74H230T, ILL, Grenoble.(1974).

[16]   DIANOUX A.J., GHOSH R.E., HERVET H., LECHNER R.E., "IN5 program package
       for experimental preparation and data reduction: user's guide" Internal
       Report 75D16T, ILL Grenoble (1975).

[17]   HOWELLS W.S., "User's guide to data processing of IN10 data" Internal
       Report 75H130T, ILL, Grenoble (1975).

[18]   LALANNE P., Thesis 3e cycle, Bordeaux I (1970).

[19]   HAHN E.L., Phys. Rev. 80 (1950) 580.

[20]   MILLS R., "Molecular motions in liquids" Ed. J. LASCOMBE, D. REIDEL
       Publishing Company, Dordrecht-Holland (1974) 391.

[21]   MAC-CALL D.W., DOUGLASS D.C., ANDERSON E.W., Phys. Fluids 2 (1959) 87.

[22]   BESNARD M., DIANOUX A.J., LALANNE P., LASSEGUES J.C., J. Phys. 38
       (1977) 1000.

[23]   BASTIANSEN O., FRITSCH F.N., HEDBERG K., Acta. Cryst. 17 (1964) 538.

[24]   JOHNSON M.W., "DISCUSS: a computer program for the calculation of
       multiple scattering effects in inelastic neutron scattering experiments"
       Internal Report 5782 Harwell AERE R7682 (1974).

[25]   PERROT M., LASCOMBE J., Proceedings Euchem Conference, Schloss Elmau,
       FRG (April 1976).

[26]   DUNCAN J.L., BURNS G.R., J. Mol. Spectry. 30 (1969) 253.

[27]   BUTCHER R.J., JONES W.J., J. Mol. Spectry. 47 (1973) 64.

[28] SINGWI K.S., SJÖLANDER A., Phys. Rev. 119 (1960) 863.

[29] LARSSON K.E., J. Chem. Phys. 59 (1973) 4612.

[30] ZEIDLER M.D., "Molecular motions in liquids", Ed. J. LASCOMBE, D. REIDEL Publishing Company, Dordrecht-Holland (1974) 421.

DISCUSSION

J. YARWOOD: Can you comment briefly on the method you use to extract the reorientation contribution $G_{2R}^E(t)$ for a depolarized E-band in the Raman spectrum?

M.E. BESNARD: The depolarized E-symmetry bands do not have an isotropic profile, so the correlation function $G_{2R}^E(t)$ cannot be rigorously extracted. Nevertheless, an orientational correlation time τ_{2R} can be obtained in the following manner: (i) The width of the vibrational profile of the E-band is assumed to be close to that of the A_1-band and to be independent of temperature; (ii) The process is assumed to be diffusional; (iii) The correlation time τ_{2R} is then calculated by means of the relation $\dfrac{1}{\tau_{2R}} = \dfrac{1}{\tau_{\text{anisotropic}}} - \dfrac{1}{\tau_{\text{vibrational}}}$, which is applicable only if the vibrational and orientational profiles are Lorentzians. Fuller details are given in the paper we have cited as Ref. [25].

W. PRESS (Chairman): How justifable is the assumption that translational and rotational motions are decoupled? Are the cyclopropane molecules very globular?

M.E. BESNARD: The hypothesis of decoupling between the translational and rotational motions is customary and permits one to write that the incoherent scattering law is given by the convolution product of the translational contribution and the rotational contribution. Although, as far as we know, there is no theoretical justification for this hypothesis, one assumes, qualitatively, that for globular molecules the hypothesis is reasonable. In particular, it seems to be acceptable for cyclopropane which, although not really globular, has a high degree of symmetry (D_3h). Additional details can be found in Ref. [3].

NEUTRON QUASI-ELASTIC SCATTERING STUDIES ON THE ROTATIONAL MOTIONS IN LIQUID ACETONITRILE

P.G. WOODCOCK, T.C. WADDINGTON, J. YARWOOD
Department of Chemistry,
University of Durham,
Durham City,
United Kingdom

Abstract

NEUTRON QUASI-ELASTIC SCATTERING STUDIES ON THE ROTATIONAL MOTIONS IN LIQUID ACETONITRILE.

Quasi-elastic neutron spectra of acetonitrile (in the liquid phase and in dilute solution) have been compared with the results of computer simulations for a symmetric top molecule with translational and reorientational diffusion coefficients obtained by infra-red, Raman and n.m.r. techniques. The agreement between observed spectra and those calculated using the simple diffusion or rotational diffusion models (including rotational terms up to $\ell = 5$) is generally good for the liquid phase. For solutions in carbon tetrachloride the decrease in quasi-elastic broadening due to a lowering of the translational and reorientational freedom is also qualitatively explained.

1. Introduction

In general, the incoherent quasi-elastic scattering spectrum from a molecular liquid [1-5] reflects all diffusional, reorientational and vibrational motions of the protons present. However, in the absence of low frequency vibrations the spectrum is, to a good approximation, controlled by the translational and rotational motions. In principle, the two contributions can be separated experimentally if (i) the translational (D_{tr}) and rotational (D_{rot}) diffusion coefficients are sufficiently different from one another. (The criterion [1] is that $2d^2 D_{rot} > D_{tr}$ where d is the distance between the scattering proton and the centre of rotation). (ii) that studies are performed [3] at low momentum transfer, Q, (iii) that the instrument resolution is sufficiently high. If all three conditions are satisfied the spectrum consists of a central 'elastic' peak broadened only by relatively slow diffusive motions with a rotationally broadened spectrum extending from zero energy transfer into the inelastic region. (figure 1 of reference 1). In practice, for simple molecular liquids, even at high resolution and low Q, the spectra appear (as in figure 1) without separation into translational and reorientational parts since condition (i) is not satisfied. The only viable method of analysis of such spectra at the present time is via model calculations involving either spectral fitting or spectral synthesis using a digital computer. A viable model is required to do this, of course, and interpretation is not easy. Indeed, this approach has only been tried for a small number of molecules [3,5,6-9]. Nevertheless, we believe that important information can be obtained (for well chosen molecules) about the molecular dynamics and their variation with temperature and surrounding

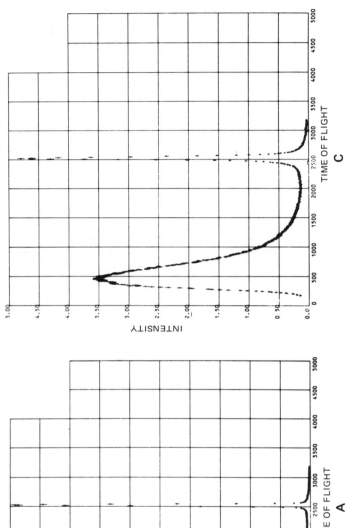

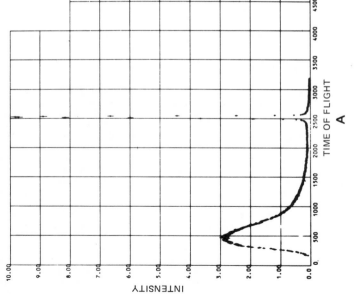

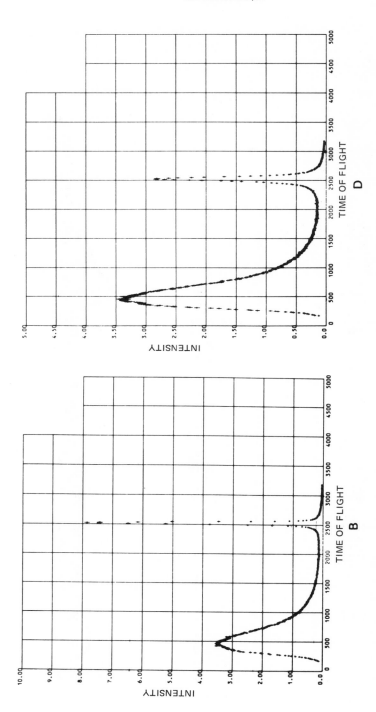

FIG.1A.   Observed time-of-flight spectra of acetonitrile liquid at 271 K (IN5).   The scattering angles are: A 8°; B 16°; C 24°; D 32°.

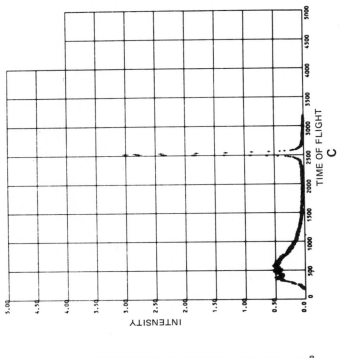

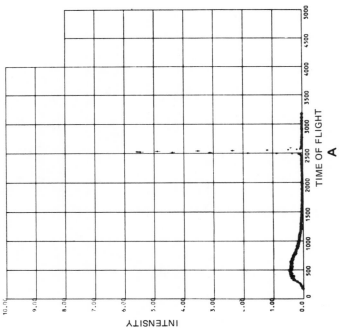

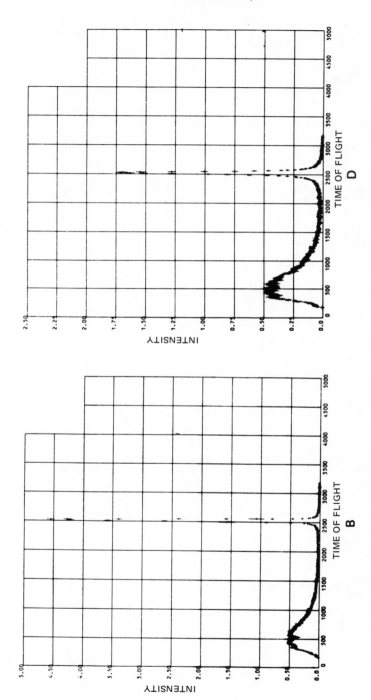

FIG.1B. Observed time-of-flight spectra of acetonitrile in carbon tetrachloride at 271 K (IN5) (concentration is 0.3 molar fraction). The scattering angles are identical with those in Fig. 1A.

environment. In particular it is possible to test the various models [4-9] of molecular reorientation which are available making use of dynamic information obtained [1,6,7,10,11] from infrared, Raman and n.m.r. spectroscopy. The present work represents an effort to discover how successfully one can reproduce the quasi-elastic and near inelastic part of the cold neutron spectrum of a symmetric top molecule (CH_3CN in the liquid and dilute solution in carbon tetrachloride) using the Sears [12] method of partial wave expansion along with a rotational diffusion model or reorientational correlation functions obtained directly from other spectroscopic techniques (the translational part being approximated by a single Lorentzian - see section 2).

2. Theoretical

In the absence of strong statistical correlation between reorientational and translational motion the incoherent scattering cross section is a simple convolution of the two individual cross sections. Thus,

$$\frac{d^2\sigma_{inc}}{d\Omega d\epsilon} = \frac{b_{inc}^2}{\hbar} \frac{k}{k_o} \exp(-\hbar\omega/2k_BT) S_{inc}(Q,\omega) \tag{1}$$

$$\text{where } S_{inc}(Q,\omega) = \int_{-\infty}^{+\infty} S_{tr}(Q,\omega) \cdot S_{rot}(Q,\omega) d\omega \tag{2}$$

(the symbols have their usual meanings).

It is usual [1-9] to assume that translational motion proceeds by simple diffusion. The scattering function $S_{tr}(Q,\omega)$ is then given by

$$S_{tr}(Q,\omega) = \frac{1}{\pi} \frac{D_{tr}Q^2}{(D_{tr}Q^2)^2 + \omega^2} \exp(-\hbar\omega/2k_BT) \tag{3}$$

where D_{tr} is the translational diffusion coefficient obtained either from n.m.r. measurements [6] or using a back scattering neutron spectrometer [3]. It then remains to calculate the scattering function $S_{rot}(Q,\omega)$. For a spherical top (isotropically scattering) molecule Sears [12] has shown that,

$$S_{rot}(Q,\omega) = \sum_{\ell=0}^{\infty} (2\ell + 1) j_\ell^2(Qd) S_\ell(\omega) \tag{4}$$

or in terms of the intermediate scattering function $I(Q,t)$

$$I_{rot}(Q,t) = \sum_{\ell=0}^{\infty} (2\ell + 1) j_\ell^2(Qd) f_\ell(t) \tag{5}$$

where $f_\ell(t)$ are reorientational time correlation functions, the first two of which may be obtained from other techniques (from the infrared for $\ell=1$ and from Raman or n.m.r. for $\ell=2$). These functions are given by,

$$f_\ell(t) = \int\limits_{-\infty}^{+\infty} S_\ell(\omega)\exp(i\omega t)dt \tag{6a}$$

$$\equiv <P_\ell[\text{Cos}\,\theta(t)]> \tag{6b}$$

where θ is the angle of rotation and P_ℓ the ℓth order Legendre polynomial. If reorientational motion is also assumed to be by rotational diffusion then, in the classical limit,

$$f_\ell(t) = \exp\{-\ell(\ell + 1)D_{rot}t\} \tag{7}$$

and the $S_\ell(\omega)$ of equations (4) and (6) may be shown [12] to be,

$$S_\ell(\omega) = \frac{1}{2\pi}\,\exp(-\hbar\omega/2k_BT)\int\limits_{-\infty}^{+\infty}f_\ell(t)\exp(-i\omega t)dt \tag{8a}$$

$$\text{or } S_\ell(\omega) = \frac{1}{2\pi}\,\exp(-\frac{\hbar\omega}{2k_{BT}})\int\limits_{-\infty}^{+\infty}\exp\{-\ell(\ell + 1)D_{rot}t\}\exp(-i\omega t)dt \tag{8b}$$

$$= \frac{1}{\pi}\,\exp(-\frac{\hbar\omega}{2k_BT})\frac{\ell(\ell + 1)D_{rot}}{(\ell[\ell + 1]D_{rot})^2 + \omega^2} \tag{8c}$$

where D_{rot} is a simple rotational diffusion coefficient. The D_{rot} of equations (7) and (8) is, of course, unique for a spherical top molecule but for a symmetric top molecule (with two non-equivalent 'modes' of rotation) two rotational diffusion coefficients are necessary in order to specify the motion. Equation (7) must then be replaced [13] by,

$$f_\ell(t) = \sum_{m=-\ell}^{+\ell} f_\ell^m(t)\,|D_{m,o}^\ell\,(\eta,\xi)|^2 \tag{9}$$

where $D_{m,o}^\ell$ are Wigner rotation matrices which include the polar (η) and azimuthal (ξ) angles of the scattering atom. For the symmetric top case equation (9) can be shown [13] to give,

$$f_\ell^m(t) = \exp\{-(\ell(\ell + 1)D_\perp + [D_{||} - D_\perp]m^2)t\} \tag{10}$$

where $D_\perp$ and $D_{||}$ are the rotational diffusion coefficients of the symmetry axis and about the symmetry axis, respectively. (Notice that (10) reduces to (7) if $D_{||} = D_\perp \equiv D_{rot}$ as in the spherical top case). The use of $f_\ell(t)$ from equation (9) is straight-forward provided that the necessary diffusion coefficients are known. Infrared and Raman or n.m.r. spectra usually give correlation times τ_{1R} (infrared) and τ_{2R} (Raman), $\tau_{2\theta}$ (n.m.r.). The calculation of a macroscopic diffusion coefficient again requires the use of a model. For small step rotational diffusion it may be shown [11] that,

$$D_{rot} = \frac{1}{6\tau_{2R}} \tag{11a}$$

$$\text{or} \quad D_{rot} = \frac{1}{2\tau_{1R}} \tag{11b}$$

(although it should be remembered that the rotation of a symmetric top molecule about its own symmetry axis may be non-diffusional [10] especially at short times). Correlation times and diffusion coefficients for acetonitrile are summarised in table 1. For values of $\ell > 2$ one must resort to the use of equation 8(b) with a single D_{rot}. The computed spectrum (without correction for the effects of instrument resolution) is then given by,

$$\frac{d^2\sigma_{inc}}{d\Omega d\varepsilon} = \frac{b^2}{\hbar} \frac{k}{k_o} \{S_T^{inc}(Q,\omega)\}$$

$$= \frac{b^2}{\hbar} \frac{k}{k_o}\{S_{tr}(Q,\omega)j_o^2(Qd) + 3j_1^2(Qd)\int_{-\infty}^{+\infty}S_{tr}(Q,\omega-\omega')\exp(\frac{-\hbar\omega'}{2k_BT})S_1(\omega')d\omega'$$

$$+ 5j_2^2(Qd)\int_{-\infty}^{+\infty}S_{tr}(Q,\omega-\omega')\exp(\frac{-\hbar\omega'}{2k_BT})S_2(\omega')d\omega'$$

$$+ \sum_{\ell=3}^{\ell=\infty}(2\ell + 1)j_\ell^2(Qd)\int_{-\infty}^{+\infty}S_{tr}(Q,\omega-\omega')\exp(\frac{-\hbar\omega'}{2k_BT})\frac{\ell(\ell + 1)D_r}{[\ell(\ell + 1)D_r]^2 + \omega'^2}d\omega'\} \tag{12}$$

where $S_1(\omega')$ and $S_2(\omega')$ are obtained via equation 8(a) employing equations (9) and (10) in order to determine $f_\ell^m(t)$.

3.   Experimental

The experimental neutron spectra (fig.1) were obtained for a 10% scatterer on the 4H5 (Harwell) and IN5 (Grenoble) time-of-flight spectrometers at instrument resolutions of 100μeV (4H5) and 30μeV (IN5) over a range of momentum transfers between $Q^2 = 0.1$ and 1.0Å^{-2}. Counting times varied between 12 and 36 hours depending on rotor speed and initial neutron wavelength. Solutions in carbon tetrachloride were made up by volume and used immediately after preparation.

4.   Program Design

The program employed for spectral synthesis using equation (12) was based on that used by Brier and Higgins (a copy was kindly provided by Dr. P.N. Brier) but has been modified and developed to do calculations for a symmetric top molecule and to output the calculated spectrum at various points in the computation in order to examine the result for each of the terms in equation (12). This enables a check to be made on the importance of each of the ℓ components of the Sears expansion over a given range of

Table I. Summary of translational and reorientational correlation times and diffusion coefficients for acetonitrile

	$\tau_{2R}(\perp)$/ps (T/K)	$\tau_{2R}(\parallel)$/ps (T/K)	$\tau_{1R}(\perp)$/ps (T/K)	$D_{rot}(\perp)$/ $(ps)^{-1}$	$D_{rot}(\parallel)$ $(ps)^{-1}$	$10^{-5}D_{trans}$/ $cm^2 \cdot s^{-1}$	Ref
LIQUID	1.0 - 1.2 (298)	0.1 - 0.14 (298)	3.3^{b} (298)	0.15 0.16 - 0.14	1.7 - 1.2		16 10a
	2.2 ± 0.2 (252)			0.076		2.3 (254) 3.2 (273) 4.7 (298)	6b 6b 15 6b
	1.6 ± 0.2 (288)			0.10		6.5 (323) 8.8 (348)	6b 15 6b
	0.7 ± 0.1 (343)			0.23			15
SOLUTION IN CCl_4[a] (288K)	2.9(0.21)	~0.3^{c}	-	0.058	0.55	0.82^{d}(0.20)	18 17
	2.6(0.40)	-		0.064		0.67^{d}(0.35)	18 17
	2.3(0.62)	-		0.072		0.93^{d}(0.50)	18 17
	1.7(0.81)	-		0.098		1.15^{d}(0.65) 1.63^{d}(0.80)	18 17 18

a. Values in parentheses give concentration in mole fraction of CH_3CN.

b. Value uncorrected for the effects of vibrational relaxation.

c. Assumed to be $\tau(\perp)/10$.

d. Values are mutual diffusion coefficients obtained from Raleigh scattering data [18].

energy transfer. The cross section computed from equation (12) was convolved with the vanadium instrument profile and subjected to a multiple scattering correction (using the program [14] 'DISCUS') before comparison with the experimental spectra.

5. Results and Discussion

Initially our calculations were carried out with a value of D_{tr} fixed at the value obtained by Zeidler [6] using n.m.r. spectroscopy (table I) and the effect of adding terms to the Sears expansion (equation 4) was investigated. It was found that at relatively low scattering angles and for small energy transfers the contribution of the $\ell = 1$ and $\ell = 2$ terms totally dominated in the reorientational part of the spectrum and that addition of further terms up

WOODCOCK et al.

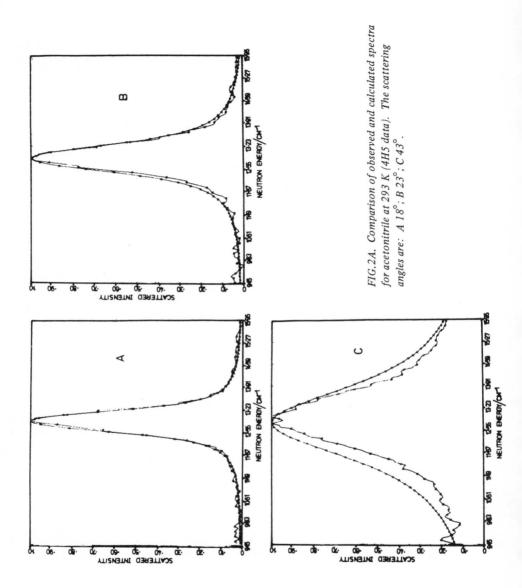

FIG.2A. Comparison of observed and calculated spectra
for acetonitrile at 293 K (4H5 data). The scattering
angles are: A 18°; B 23°; C 43°.

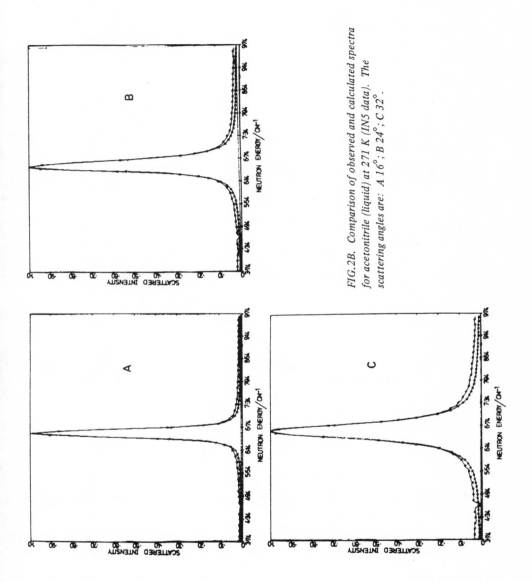

FIG.2B. Comparison of observed and calculated spectra for acetonitrile (liquid) at 271 K (IN5 data). The scattering angles are: A 16°; B 24°; C 32°.

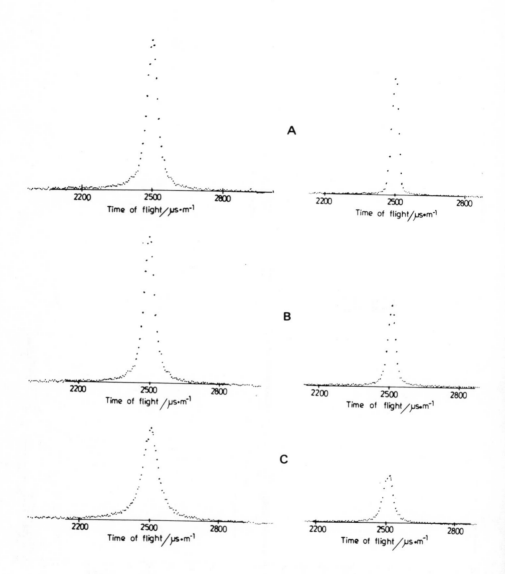

FIG. 3. Comparison of observed quasi-elastic broadening of spectra from CH_3CN and CH_3CN in CCl_4 (0.3 molar fraction) at 271 K (IN5 data). The scattering angles are A $8°$; B $16°$; C $32°$.

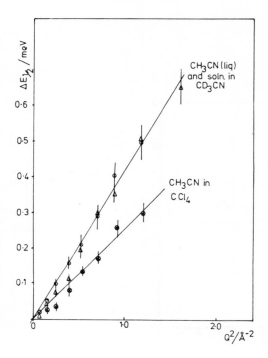

FIG.4. Comparison of quasi-elastic peak width versus Q^2 plots for CH_3CN and CH_3CN in CCl_4 at 293 K (4H5 data).

to ℓ = 5 contributed <1% to the scattering cross section. This is encouraging since the D_r values for ℓ = 1 and ℓ = 2 are, in principle, measurable, and since computations on other simple polyatomic molecules [7,8,12] also show that, at least at small scattering angles, one expects [12] the contribution from terms in ℓ > 2 to be small. We subsequently allowed D_{tr} to vary within reasonable limits and found that the best fits we could obtain to the observed Q.E profiles at the lowest angle for the liquid were:

293K D_{tr} = 4.80 x 10^{-5} cm$^2 \cdot$ s^{-1}

271K D_{tr} = 3.25 x 10^{-5} cm$^2 \cdot$ s^{-1}

(The quality of the fit is demonstrated by figures 2A and 2B at angles 16° and 18°, respectively). At these small values of Q^2 the reorientational contribution is negligible for small energy transfers and the computed spectrum is almost totally insensitive to the D_{rot} values used. Finally, we have adjusted the reorientational diffusion coefficients until a reasonable fit is achieved at angles up to 43° (on 4H5) (corresponding to Q $\cong$ 0.6Å^{-1}) (see figures 2A and 2B). Since reorientation about the symmetry axis (as measured by $D_{rot}(\parallel)$) is so fast

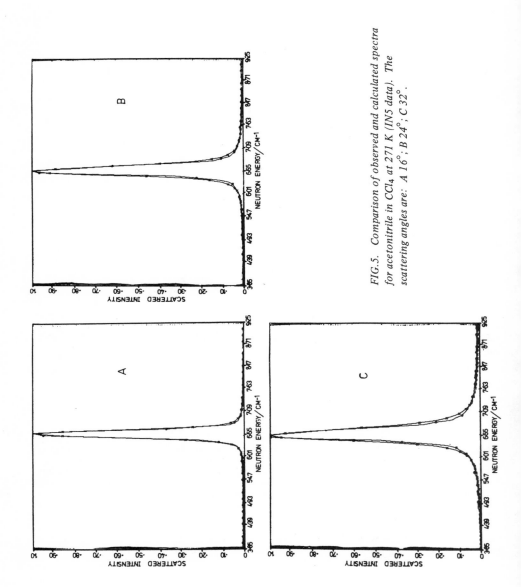

FIG.5. Comparison of observed and calculated spectra for acetonitrile in CCl_4 at 271 K (IN5 data). The scattering angles are: A 16°; B 24°; C 32°.

the contribution due to this motion at relatively small energy transfers
is very small. It is therefore impossible to use this diffusion coefficient
as a parameter and we have fixed the value at that given in table I (at the
appropriate temperature). Variation of $D_{rot}(\perp)$ in equation 10 does, of course,
affect the computed quasi-elastic spectrum and the best fit (figure 2) we have
achieved is obtained with

$$293K \qquad D_{rot}(\perp) = 1.0 \times 10^{12} \text{ s}^{-1}$$

$$271K \qquad D_{rot}(\perp) = 0.6 \times 10^{12} \text{ s}^{-1}$$

It is clear that these values are considerably faster (by a factor of about 5)
than those tabulated in figure 5. Indeed, it appears that the situation is
such that one can adequately reproduce the observed spectrum with a <u>single</u> D_{rot}
value of about that obtained from the n.m.r. spectra for $D_{rot}(\parallel)$. This would
mean that the $D_{rot}(\perp)$ values obtained from Infrared Raman spectroscopy are too
slow to affect the quasi-elastic neutron spectra at low Q values. The $D_{rot}(\parallel)$
value leads, of course, to a very much broader rotational (Lorentzian)
contribution which affects the computed spectrum in the 'wings'. There is no
positive evidence that the rotational diffusion model is invalid [19] but some
evidence from the required D_{tr} values that neutron and n.m.r. data do not
represent the same measure of 'translational' diffusion. However, the resolution
achieved with IN5 was probably insufficient to obtain a good measure of D_{tr}.

When acetonitrile is dissolved in CCl_4 the viscosity increases sharply
[17] and the translational [18] and rotational diffusion coefficients decrease
rapidly (table I) with increasing CCl_4 concentration (the solution is extremely
non-ideal [18] and the mutual diffusion coefficients reach a minimum value at
intermediate concentrations). This loss of freedom of the molecules causes a
considerable decrease in the Q.E. broadening observed (figure 3) and in the
'apparent' diffusion coefficient obtained from Q.E. half-width analyses
(figure 4). We have followed the same fitting procedures as for the pure
liquid and the resulting best fit parameters are,

$$271K \qquad D_{tr} = 1.6 \times 10^{-5} \text{cm}^2 \cdot \text{s}^{-1} \qquad D_{rot}(\perp) = 0.2 \times 10^{12} \text{ s}^{-1}$$

As may be seen from figure 5 the fit using these parameters is not perfect
but it is clear that the decrease in Q.E. broadening seen from figure 4 is
qualitatively explained in terms of decreasing translational and rotational
freedom in the mixture.

References

[1]   T. Springer, Molecular Motions in Liquids (Ed. J. Lascombe)
       D. Reidel Pub. Co., Dordrecht, 1973, pp.411-417.

[2]   T. Springer, Springer Tracts in Modern Physics, Vol.64 (Springer-
       Verlag 1972).

[3]   F. Volino and A.J. Dianoux, Proceedings of the EUCHEM Conference on
       'Structure and Dynamics of Organic Liquids, Mittenwald, 1976.

[4]   J.G. Powles, 'Atomic and Molecular Motions in Liquids', Chapter 6 of
       Chemical Applications of Thermal Neutron Scattering (Ed. B.T.M. Willis)
       (Oxford University Press, 1973).

[5]   K.E. Larsson, (a) Faraday Symposium of the Chemical Society No.6
       (1972) 122; (b) J. Chem. Phys., 59 (1973) 4612; (c) Ber. Bunsenges.
       Physik. Chem., 75 (1971) 352; (d) Phys. Rev., A3 (1971) 1006.

[6]   (a) M.D. Zeidler, Molecular Motions in Liquids (Ed. J. Lascombe), Reidel Pub. Co., Dordrecht, 1974, p.421; (b) M.D. Zeidler, Ber. Bunsenges. Physik. Chem., 75 (1971) 769.

[7]   P.N. Brier and J.S. Higgins, Neutron Inelastic Scattering. (I.A.E.A., Vienna, 1972), p.461; Mol. Phys., 21 (1972) 721.

[8]   (a) B.A. Dasannacharya, C.L. Thaper and P.S. Goyal, Neutron Inelastic Scattering. (I.A.E.A. Vienna 1972), p.477.

[9]   A summary of recent work is given by G. Allen and J.S. Higgins, Rep. Prog. Phys., 36, 1073 (1973).

[10]   (a) J.E. Griffiths, 'Vibrational Spectra and Structure', Vol.6 (Ed. J. Durig), Elsevier, Amsterdam 1977; (b) R.T. Bailey 'Molecular Spectroscopy', Vol.2 (Ed. Barrow, Long and Millen) The Chemical Society, London 1974; (c) J. Yarwood and R. Arndt, Molecular Association, Volume 2 (Ed. R. Foster) (Wiley-Interscience 1978) Chapter OO.

[11]   (a) R.G. Gordon, J. Chem. Phys., 44 (1966) 1830; (b) P.S. Hubbard, Phys. Rev., 131 (1963) 1155; (c) R.E.D. McClung, J. Chem. Phys., 51 (1969) 3842; 57 (1972) 5478.

[12]   V.F. Sears, Can. J. Phys., 44 (1966) 1279, 1299; Can J. Phys., 45 (1967) 237.

[13]   B.J. Berne, Physical Chemistry An Advanced Treatise, Vol.8B, (Ed. H. Eyring, D. Henderson and W. Jost) (Academic Press, New York, 1971) p.539-713 and references therein.

[14]   M.W. Johnson, Report No. AERE-R7682, March 1974.

[15]   J. Yarwood, G. Döge and R. Arndt, Chem. Phys., (in press).

[16]   (a) W.G. Rothschild, J. Chem. Phys., 57 (1972) 991; C. Breuillard-Alliot and J. Saussen-Jacob, Mol. Phys., 28 (1974) 905.

[17]   C.H. Wang and S.L. Whittenberg, J. Chem. Phys., 66 (1977) 4255.

[18]   K.J. Czwormak, H.C. Anderson and R. Pecora, Chem. Phys., 11 (1975) 451.

[19]   T.E. Bull, J. Chem. Phys., 62 (1975) 222.

DISCUSSION

H. POSCH: The assumption of a small-angle rotational diffusion model for the tumbling motion is probably good. But how meaningful is such an assumption for the spinning motion?

J. YARWOOD: It is true that for spinning motion of acetonitrile (represented by $D_{rot}(\|)$) the assumption of rotational diffusion tends to break down because the rate of reorientational motion is ten times greater than that represented by $D_{rot}(\perp)$ (the 'tumbling' motion). As I pointed out, however, the neutron data obtained on IN5 cannot be simulated using $D_{rot}(\|)$ as a parameter because the calculated profiles – at least at relatively low energy transfers – are very insensitive to the value of $D_{rot}(\|)$ owing to the fact that the Lorentzian

profile due to spinning motion is weak and very broad. Calculations to higher
energy transfer and at higher Q values should enable us to do further checks on
the validity of the diffusion model.

R.E. LECHNER: You have obtained equally good fits to your data with
rotational diffusion coefficients differing by a factor of 2. Was the translational
diffusion constant fixed in these fits?

J. YARWOOD: As I pointed out in my presentation, we attempted to 'fit'
the rotational part of our quasi-elastic spectra using a fixed D_{tr}, so the answer is
yes. I do agree though that, in the absence of IN10 data, it would be valid to try
fitting a series of spectra over a wide Q range using a pair of variable parameters.
However, the factor of 2 may simply be due to the relatively poor resolution
compared with the width of the rotational part of the spectrum.

A.J. DIANOUX: I was surprised at the factor of three difference that you
report between the values of the self-diffusion coefficient extracted from neutron
scattering and NMR. If the neutron spectra are taken at low enough Q values
and with good enough resolution, these two methods give identical results, as they
should (see paper IAEA-SM-219/107, Vol. 1, these Proceedings). Since, with
$D \cong 10^{-5}$ cm^2/s, the broadening of the quasi-elastic line is only of the order of
1 μeV for Q = 0.1 Å^{-1}, one really needs good resolution to see it.

J. YARWOOD: I believe you are probably right, although it would be
useful and instructive to have IN10 data so that we could *check* that NMR and
neutron data do give the same answer for CH_3CN.

B.A. DASANNACHARYA: The higher order terms in the Sears expansion
would contribute largely to high-energy transfers, and fitting in the quasi-elastic
region with large ℓ values should not be sensitive. What is your experience in this
regard?

J. YARWOOD: You are right. One would have to do calculations in the
near inelastic region in order to be sure how many ℓ values are required.

B.A. DASANNACHARYA: Have multiple scattering corrections been made?

J. YARWOOD: Yes, we have performed multiple scattering corrections.
At low energy transfers, however, they seem to be extremely small. The
figures shown in the paper do *not* include the multiple scattering corrections.

J. TOMKINSON: Your results show a difference in the observed diffusion
constants, as between the pure liquid acetonitrile and its solution in CCl_4. Would
you like to comment on how this comes about?

J. YARWOOD: The reason usually given for the decrease in both rotational
and translational diffusion coefficients with the CCl_4 solution is that the viscosity
goes up considerably and the 'freedom' for molecular motions decreases. The
macroscopic viscosity reflects the microscopic interactions in the liquid and these
are evidently larger in CCl_4 than in CH_3CN. This is *probably* due to the sheer bulk
of CCl_4 molecules but may also be related to electrical interactions, especially
between CH_3CN and CCl_4.

INCOHERENT NEUTRON SCATTERING STUDY OF MOLECULAR REORIENTATION AND ROTATIONAL ISOMERIZATION IN PLASTIC SUCCINONITRILE

J.P. AMOUREUX, M. BEE, R. FOURET
Laboratoire de dynamique des cristaux moléculaires,
Université de Lille,
Villeneuve d'Ascq,
France

R.E. LECHNER
Institut Laue-Langevin,
Grenoble

Abstract

INCOHERENT NEUTRON SCATTERING STUDY OF MOLECULAR REORIENTATION AND ROTATIONAL ISOMERIZATION IN PLASTIC SUCCINONITRILE.

The succinonitrile molecule $[N \equiv C-(CH_2)_2-C \equiv N]$ can assume three rotationally isomeric forms, a trans (t) and two gauche (g) conformations. In the plastic phase $(233 < T < 331°K)$ the three isomers exist in a thermodynamic equilibrium. Quasi-elastic neutron spectra measured at 302 K are presented and analysed in terms of a model taking into account the two coupled molecular motions which mainly contribute to the low energy scattering: (a) when in its t-form the molecule performs $\pi/2$-reorientations around its long axis with a jump rate k. (b) conformational changes occur with a jump rate k' from a g to the t-form and with a jump rate k" from the t to each of the g-forms. A preliminary comparison of the theory to the experimental spectra shows that k, k' and k" are all of the order of 10^{11} s^{-1} and suggests that k is somewhat larger than k' and k".

1. INTRODUCTION

The succinonitrile molecule, $[NC \equiv (CH_2)_2 \equiv CN]$, can assume four rotationally isomeric forms, a cis (c), a trans (t) and two gauche (g) configurations. They have C_{2v}, C_{2h} and C_2 symmetry, respectively [1]. For steric reasons, due to the polar nature of the two cyano groups, and by analogy with related molecules, the cis isomer is considered as the least stable of the three configurations. In the solid there is a strong correlation between the isomer concentrations and the crystalline structure. At low temperature the system is monoclinic, orientationally ordered, and contains exclusively the two gauche forms (g and $\bar{g}$) of the molecule. At 233°K the crystal transforms to an orientationally disordered "plastic" phase with b.c.c. symmetry (a = 6.37 Å), which is stable up to the melting point (331°K). In this phase the two g and the t-form of the molecule exist in a thermodynamic equilibrium. The concentrations are temperature dependent, but vary slowly over the temperature range of the plastic phase. There are about 22 % t-molecules

at room temperature and about 20 % near the plastic transition [2] . The
remaining molecules have with equal probability one of the two g-configura-
tions (the concentration of the c-configuration being negligible).   The g-
configurations are related to the t-form by ± 120°-rotations of either one
of the two $-CH_2-C \equiv N$ groups around the central C-C bond of the molecule.

From measurements of the polarization effect on Raman spectra [3] and
from X-ray structure work [4] the following detailed picture of the static
structure evolves : The central C-C bonds of the molecules are preferentially
aligned along the four threefold axes of the cubic unit cell. Each isomer
can occupy three different equilibrium orientations differing from each-other
by 120°-rotations around these axes. This means that each isomer has twelve distinguishable and equally probable equilibrium orientations within the crystal
lattice. The corresponding atomic equilibrium positions are the same for all
molecular conformations and are therefore independent of the isomer concentrations.

2. THE ROTATIONAL MOTION : RESULTS FROM PREVIOUS EXPERIMENTS

Information on the dynamical nature of the above described orientational disorder is available from a number of different experiments.
Dielectric relaxation [5-7] , NMR [8-9] , heat capacity [10], Rayleigh
scattering[11-15] and acoustic wave dispersion [16] studies have established
the existence of rapid rotational motions A) of the whole molecule and
B) of the two nitrile groups within the molecule. That both types of motion
consist in reorientations between a finite number of equilibrium orientations is obvious from the fact that such equilibrium orientations exist.
Perhaps the simplest way to obtain the above described distribution of
orientations would be to let each molecule reorient by 120° rotational jumps
around the four cube diagonals of the unit cell. For steric reasons it seems
however clear [3,4,7], that whole-molecule reorientations are most likely
to occur when the molecule is in its trans-form. In this configuration the
molecule is almost linear and has a relatively small moment of inertia about
its long axis which is preferentially aligned (approximately) along one of
the fourfold symmetry axes of the lattice. Reorientations around these axes
would consist in 90°-rotational jumps. This particular motion alone does
however not yield the complete orientation distribution described above.
In order to achieve this, 120°-reorientations of each nitrile group around
the C-C bond of the molecule must also be allowed. The latter motion com-
prises essentially the isomerisation processes t $\leftrightarrow$ g and t $\leftrightarrow$ $\bar{g}$, the
reaction g $\leftrightarrow$ $\bar{g}$ being excluded because of the high potential barrier
involved. In the following it will be assumed that whole-molecule reorientations other than $\pi/2$-rotations of trans molecules as described above may
be neglected so that the discussion of the rotational motion can be restricted to this and to the motions of isomerisation. The former will be
referred to as motions of type A), the latter as motions of type B).

The rotational correlation times obtained with different experimental
techniques at the same temperature scatter appreciably, for example at 25°C
the observed values lie between 1 $\times 10^{-11}$s and 7 $\times 10^{-11}$s (see Table 1).
This is probably due to the fact that the different experiments in general
are not sensitive exactly to the same aspects of the rotational motion.
Therefore different definitions of correlation times are involved and the
results cannot be readily compared with each-other. Dielectric relaxation,
acoustic wave dispersion and even light scattering techniques measure
effects due to the molecular motion on macroscopic scales. It can thererore
be expected that in general the correlation of rotational motions of different molecules may have some direct influence on the observed correlation

TABLE 1 : Rotational correlation times of succinonitrile at 25°C
as observed with different experimental techniques.

Experimental Technique	correlation time	value	reference
dielectric relaxation	τ_D	5.7×10^{-11} s	[5]
-"-	τ_D	6.9×10^{-11} s	[7]
NMR	τ_r	4.0×10^{-11} s	[9]
Rayleigh scattering	τ	5.9×10^{-11} s	[11]
-"-	τ	5.7×10^{-11} s	[12]
-"-	τ_1	6.2×10^{-11} s	[13]
-"-	τ_2	4.4×10^{-11} s	[13]
-"-	τ_1	6.4×10^{-11} s	[14]
-"-	τ_2	4.4×10^{-11} s	[14]
Acoustic wave dispersion	τ_A	1.0×10^{-11} s	[16]
Neutron scattering	τ_N	2.7×10^{-11} s	present work

times. That appreciable orientation correlations do exist in plastic
succinonitrile was shown recently by an analysis of X-ray diffuse scattering results [17] . NMR is also sensitive to correlated reorientations of
neighbouring molecules although perhaps to a lesser extent since the contributions of different interproton vectors $\vec{r}$ to the correlation function
of $Y_2^m(r)/r^3$ are proportional to r^{-6} (r being the proton-proton distance).
Incoherent quasielastic neutron scattering, the technique used in the
present work, permits to observe the proton self correlation function via
its space-time Fourier transform : the incoherent scattering function
$S_s(Q,\omega)$ [18] ; i.e., contrary to the other techniques, with the possible
exception of NMR, one exclusively studies single particle motions and
therefore the orientational relaxation of single vectors rather than whole
vector ensembles.

It is clear that a quantitative comparison of results from such different techniques would be feasible only if in each case the analysis were
based on the same microscopic models for the rotational motion including
orientational correlation effects where relevant. A qualitative comparison
can however be made. For this purpose we have included in Table 1 an apparent correlation time τ_N determined from the quasielastic widths $\Gamma (= \text{HWHM})$
observed in the present experiment(and corrected for the instrument resolution);τ_N is defined in the same way as the correlation time τ of ref.[11],

namely as $\tau_N = (2\pi \ \Gamma)^{-1}$. It is seen from Table 1 that the correlation time
obtained from dielectric relaxation [5,7] , τ_D, and one of the two correlation times from Rayleigh scattering [13,14], τ_1, have rather similar values
and are larger than τ_r (NMR [9]), τ_2 (Rayleigh scattering [13,14]), τ_A
(acoustic wave dispersion [16]) and τ_N (this experiment). In fact τ_D cannot
correspond to motions of type A) since the dipole moment of the trans-
molecule is practically zero; it therefore must reflect the motion of isomerisation alone. The same motion is also connected with τ_1, which describes
the relaxation of the difference of the diagonal components $(\alpha_{11}-\alpha_{22})$ of the
(macroscopic) polarizability tensor. The other correlation times, however,
τ_r, τ_2, τ_A and τ_N might only be average correlation times in the sense that
their values may be determined by the combined effect of both types of motion,
A) and B). This would be so if the two intrinsic correlation times corresponding to processes A) and B) were not too different from each-other and
thus the effects of both would have been seen in the relevant frequency
ranges of the different experiments. We have recently shown by an analysis
of the measured elastic incoherent structure factor (EISF) [19] that this
is in fact the case for neutrons. The EISF is the (Q-dependent) integral
elastic intensity [20]. It contains geometrical information on the motion,
which in this experiment permitted us to conclude that both types of motion
A) and B) were sufficiently **fast** to be resolved from the (incoherent) elastic
peak. The quasielastic spectra observed in this experiment reflect the
dynamical aspect of the molecular rotation. In the present paper we present
a model calculation allowing for both kinds of motion described above. This
model (called model C in [19]) is compared to the measured neutron spectra
in order to determine the relevant correlation times.

3.   EXPERIMENTAL

Neutron time-of-flight (TOF) spectra were taken using the multi-chopper
spectrometer IN5 of the Institute Laue-Langevin at three different incident
wavelengths λ_0 (5.94, 8.04 and 10.4 Å) with a sample of powdered succinonitrile at three different temperatures (302°K, 312°K, 326°K) in the plastic
phase. The elastic resolution of the instrument was 114 μeV, 48 μeV and
24 μeV (FWHM; for the three different wavelengths, respectively). The sample
was slab-shaped and was held between thin aluminium sheets; its thickness was
about 0.3 mm. Four typical TOF-spectra are shown in Fig. 1 for T = 302°K, an
incident wavelength λ_0 = 10.44 Å and scattering angles φ of 13, 42, 72 and
130.5°. All spectra were corrected for detector efficiency, container scattering, absorption and self shielding, and normalized with respect to each other
by comparison with a vanadium standard. It is seen from Fig. 1 that the
spectra contain a pronounced quasielastic contribution (centered around zero
energy transfer $\hbar\omega$) which is well separated from a broad inelastic spectrum.
The quasielastic peak contains clearly a narrow and a broad component especially at the larger angles. In the present paper our interest will be
concentrated on this low energy transfer part of the data, because it is
this part which reflects the random rotational motion of the molecules.

4.   CONFIGURATION PROBABILITIES AND THE INCOHERENT SCATTERING LAW

Since due to the relatively high energy resolution used in our experiment most of the inelastic scattering (corresponding to periodic lattice
and intramolecular motions) is well separated from the quasielastic part of
the spectra, it will be sufficient to limit the discussion to the rotational
scattering function $S_S^R(Q,\omega)$ [20,21]. Our model allows for motions A) and B)

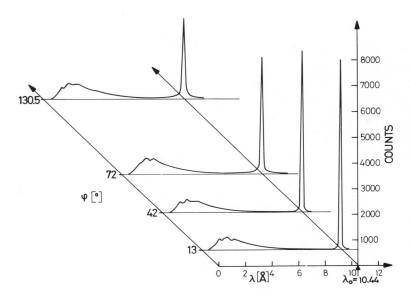

FIG.1. Typical examples of corrected experimental time-of-flight spectra of plastic succinonitrile at 302 K. Incident wavelength $\lambda_0 = 10.44$ Å; scattering angles $\varphi = 13, 42, 72$ and 130.5°. Each spectrum contains 508 experimental points, equidistant on the scattered neutron wavelength scale. This large number of points cannot easily be reproduced in the figure; therefore the spectra are represented by full lines.

as described in Section 2. The scattering function for such instantaneous "jumps" between a finite number of allowed configurations reads, for a powder sample (requiring an average over all directions of $\vec{Q}$),

$$S_s^R(Q,\omega) = \frac{1}{2\pi} \int d\Omega_Q \int_{-\infty}^{-\infty} e^{-i\omega t} \, I_s(\vec{Q},t) dt \tag{1}$$

The intermediate scattering function is given by

$$I_s(\vec{Q},t) = \sum_{\Omega} \sum_{\Omega_0} e^{i\vec{Q}[\vec{R}(\Omega)-\vec{R}(\Omega_0)]} \cdot P(\Omega,\Omega_0,t) \cdot P(\Omega_0) \tag{2}$$

where the sums are taken over all initial (Ω_0) and final (Ω) configurations of the molecule and $\vec{R}(\Omega)$ is the position vector (of the proton being considered) for the configuration Ω.

The conditional probabilities $P(\Omega,\Omega_0,t)$ for the different molecular configurations are obtained from a set of rate equations taking into account the distribution $P(\Omega_0)$ of initial configurations.

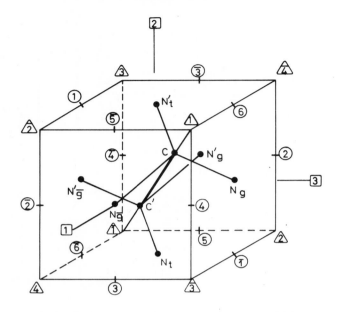

FIG.2.   Cube oriented as the b.c.c. unit cell of the lattice.   A succinonitrile molecule is shown
schematically with its central C-C bond aligned along the cube diagonal number 1.   The numbers
indicate the points where the main symmetry axes of the cube cut its faces or edges.

Let k be the probability per unit time for a $\pi/2$-rotational jump of
the t-molecule, whereby its central C-C axis reorients from one cube diagonal to another; let k' be the probability per unit time for a transition
from a gauche (g or $\bar{g}$) to the trans conformation and k" the probability for
the inverse process.

In addition to these jump rates we need to define the molecular
configurations and the associated configuration probabilities. For this
purpose we will use Fig. 2 showing a cube, which is oriented as the unit
cell of the b.c.c. lattice. It is indicated, where the main symmetry axes
of this cube cut its faces or edges and the respective points are numbered.
A succinonitrile molecule is shown schematically with its central C-C bond
aligned along the cube diagonal number 1. With the orientation of the C-C
bond chosen, nine different configurations of the molecule are possible
within the frame of our model. These are obtained by 120°-rotations of the
three possible molecule conformations around the C-C bond. Similarly -
considering the C-C bond as a vector fixed in the molecule - there are nine
different configurations associated with each of the eight cube diagonal
directions, so that the total number of different molecular configurations
is 72.

Let us introduce the notation $P^i_{g_j}$, $P^i_{\bar{g}_j}$ and $P^i_{t_j}$ for the conditional
probabilities $P(\Omega,\Omega_\rho,t)$ of these configurations. Here for instance g^i_j denotes
a gauche molecule which has its C-C axis aligned along the cube diagonal i,

and its twofold axis direction coinciding with the twofold cube axis j. Note
that the twofold axis direction of the gauche molecule is defined by the
vector pointing from the center of the C-C bond to the center of the straight
line joining the two nitrogen atoms of the molecule. The definition of the
other kind of gauche configuration, $\bar{g}^i_j$, is analogous. For the trans-molecule
t^i_j , the subscript i again denotes the cube diagonal parallel to the central
C-C bond direction of the molecule, whereas j is the number of the fourfold
cube axis along which the molecule is aligned (roughly parallel to the
straight line joining the two nitrogen atoms in the trans-conformation).

Corresponding to the dynamical equilibrium existing between the 72
different molecular configurations, we have to solve a system of 72 rate
equations. Obviously we cannot go here into all the details but let us just
give three typical examples :

$$\frac{d}{dt} \; P^1_{g1} \; = - \, 2k'P^1_{g1} \; + \, k''P^1_{t2} \; + \, k''P^1_{t3}$$

$$\frac{d}{dt} \; P^{\bar{1}}_{g1} \; = - \, 2k'P^{\bar{1}}_{g1} + \, k''P^{\bar{1}}_{t2} \; + \, k''P^{\bar{1}}_{t3} \qquad\qquad (3)$$

$$\frac{d}{dt} \; P^1_{t1} \; = k'P^1_{g2} + k'P^1_{g3} - (4k'' + 2k)P^1_{t1} \; + \, k' \, P^1_{\bar{g2}} \; + \, k'P^1_{\bar{g3}}$$

$$+ \; kP^{\bar{2}}_{t1} \; + \, kP^{\bar{3}}_{t1}$$

The (72 × 72)-matrix of this system of equations can be decomposed into two
independent (36 × 36)-matrices by introducing the two new bases σ and δ
formed by the elements

$\sigma^\alpha_{g\beta}$, $\sigma^\alpha_{t\beta}$, $\sigma^\alpha_{\bar{g}\beta}$ and

$\delta^\alpha_{g\beta}$, $\delta^\alpha_{t\beta}$, $\delta^\alpha_{\bar{g}\beta}$ resp., which are defined as the sums and the differences

of all the pairs of "parallel" and "antiparallel" configuration
probabilities as follows :

$$\sigma^\alpha_{g\beta} \; = P^\alpha_{g\beta} + P^{\bar{\alpha}}_{g\beta}$$

... etc.   (4)

$$\delta^\alpha_{g\beta} \; = P^\alpha_{g\beta} - P^{\bar{\alpha}}_{g\beta}$$

... etc.

The basis σ yields a 36-dimensional matrix representation of the octa-
eder symmetry group, the basis δ a 36-dimensional matrix representation
of the symmetry group of the tetraeder. Both can be decomposed into
irreducible representations of lower dimensions as follows [22] :

$$\Gamma_\sigma = 2A_{1g} + A_{1u} + 2E_g + E_u + 2T_{1g} + T_{1u} + 4T_{2g} + 2T_{2u}$$

$$\Gamma_\delta = 2A_1 + A_2 + 3E + 4T_1 + 5T_2 \qquad\qquad (5)$$

The bases of these irreducible representations are found with the aid of
projection operators [23]. Thus the original set of 72 rate equations

TABLE 2 : List of the different eigenvalues

α_0	0	
$\alpha_1, \alpha_2, \alpha_3, \alpha_4$	eigenvalues of matrix D (see Appendix A)	
α_5	$-(k' + 2k'') + \sqrt{\Delta}$	
α_6	$-(k' + 2k'') - \sqrt{\Delta}$	$\Delta = (2k'' - k')^2 + 2k'k''$
α_7	$-(k' + 2k'' + k) + \sqrt{\Delta'}$	
α_8	$-(k' + 2k'' + k) - \sqrt{\Delta'}$	$\Delta' = (2k'' - k' + k)^2 + 2k'k''$
α_9	$-(k' + 2k'' + 2k) + \sqrt{\Delta''}$	
α_{10}	$-(k' + 2k'' + 2k) - \sqrt{\Delta''}$	$\Delta'' = (2k'' + k' + 2k) - 8k'k''$
α_{11}	$-2k'$	
α_{12}	$-(2k' + 4k'')$	

is replaced by a number of lower dimensional systems, the eigenvalues
of which can easily be found. There is a total of 13 different eigenvalues
α_j , which are listed in Table 2 (see also Appendix A).

In order to evaluate expression (2) it is not necessary to calculate
the conditional probabilities $P(\Omega, \Omega_0, t)$ for all the 72 initial configurations. In fact for symmetry reasons it is sufficient to consider 12
different initial configurations corresponding to the fact that there are
three different molecular conformations (g, $\bar{g}$ and t) and four protons in
the molecule. Furthermore we note that there are only two different values
of the initial configuration probability $P(\Omega_0)$, namely

$$P_g(\Omega_0) = \frac{1}{24} \cdot \frac{k''}{k' + 2k''}$$

for the 24 g   as well as
for the 24 $\bar{g}$ configurations, and

$$P_t(\Omega_0) = \frac{1}{24} \frac{k'}{k' + 2k''}$$

for the 24t configurations.

Inserting the functions $P(\Omega, \Omega_0, t)$ and $P(\Omega_0)$ into Eq. (2) and using (1) we
finally obtain the rotational scattering function

$$S_s^R(Q, \omega) = A_0(Q) \ \delta(\omega) + \sum_{j=1}^{12} A_j(Q) \cdot \mathcal{L}(\alpha_j, \omega) \tag{6}$$

in terms of the Lorentzian functions $\mathcal{L}(\alpha_j, \omega) = \frac{1}{\pi} \cdot \frac{|\alpha_j|}{\alpha_j^2 + \omega^2}$ with energy

widths determined by the eigenvalues α_j and the structure factors $A_j(Q)$. The
latter are complicated functions of the proton site-site distances r_i [19]
and the equilibrium probabilities $P(\Omega_0)$. Explicit expressions are given in
Appendix B.

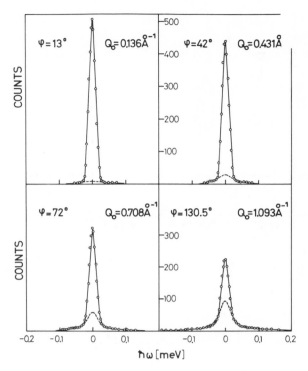

FIG.3.   Quasi-elastic spectra of plastic succinonitrile at 302 K measured with $\lambda_0 = 10.44$ Å (same scattering angles as in Fig. 1). Experimental points are represented by circles (for clarity only part of the experimental points are given). The full line is the fit of the model described in the text, the dashed lines indicate the separation of the spectra into elastic and quasi-elastic contributions (from fit).

For completeness it should be mentioned that models A and B described in ref. [19] are obtained from Eq. (6) if one sets $k' = k'' = 0$ (for model A) or $k = 0$ (for model B).

5.   COMPARISON OF MODEL TO EXPERIMENTAL RESULTS AND DISCUSSION

In order to compare our model to the measured neutron spectra we have multiplied expression (6) with a Debye–Waller factor which was directly obtained from the Q-dependence of the measured quasielastic integral; furthermore a flat inelastic "background", calculated in a consistent way from a Debye density of states (where the Debye temperature was obtained from the Debye–Waller factor) was added [19] ; the whole expression was folded with the instrument resolution function [24] and least squares' fitted to the experimental spectra.

Since the two conformation jump rates k' and k'' are connected by the relation $k' = 2k''R$ (where $R = 0.282$ at 302°K and slowly varying with temperature [2]) there are – except for a global normalization factor F for the

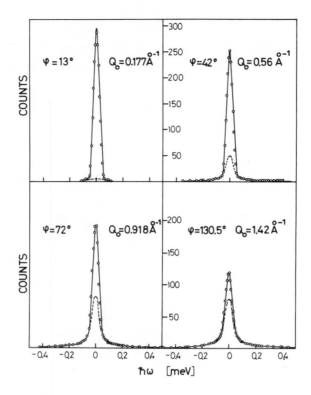

FIG.4. Quasi-elastic spectra of plastic succinonitrile at 302 K measured with $\lambda_0 = 8.04$ Å (same scattering angles as in Fig.1). Experimental points and curves as in Fig. 2.

spectra – only two independent fit parameters, namely k and k'. We have applied the following fit procedure. First the model was fitted simulta- neously to the spectra taken at the five largest scattering angles (112.5≤ φ≤ 135.5°) in order to determine k and k'. Then these two parameters were fixed and the model was fitted with only one parameter, the normalization factor F, to the other spectra. This procedure was applied to the spectra measured at 302°K with incident wavelengths λ_o = 8.04 and 10.44 Å. Good fits were obtained at all scattering angles (see Figs. 3 and 4) and there was little variation in the resulting F-values. However, as one might expect, it is not possible to obtain very precise values of k and k' from a fit at only a few scattering angles. In the present preliminary analysis we find for the correlation time τ_i = 1/k' an approximate value of 2.5 ± 1.0 x 10^{-11}s whereas the correlation time τ_t = 1/k seems to be about five times smaller. It is less well defined because of the relatively small concentration of t–molecules. These results are in qualitative agreement with those found with other tech- niques (see Table 1).

More precise values of the correlation times can in principle be obtained from our spectra, since this information is contained in their shape.
Such an analysis requires the use of all measured spectra and a careful
consideration of the following points :
i)   The spectra should be corrected for multiple scattering since this affects
     the widths of the quasielastic spectra.
ii) With different incident wavelengths (i.e. different resolutions and
     Q-ranges) different aspects of the measured scattering functions are
     amplified. It is therefore desirable to fit the model simultaneously
     at all scattering angles as well as for the different incident neutron
     wavelengths of the experiment.
iii) The uncertainties of the determination of the Debye-Waller factor and of
     the inelastic parts of the spectra will then also be reduced.
     It should be noted that the same problems also affect other recent
neutron results on the same subject [25]. We intend to present a more complete analysis as indicated above in another paper [26], where we will also
discuss the temperature dependence of our spectra.

ACKNOWLEDGEMENTS

We gratefully acknowledge the technical assistance obtained during
the experiment from Y. Blanc and F. Douchin.

Appendix A

THE EIGENVALUES $\alpha_1, \alpha_2, \alpha_3, \alpha_4$

α_1 to α_4 are the eigenvalues of the matrix

$$
D = \begin{pmatrix}
-2k' & 0 & 0 & 2k'' \\
0 & -2k' & k'' & k'' \\
0 & 4k' & -4(k+k'') & 0 \\
2k' & 2k' & 0 & -2(k+2k'')
\end{pmatrix}
\tag{A1}
$$

which requires numerical diagonalization. We have fitted an empirical
function of the following form to the numerical result :

$$
\alpha_j = k'' \cdot (p_1 + p_2 \cdot \rho + p_3 \cdot e^{-p_4 \rho} + p_5 \cdot e^{-p_6 \rho} + p_7 \cdot e^{-p_8 \rho})
\tag{A2}
$$

where $\rho = k/k''$, $k' = 2k''R$ and $R = N_t/N_g$ with N_t and N_g being the
concentrations of trans- and gauche-molecules, respectively. The coefficients
obtained from the fit of expression (A2) are listed in table A.

TABLE A. COEFFICIENTS OF EXPRESSION (A2)

R	j	P_1	P_2	P_3	P_4	P_5	P_6	P_7	P_8
0.282	1	-4.08655	-1.99912	-0.585765	0.228649	0.321820	15.05	0.	0.
(302°K)	2	-1.1089	0.	0.509524	0.86016	0.146854	0.0408266	0.452522	0.213758
	3	-1.12372	0.	0.052732	0.072139	0.206322	0.546098	0.086763	1.36071
	4	-4.04301	-3.99948	-0.449178	0.444963	-0.63581	4.4471	0.	0.
0.285	1	-4.09198	-1.99904	-0.611056	0.246737	0.348402	21.1794	0.	0.
(312°K)	2	-1.12202	0.	0.464563	0.219595	0.151755	0.0408801	0.505701	0.865294
	3	-1.13611	0.	0.0382721	0.0565724	0.130602	0.331583	0.181928	1.42307
	4	-4.07321	-3.99965	-0.277305	0.268482	-0.829834	2.12216	0.	0.
0.289	1	-4.09318	-1.99902	-0.619469	0.246173	0.351929	18.6441	0.	0.
(326°K)	2	-1.13754	0.	0.467745	0.22102	0.157112	0.0418312	0.512682	0.862545
	3	-1.15216	0.	0.0376971	0.0547394	0.129355	0.321221	0.189691	1.37279
	4	-4.0346	-3.99962	-0.280932	0.272606	-0.840467	2.11911	0.	0.

Appendix B

THE STRUCTURE FACTORS $A_j(Q)$

Be $[M^\sigma]$ and $[M^\delta]$ the (4×4) matrices with elements $m_{\ell j}^\sigma$ and $m_{\ell j}^\delta$ defined as functions of the eigenvalues α_1 to α_4 by the relations

$$m_{1j}^\sigma = m_{1j}^\delta = 1 \qquad\qquad m_{4j}^\sigma = m_{4j}^\delta = \frac{2k' + \alpha_j}{4k''}$$

$$m_{2j}^\sigma = \frac{k'(2k' + \alpha_j)}{(2k' + \alpha_j)(4k'' + 4k + \alpha_j) - 4k'k''} \qquad m_{3j}^\sigma = m_{2j}^\sigma \times \frac{4k'' + 4k + \alpha_j}{2k'}$$

$$m_{2j}^\delta = \frac{k'(2k' + \alpha_j)}{(2k' + \alpha_j)(4k'' + \alpha_j) - 4k'k''} \qquad m_{3j}^\delta = m_{2j}^\delta \times \frac{4k'' + \alpha_j}{2k'}$$

Be $H_{\beta j}^{\gamma\sigma}$ and $H_{\beta j}^{\gamma\delta}$ (j=1 to 4) the elements of the vectors $\vec{H}_\beta^{\gamma\sigma}$ and $\vec{H}_\beta^{\gamma\delta}$ (γ=1,2 and β = 1,2,3) which are solutions of the linear systems

$$[M^\sigma] = \vec{H}_\beta^{\gamma\sigma} = [M^\delta]\,\vec{H}_\beta^{\gamma\delta} = \vec{V}_{\gamma\beta} \qquad \text{with}$$

$$\vec{V}_{11} = (0,\ 0,\ 1/8,\ 0) \qquad\qquad \vec{V}_{21} = \vec{V}_{22} = (0,\ 0,\ 0,\ 1/8)$$

$$\vec{V}_{12} = (1/4,\ 0,\ 0,\ 0) \qquad\qquad \vec{V}_{23} = (0,\ 1/4,\ 0,\ 0)$$

$$\vec{V}_{13} = (0,\ 0,\ 1/8,\ 0)$$

Let us define the vectors $\overrightarrow{L_i^\gamma(\alpha_j)}$ (which have 12 components) by the relation

$$L_{i,\beta+3(\ell-1)}^\gamma (\alpha_j) = \frac{1}{4}\,(m_{\ell j}^\sigma\, H_{\beta j}^{\gamma\sigma} + s_i\, m_{\ell j}^\delta\, H_{\beta j}^{\gamma\delta})$$

where

$$s_i = 1 \quad \text{for} \quad i = 1,\ 3,\ 4,\ 7,\ 8,\ 11$$

$$s_i = -1 \quad \text{for} \quad i = 2,\ 5,\ 6,\ 9,\ 10,\ 12$$

The structure factors $A_j(Q)$ appearing in Eq. (6) of the text can be expressed as follows

$$A_j(Q) = \sum_{i=1}^{12} c_{ij}\, j_0(Qr_i) \qquad j = 0 \text{ to } 12 \tag{B1}$$

where the coefficients c_{ij} for $j = 1$ to 4 are given by

$$c_{ij} = \frac{1}{4} \sum_{p=1}^{12} \left[n_{ip}^1 \; L_{ip}^1(\alpha_j) \times \frac{2k''}{k' + 2k''} + n_{ip}^2 \; L_{ip}^2(\alpha_j) \; \frac{k'}{k' + 2k''} \right] \qquad (B2)$$

and the elements n_{ip}^γ are given in the tables B1 and B2.

$\gamma = 1$ **TABLE B1. THE ELEMENTS n_{ip}^1**

$\,^p$ $\!\!_i$	1	2,3	4	5,6	7	8,9	10	11,12
1	4	2	0	4	4	6	8	4
2	-4	-2	0	0	-4	-2	-8	-4
3	0	0	0	-4	0	-4	0	0
4	4	6	8	4	12	10	8	12
5	-2	-3	-4	2	-6	-1	-4	-6
6	-4	-2	0	-8	-4	-10	-8	-4
7	0	-4	-8	-4	-8	-8	0	-8
8	-4	-2	0	0	-4	-2	-8	-4
9	6	5	4	6	10	11	12	10
10	2	-1	-4	-2	-2	-3	4	-2
11	-4	-2	0	0	-4	-2	-8	-4
12	2	3	4	2	6	5	4	6

$\gamma = 2$ **TABLE B2. THE ELEMENTS n_{ip}^2**

$\,^p$ $\!\!_i$	1,2	3	4,5	6	7,8	9	10,11	12
1	4	0	0	8	4	8	8	0
2	-4	0	0	0	-4	0	-8	0
3	0	0	0	-8	0	-8	0	0
4	4	8	8	0	12	8	8	16
5	-2	-4	-4	8	-6	4	-4	-8
6	-4	0	0	-16	-4	-16	-8	0
7	0	-8	-8	0	-8	-8	0	-16
8	-4	0	0	0	-4	0	-8	0
9	6	4	4	8	10	12	12	8
10	2	-4	-4	0	-2	-4	4	-8
11	-4	0	0	0	-4	0	-8	0
12	2	4	4	0	6	4	4	8

The site-site distances r_i are listed in Table 1 of ref. [19].
For the remaining coefficients c_{ij} (j = 0 and 5 to 12) we define the
following expressions :

$$A_{(\pm)} = \frac{(\pm)1}{24(k'+2k'')\sqrt{\Delta}}\left(2k'^2 + 2k''^2 - k'k'' \pm (2k'+k'')\sqrt{\Delta}\right)$$

$$B(\pm) = \frac{(\pm)1}{16(k'+2k'')\sqrt{\Delta'}}\left(2k'^2 + 2k''^2 - k'k'' - k(2k'-k'') \pm (2k'+k'')\sqrt{\Delta'}\right)$$

$$C(\pm) = \frac{(\pm)1}{48(k'+2k'')\sqrt{\Delta''}}\left(k'^2 + 4k''^2 + 4k'k'' - 2kk' + 4kk'' \pm (k'+2k'')\sqrt{\Delta''}\right)$$

$$D = \frac{k''}{k'+2k''}$$ (see Table 2 for the definitions of Δ, Δ' and Δ'')

These expressions are used in Table B3 in order to present all the
coefficients c_{ij}.

TABLE B3.   COEFFICIENTS c_{ij}

i \ j	0	1 to 4	5	6	7	8	9	10	11	12
1	$\frac{1}{24}$		A_+	A_-	B_+	B_-	C_+	C_-	D	0
2	$\frac{1}{12}$		0	0	0	0	$-2C_+$	$-2C_-$	0	0
3	$\frac{1}{24}$		A_+	A_-	0	0	C_+	C_-	0	0
4	$\frac{1}{12}$	c_{ij}	$-A_+$	$-A_-$	$-B_+$	$-B_-$	$2C_+$	$2C_-$	$-D$	0
5	$\frac{1}{12}$	given	0	0	0	0	$-2C_+$	$-2C_-$	0	0
6	$\frac{1}{6}$	by	0	0	0	0	$-4C_+$	$-4C_-$	0	0
7	$\frac{1}{6}$	Eq.(B2)	$-2A_+$	$-2A_-$	0	0	$4C_+$	$4C_-$	0	0
8	$\frac{1}{12}$		$-A_+$	$-A_-$	B_+	B_-	$2C_+$	$2C_-$	0	0
9	$\frac{1}{12}$		0	0	0	0	$-2C_+$	$-2C_-$	0	0
10	$\frac{1}{24}$		0	0	0	0	$-C_+$	$-C_-$	0	0
11	$\frac{1}{12}$		$2A_+$	$-2A_-$	$-B_+$	$-B_-$	$2C_+$	$2C_-$	0	0
12	$\frac{1}{24}$		0	0	0	0	$-C_+$	$-C_-$	0	0

REFERENCES

[1] JANZ, G.J. and FITZGERALD, W.E., J. Chem. Phys. 23 (1955) 1973.
[2] FONTAINE H. and FOURET, R., Adv. in Mol. Relax. Processes 5 (1973) 391.
     Elsevier Sci. Publ. Comp., Amsterdam.
[3] FONTAINE, H., LONGUEVILLE, W. and WALLART, F., J. Chimie Physique 68
     (1971) 1593.
[4] FONTAINE, H. and BEE, M., Bull. Soc. fr. Mineral. Cristallogr. 95 (1972)
     441.
[5] CLEMETT, C. and DAVIES M., J. Chem. Phys. 32 (1960) 316.
[6] WILLIAMS, D.E. and SMYTH, C.P., J. Am. Chem. Soc. 84, 1808 (1962).
[7] LONGUEVILLE, W., FONTAINE H. and CHAPOTON, A., J. Chimie Physique 68
     (1971) 436.
[8] PETRAKIS, L. and RAO, A., J. Chem. Phys. 39 (1963) 1633.
[9] POWLES, J.G., Afrozi Begum and NORRIS, M.O., Mol. Physics 17 (1969) 489.
[10] WULFF, C.A. and WESTRUM, E.F. Jr., J. Chem. Phys. 67 (1963) 2376.
[11] BOYER, L., VACHER, R., CECCHI, L., ADAM, M. and BERGE, P., Phys. Rev.
     Lett. 26 (1971) 1435.
[12] ADAM, M., BOYER, L., VACHER, R., BERGE, P. and CECCHI,L. J. Physique, 32,
     Colloque C5a, suppl. No. 10, p. C5a-233 (1971).
[13] BOYER, L., VACHER, R. and CECCHI, L., J. Physique 36 (1975) 1347.
[14] BISCHOFBERGER, T., Thesis, IBM-Zürich Research Report RZ 777 (1976).
[15] BISCHOFBERGER, T., and COURTENS, E., Phys. Rev. Lett. 35 (1975) 1451.
[16] FONTAINE, H., FOURET, R., BOYER L., and VACHER R., J. Physique 33
     (1972) 1115.
[17] DESCAMPS, M., COULON, G., Chemical Physics (1976), to be published.
[18] see for example T. Springer, Springer Tracts in ModernPhysics 64 (1972),
     Springer-Verlag, Berlin, Heidelberg, New York.
[19] LECHNER, R.E., AMOUREUX, J.P., BEE, M. and FOURET, R., submitted to
     Comm. on Physics (1977).
[20] For a review of work on related problems see : LEADBETTER, A.J.,and
     LECHNER, R.E., in "The Plastic Crystalline State", Ed. SHERWOOD, J.N.,
     John Wiley and Sons (to appear in 1977).
[21] See also : LECHNER, R.E.,and HEIDEMANN, A., Comm. on Physics 1 (1976)
     213.
[22] See for example : LEECH, J.W. and NEWMAN, D.J., "How to Use Groups",
     Methuen and Co. Ltd, 1969, p. 31-34.
[23] Ref.[22],p. 44.
[24] See Appendix in VOLINO, F., DIANOUX, A.J., LECHNER, R.E. and HERVET, H.,
     J. Phys. Colloq. 36 (1975) C1-83.
[25] LEADBETTER, A.J., TURNBULL, A., Faraday Transactions II (1977), in
     print.
[26] AMOUREUX, J.P., BEE, M., FOURET, R., and LECHNER R.E., to be published
     in Journal de Physique.

DISCUSSION

W. PRESS *(Chairman):* You mentioned 72 discrete orientations of the succinonitrile molecules in the plastic phase. Wouldn't a description of the orientational order by some (continuous) distribution function be more appropriate, in view of the different conformations which are possible?

R.E. LECHNER: No. It must be emphasized that the 72 molecular configurations correspond to only 24 equilibrium positions of the individual proton. It is true that the static proton-density distribution could be described by some continuous function peaked at these 24 sites. However, for the dynamical problem it is more convenient to use an ensemble of discrete configurations and hence to obtain a meaningful definition of the two correlation times of isomerization and whole-molecule reorientation, respectively.

T.C. WADDINGTON: Can you obtain the barriers to the trans-gauche iso-merization of the succinonitrile molecule, and to the whole-body reorientation of the molecule about its long axis, from the temperature dependence of your data?

R.E. LECHNER: Yes, we will be able to obtain this information from our spectra measured at several different temperatures. This analysis has not yet been, done, however.

J.-B. SUCK: You quoted an error of about 30%. Was this due to your choice of the part of the measured intensity you attributed to elastic and to quasi-elastic scattering?

R.E. LECHNER: No. These errors are caused mainly by the effects of multiple scattering, which we have not corrected for, and by an uncertainty in the subtraction of a small inelastic 'background'. Another contributing factor is that we have obtained the correlation times by a preliminary fit of the model to only a few scattering angles. We intend to reduce these errors considerably in a more elaborate analysis.

R.M. PICK: Looking at the τ values you have obtained, I have the feeling that you could reconstruct the correlation times measured by NMR, on the one hand, and by Rayleigh scattering and dielectric relaxation, on the other hand. How do these values compare? In particular, can you get information on the degree of correlation between the molecules in these two measuring techniques?

R.E. LECHNER: A detailed comparison with results obtained using other techniques would require an analysis of these other results on the basis of our microscopic model. We have not done this. However, a qualitative comparison (Table 1 in the paper) shows that, for instance, the correlation times obtained from dielectric relaxation (τ_D) and from Rayleigh scattering (τ, τ_1) are higher by factors of 2 or 3 than what we obtain for the motion of isomerization. This may be due to orientational correlation between different molecules; however, I think the spatial range of such correlations must be relatively short.

B.A. DASANNACHARYA: Is the correlation time that you are describing identical with proton residence time or is it a model-dependent τ? If the latter, this may lead to difficulties in comparisons with other experiments, which also often use model-dependent relaxation times. Could you please comment on this?

R.E. LECHNER: For models A and B the correlation times mentioned are proton residence times defined in the usual way. In model C, however, the residence time is not defined in such a simple way, because, for one thing, the configuration probability of a trans-molecule can decay by several different processes. It is therefore better to define 'jump' probabilities by taking the inverse correlation times, as we have done in our paper.

ROTATIONAL MOTIONS IN SOME MOLECULAR SOLIDS: CLATHRATE HYDRATES, PLASTIC SILANE

W. WEGENER, J. VANDERHAEGHEN, [†]
S. HAUTECLER, E. LEGRAND
SCK/CEN,
Mol

L. VAN GERVEN
Katholieke Universiteit Leuven,
Leuven,
Belgium

Abstract

ROTATIONAL MOTIONS IN SOME MOLECULAR SOLIDS: CLATHRATE HYDRATES, PLASTIC SILANE.

Systems in which molecules have high rotational freedom are studied: (a) the clathrate deuterates of ethylene oxide (EOC) and tetrahydrofuran (THFC); (b) solid silane (SiH_4) in its plastic phase. The TOF spectra of polycrystalline samples are measured at several temperatures. The quasi-elastic (QE) scattering using models involving re-orientational jumps around fixed or randomly changing axes is analysed. Their predictions concerning the Q-behaviour of the QE and the elastic intensities and line shapes are compared with experimental results. The following models appear to be the most adequate ones: $180°$-jumps around the polar molecular axis (for EOC); $120°$-jumps around the threefold cage axes (THFC); $120°$-jumps around the threefold molecular axes (SiH_4). The residence times obtained from model fits are consistent with dielectric and NMR data; from their temperature dependence activation energies of 0.35, 0.20, and 0.25 kcal $\cdot$ mol^{-1}, respectively, are derived. Effective-frequency distributions are calculated from the low-temperature inelastic spectra and their maxima are tentatively assigned to librations (EOC, THFC) and vibrations (SiH_4) of the molecules. On the assumption of cosine-type hindrance potentials barrier heights and activation energies are derived; their values are consistent with those gained from the QE data and with IR and NMR data.

1. INTRODUCTION

The molecular crystal SiH_4 in its plastic phase as well as the clathrate hydrates of ethylene oxide (EOC) and tetrahydrofuran (THFC) are examples of orientationally disordered solids. In these clathrates the

---

[†] Research fellow of the Belgian "Interuniversiteir Instituut voor Kernwetenschappen" in the Laboratory of Solid State Physics and Magnetism, Katholieke Universiteit Leuven.

guest molecules are encaged in nearly spherical cavities of a H_2O host lattice and can be regarded as nearly isolated from each other; since the guests are not chemically bound   to the cages, they show a high rotational mobility. Also in the case of plastic SiH_4 the rotational motions are just slightly hindered as a consequence of the large rotational constant and the weak angle-dependence of the intermolecular forces (octupole-octupole interactions). One can thus expect in all three systems random reorientations. Indications for such motions have been found for EOC in dielectric [1] and NMR works [1], [2]; a theoretical study is presented in [3]. Also for THFC, NMR results [4] have been interpreted in terms of reorientations. SiH_4 has at 63.5 K a solid-solid transition. From large bandwidths in IR and Raman spectra in the high-temperature phase I it has been concluded [5] that this phase is orientationally disordered. This interpretation is supported by a NMR study [6], in which molecular reorientations have been found down to 25 K.

In our incoherent inelastic neutron scattering investigation of EOC, THFC, and SiH_4 we found in the high temperature regions (EOC and THFC: $T \gtrsim 150K$; SiH_4: phase I) a strong quasielastic (QE) component, which can be attributed to molecular random reorientations. At low temperatures this component vanishes, while a structure appears in the inelastic region. We could gain information about the nature of the reorientations by comparing the T and Q dependence of the QE and elastic components with model predictions. Furthermore we derived effective frequency distributions, and the peaks found in the low temperature spectra were assigned to molecular librations (EOC, THFC) and vibrations (SiH_4).

2. STRUCTURAL INFORMATION

2.1. Clathrate hydrates

Similarly to the different structures of ice, the clathrate host lattices are built up by hydrogen-bonded H_2O molecules. Their arrangement can be described in terms of polyhedral "cages" linked   together and fil-

ling the space. Each of them can be occupied by just one molecule of a dis-

solved substance, the host lattice being stabilized by the presence of such

guests. According to X-ray studies [7] the EOC and THFC hydrates have struc-

tures called "I" and "II" in [8].

In structure I (Pm3n, a = 12.03 Å) the unit cell contains 46 H_2O

molecules forming 2 dodecahedra and 6 larger tetrakaidecahedra. The 14-he-

dra (symmetry $\bar{4}$2 m) are limited by 12 pentagonal faces and by 2 hexagons per-

pendicular to the $\bar{4}$-axis : these cavities look like an oblate spheroid

with its shorter axis in the $\bar{4}$-direction. The structural data of the trian-

gular EO molecule (C_2H_4O) are given in [9]; the principal moments of inertia

are I_x = 59.504, I_y = 32.919, I_z = 37.923 (all in 10^{-40} $g.cm^2$; the z-axis

being the twofold (polar) axis and the y-axis being parallel to the C-C

bond). In EOC the guest molecules occupy at 248 K mainly the 14-hedra [7]

(less than 6 % are in the small cages). The guests in the big cages show

orientational disorder : according to [7] , at T = 248 K one half of them

occupy two equilibrium positions, in which the O-atoms lie on the $\bar{4}$-axis

and the C-C bonds are in the symmetry planes containing the $\bar{4}$-axis; the

other half of the guests occupy disordered positions somewhat displaced

and rotated from the equilibrium ones. However, the existence of these

preferred positions has been questioned in the theoretical study [3]. More-

over a very recent neutron diffraction investigation at 80K [10] yielded

a 24-fold orientational disorder; in the analysis presented here these

results have not yet been taken into account.

The host lattice of the THFC hydrate has the structure type II

(Fd3m, a = 17.3 Å). The unit cell contains 136 H_2O molecules forming 16

dodecahedra and 8 larger hexakaidecahedra. The THF molecules fill exclusi-

vely the 16-hedra (symmetry $\bar{4}$3m). Structural data of the THF molecule

(C_4H_8O) can be found in [11] ; the principal moments of inertia are
I_x = 217.8, I_y = 122.1, I_z = 99.2 (all in 10^{-40}g cm^2, the axes being defined as in the EOC case). In [7], no decision could be made between free
rotation of the guest molecules and a distribution over 24 possible equilibrium positions.

2.2. Silane

For silane very limited structural information has been obtained
from optical spectroscopy [5] , [12], powder X-ray diffraction [13] and
neutron diffraction [14], and often controversary conclusions have been
drawn. The only point on which the different authors agree is that the
symmetry of phase I is lower than cubic, in agreement with the birefringence
observed in this phase. In [13] a b.c.t. structure (a = 12.5 Å, c = 14.2 Å
at 77 K) has been suggested. Therefore in [13] and [14] the plastic nature
of SiH_4I has been questioned, most of the plastic crystals having a cubic
structure. But this is not a general rule [15]; indeed the high entropy
change at the transition is a strong indication for the existence of random
reorientations. The moment of inertia of the tetrahedral SiH_4 molecule is
I = 9.73 · 10^{-40} g·cm^2. For the low-temperature phase(s) there is even less
structural information available. From [14] it is known that in SiD_4 there
are at least two more solid phases with rather low symmetry; but in the NMR
results on SiH_4 [6] no indication of a second transition has been found down
to 4K.

3. EXPERIMENTAL RESULTS AND DATA REDUCTION

Our experiments have been performed on a TOF spectrometer [16] located at the BR2 reactor. The incoming neutron energy was E_0 = 4.77 meV

(4.141 Å); data were collected simultaneously at scattering angles ranging from 15° to 100°, Bragg angles being avoided. The corresponding momentum transfer range for elastic scattering was $0.4 \text{ Å}^{-1} < Q < 2.5 \text{ Å}^{-1}$. At the energy E_0 the resolution was 0.25 meV. The measuring temperatures were 30, 90, 164, 214, 271 K for EOC; 31, 92, 159, 193, 212 K for THFC; 25, 35, 50, 68, 78, 85 K for SiH_4. The temperature could be kept constant better than 1 K (for the highest value). Flat aluminium sample holders were placed in transmission geometry under an angle of 45° with the incoming beam. The polycrystalline clathrate samples were prepared in situ by cooling down from room temperature solutions of the guest substances in heavy water; the sample transmissions were about 70 %. Neutron diffraction tests showed no indication of a contamination by ordinary ice grains. The polycrystalline SiH_4 sample (60 % transmission) was prepared by condensing the gas in a sample holder after purifying it from H_2.

Some typical TOF spectra representing raw data are given in Fig. 1 for EOC deuterate and SiH_4. All show a broad inelastic component; the 3 SiH_4 spectra contain a very broad QE component, the EOC spectra a less pronounced one, which vanishes at the lowest temperature (30 K). The narrow elastic lines represent the resolution function R of the spectrometer.

All spectra have been corrected for background and detector efficiency, normalized to vanadium scattering and transformed to $\hbar\omega$-scale. After that the inelastic part has been separated; this was done by approximating the QE component by one single Lorentzian (folded with R) and the inelastic component by $\exp(\alpha + \beta\omega + \gamma\omega^2)$. Using the results of a least-squares fit, this part could then be subtracted. In the case of SiH_4 Fig. 1 shows that the inelastic component was not clearly separable from the QE line because of the great width of the latter one. Here the fits were difficult and introduced a relative high uncertainty in the data reduction. Finally the QE data

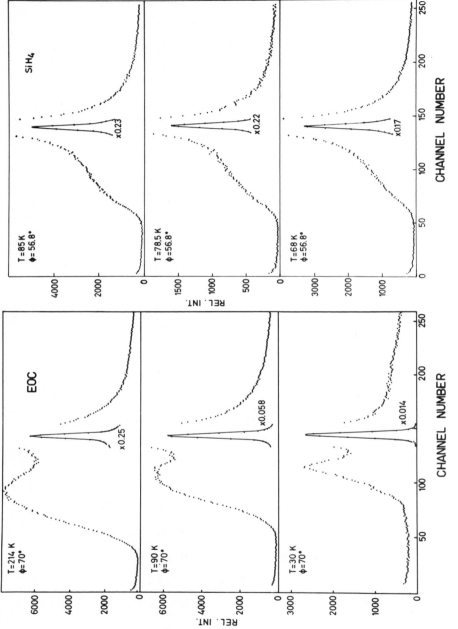

FIG.1. TOF spectra of neutrons scattered under a 70° angle by EOC deuterate (left-hand side) and under a 56.8° angle by plastic silane (right-hand side) for various temperatures; the spectra represent raw data.

for EOC and SiH_4 have been corrected for multiple scattering using a Monte-Carlo program [17]; as scattering function only the QE and the elastic past were introduced. For the THFC results this correction has not yet been performed.

The data reduction described so far referred to the QE-region; for the analysis of the inelastic part no multiple scattering correction has been applied. Effective frequency distributions of the molecular motions have been derived by applying the transformation described in [18].

4. ANALYSIS

4.1. QE component

4.1.1. General

Because of the large incoherent scattering cross-section of the proton the intensity in the neutron spectra is mainly caused by scattering from the H atoms of the guest, respectively, SiH_4 molecules; the QE component has to be interpreted as due to the random molecular reorientations. To gain information about the nature of these motions we have considered two types of theoretical models and compared their predictions with our experimental results. Both involved rotational jumps which occur randomly and instantaneously (the mean time between two jumps, the residence time τ, is long compared with the jump duration) :

a) Jumps around fixed axes and over fixed angles, both determined by the symmetries of the molecule and of its surroundings. From rate equations for residence probabilities one can calculate the classical incoherent scattering function for one proton fixed to a reorienting molecule in a polycrystal :

$$S_{inc.}^{cl.}(Q,\omega) = e^{-2W} \left[C_o(Q)\delta(\omega) + \sum_{i=1}^{\ell} C_i(Q) \cdot L_i(\omega) \right] \tag{1}$$

The $L_i(\omega) = \frac{1}{\pi} \lambda_i/(\lambda_i^2 + \omega^2)$ are Lorentzians, the λ_i being related to the residence time(s) ; e^{-2W} is a (global) Debye-Waller factor taking into account the influence of librations between jumps and of molecular vibrations. This type of model has been applied to EOC, THFC, and SiH_4.

b) Ivanov jump diffusion [20], which allows rotational jumps around all possible axes with the same probability (isotropic rotation) and over all angles ε with a given probability distribution $p(\varepsilon)$; between two jumps again librations can occur. Using the SEARS formalism [19] and the rotational autocorrelation functions F_ℓ (t) given in [20], one can derive the scattering law:

$$S_{inc}(Q,\omega) = e^{-2W} \left[j_0^2 (Qd) \; \delta(\omega) + \sum_{\ell=1}^{\infty} (2\ell + 1) j_\ell^2 (Qd) \; \tilde{F}_\ell(\omega) \right] \qquad (2)$$

with $F_\ell(t) = \exp(-|t|/\tau_\ell)$, $1/\tau_\ell = 1/\tau \; (1 - (2\ell + 1 \int_0^\pi d\varepsilon \; p(\varepsilon) \; \dfrac{\sin (1 + \frac{1}{2})\varepsilon)}{\sin \varepsilon/2}$

$\tilde{F}_\ell(\omega)$ is the Fourier transform of $F_\ell(r)$, $j_\ell(x)$ a spherical Bessel function, d the distance proton-molecular centre of gravity. This type of model has been applied here only to EOC.

The analysis was done in several steps: 1.) From (1) and (2) the ratio $r(Q) = I_{QE} / (I_{QE} + I_{EL})$ between QE and total intensity versus Q has been calculated and compared with the experimental data; in this ratio the Debye-Waller is not involved. 2.) From the scattering laws theoretical shapes of the QE lines could be calculated and fitted to the experimental spectra. 3.) The constancy of the resulting residence times versus Q gave a further check of the model adequacy.

4.1.2. E O c l a t h r a t e

The X-ray study [7] indicates two preferred guest molecule positions, thus two types of reorientations are possible : 1.) 180°-jumps around the

$\bar{4}$ cage axis ("$\bar{4}$-jump", bringing the molecule into an identical position
without movement of the polar axis), 2.) 180°-rotations around a twofold
cage axis, ("2-jump", bringing the molecule from one into the other position
and reversing the dipole moment). We have considered two cases : model I
($\bar{4}$-jumps and 2-jumps allowed) and model II ($\bar{4}$-jumps alone). The corresponding curves r = r(Q) are shown in Fig. 2, together with that for isotropic
rotation (model III), which does not depend on the special distribution
p(ε) in (2).

4.1.3. T H F c l a t h r a t e

The adequacy of two models has been tested; model I involved 120°-
jumps of the guest molecule around the threefold axes and model II 180°-jumps
around the same axes.

4.1.4. S i l a n e

Because of the lack of structural information the choice of axes and
jump angles has to be based mainly on the tetrahedral symmetry of the molecule. One can consider the following types of reorientations : model I :
120°-jumps around the threefold axes, one of them being nonequivalent to the
three other ones (due to the noncubic lattice structure); model II : as I,
but with 4 equivalent axes; model III : 120°-jumps around one fixed threefold
axis; model IV : 90°-jumps around 3 equivalent twofold axes; model V : a
combination of II and IV. The curves r = r(Q) corresponding to these models
are shown in Fig. 2. Because of the uncertainty introduced in the SiH$_4$ data
by the separation of the inelastic component, models containing too much
Lorentzians or too **many** parameters had to be skipped; only model II and III
remained for the analysis.

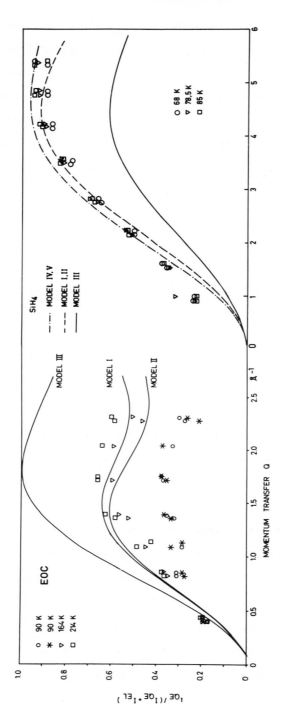

FIG. 2. Ratio of quasi-elastic intensity (I_{QE}) to total intensity ($I_{QE} + I_{EL}$) versus momentum transfer for EOC (left-hand side) and SiH_4 (right-hand side). The curves are predictions of different models (described in the text) involving jump orientations of the molecules. The points correspond to experimental results.

4.2. Inelastic regions

The formalism of [18] has been applied to obtain effective-frequency distributions of molecular motions; this transformation is based on the one-phonon approximation, and no multiple-scattering correction had been applied. The positions of the maxima found in the low-temperature curves are given in Table I together with suggested peak assignments.

5. DISCUSSION

5.1. EO chathrate

By comparison of the theoretical curves $r = r(Q)$ with the experimental data one can exclude model III (isotropic rotation). Thus this type of motion was not present in the region of time and temperature covered by our experiment. The models assuming fixed axes and angles for the jumps were found to be more adequate. The line-shape fits with model ($\bar{4}$- and 2-jumps) gave, however, very high residence times for the 2-jumps ($\tau_2 > 10$ps at 214K) with large statistical uncertainties, explained by resolution effects : for $\tau \gtrsim 8$ ps the QE line width becomes smaller than the elastic line width. Thus the 2-jumps could not be "seen" well in our experiment. Because they involve changes in the dipole direction, our results can be compared with dielectric relaxation times of about 10 ps obtained in [21]. Line-shape fits including $\bar{4}$-jumps alone gave satisfactory results (Fig 3); the residence times were fairly independent of Q. With decreasing temperature also the $\tau_{\bar{4}}$ values come into the neighbourhood of the instrumental resolution : in Fig. 2 the 90 K results show stronger deviations from the model predictions; a repetition of these measurements gave essentially the same values. For long residence times separation of components and multiple scattering corrections become more difficult. The assumption of "instantaneous" jumps is found to be reasonable by comparing with the most probable time for a **free** rotation

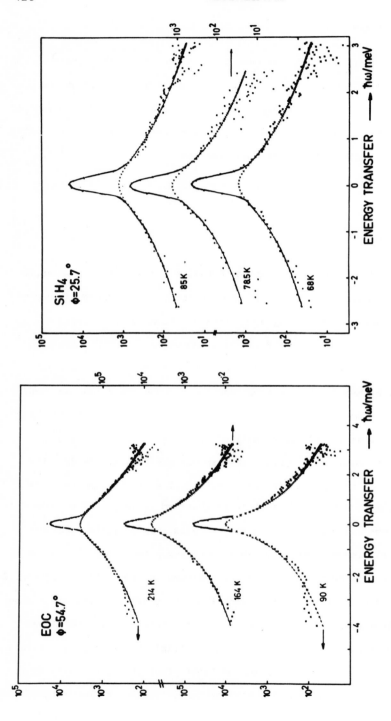

FIG.3. Fitted curves (full lines) to experimental results in the quasi-elastic region in spectra of neutrons scattered in EOC (left-hand side) and SiH₄ (right-hand side). The experimental points (*) are obtained after several corrections, including subtraction of inelastic component and multiple-scattering correction. The crosses (X) represent the theoretical quasi-elastic scattering derived from the models II for EOC and SiH₄ (explained in the text).

around the polar axis. It must be stressed that (1) contains only the proton

jump distance and not the polar-axis direction; strictly **speaking** we can con-

clude only that a model assuming 180°-rotations around the molecular axis

gives a satisfactory description of our data.

The activation energy E_A =(0.35 ± 0.05) kcal·mol^{-1} derived from the

Arrhenius plot (Fig. 4) is lower than the result of 0.9 kcal·mol^{-1} obtained

in [2] for T < 160 K from proton magnetic relaxation. Also dielectric studies

[22], [1] gave mean E_A values of 1.26 kcal·mol^{-1}. This in not **inconsistent**

with our result corresponding to reorientations around the polar axis, while

dielectric studies involve motions of this axis.

In the inelastic spectra of EOC at 30 K several peaks appeared, which

vanished for higher temperatures. They were more clearly visible after

transformation to effective-frequency distributions : in Table I their posi-

tions are given. We have tentatively assigned the two main peaks A, B to

1 → 0 transitions belonging to **librations** around the x-, respectively, the

y-axis. Their frequencies ω_A, ω_B agree fairly well with values given in [22]

(estimations from far IR absorption; for nonpolar principal axes) and in [23]

(IR absorption peaks at 4.3 K). If one assumes for rotations around the

nonpolar axes a twofold cosine-type hindrance potential, the low-temperature

activation energies are derived as $E_A^{(x)} \approx E_A^{(y)}$ = (1.27 ± 0.21) kcal·mol^{-1}.

This value agrees well with E_A = 1.28 kcal·mol^{-1} (average over 31 K < T < 90 K)

given in [22] from dielectric data, thus associated with reorientations dis-

placing the polar axis. All other possible assignments of the peaks A, B

gave too high values at least for one of the activation energies $E_A^{(x)}$, $E_A^{(y)}$.

Peak C has tentatively been assigned to the 1 → 0 transition for a libration

around the z - axis (parallel to the $\bar{4}$ cage axis). The assumption of a twofold

potential led to a much too high E_A value; however, the cage shape suggests

that a sixfold potential is more appropriate; the corresponding low temperature

TABLE I. PEAK POSITIONS (cm^{-1}) IN THE EFFECTIVE-FREQUENCY DISTRIBUTIONS OF EOC, THFC, AND SiH$_4$ AS DERIVED FROM LOW-TEMPERATURE INELASTIC NEUTRON SPECTRA (INS), COMPARED WITH INFRA-RED DATA (IR)

L(α): libration around principal α-axis, T: vibration.

peak	EOC			THFC			SiH$_4$ (phase II)		
	IR	NIS	comment	IR	NIS	comment	IR	NIS	comment
A	32 [22] 35 [23]	29 ± 2	L (x)	-	19 ± 3	(small bump)	35 [5]	32 ± 2	T
B	43 [22]	39 ± 4	L (y)	25 [24]	28 ± 2	L (x)	53 [5]	49 ± 5	T
C	64 [23]	57 ± 4	L (z)	38 [24]	38 ± 3	L (y)	61 [5]	65 ± 8	T
D							85 [5]	77...89	(small bump occa- sionally

activation energy is $E_A^{(z)}$ = (0.40 ± 0.10) kcal·mol^{-1}. This is in good agreement with the value (0.35 ± 0.05) kcal·mol^{-1} derived from the temperature dependence of the residence time.

5.2. THF Clathrate

The analysis of the THFC data was performed in the same manner as for EOC. The theoretical and experimental r = r(Q) curves agreed slightly better for model I (120°-jumps) than for model II (180°-jumps), the latter giving residence times larger by a factor 2. From our analysis a clear decision in favour of I or II was not yet possible. The activation energies were in

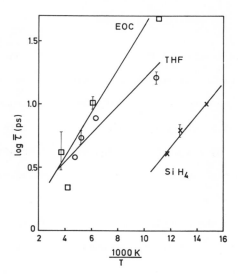

FIG.4. Arrhenius plots of the residence times for re-orientations of EO and THF molecules in clathrate deuterates and of SiH₄ in the plastic phase I. The fitted straight lines have been used to determine activation energies.

both cases E_A = (0.20 ± 0.05) kcal mol^{-1}; from dielectric measurements a value of 0.3 kcal·mol^{-1} has been derived [3]. For model I the Arrhenius plot is shown in Fig. 4. The positions of two peaks B, C and a small bump A in the effective frequency distribution are given in Table I. They agree well with IR frequencies [24]; because these belong to librations around nonpolar axes, we associate ω_B, ω_C with 1 → 0 transitions for such motions. Since the cage has nearly spherical shape, one can assume nearly equal wall heights ($V_x \approx V_y$) for the hindrance potentials around the x- and y-axes; therefore using the relation $\omega_x/\omega_y \approx \sqrt{V_x I_y/V_y I_x} \approx \sqrt{I_y/I_x}$ one can assign ω_B, ω_C to librations around the x-respectively the y-axes. A peak corresponding to the z-axis librations could not be identified.

5.3. Silane

Fig. 2 shows that model III can be excluded; that means (see 4.1.4) that only model II had to be used in the analysis. The resulting line-shape fits (Fig. 3) show that the assumption of 120°-jumps around 4 equivalent triad axes gives a satisfactory description of our results. However, the uncertainty introduced by the difficult separation of the inelastic component leads to a large scattering of the residence time values. From their temperature dependence we obtained as activation energy E_A = (0.25 ± 0.06) kcal·mol^{-1} for reorientations in the plastic phase I. The effective frequency distribution (derived from 25 K data, thus in phase II) shows 3 peaks A, B, C, and a shoulder D. In Table I the corresponding frequencies are compared with the IR data of [5]. We assigned tentatively A, B, C to translational and D to librational transitions. This interpretation is supported by the following arguments : a) [25] describes the specific heat using a frequency distribution containing a Debye- and an Einstein term (ω_D = 66 cm^{-1}, ω_E = 133 cm^{-1}) for the translations and the vibrations; in [26] ω_D = 65.5 cm^{-1} is given for. T ≈ 14 K, where the librations do not contribute to the specific heat. The closeness of ω_A, ω_B, ω_C to the Debye frequency suggests their translational nature. b) A specific heat calculation using ω_E = 113 cm^{-1} for the librational and the low-energy part of our experimental distribution for the translational part gave satisfactory agreement with the curve of [25]. c) In [6] from NMR data for reorientations in phase II (probably around threefold axes) activation energies of (1.92 ± 0.06) kcal·mol^{-1} and (1.10 ± 0.03) kcal·mol^{-1} have been obtained for T > 47 K and T < 47 K, respectively. Using a threefold cosine potential with a barrier height of 1.6 kcal·mol^{-1} we have calculated a frequency of 110 cm^{-1} for the 1 → 0 transition. Of course, we do not mean that an Einstein level is an adequate description of the librational motions, but we believe that the translational and the librational modes are clearly separated.

ACKNOWLEDGEMENTS

The authors wish to thank Dr. Nève de Mévergnies for his constant interest in their work. Technical assistance by Mssrs. J. Brouwers, M. Van Roy and J. Baudeweyns is greatly appreciated. One of us (J.V.) is grateful to IIKW for granting financial support in the framework of a research project on the study of molecular solids by neutron scattering and NMR.

REFERENCES

[1] GARG, S.K., MORRIS, B., DAVIDSON, D.W., J. Chem. Soc. Faraday Trans. II 68 (1972) 481.

[2] HAYWARD, R.J., PACKER, K.J., Mol. Phys. 25 (1973) 1443.

[3] DAVIDSON, D.W., Can. J. Chem. 49 (1971) 1224.

[4] GARG, S.K., DAVIDSON, D.W., RIPMEESTER, J.A., J. Magn. Resonance 15 (1974) 295.

[5] FOURNIER, R.P., SAVOIE, R., NGUYEN DINH THE, BELZILE, R., CABANA, A., Can. J. Chem. 50 (1972) 35.

[6] JANSSENS, G., VAN HECKE, P., VAN GERVEN, L., Chem. Phys. Letters 42 (1976) 445.

[7] MCMULLAN, R.K., JEFFREY, G.A., J. Chem. Phys. 42 (1965) 2725 and MAK, T.C.W., MCMULLAN, R.K., J. Chem. Phys. 42 (1965) 2732.

[8] Von STACKELBERG, M., MÜLLER, H.R., Z. Elektrochem. 58 (1954) 25.

[9] CUNNINGHAM, G.L., BOYD, A.W., MYERS, R.J., GWINN, W.D., LE VAN, W.I., J. Chem. Phys. 19 (1951) 676.

[10] HOLLANDER, F., JEFFREY, G.A., J. Chem. Phys. 66 (1977) 4699.

[11] EYSTER, J.M., PROHOFSKY, E.W., Spectrochim. Acta 30A (1974) 2041.

[12] WILDE, R.E., SRINIVASAN, T.K.K., J. Phys. Chem. Solids 36 (1975) 119.

[13] SEARS,W.M., MORRISON,J.A., J. Chem. Phys. 62 (1975) 2736.

[14] LEGRAND,E., PRESS,W., Sol. State Comm. 18 (1976) 1353.

[15] STAVELEY,L.A.K., Ann. Rev. Phys. Chem. 13 (1962) 351.

[16] WEGENER,W., HAUTECLER,S., in : Research with BR2 Neutron Beams, Report BLG 519 (1977).

[17] COPLEY,J.R.D., Comp. Phys. Comm. 7 (1974) 289.

[18] PRASK,H., BOUTIN,H., YIP,S., J. Chem. Phys. 48 (1968) 3367.

[19] SEARS,V.F., Can. J. Phys. 45 (1967) 237.

[20] IVANOV,E.N., Soviet Phys. - J. Exper. Theor. Phys. 18 (1964) 1041.

[21] DAVIES,M., WILLIAMS,K., Trans. Faraday Soc. 64 (1968) 529.

[22] DAVIDSON,D.W., in : Water, Vol. 2, Ed. F. FRANKS, Plenum Press, New York - London (1973) 115.

[23] BERTIE,J.E., JACOBS,S.M., Can. J. Chem. 55 (1977) 1777.

[24] KLUG,D.D., WHALLEY,E., Can. J. Chem. 51 (1973) 4062.

[25] CLUSIUS,K., Z. Phys. Chem. B23 (1933) 213.

[26] KLEIN,M.L., MORRISON,J.A., WEIR,R.D., Disc. Faraday Soc. 48 (1969) 93.

DISCUSSION

A. HÜLLER: Is your jump model for the rotational motion at 214 K consistent with a potential strength of only 0.35 kcal/mol?

W. WEGENER: The question concerns EOC. The existence of potential minima deep enough to define preferred orientations is supported by X-ray diffraction and by the fact that our results could not be described by the model assuming random changes of the axes and angles, which would correspond to many shallow minima (see Fig.2). At the highest temperatures, however, the residence times are not really small compared with the 'classical jump times'; although it provides good line-shape fits, the instantaneous jump model thus seems somewhat oversimplified. The value of 0.35 kcal/mol for the 'activation energy' derived from an Arrhenius plot of the residence times is therefore questionable. The difficulty you are thinking of could possibly be related to invalidity of the assumption of a constant E_A value over the full range of temperature.

NATURE OF ROTATIONAL MOTIONS IN THE SOLID PHASES OF NEOPENTANE AND TERTIAL BUTYL CHLORIDE

K.E. LARSSON, T. MÅNSSON, L.G. OLSSON
The Royal Institute of Technology,
Institute of Reactor Physics,
Stockholm,
Sweden

Abstract

NATURE OF ROTATIONAL MOTIONS IN THE SOLID PHASES OF NEOPENTANE AND
TERTIAL BUTYL CHLORIDE.

A cold-neutron-scattering study was performed on the solid phases of neopentane and
t-butyl chloride. For neopentane with phase transition temperatures of 140 and 257 K
(melting point), measurements were made at 135, 148, 173, 213 and 253 K. A separate study
was performed in the liquid phase at 265 K. In t-butyl chloride with phase transitions at
183, 219 and 247 K (melting point), measurements were performed at 173, 205 and 235 K.
The aim of the measurements was the nature of the rotations of the rigid, globular molecules
in various phases. As a result of the present study it is found that the molecules are "frozen
in" in the lowest temperature phases. In the plastic phases, 140–257 K for neopentane and
183–247.5 K for t-butyl chloride, the important conclusion is that neither free rotations
nor well developed librations exist in these phases. The rotational motion is relatively well
approximated by Langevin rotational diffusion but also with a two-step stochastic model,
the relaxation times of which turn out to be so short that it is not possible to make a distinction between this model and the Langevin model. The only tendency of somewhat dominating
librations in plastic phases is observed in neopentane in a temperature range of about
140–170 K, i.e. close to the transition point.

1. INTRODUCTION

A variety of spectral methods has been used to investigate the structure
and atomic dynamics of the globular molecules neopentane, $C(CH_3)_4$, and
tertial butyl chloride, $(CH_3)_3$-C-Cl, in their solid phases [1–5]. Both exhibit
plastic phases, the plastic phase for neopentane ranging from 140 to 257 K and
the two plastic phases for t-butyl chloride ranging from 183 to 219 K, phase II,
and further from 219 to 247.5 K, phase I, respectively. It was shown that not
only the static structure changes at these phase transitions — from hexagonal to
fcc in neopentane and from monoclinic to tetragonal to fcc in t-butyl chloride,

all with increasing temperature — but also the nature of the rotational motion of molecules, tending to some kind of rotational disorder. The exact nature of these rotational motions is unclear as yet. Various hypotheses involving such contrasts as free rotations as one extreme case and well developed librations followed by rotational jumps as the opposite extreme were proposed in the past.

In general, the spectral methods applied to study the rotational dynamics were selective such that one particular component of the motion was investigated. Typically, in spherical-harmonics expansion of the angular orientational correlation function, only the term $\ell = 1$, as by the use of dielectric relaxation and infra-red absorption spectroscopy methods, or $\ell = 2$, as by the use of Raman scattering or NMR-relaxation methods, were picked out for study. In an inelastic, incoherent neutron scattering experiment *all* the proton motions are studied simultaneously and, therefore, the full correlation function is studied in such an experiment, which may be regarded as a source of complication. The useful property of momentum sensitivity adds, however, an advantage to the neutron studies. A difficulty may arise because of the large moments of inertia of the two molecules under discussion, $I = 2.2 \times 10^{-38}$ g · cm² for neopentane, $I_\parallel = 1.8 \times 10^{-38}$ g · cm² and $I_\perp = 3.2 \times 10^{-38}$ g · cm² for t-butyl chloride. $I_\parallel$ and $I_\perp$ are the moments of inertia parallel and perpendicular to the C-Cl axis, which is the symmetry axis. Such values of I lead to most probable classical rotational frequencies, Ω_R, of the order of 10^{12} r · s^{-1} corresponding to rotational energy transfers of the order of ± 0.7 meV in an inelastic energy transfer. High resolution is, undoubtedly, necessary. Cold neutrons of an energy of 3.7 meV with an energy spread of about 0.15 meV were, therefore, used in the present study. The aim of the study was to clarify as much as possible of the nature of the molecular rotational motions.

Our particular choice of the molecular pair was dictated *both* by the fact that the two molecules are, to a good approximation, spherical and in this respect similar *and* because they are different in two respects: the t-butyl chloride molecule exhibits a dipole moment of 2.14 debye and has a cylindrically symmetric mass distribution round the C-Cl binding line, whereas there is no dipole moment from the neopentane molecule, which has, moreover, a spherically symmetric mass distribution. One could guess that the rotational motions of the pair in the plastic phases would differ in some characteristic way.

2.   MEASUREMENTS AND EXAMPLES OF EXPERIMENTAL RESULTS

A hybrid crystal-chopper time-of-flight spectrometer for cold neutrons at the R2 reactor in Studsvik was used to analyse neutrons from approximately 90% transmission specimens of slab geometry. Greatest importance in the

current neutron scattering studies must be ascribed to numerous corrections
to be performed with utmost care. These corrections are:

(a)   Normalization of the various sets of measured spectra, observed at scattering
angles from 15 to 85°, in several detector positions, to the incident neutron flux
by monitors in the incident neutron beam.

(b)   Normalization according to detector efficiency.

(c)   Background subtraction. The white background is, in general, subtracted
separately.

(d)   The wavelength dependence on the neutron detection ($^{10}BF_3$ gas).

(e)   Multiple scattering is calculated by using the model giving the best fit and
added to the calculated single-scattering cross-section [6]. Multiple scattering
by the thin sample container walls is neglected in the present study.

The aluminium holders (in the case of t-butyl, chloride teflon tubes) were
held at the desired temperatures in a cryostat controlled to an accuracy of ±1 K.
The neopentane runs were made at 135 K in the crystalline phase, at 148, 173,
213, 239 and 253 K in the plastic phase and at 265 K in the liquid phase. t-butyl
chloride was run at 173 K in phase III — the crystalline phase —, at 205 K in
phase II and at 235 K in phase I, where II and I are plastic phases.
As is illustrated in Fig.1, the scattered-neutron spectra from neopentane
change rather drastically in going from the crystalline to the plastic phase and,
in addition, within the plastic phase as the temperature is increased. The change
in passing the melting point is relatively smaller. In Fig.2, we observe that a
dramatic change of the spectrum from t-butyl chloride occurs in going from
phase III (crystalline) to phase II (plastic), whereas the change in going from
phase II to phase I is minor. Several different angles of observation were used
and the spectra observed in various directions show the same general behaviour
as illustrated in Figs 1 and 2. The most striking observation is that the elastic
line in the crystalline phase is strongly broadened in the plastic phase and a
considerable intensity increase is simultaneously observed in the energy transfer
range from 0 to about 7 meV (1200 to 700 $\mu s \cdot m^{-1}$).

3.   MODELS AND INTERPRETATION

Our philosophy of analysis is to construct and use models that describe
all three proton motions observed, i.e. the translational and rotational motions
of the rigid molecule and the torsional motion of the methyl groups round the
C-C lines of binding. Higher-energy motions are not observed in the cold-neutron-
scattering experiment. We are, thus, not trying to isolate any "quasi-elastic peaks",

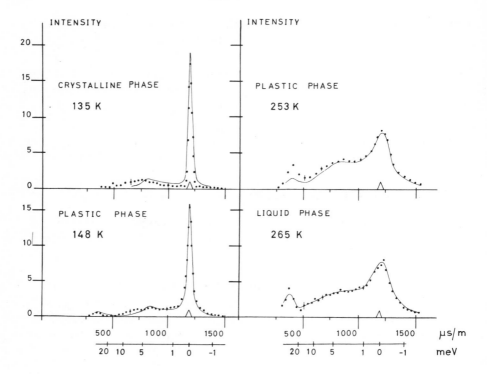

FIG.1. *The temperature dependence of the measured and calculated t-o-f spectra for neopentane at one angle of observation, 66° (for the liquid state 60°). The dots are the experimental data and the solid lines the stochastic two-step model combined with the proper centre-of-mass motion (Section 3.3). In the crystalline phase, 135 K, τ_0 was set equal to 1×10^{-11} s, a limit chosen for computer-technical reasons. Obviously, this time is much too short. — The multiple scattering has been added to the calculated cross-sections. The Bessel function J_0^2 (κr) is equal to zero for the angle of 66° and zero energy transfer. The spectra are approximately normalized to the same intensity at κ = 0.*

a very uncertain and arbitrary method, which was much used in the past before the full advanced use of computers was developed. We rather chose to calculate the entire spectrum observed. The physical assumptions we have to use still involve a certain degree of unavoidable arbitrariness. Our primary assumption is that the transitions, rotations and torsions are uncoupled. The general cross-section formulation used is, thus, given by

$$\frac{d^2 \sigma_{inc}}{d\Omega d\omega} = N a_{inc}^2 \frac{k}{k_0} \exp\left(\frac{\hbar\omega}{2k_B T}\right) \frac{1}{\pi} \int_0^\infty I_{cm} (\kappa,t)\, I_{rot} (\kappa,t)\, I_{tors} (\kappa,t) \cos \omega t\, dt$$

$$(1)$$

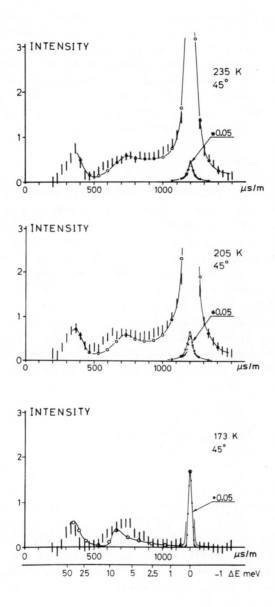

FIG.2.   Observed neutron spectra in phase I at 235 K, phase II at 205 K and phase III at
173 K (vertical dashes) in t-butyl chloride at an angle of observation of 45°. The solid line
with rings corresponds to theoretically calculated effective spectra, including multiple
scattering. In phase III, the solid line corresponds to the Debye model for CH_3-group motion,
in phases II and I to the stochastic two-step rotational-diffusion model folded with the Debye
spectrum for CH_3-group motion.

where $I_{cm}(\kappa,t)$, $I_{rot}(\kappa,t)$ and $I_{tors}(\kappa,t)$ are the intermediate scattering functions for translation, rotation and torsion, respectively, $\hbar\kappa$ is the momentum transfer, $\hbar\omega$ the energy transfer in the scattering process, t the time, and k and k_0 are the wave vectors of the scattered and ingoing neutrons, respectively. T is the absolute temperature of the sample, a_{inc} is scattering length of the proton, and $\dot{N}$ the number of scattering protons. To obtain information on rotations of the rigid molecule we have to make reasonable and — as far as possible — accurate assumptions for the translational and torsional motions.

3.1. Translational motions

We start from the general observation that the rotational energy transfers, if present, are centred at relatively small energies. From the general appearance of the spectra observed in the crystalline phases of both samples (Figs 1 and 2), we conclude that the neutrons do not observe any type of rotation here. The rotations, if existing at all, must consist of long life-time librational motions of the molecule as a rigid unit. On the neutrons' time scale of observation of $t < 10^{-11}$ s, they are completely frozen in. The spectra in these two temperature phases must, therefore, have their origin in translations and motion of the methyl groups, the latter affecting only the high-energy end of the spectrum — $t < 500\ \mu s \cdot m^{-1}$ or $\Delta E > 20$ meV — which is rather uninteresting for our present study. The spectrum in the lower-temperature phase corresponding to energy transfers of up to about 20 meV is therefore fitted with a Debye spectrum of a suitable form:

$$f(\omega) = 0.125\ \frac{3\omega^2}{\omega_{D_1}^3} + 0.625\ \frac{3\omega^2}{\omega_{D_2}^3} + 0.250\ \frac{3\omega^2}{\omega_{D_3}^3} \tag{2}$$

with $\omega_{D_1} = 0.44 \times 10^{13}$, $\omega_{D_2} = 0.63 \times 10^{13}$ and $\omega_{D_3} = 0.75 \times 10^{13}$ rad·s^{-1} for neopentane and an identical form for t-butyl chloride but with $\omega_{D_1} = 1.0 \times 10^{13}$, $\omega_{D_2} = 1.2 \times 10^{13}$ and $\omega_{D_3} = 1.4 \times 10^{13}$ rad·s^{-1}. These frequency functions, combined with the phonon expansion formula [7], give a fair picture of the neutron spectrum caused by translational motion. The frequency functions were assumed to be temperature-independent and were used in all solid phases. The fit obtained in the low-temperature phases is exemplified for T = 173 K in t-butyl chloride in Fig.2.

There is no possibility of changing the shape of the translational spectrum when entering into the plastic phases, because no additional information exists on these spectra and their possible change when the structure of the samples changes. We thus rely on the assumption that the translational spectra remain unchanged over the temperature phases.

3.2. Torsional motions

The neutron spectra scattered from the torsional motion of the CH_3 groups in various molecules were studied by several experimenters [8]. In general, the barrier for the methyl group against rotation is so high that the mean life-time between rotational jumps is much longer than the neutron observation time, which is $< 10^{-11}$ s and is dictated by the resolution of the instrument. The neutrons observe the methyl groups as performing a librational motion going on for ever. According to this observation and using the analysis and expressions of Grant et al. [8] we assume that

$$I_{tors}(\kappa,t) = (1 - p) + p\, I'_{tors}(\kappa,t) \qquad\qquad (3)$$

where p is the probability for de-excitation of the torsions by the neutron. This factor is slightly temperature-dependent and has a value close to 0.1. A form, Gaussian in t, was empirically applied to describe $I'_{tors}(\kappa,t)$, the broad band round the first excited level of torsions. Transformed to the (κ,ω)-space the function $S'_{tors}(\kappa,\omega)$ is a Gaussian in ω centred about 33 meV and having a width (FWHM) of 20 meV. The width is thus assumed κ-independent, which is reasonable because near 33 meV the κ-values do not change much with the angle of observation in a cold-neutron-scattering experiment. From Figs 1 and 2, it is seen that these empirical assumptions give a reasonable description for the observed spectrum.

3.3. Rotational motion

With the preliminaries as given in sections 3.1. and 3.2., we may approach our main problem: to investigate the nature of the rotational motions in the plastic phases, which obviously are responsible for the broadening of the elastic peak and the intensity increase for smaller energy transfers, $\Delta E < 7$ meV. The investigation covers the full scale of models from undamped librations to free rotation with Langevin rotational diffusion as an intermediate case with strong damping. Since the mass distribution is spherical in neopentane and axially symmetric in t-butyl chloride, different formulations must, in general, be used to describe the rotational dynamics. For one particular model, however, the cross-section was only formulated for a spherical mass distribution. In that case, an average moment of inertia (arithmetic mean) was used for t-butyl chloride and the molecule was subsequently treated as if it had a spherical mass distribution.

In general, the motions were assumed to occur isotropically, which allows us to use Sears' formulation [9] of the scattering functions:

$$I_{rot}(\kappa, t) = \sum_{\ell=0}^{\infty} (2\ell + 1) j_\ell(\kappa b)^2 F_\ell(t) \tag{4}$$

Here $j_\ell(\kappa b)$ is the spherical Bessel function of order ℓ, b is the distance from the proton to the axis of rotation, and $F_\ell(t)$ is the rotational relaxation function of order ℓ. In one of the models tested the rotation is not assumed to occur isotropically and, therefore, Eq.(4) cannot be used. This case will be described separately. In all cases, the physics of the rotational mechanism is contained in the relaxation or correlation function $F_\ell(t)$. The following models were tested in appropriate phases or temperature ranges and for the appropriate type of molecule:

(a) The molecules rotate freely. The corresponding rotational relaxation functions for the cases of spherically and axially symmetric molecules are formulated [9, 10] and given in Appendix I-1. These models are tested for neopentane near melting and for t-butyl chloride in phase I.

(b) The molecules perform undamped libration. The corresponding exact relaxation functions are unknown. An approximate form was guessed and used in formula (4) for isotropic rotation. This form constitutes one extreme limit in the more general stochastic two-step rotational diffusion model [11]. The guessed form — see Appendix I-2 — contains three parameters, of which only two are independent. The form of the spectrum

$$S_\ell(\omega) = \frac{1}{\pi} \int_0^{\infty} F_\ell(t) \cos \omega t \, dt$$

consists of a central peak of intensity F_{lib} surrounded by two Gaussian distributions centred about $\pm \omega_0$, of width $\sigma(\ell(\ell+1))^{1/2}$ and of integrated intensity $1 - F_{lib}$. The parameters F_{lib}, ω_0 and σ are interconnected via the relation

$$\omega_0 = \frac{\Omega_r}{\left((1 - F_{lib})(1 + \left(\frac{\sigma}{\omega_0}\right)^2)\right)^{1/2}} \tag{5}$$

The physical meaning of the parameters ω_0 and σ is obvious. F_{lib} is a constant with a value $0 < F_{lib} < 1$. $F_{lib} = 1$ — no inelastic scattering — means that only the ground state is populated (deep potential well). $F_{lib} = 0$ — all scattering inelastic — means that the librational spectrum is highly excited (shallow potential well).

This model is tested for t-butyl chloride in phase II. As the formula is worked out for a spherically symmetric mass distribution, an average moment of inertia is used in the computation.

(c) The molecules perform a stochastic, isotropic, rotational diffusion consisting of an infinite succession of two consecutive steps, of which one is a free rotation more or less damped, and the other one is a libration more or less damped. The relaxation times for the two processes are τ_1 for free rotation and τ_0 for libration. The two steps are described by the partial relaxation functions given in Appendix   I-1 and I-2. When $\tau_0 \gg \tau_1$, we have the limit (2) above and when $\tau_1 \gg \tau_0$ we are in the limit (1). In general, we find a complicated mixture if $\tau_0 \sim \tau_1$ and both times are short, such that $\Omega_r \tau_1 \sim \omega_0 \tau_0 \sim 1$. The analytical expression for $S_\varrho(\omega)$ is well known ([11], Eq.(14)). Parameters at disposal are τ_0 and τ_1 and the two independent parameters F_{lib} and ω_0 for librational motion as mentioned under (2). A form suitable for computation is given in Appendix I-3. The same form was used for both molecules. It is to be noted that the formulas were worked out for a spherically symmetric mass distribution (spherical top) and fit the neopentane case ideally. For the case of t-butyl chloride, an average moment of inertia is defined (arithmetic mean) and used in the computations involving this model assumption.

(d) The molecules perform isotropic Langevin rotational diffusion. This is indistinguishable from the previous case when τ_0 and τ_1 become small, i.e. of the same order as the relaxation times, $\tau = I/\xi$, defined from a Langevin diffusion equation, where ξ is the friction coefficient and I the moment of inertia. In the case of neopentane we deal with a spherically symmetric molecule and we have only one friction coefficient ξ treated as a disposable parameter. In the case of t-butyl chloride, we have to deal with an axially symmetric molecule (treated as a symmetric top) and, therefore, we have two friction coefficients $\xi = \xi_{33}$ and $\xi = \xi_{11} = \xi_{22}$, where index 33 refers to rotation round the C-Cl axis and indices 11 or 22 refer to rotation about the two axes perpendicular to the first one. These two coefficients are disposable parameters. In principle, this type of motion, characterized by a torque consisting of a friction term proportional to the angular velocity and another caused by white noise, is the simplest of all. The problem of evaluating the $F_\varrho(t)$: s is complicated and involves several simplifications [12, 13]. Approximate expressions for $F_\varrho(t)$ are given in Appendix I-4. Rotational diffusion constants are defined by the Einstein relations, $D_{ii} = k_B T/\xi_{ii}$ for the three axes of rotation.

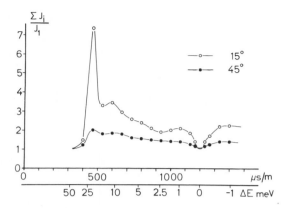

FIG.3. *Ratio of total scattering from t-butyl chloride sample to single scattering as a function of energy transfer at angles of observation of 15° and 45°.*

   (e) The molecules perform uniaxial rotational diffusion. Such a motion could possibly be envisaged for the t-butyl chloride molecules in phase II, if the molecules performed rotational diffusion about the C-Cl axis. In principle, this case differs little from the previous case of isotropic Langevin diffusion. The physical meaning of this case is quite clear: in this case, the rotational motion about the two axes perpendicular to the C-Cl axes is assumed to be completely hindered. Because of the uniaxial nature of the motion, Sears' formulas (Eq.(3)) cannot be used. The correct formulation for $I_{rot}(\kappa,t)$ has been derived for the case of simple rotational diffusion [14]. We adopt this κ-dependence but use the time relaxation functions $F_\varrho(t)$ appropriate to Langevin diffusion, i.e. the $F_\varrho(t)$: s obtained from the previous case (4) when $\xi_{11} = \infty$. The only disposable parameter is the friction constant ξ_{33}. The appropriate formulas are given in Appendix I-5.

   In each case, when necessary, the Fourier transforms needed to obtain the scattering functions were calculated by means of a fast Fourier transform aligorithm [15, 16]. The important multiple-scattering correction was calculated in the following way: the first-order scattering as given by the cross-section of Eq.(1) above was computer-calculated and used as an input to the multiple-scattering calculation code, originally developed by Cocking [6]. The second-order scattering obtained plus a correction for higher-order terms were then added to the first-order scattering. The result is an effective cross-section, depending on sample geometry, orientation and thickness, corresponding to the observed one. This is then compared directly to the measured spectra. An example of the size of the entire scattering as compared to the fundamental first-order scattering is given in Fig.3. It may be noted here that the effective cross-section in the high-frequency end of the spectrum ($\Delta E > 20$ meV), where the correction is large, is rather model-insensitive. Very little can, therefore, be predicted on the nature of molecular motions leading to energy transfers larger than about 20 meV. Fortunately, the important rotational scattering corresponds to smaller energy transfers. Finally, it should be noted that terms up to $\ell = 10$ or 12 were included in the computations of rotational cross-sections.

In all cases, the computer-calculated effective cross-sections were normalized to the measured ones in the same way, i.e. at the elastic peak (the peak value) of just one angle of observation, which was a 15° angle of observation for t-butyl chloride and an angle of 20° for neopentane. The rest then follows from this. Considering the rapid variation of the cross-section both with energy transfer, $\hbar\omega$, and with angle, or scattering vector, κ, this is a rather stringent test of the models.

4.   RESULTS

4.1. Neopentane

First of all, the experimental results show that the rotational motions are frozen in below the plastic transition temperature of 140 K. The rotations are set free above 140 K. As is indicated in Fig.1, the two-step stochastic model (3.3.(c)) fits the data well over the whole plastic phase with proper choice of the relaxation times τ_0 and τ_1, ω_0 and F_{lib}. This is also indicated in Figs 4A and B (solid lines). As is also shown in the same figure, the Langevin rotational diffusion model (3.3.(d)) fits the data approximately as well. On the other hand, if one lets the free rotation component dominate, the fit is destroyed. The important observation is (Fig.5) that the times τ_1 and τ_0 remain short, $0.4 \times 10^{-12} < \tau_0, \tau_1 < 7 \times 10^{-12}$ s, which, in general, means that angular steps are small, $\Omega_R \tau_1 \sim 0.5$ radians, $\Omega_R = (k_B T/I)^{1/2}$, which gives a mean angular step of about 30°. It is only in the neighbourhood of the transition point that librations are reasonably well developed as $\omega_0 \tau_0 \sim 18$ at 148 K, which indicates a damping to 1/e over three librational periods. On the other hand, $\omega_0 \tau_0 < 1$ in the upper temperature region of the plastic phase. Pertinent data for neopentane are collected in Table I. It is easily understood that, with such strong damping, a distinction between Langevin diffusion and some type of step model is impossible. We should remember that, at least, ten terms are added ($\ell=1, ... 10$) in Sears' expansion. This tends to smear out any details that might introduce a difference between the two models. A comparison between the rotational relaxation functions $F_\varrho(t)$ for the two fitted models indicates that the difference between the two sets of $F_\varrho(t)$:s is so small that it will not be observed in the final summed and folded result. An example of $F_1(t)$ and $F_2(t)$ is given in Fig.6. Conclusions on liquid neopentane have already been published [17]. These

213 K

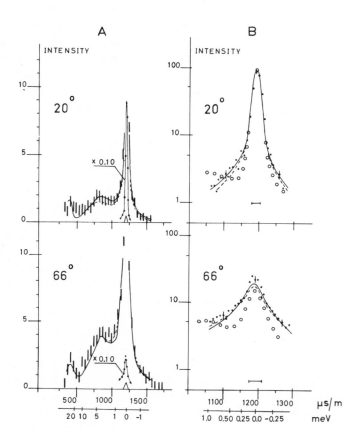

FIG.4A.   Calculated and measured t-o-f spectra for neopentane at 213 K.   Vertical bars or
dots are the experimental data.   Solid and broken lines denote the two-step model
$(\tau_1 = 0.8 \times 10^{-12}$ and $\tau_0 = 1.4 \times 10^{-12}$ s) and rotational Langevin model, respectively.   Both
models are combined with a Debye spectrum for the translational motion.

   B.   Quasi-elastic peak.   The denotations are the same as in Fig.4A.   For comparison,
the rings indicate the two-step model with the rotational mode of motion dominating
$(\tau_1/\tau_0 = 3.2)$, and the horizontal bar at the energy transfer 0 shows the available time
resolution of the spectrometer.   The multiple-scattering contribution has been added to the
calculated cross-sections.

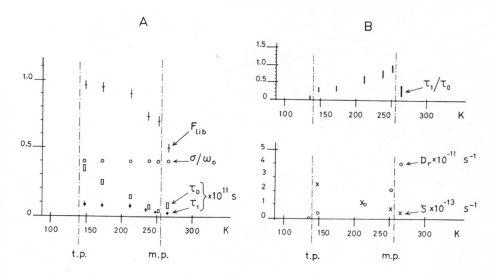

FIG.5. *Experimentally obtained temperature dependence of the parameters governing the models tried for neopentane. (A) Two-step model. The rotational and librational relaxation times τ_1 and τ_0 are denoted by dots and rectangles, respectively, the parameter F_{lib} by bars and the ratio σ/ω_0 by rings. (B) The bars denote the ratio τ_1/τ_0, derived by the two-step model; the rings denote the rotational-diffusion constant obtained from the Langevin model. Crosses are the corresponding friction coefficients.*

TABLE I. LIBRATIONS DERIVED FROM TWO-STEP MODEL FIT

T (K)	F_{lib}	$\omega_0 \times 10^{-12}$ $(rad \cdot s^{-1})$	$\tau_0 \times 10^{12}$ (s)	$\omega_0 \tau_0$	Remarks
265 [a]	0.5	1.3	< 1.0	< 1.7	
253	0.7	2.1	0.3	0.5	strongly damped
239	0.75	2.3	0.6	1.4	libration
213	0.86	2.9	1.4	4.0	
173	0.95	4.4	2.4	10	well defined
148	0.97	5.2	3.5	18	libration

[a] Liquid.

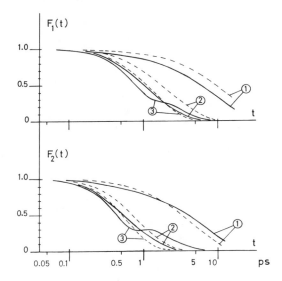

FIG.6. *Some rotational relaxation functions calculated from the models giving the best overall agreement with the measured data on neopentane. Solid lines denote the two-step model and broken lines the rotational Langevin diffusion. Curves labelled with 1, 2 and 3 indicate the temperature dependence at 148, 253 and 265 K, respectively.*

results indicate that there is no important change of rotational motion in passing the melting point. If anything, there is a tendency for the molecules to have an increased mean time for libration in the liquid near the melting point. A similar tendency was observed in molecular-dynamics calculations [18]. On the whole, however, the real melting point for rotations is at the phase transition at 140 K.

4.2. t-butyl chloride

As has already been stated and exemplified in Fig.1, the spectrum observed in phase III at 173 K is characterized by the fact that the elastic peak is sharp — given by resolution width — and a very weak intensity is observed in the near-elastic region up to $\Delta E \sim 2$ meV. It is concluded that only the lattice vibrational motions are observed exactly as for neopentane below 140 K. The rotation is "frozen in", relaxation time $\gg 10^{-11}$ s, and may have degenerated to very small amplitude librations not observable here.

Next, we turn to the plastic phases II and I. As is seen from Fig.2, there are two fundamental changes in going from phase III, i.e. (a) there is a broadening of the elastic peak and (b) there is now a large intensity observed for near-elastic scattering contributing both below and above $\Delta E \sim 2$ meV. This intensity is of rotational origin as is proved by the following results. First, the extreme

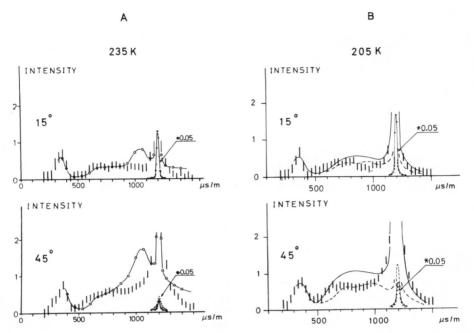

FIG.7A.   *Free rotational model combined with Debye spectrum and CH₃ torsion model (solid lines with rings) in phase I of t-butyl chloride at 235 K and at angles of observation of 15° and 45°, compared to observed data (vertical dashes).*

B.   Undamped libration, $\tau_0 = \infty$, $\tau_1 = 0$ (dashed line) and damped libration, $\tau_0 = 2.5 \times 10^{-12}$ s, $\tau_1 = 0$ (solid line) combined with Debye spectra and CH₃ spectra at 205 K in phase II compared to observed data (vertical dashes) at angles of observation of 15° and 45°.

assumptions on rotation were tested. We tried free rotational motions (Appendix I-1) in phase I, where such a case could possibly occur. As is illustrated in Fig.7A, this assumption is safely ruled out.

The next extreme model would be the opposite, which is undamped isotropic (randomly distributed in direction) librations (Appendix I-2) in phase II. The reason for such an assumption would be that it was concluded from NMR-studies [5] that the molecule only rotates round the C-Cl axis in this phase with a very long relaxation time of about 10^{-8} s. The best we could do was to select $F_{lib} = 0.65$ and $\sigma/\omega_0 = 1$ giving $\omega_0 = 1.2 \times 10^{12}$ rad · s⁻¹ (compare Eq.(5)). As is seen in Fig.7B (dashed lines) such an assumption can never fit our data. The predicted elastic peak is too narrow (a $\delta(\omega)$-function) and its κ-dependence is wrong. To come closer to the observed data regarding the elastic peak, the mean life-time τ_0 of the libration has to be decreased from very long, $\tau_0 \to \infty$, to the order of $\tau_0 \sim 2.5 \times 10^{-12}$ s (solid line in Fig.7B). This leads to a more realistic — although not good — fit.

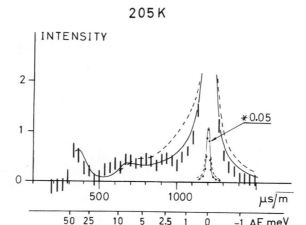

FIG.8. Uniaxial rotational Langevin diffusion (dashed line) and isotropic rotational Langevin diffusion (solid line) combined with the centre-of-mass motion and CH_3-group motion and compared to experimental data on t-butyl chloride (vertical dashes) at an angle of observation of 32° in phase II at 205 K. The rotational-diffusion constant $D_{11} = 3.8 \times 10^{11}$ s^{-1} in both cases. $D_{33} = 0.35 \times 10^{11}$ s^{-1} in the case of isotropic rotational diffusion and $D = 0$ for uniaxial rotational diffusion. The fit to the peak value is equally good at all other angles of observation.

In this context, it should be noted that we also tried one [20] of the current [19–21] jump models — valid for strongly unisotropic libration — to fit the elastic and near-elastic peak. Various assumptions involving re-orientation about the C-Cl axis, i.e. 120° rotation, 60° rotation and 30° rotation were tried. The mean time, τ, between re-orientations had to be of order $(2–3) \times 10^{-12}$ s to describe the width of the quasi-elastic peak. In total, the observed near elastic intensity could *not* be reproduced by such a model. This seems quite obvious as such a model does not contain the inelastically scattered librational component. The important observation is, however, that the relaxation time in any case had to be rather finite, $\cong 10^{-12}$ s, to reproduce the observed width of the quasi-elastic peak. In any case, the hypothesis of nearly undamped libration in phase II and of course also in phase I is ruled out.

We now turn to the assumption of uniaxial Langevin diffusive rotation (Appendix I-5) round the C-Cl axis. As is illustrated in Fig.8 (dashed line) this assumption does not lead to an acceptable fit. In the calculation presented in the figure, the rotational diffusion constant, D_{33}, was taken as 3.8×10^{11} s^{-1}. This is the value which gave the best fit in the case of isotropic diffusion (see below). The variation with momentum transfer of the peak intensity of the elastic peak is, however, well represented by the model.

TABLE II. PARAMETERS OF FITTED MODELS

Model or motion	Temperature (K)	173	205	235
Isotropic Langevin diffusion	$\xi_{11} \times 10^{25}$ g·cm²·s⁻¹	large	8 ± 2	4 ± 0.8
	$\xi_{33} \times 10^{25}$ g·cm²·s⁻¹	— ” —	0.75 ± 0.15	1.25 ± 0.25
	$D_{11} \times 10^{-11}$ s⁻¹	small	0.35 ± 0.1	0.8 ± 0.2
	$D_{33} \times 10^{-11}$ s⁻¹	— ” —	3.8 ± 0.8	2.6 ± 0.5
	$\tau_{11} = I_{11}/\xi_{11} \times 10^{13}$ s	— ” —	0.3	0.8
	$\tau_{33} = I_{33}/\xi_{33} \times 10^{13}$ s	— ” —	2.6	0.7
Stochastic two-step diffusion	$\tau_0 \times 10^{12}$ s	≫ 10	0.5 ± 0.2	1.5 ± 0.5
	$\tau_1 \times 10^{12}$ s		0.2 ± 0.1	0.5 ± 0.2
	F_{lib}	≲ 1	0.90 ± 0.03	0.77 ± 0.03
	$\Omega_r \times 10^{-12}$ rad·s⁻¹		1.02	1.09
	$\omega_0 \times 10^{-12}$ rad·s⁻¹		2.9	2.2
	τ_1/τ_0	~ 0	0.4	0.3
	$\tau_0 \omega_0$ rad		0.46 π	1.04 π
	$\tau_1 \Omega_r$ rad		0.065 π	0.17 π
Torsion of CH₃	$\omega_{CH_3} \times 10^{-13}$ rad·s⁻¹	5.3	5.3	5.3
Debye frequencies of commotion	$\omega_{D1} \times 10^{-13}$ rad·s⁻¹	1	1	1
	$\omega_{D2} \times 10^{-13}$ rad·s⁻¹	1.2	1.2	1.2
	$\omega_{D3} \times 10^{-13}$ rad·s⁻¹	1.4	1.4	1.4

Up to this point, none of the assumptions on the nature of the rotational motion was successful. When, however, the two remaining models are tested, the situation is changed.

We next investigated the possibility of applying the two-step stochastic model (Appendix I-3) to both phase I and II. In this case, an average moment of inertia had to be used, equal for the three different axes of inertia because the model was formulated only for such a case. The parameters of interest in this calculation are the average times for libration, τ_0, and free rotation, τ_1, respectively; further, the nature of the libration is determined by F_{lib} as discussed in Sections 3.3.(b) and (c) and by ω_0, the mean librational frequency. The width of the librational band was selected such that $\sigma/\omega_0 = 0.5$.

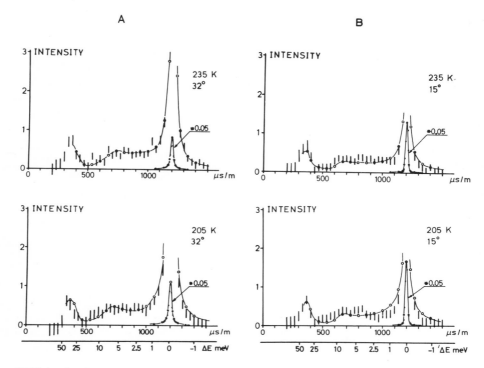

FIG.9A.   *Stochastic two-step rotational-diffusion model combined with Debye model for centre-of-mass motion and Gaussian spectrum for CH$_3$-group motion (solid line with rings) compared to experimental data on t-butyl chloride (vertical dashes) at an angle of observation of 32° in phase I at 235 K and in phase II at 205 K. The fit is of a similar nature at all angles of observation.*

   B.   Isotropic rotational Langevin diffusion model for axially symmetric molecules combined with the same models for centre-of-mass and CH$_3$-group motion as in A (solid line with rings) in phase I at 235 K and in phase II at 205 K and at an angle of observation of 15°, compared with experimental data (vertical dashes). The fit is similar at all angles of observation.

The result of a large number of computations for the three angles of observation 15°, 32° and 45° and for the two temperatures 205 K (phase II) and 235 K (phase I) gave the parameter set shown in Table II. An example of the fit obtained is given in Fig.9A. The fit is rather impressive, remembering that the computed effective cross-sections are normalized to observation only at one point: the elastic peak at a 15° angle of observation. The fit is slightly better in phase I than in phase II. It is observed from Table II that the relaxation times τ_0 and τ_1 had to be selected short, $\cong 10^{-12}$ s.

   The final model to be tested is the isotropic, Langevin rotational diffusion case. As is discussed in Section 3.3.(d), the molecule is now treated more

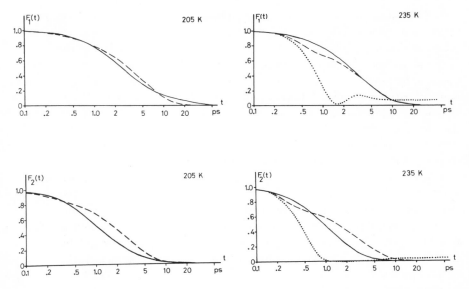

FIG.10.   Rotational relaxation functions $F_1(t)$ for $\ell = 1$ and $F_2(t)$ for $\ell = 2$ at 205 K and 235 K for isotropic Langevin diffusion, Mishima model (solid line) corresponding to best fit to observed data on t-butyl chloride. Free rotation in phase I is given for comparison (dotted line); compare Fig.7A.

correctly as having an axially symmetric mass distribution. Figure 9B shows that the fit is of equal quality in both phases I and II. A close comparison between Figs 9A and 9B shows that both models fit the data almost equally well. May be, there is a characteristic tendency for the Langevin model to round off the corner too much between the quasi-elastic and the inelastic region, at $\Delta E \cong + 1$ meV. This effect is particularly pronounced in phase II at 205 K.

It is again noted that the rotational relaxation functions $F_\ell(t)$ for the two models differ only slightly when the parameters of best fit to data are applied. Figure 10 gives $F_1(t)$ and $F_2(t)$ as examples.

5.   CONCLUSIONS

It is found from the present analysis of the neutron data that all extreme assumptions on the rotational motion in the plastic phases were ruled out for t-butyl chloride as well as for neopentane. Free rotation is, of course, rather improbable even at the high-temperature end because the molecules lack the space necessary for such a motion.

The failure of extreme librational and jump models indicates several things: (a) the potential wells hindering rotation are not deep enough to hinder barrier passages effectively. This conclusion holds irrespectively of whether the molecule shows a dipole moment or not; (b) the molecules, when rotating from one well to another, perform this in a rather irregular and random way, the steps being of varying lengths. The very precise prediction of jump lengths characteristic of a jump model does not correspond to what is observed in nature, at least for neopentane and t-butyl chloride; (c) it is not allowed to neglect the time of rotation from one well to another. The use of Frenkel models is, therefore, doubtful for both types of molecules in their plastic phases.

A remarkable observation is the shortness of the relaxation times derived from these fits for both types of molecules, irrespective of the model tried. All angular steps appear small, in the range $10-30°$, and the residence time for a particular orientation is, in general, too short to permit the development of a true libration. Therefore, the motion is relatively well approximated by a Langevin type of rotational diffusion. A more sophisticated model with a better physical foundation may reproduce the data slightly better, but the improvement is expected to be small owing to the relative insensitivity of the neutron scattering method. This is due to the facts already mentioned: (a) the neutrons observe *all* proton motions; (b) multiple-scattering corrections are hard to perform perfectly.

As is shown by the observations on neopentane near the plastic transition temperature in the plastic phase, there is a tendency for the librations to develop more clearly. Similarly, in phase II on t-butyl chloride a freezing-in of the rotational motion develops: according to Table II, the ratio of the relaxation times $\tau_{33} = I_{33}/\xi_{33}$ and $\tau_{11} = I_{11}/\xi_{11}$ has a value close to 1 in phase I and a value of about 9 in phase II. This means that in phase I the molecules tumble with equal probability round the C-Cl axis (τ_{33}) and the two axes are perpendicular to this axis ($\tau_{11} = \tau_{22}$). In phase II, the rate of motion is 9 times more probable about the C-Cl axis, which means that the motion about the two axes perpendicular to the C-Cl axis gradually disappears in this phase: the molecules tend to line up. But still the relaxation times are very short. Our observations are, in this respect, in disagreement with recent NMR-observations [5]. We believe that other effects are observed in such measurements. The neutron observations are very direct and the interpretation is quite straightforward. We find that the randomness of the rotational motion is gradually lost when the important phase transition point is approached. These observations show that the neutron scattering technique, if utterly refined and if translational and torsional motions are known, should reveal finer details of rotational motions of molecules.

APPENDIX I

The following models for rotational motion were used:

I-1. Free rotation

I-1.1. Spherically symmetric molecules [9, 12]

$$F_\ell(t) = \frac{1}{2\ell+1} \left[1 + 2 \sum_{\xi=1}^{\ell} \left(1 - \frac{\xi^2 k_B T t^2}{I} \right) \exp\left\{ -\frac{\xi^2 k_B T t^2}{2I} \right\} \right] \qquad (A1')$$

where the symbols are already used and explained in the text.

I-1.2. Axially symmetric molecules [10]

$$F_\ell(t) = \int_0^\infty dJ \int dK \, 2J P_{JK}(T) \sum_{J'K'}{}' \cos\left((E_{JK} - E_{J'K'})t/\hbar\right)$$

$$\times \frac{(\ell-|K-K'|)!}{(\ell+|K-K'|)!} \left| P_\ell^{|K-K'|}(\cos\theta) \right|^2 \left| \begin{matrix} J & \ell & J \\ K & K' & -K K \end{matrix} \right|^2 \qquad (A'')$$

where

$$E_{JK} = \left(\frac{1}{2I}\right) J^2 + \left(\frac{c}{2I}\right) K^2,$$

$$P_{JK}(T) = e^{-E_{JK}/k_B T} \Big/ \sum_{J'K'} (2J' + 1) e^{-E_{J'K'}/k_B T}$$

$c = (I - I_z)/I_z$, θ is the angle between the axis and the line joining proton position with the centre of mass, I is the moment of inertia for an axis perpendicular to the symmetry axis and I_z is the same around the symmetry axis. E_{JK} are the rotor energies and $\begin{bmatrix} J_1 & J_2 & J_3 \\ m_1 & m_2 & m_3 \end{bmatrix}$ denote the Clebsch-Gordan coefficients.

I-2. **Isotropic undamped libration [11]. Molecular mass distribution assumed spherically symmetric:**

$$F_\ell(t) = F_{lib} + (1 - F_{lib}) \exp\{-[\sigma^2 t^2 \ell(\ell+1)/2]\} \cos\{[\ell(\ell+1)]^{1/2}\,\omega_0 t\}$$

$$(A2')$$

F_{lib}, ω_0 and σ are parameters, between which the relation given by Eq.(5) in the text holds. With damping the $F_\ell(t)$:s are changed to $F'_\ell(t)$:

$$F'_\ell(t) = e^{-t/\tau_0}\, F_\ell(t)$$

$$(A2'')$$

ω_0 is the libration frequency, σ is the half-width of librational spectrum, $0 < F_{lib} < 1$.

I-3. **Isotropic, stochastic, two-step rotational diffusion model [11]. Molecular mass distribution assumed spherically symmetric**

In this case, the Fourier transform $S_\ell(\omega)$ of $F_\ell(t)$ is given:

$$S_\ell(\omega) = \frac{1}{\pi(\tau_0 + \tau_1)}\, \mathrm{Re}\left[\frac{\tau_0\, a_\ell + \tau_1\, b_\ell + 2a_\ell b_\ell}{1 - a_\ell b_\ell/\tau_0\tau_1}\right]$$

$$(A3)$$

where

$$a_\ell = \frac{F_{lib}}{1/\tau_0 + i\omega} + \frac{(1-F_{lib})\pi^{1/2}}{2^{3/2}\,\sigma[\ell(\ell+1)]^{1/2}} \sum_{p=1}^{2} \exp(z_p^2)\,\mathrm{erfc}(z_p)$$

$$b_\ell = \frac{1}{2\ell+1}\left\{\frac{1}{2} + \sum_{n=1}^{\ell} \frac{z_n 2^{3/2}}{n\Omega_r}\left[1 - z_n\pi^{1/2}\exp(z_n^2)\,\mathrm{erfc}(z_n)\right]\right\}$$

$$z_p = \frac{1/\tau_0 + i\omega}{2^{1/2}\,\sigma[\ell(\ell+1)]^{1/2}} + i(-1)^{p+1}\omega_0/(2^{1/2}\sigma)$$

$$z_n = (1/\tau_1 + i\omega)/2^{1/2}\, n\Omega_r$$

I-4. Isotropic, diffusive Langevin rotation of axially symmetric molecules [13]

$$F_\ell(t) = \sum_{m=0}^{\ell} C_\ell^m \, [P_\ell^m \, (\cos\theta)] \exp\{[m^2 - \ell(\ell+1)] \, h_1(t) - m^2 h_3(t)\} \qquad (A4)$$

where

$$h_1(t) = \int_0^t D_{11}(\tau)d\tau, \qquad h_3(t) = \int_0^t D_{33}(\tau)d\tau,$$

$$D_{ii}(t) = \int_0^t \langle\omega_i(0)\,\omega_i(t)\rangle \, d\tau \quad \text{and} \quad \langle\omega_i(0)\,\omega_i(t)\rangle$$

is the angular-velocity auto-correlation function given by

$$\langle\omega_i(0)\,\omega_i(t)\rangle = e^{-\frac{\xi_{ii}t}{I_i}} \frac{k_B T}{I_i} \left\{ 1 - \frac{1}{2}\left(\frac{k_B T}{I_i}\right)\frac{(I_i - I_k)^2}{I_j I_k} t^2 \right.$$

$$\left. + \frac{1}{8}\left(\frac{k_B T}{I_i}\right)^2 \frac{(I_i - I_k)^4}{I_j^2 I_k^2} - t^4 \right\}$$

with i, j, k = 1, 2, 3, cyclic.

The ξ_{ii} are the diagonal terms in the friction coefficient tensor. In this treatment the off-diagonal terms are assumed to be zero, furthermore, $I_1 = I_2 \neq I_3$ and $\xi_{11} = \xi_{22}$. The disposable parameters are ξ_{11} and ξ_{33}.

$$C_\ell^m = 2 \, \frac{(\ell-m)!}{(\ell+m)!} \quad \text{for} \quad \ell \geq 1; \quad C_\ell^0 = 1.$$

$P_\ell^m (\cos\theta)$ is the associated Legendre polynomial.

I-5. **Uniaxial, diffusive Langevin rotation of axially symmetric molecules [13, 14]**

The basic formulas were derived for simple diffusion. The intermediate scattering function for rotational motion is

$$I_{rot}(\kappa,t) = \langle J_0^2 (\kappa d)\rangle_{polycr} + 2 \sum_{n=1}^{\infty} \{\langle J_n^2 (\kappa d)\rangle_{polycr} F_n(t)\} \tag{A5}$$

where $J_n(\kappa d)$ are Bessel functions of order n, d is the distance from the centre of mass of the molecule to the scattering proton and

$$\langle J_n^2 (\kappa d)\rangle_{polycr} = \frac{1}{2} \int_{-1}^{1} J_n^2 (\kappa d \sin \theta) \, d (\cos \theta)$$

where the average takes care of the polycrystalline structure of the sample; $F_n(t) = \exp \{- n^2 h(t)\}$ with $h(t) = (k_B T/b^2 I_3) (bt - 1 + \exp (- bt))$ and $b = \xi_{33}/I_3$.

REFERENCES

[1] LIVINGSTONE, R.C., ROTSHILD, W.G., RUSH, J.J., J. Chem. Phys. 59 (1973) 2498.
[2] DE GRAAF, L., SCIESIŃSKI, J., Physica 48 (1970) 79.
[3] LASSIER, B., BROT, C., J. Chem. Phys. 65 (1968) 1723.
[4] GUTHRIE, G.B., McCULLOUGH, J.P., Phys. Chem. Sol. 18 (1961) 531.
[5] O'REILLY, D.E., PETERSON, E.M., SCHEIE, C.E., SEYFARTH, E., J. Chem. Phys. 59 (1973) 3576.
[6] COCKING, S.J., AERE Report R 5867, Thesis (1968).
[7] SJÖLANDER, A., Ark. Fys. 14 (1958) 315.
[8] GRANT, D.M., PUGMIRE, R.J., LIVINGSTONE, R.C., J. Chem. Phys. 52 (1970) 4424.
[9] SEARS, W.F., Can. J. Phys. 44 (1966) 1279, 1299; 45 (1967) 237.
[10] AGRAWAL, A.K., YIP, S., Phys. Rev. A (1970) 970.
[11] LARSSON, K.E., J. Chem. Phys. 59 (1973) 4612.
[12] STEELE, W.A., J. Chem. Phys. 38 (1963) 2404, 2411.
[13] MISHIMA, K., J. Phys. Soc. Jpn. 31 (1971) 1796.
[14] JANIK, J.A., JANIK, J.M., OTNES, K., Physica 83B (1976) 259.
[15] COOLEY, J.W., TUKEY, J.W., IEEE Audio Transactions (June 1967).

[16] BRENNER, W., MIT Lincoln Laboratory (June 1968).
[17] OLSSON, L.G., DAHLBORG, U., LARSSON, K.E., J. Chem. Phys. 65 (1976) 721.
[18] O'DELL, J., BERNE, B.J., J. Chem. Phys. 63 (1975) 2376.
[19] STOCKMEYER, R., STILLER, H., Phys. Status Solidi 27 (1968) 269.
[20] SKÖLD, J., Chem. Phys. 49 (1968) 2443.
[21] BROT, C., LASSIER-GROVES, B., Ber. Bunsenges. Phys. Chem. 80 (1976) 31.

DISCUSSION

L.A. DE GRAAF: I would disagree with your conclusions about the reorientational motions in neopentane. At the Jülich meeting about two years ago we also showed data on neopentane (to be published shortly). Our data were transformed to κ,t space and corrected for resolution, multiple scattering and translational motions to give $I_R(\kappa,t)$, the rotational part of the inter-mediate scattering functions. From this, $I_R(\kappa,\infty)$ (the elastic incoherent struc-ture factor) and the reorientational correlation functions $F_1(t)$, $F_2(t)$ and $F_3(t)$ were obtained. From $I_R(\kappa,\infty)$, and from $F_3(\infty)$ — which goes to a finite value — it can be concluded that the proton distribution does not randomize, i.e. quasi-equilibrium sites exist, and $180°$ jumps are most probable. The ratio of τ_1 to τ_2 obtained from $F_1(t)$ and $F_2(t)$ (which are in agreement with infra-red and Raman data reported by Livingston and co-workers) is between 2.5 and 3, which in a simple picture would indicate small-angle jumps.

Our feeling is that these results are not completely contradictory when a memory of rotational momentum is taken into account. Moreover, in the molecular dynamics calculations on β-N_2 made by Quentrec, similar behaviour is observed. I think that for a complete solution of this problem more molecular-dynamics calculations are needed.

K.E. LARSSON: I have a strong feeling that it is a very difficult procedure to perform Fourier transforms on the measured neutron spectrum and especially on the constant-angle presentation of the spectrum. To determine the various rotational relaxation functions $F_1(t)$, $F_2(t)$ and $F_3(t)$ from a transformed and manipulated intermediate scattering function is, in my opinion, well nigh im-possible. From your description of the procedure used I cannot form an exact judgement regarding the accuracy and other more fundamental points that may be involved. In general, I think a more straightforward method is to divide the analysis into two parts: (a) first to perform a careful and accurate measure-ment and make all corrections; and then (b) to calculate a theoretical intensity distribution for comparison with the experimental one. To carry out a mixture of steps would seem more difficult and less reliable. The separation of one spectral part from another — for example, quasi-elastic from inelastic — is difficult and may in many cases introduce unacceptable uncertainties.

DYNAMICS OF TRANSLATIONS AND ROTATIONS IN MOLECULAR CRYSTALS

K.H. MICHEL [†]
Institut für Theoretische Physik der
    Universität des Saarlandes,
Saarbrücken,
Federal Republic of Germany

J. NAUDTS,
Natuurkunde,
University of Antwerp,
Wilrijk,
Belgium

Abstract

DYNAMICS OF TRANSLATIONS AND ROTATIONS IN MOLECULAR CRYSTALS.

The dynamics of rotations and translations in molecular crystals is derived from a microscopic Hamiltonian. The dynamic variables are the lattice displacements, their conjugate momenta and, in the case of orientationally disordered phases, the appropriate symmetry-adapted functions. The dynamic equations used in this paper are relevant to neutron and Brillouin scattering. The inelastic-neutron-scattering law, including interference between translation and rotations, is given. Experiments in KCN are explained.

1. Introduction

In molecular liquids [1], the importance of the coupling between translational and rotational degrees of freedom has been recognized for a long time. There, mixed transport coefficients account for the coupling between the dynamic equations. This effect has been studied in many theoretical [2] and experimental [3] investigations. On the other hand, in molecular crystals [4] there exists a static coupling between translations and rotations. This coupling is of special importance near structrural phase transitions where an ordering

---

[†] Present Address: Natuurkunde, University of Antwerp, 2610, Wilrijk, Belgium.

of molecular orientations is accompagnied by a change of lattice structure. As an example we mention the anomalous temperature behavior of the elastic constants c_{44} in KCN and NaCN
measured first by Haussühl [5] by means of ultrasonic methods
and confirmed by neutron [6] and Brillouin [7] scattering experiments. Recently, the present authors have developed a
microscopic theory which explains these experiments. In principle, the static coupling between translations and rotations
has been known for a long time [8]. However, except for
the case of solid hydrogene [9] where the molecules exhibit a
nearly free rotation spectrum, the theory of rotational motion is mainly restricted to the assumption of small-amplitude
rotational oscillations. Obviously, this assumption breaks
down near an orientational phase transition. In order to deal
with this situation, it is most appropriate to use symmetry-
adapted functions as dynamic variables [10] for the rotational
motion. A theoretical description of the coupling of translational motion with large-amplitude molecular reorientations
should take into account these observations. Our theory is
therefore based on a Hamiltonian which contains the center-
of-mass displacements as translational coordinates and where
in addition symmety-adapted functions describe molecular orientations [11].

The present paper is devoted to a dynamical description
of the coupled rotational and translational motion, based on
the microscopic Hamiltonian of ref. [11]. The dynamic equations are used to derive the relevant correlation functions
which enter the neutron, Brillouin and Raman scattering laws.
In this framework we will give a complete expression for the

dynamic neutron scattering law in the case of coupled translations and rotations. In particular interference terms between
these two types of motion are derived.

2. The Model Hamiltonian

To be specific, we use as a model M(XY) compounds like
KCN or NaCN but the generalization of our considerations to
other substances will be obvious. In the high temperature
phase [12], $(T>T_c \approx 168$ K$)$, KCN has a cubic NaCl-type structure where the linear (CN)$^-$ ions are surrounded by spherical
K$^+$ atoms in octahedral position. The (CN)$^-$ ions have no orientational order. At T_c, there is a (first-order) phase transition to an orthorombic structure where the (CN)$^-$ ions are
oriented along the b-axis. The sense of the (CN)$^-$ ions is not
fixed at this transition. In order to describe this situation,
we have recently [11] proposed a model of a crystal which consists of dumbbell molecules surrounded by spherical atoms in
octahedral position. In addition to forces interacting between the centers of mass of the constituting particles, we
assume that the two ends of each dumbbell experience a repulsive Born-Mayer potential from the spherical atoms in octahedral positions. This latter potential depends on the orientation of the dumbbells. Performing then a series expansion
to center-of-mass coordinates of the unit cell, we have obtained the following Hamiltonian [11]:

$$H = H^T + H^R + H^{TR} \tag{2.1}$$

where H^T represents the pure translational part:

$$H^T = \sum_i \frac{p_i^+(\vec{k}) \, p_i(k)}{2m} + \sum_{i,j} M_{ij}(\vec{k}) \, s_i(\vec{k}) \, s_j(\vec{k}) \ , \quad i=1,2,3 \tag{2.2a}$$

H^R the rotational part

$$H^R = \sum_i \frac{L_i^\dagger(\vec{k}) L_i(\vec{k})}{2I} + V^o(\vec{k}=o) \tag{2.2b}$$

and H^{TR} the interaction between translations and rotations:

$$H^{TR} = i \sum_k \hat{v}_{\alpha i}(\vec{k}) \; Y_\alpha^\dagger(k) \, s_i(\vec{k}) \; , \qquad \alpha = 1\text{-}5 \tag{2.2c}$$

Here Fourier transforms are defined by $F(\vec{k}) = N^{-1} \sum_n e^{i\vec{k}.\vec{X}(\vec{n})} F(\vec{n})$, N and $\vec{n}$ being respectively total number and label of unit cells. The p_i are the momenta conjugate to the translational center-of-mass displacements s_i. They satisfy the usual commutation rules. M_{ij} is the second-order translational coupling coefficient, m is the total mass (1K-atom + 1 dumbbell) per unit cell, L the angular momentum of the dumbbell and I its moment of intertia. V^o is the zeroth order expansion coefficient of the orientation-dependent potential. It represents the dumbbell in the perfect octahedral potential and is expandable in terms of cubic harmonics. Finally V^{TR} represents the first-order term (in s_i) of the interaction between translations and orientations. The orientations appear under the form of symmetry-adapted functions given by the five spherical harmonics of order 2: $Y_1 = Y_2^o$, $Y_2 = \sqrt{\frac{3}{2}} (Y_2^2 + Y_2^{-2})$, $Y_3 = i(Y_2^2 - Y_2^{-2})$, $Y_4 = (Y_2^1 - Y_2^{-1})$, $Y_5 = -i(Y_2^1 + Y_2^{-1})$. The matrix of coupling coefficients reads:

$$\tilde{\vec{v}}^\tau = \frac{2a}{m} \begin{pmatrix} k_x A & -k_x A & k_y B & 0 & k_z B \\ k_y A & k_y A & k_x B & k_z B & 0 \\ -2k_z B & 0 & 0 & k_y B & k_x B \end{pmatrix} \tag{2.3}$$

Here the x,y,z (or 1,2,3) directions are taken along the cubic axes of the crystal with lattice constant 2a. The coefficients A and B are functions of the parameters of the Born-Mayer potential as well as of the length 2d of the dumbbell. As we have shown [11], the bilinear interaction $\hat{v}$ Ys can be transformed into an effective orientational interaction between the dumbbells:

$$V_{eff}^{RR} = -\frac{1}{2} \sum_{\vec{k}} Y_\alpha^\dagger(\vec{k}) \ C^{\alpha\beta}(\vec{k}) Y_\beta(\vec{k}) \qquad (2.4)$$

where $\widetilde{C}(k) = \widetilde{\widehat{v}}(\widetilde{M}^{-1})\widetilde{\widehat{v}}^\tau$. ($\tau$ = transposed). The importance of such an effective interaction mediated by the lattice has been demonstrated independently from ultrasonic measurements [13].

3. Dynamic Equations

   The thermal average of an operator A_ν is defined by

$$\langle A_\nu \rangle = Sp[\exp(-H/T)A_\nu]/Sp[\exp(-H/T)] \qquad (3.1)$$

where T denotes the temperature and Sp stands for the trace. In linear-response theory, the response function of two operators A_ν and A_μ is related to the Laplace transform of the retarded Green's function [14]:

$$\chi_{\nu\mu}(z) = -\langle\!\langle A_\nu^\dagger;A_\mu\rangle\!\rangle_z = i\int_0^\infty dt \ e^{izt}\langle[A_\nu^\dagger(t),A_\mu(o)]\rangle \qquad (3.2)$$

Here $z = \omega + i\varepsilon$, $\varepsilon \to o$. The Laplace transform of Kubo's relaxation function and the response function are related by

$$\Phi_{\nu\mu}(z) = \frac{1}{z}[\chi_{\nu\mu}(z) - \chi_{\nu\mu}(o)] \qquad (3.3)$$

We will use the notation $\chi_{\nu\mu}(o) \equiv (A_\nu, A_\mu)$. The dynamic form factor measured by neutron scattering is given by

$$S_{\nu\mu} = - \omega[1 - \exp(-\omega/T)]^{-1}\Phi''_{\nu\mu}, \qquad \omega \in \underset{\sim}{R} \tag{3.4}$$

We start from the assumption that, for the time scale of interest, the dynamics of the system is governed by a set of secular variables $\{A_\mu\}$, μ being the label of these variables. Applying the Mori-Zwanzig projection operator technique [15] in the formulation given by ref. [16], the relaxation function $\Phi_{\nu\mu}$ is found to satisfy the basic equation

$$\left[z\delta_{\mu\nu} - \Omega_{\mu\nu} + \Sigma_{\mu\nu}(z)\right] \Phi_{\nu\rho}(z) = \chi_{\mu\rho}(o) \tag{3.5}$$

Here Ω denotes the matrix of restoring forces which accounts for oscillatory motion and Σ the dissipation matrix which accounts for damping. For the model described in Sect. 2, the set of dynamic variables is given by $\{s_i(\vec{k}), p_i(\vec{k}), \bar{Y}_\alpha(k)\}$. Here we use instead of Y_α the orthogonalized quantity $\bar{Y}$ defined by

$$\bar{Y}_\alpha(\vec{k}) = Y_\alpha(\vec{k}) - s_i(\vec{k}) D_{ij}(\vec{k}) (s_j(\vec{k}), Y_\alpha(k)) \tag{3.6}$$

with $D_{ij}(k) = (s(\vec{k}), s(\vec{k}))^{-1}_{ij}$.

Then the relevant matrices entering Eq. (3.5) are given by

$$\tilde{\chi}(o) = \begin{pmatrix} \tilde{D} & \tilde{O} & \tilde{O} \\ \tilde{O} & \tilde{1} & \tilde{O} \\ \tilde{O} & \tilde{O} & \tilde{X}^{-1} \end{pmatrix} \tag{3.7}$$

with $X_{\alpha\beta} = (\bar{Y}(\vec{k}), \bar{Y}(\vec{k}))^{-1}_{\alpha\beta}$. The restoring force matrix $\tilde{\Omega}$ is found to be

$$\tilde{\Omega} = \begin{pmatrix} \tilde{O} & i\tilde{I} & \tilde{O} \\ -i\tilde{D} & \tilde{O} & \tilde{\beta}\tilde{X} \\ \tilde{O} & \tilde{\beta}^{\tau} & \tilde{O} \end{pmatrix} \qquad (3.8)$$

where the coupling matrix β is given by

$$\tilde{\beta}^{\tau} = (\bar{Y}, \mathcal{L}p) \qquad (3.9)$$

with $\mathcal{L}p = [H, p]$. The dissipation matrix Σ is given by

$$\tilde{\Sigma}(i\epsilon) = i \begin{pmatrix} \tilde{O} & \tilde{O} & \tilde{O} \\ \tilde{O} & \tilde{O} & \tilde{O} \\ \tilde{O} & \tilde{O} & \tilde{\lambda} \end{pmatrix} \qquad (3.10)$$

where $\tilde{\lambda} = \tilde{\Lambda}_{\bar{Y}\bar{Y}}\tilde{X}$, with $\Lambda_{\bar{Y}\bar{Y}}$ being an orientational transport co-efficient. Here we have taken the limit $\omega = o$ since the secular variables are slow in comparison with the non-secular parts of the $\bar{Y}$-currents in $\Lambda_{\bar{Y}\bar{Y}}$. Inserting the matrices (3.7)-(3.10) into Eq. (3.5) and considering only the first column of the Φ-matrix, we find three coupled sets of matrix equations for $\tilde{\Phi}_{ss}(z)$, $\tilde{\Phi}_{ps}(z)$ and $\tilde{\Phi}_{\bar{Y}s}(z)$. Elimination of $\tilde{\Phi}_{ps}(z)$ then yield the two coupled matrix equations

$$(\tilde{I}z^2 - \tilde{D})\tilde{\Phi}_{ss}(z) - i\tilde{\beta}\tilde{X}\tilde{\Phi}_{\bar{Y}s}(z) = z\tilde{D}^{-1} \qquad (3.11a)$$

and

$$(\tilde{I}z + i\tilde{\lambda})\tilde{\Phi}_{\bar{Y}s}(z) + iz\tilde{\beta}^{\tau}\tilde{\Phi}_{ss}(z) = i\tilde{\beta}^{\tau}\tilde{D}^{-1} \qquad (3.11b)$$

Here the first equation describes essentially the translational motion which is coupled to the rotational motion trough
the matrix $\tilde{\beta}$. The second equation essentially describes the
relaxation of orientational correlations; these are in turn
coupled to the translations. Elimination of $\tilde{\Phi}_{\bar{Y}s}$ from this
coupled set yields a closed equation for the translations where
the influence of the rotations shows up trough the coupling $\tilde{\beta}$:

$$[\tilde{1}z^2 - \tilde{D} - z\tilde{\beta}\tilde{X}(\tilde{1}z + i\tilde{\lambda})^{-1}\tilde{\beta}^T]\ \tilde{\Phi}_{ss}(z) =$$

$$= [\tilde{1}z - \tilde{\beta}\tilde{X}(\tilde{1}z + i\tilde{\lambda})^{-1}\beta^T]\tilde{D}^{-1} \tag{3.12}$$

In a similar way we find the equation for the mixed relaxation functions $\tilde{\Phi}_{\bar{Y}s}$ and $\tilde{\Phi}_{s\bar{Y}}$:

$$[\tilde{1}z + i\tilde{\lambda} - z\tilde{\beta}^T(\tilde{1}z^2 - \tilde{D})^{-1}\tilde{\beta}\tilde{X}]\tilde{\Phi}_{\bar{Y}s}(z) = i\tilde{\beta}^T\tilde{D}^{-1}$$

$$- iz^2\tilde{\beta}^T(\tilde{1}z^2 - \tilde{D})^{-1}D^{-1} \tag{3.13}$$

$$[(\tilde{1}z^2 - \tilde{D}) - z\tilde{\beta}\tilde{X}(\tilde{1}z + i\tilde{\lambda})^{-1}\tilde{\beta}^T]\tilde{\Phi}_{s\bar{Y}}(z) =$$

$$= i\tilde{\beta}\tilde{X}(\tilde{1}z + i\tilde{\lambda})^{-1}\tilde{X}^{-1} \tag{3.14}$$

Finally the orientation-orientation relaxation function satisfies

$$[(\tilde{1}z + i\tilde{\lambda}) - z\tilde{\beta}^T(\tilde{1}z^2 - \tilde{D})^{-1}\tilde{\beta}\tilde{X}]\tilde{\Phi}_{\bar{Y}\bar{Y}}(z) = \tilde{X}^{-1} \tag{3.15}$$

Equations (3.12)-(3.15) determine the relevant correlation
functions which enter the inelastic neutron scattering law as

we will show in the next section. In deriving the present
equations, we have carefully taken into account the dimensionality of the dynamic variables and their symmetry. In addition, our Hamiltonian (2.1) together with the concept of effective interaction allows the determination of all matrix elements which occur in our equations. In particular, one has [17]

$$\tilde{D} = [\tilde{1} + \tilde{Q}M^{-1}]^{-1}\tilde{M} \tag{3.16}$$

with

$$\tilde{Q} = \tilde{v}\tilde{\chi}^R\tilde{v}^{\tau} \tag{3.17}$$

where

$$\chi^R_{\alpha\beta} = (Y_\alpha, Y_\beta) \tag{3.18}$$

is the static rotation-rotation susceptibility. Note that
the quantity D determines the elastic constants:

$$D_{ij} = \frac{V_z}{m} k_n k_\ell C_{in,j\ell} \tag{3.19a}$$

while M_{ij} yields the bare (renormalized) harmonic elastic
constants in the absence of orientational motion:

$$M_{ij} = \frac{V_z}{m} k_n k_\ell \, C^\circ_{in,j\ell} \tag{3.19b}$$

where V_z is the volume of the cell. The rotational susceptibility is now evaluated in terms of the effective interaction and
the one-particle rotational potential. One finds [11]

$$\tilde{\chi}^R(\vec{k}) = (\tilde{1}T - \tilde{\Gamma}(\vec{k}))^{-1}\tilde{R} \tag{3.20}$$

with

$$\Gamma_{\alpha\beta}(\vec{k}) = R_{\alpha\gamma}(\vec{k}) \ C_{\gamma\beta}(\vec{k}) \tag{3.21}$$

where R denotes the single-particle susceptibility:

$$R_{\alpha\beta} = (Sp \ exp(-V^o/T) \ Y_\alpha^+ Y_\beta)/(Sp \ exp(-V^o/T)) \tag{3.22}$$

An explicit discussion of the temperature dependence of the elastic constants and the connection with the structural phase transition has been given in ref. [11].

The rotation-elastic coupling $\tilde{\beta}$ is rewritten as:

$$\tilde{\beta} = \tilde{\tilde{v}}^\tau \tilde{X}^{-1} \tag{3.23}$$

Finally, the susceptibility $\tilde{X}$ is found to be

$$\tilde{X}^{-1} = \tilde{\tilde{v}}^{-1} (\tilde{M} - \tilde{D}) (\tilde{\tilde{v}}^\tau)^{-1} \tag{3.24}$$

Consequently all static quantities which enter the dynamic equations are completely determined in terms of d, a, A, B and M. Concerning the dissipation coefficient $\tilde{\lambda} = \Lambda_{\bar{Y}\bar{Y}} \tilde{X}$ we assume that $\tilde{X}$ is the main quantity in determining the temperature dependence while $\Lambda_{\bar{Y}\bar{Y}}$ is rather constant.

4. Inelastic-Neutron-Scattering Law

For a crystal with N cells (index $\vec{n}$) and Γ scattering centers per unit cell, the inelastic-neutron-scattering cross-section reads [18]

$$\frac{d^2\sigma}{d\Omega d\omega} = \frac{1}{2\pi}\frac{q'}{q}\sum_{n\ n'}\sum_{\mu\ \mu'} a_\mu a_{\mu'} \int dt\ e^{i\omega t} \langle e^{-i\vec{Q}\cdot\vec{R}_\mu^n(t)} e^{i\vec{Q}\cdot\vec{R}_{\mu'}^{n'}(t)} \rangle \qquad (4.1)$$

Here $\vec{Q} = \vec{q}'-\vec{q}$ is the difference of the wave vectors of the incoming and outgoing neutron. The position of the μ-th scattering center with scattering length a_μ in the $\vec{n}$-th cell is given by

$$\vec{R}_\mu^n = \vec{X}^n + \vec{b}_\mu + \vec{u}_\mu^n \qquad (4.2)$$

where $\vec{X}^n$, $\vec{b}_\mu$ and $\vec{u}^n$ denote respectively the origin position within the $\vec{n}$-th cell, the equilibrium position of the μ-th particle in the $\vec{n}$-th cell and the displacement of this particle away from its equilibrium position. In the case of a dumbbell surrounded by spherical (K)-atoms in octahedral position, we have two types of scattering centers. Firstly, the spherical atom, index +, has the coordinates

$$\vec{R}_+^n = \vec{X}^n + \vec{b}_+ + \vec{u}_+^n \qquad (4.3a)$$

Secondly, the two ends of the dumbbell (index-) are located at

$$\vec{R}_{-,\sigma}^n = \vec{X}^n + \vec{b}_- + \vec{u}_-^n + \sigma\vec{d}(\Theta_n,\varphi_n)\ ,\ \sigma = \pm 1 \qquad (4.3b)$$

Here $\vec{b}_-$ is the equilibrium position of the center of mass of the dumbbell, $\vec{u}_-^n$ the corresponding displacement while $\pm\vec{d}$ localizes the extremities of the dumbbell. Obviously, the polar angles (Θ,φ) determine the orientation of the dumbbell while its length 2d is assumed to be rigid (neglect of internal modes). Expressions (4.3a) and (4.3b) are inserted into the right-hand side of Eq. (4.1). After some algebra, the inelastic-coherent-neutron-scattering law can be rewritten in the following form:

$$\frac{d^2\sigma}{d\Omega d\omega} = \frac{1}{2\pi} \frac{q'}{q} \sum_{\vec{k}} \Delta(\vec{Q} + \vec{k}) \{F_{ij}^{TT}(\vec{Q}) S_{ij}^{ss}(\vec{k},\omega) + F_{i\alpha}^{TR}(\vec{Q}) S_{i\alpha}^{sY}(\vec{k},\omega) +$$

$$+ F_{\alpha i}^{RT}(\vec{Q}) S_{\alpha i}^{Ys}(\vec{k},\omega) + F_{\alpha\beta}^{RR}(\vec{Q}) S_{\alpha\beta}^{YY}(\vec{k},\omega)\} \qquad (4.4)$$

Here the correlation functions $S(\vec{k},\omega)$ are defined by

$$S_{ij}^{ss}(\vec{k},\omega) = \int dt\ e^{i\omega t} <s_i^\dagger(\vec{k},t) s_j(\vec{k},o)> \qquad (4.5a)$$

$$S_{i\alpha}^{sY}(\vec{k},\omega) = \int dt\ e^{i\omega t} <s_i^\dagger(\vec{k},t) Y_\alpha(\vec{k},\ o)> \qquad (4.5b)$$

$$S_{\alpha i}^{Ys}(\vec{k},\omega) = \int dt\ e^{i\omega t} <Y_\alpha^\dagger(\vec{k},t) s_i(\vec{k},o)> \qquad (4.5c)$$

$$S_{\alpha\beta}^{YY}(\vec{k},\omega) = \int dt\ e^{i\omega t} <Y_\alpha^\dagger(\vec{k},t) Y_\beta(\vec{k},o)> \qquad (4.5d)$$

Here we have already made the transformation to center-of-mass coordinates:

$$\vec{u}_{+,i}^n \to \sqrt{\frac{m_+'}{m}}\ \vec{s}_i^n \quad , \quad \vec{u}_{-,i}^n \to \sqrt{\frac{m_-'}{m}}\ \vec{s}_i^n \qquad (4.6)$$

The form factors $F(\vec{Q})$ are given by:

$$F_{ij}^{TT}(\vec{Q}) = \frac{N}{n} \{a_+^2 m_+ e^{-2W_+} + 4a_+a_-\sqrt{m_+m_-}\ \cos\left[\vec{Q}.(\vec{b}_-+\vec{b}_+)\right] e^{-(W_++W_-)}$$

$$+ 4a_-^2 m_- e^{-2W_-}\}Q_i Q_j \qquad (4.7a)$$

$$F_{i\alpha}^{TR}(\vec{Q}) = iNa_+a_-\sqrt{\frac{m_+'}{m}}\ e^{-(W_-+W_+)}\ 8Nj_\ell(Qd) Q_i Y_\alpha^*(\theta',\ \varphi') c_\alpha \qquad (4.7b)$$

$$F_{\alpha i}^{RT} = (F_{i\alpha}^{TR})^{\star} \tag{4.7c}$$

$$F_{\alpha\beta}^{RR} = Na_-^2 \, e^{-2W-} \, [\, 8\pi j_2 \, (Qd)]^2 Y_\alpha \, (\Theta,\varphi) Y_\beta^{\star} \, (\Theta',\varphi') c_\alpha c_\beta \tag{4.7d}$$

where $c_\alpha = 1$ for $\alpha = 1,3,4,5$ and $c_2 = \sqrt{2/3}$. Expression (4.4), together with the definitions (4.7a-d), constitutes a generalization of the scattering laws derived by Sears [19]. In particular, we do not make the weak-hindering approximation which amounts to an ab-initio factorization of translations and rotations in the scattering law. For this reason we here obtain interference terms between translational and rotational motions. We recall that we have already met these interference terms by deriving the dynamic equations in Sect. 3. We note that in order to use the results of Sect. 3, we have to take into account the fact that the neutron scattering law (4.4) is expressed in terms of the unorthogonalized functions Y_α. Therefore we have to use the relation

$$S_{\alpha\beta}^{YY}(\vec{k},\omega) = S_{\alpha\beta}^{\overline{Y}\overline{Y}}(\vec{k},\omega) + c_i^\alpha c_j^\beta \, S_{ij}^{ss}(\vec{k},\omega) \tag{4.8}$$

and similarly

$$S_{\alpha j}^{Ys}(\vec{k},\omega) = S_{\alpha j}^{\overline{Y}s}(\vec{k},\omega) + c_i^\alpha S_{ij}^{ss}(\vec{k},\omega) \tag{4.9}$$

where $c_i^\alpha = D_{i\ell}(s_\ell, Y_\alpha)$. Using group-theoretical arguments, one can show that only diagonal matrix elements in α,β occur. Since we know the relaxation functions from Sect. 3, we can use the fluctuation-dissipation theorem (3.4) to determine the scattering laws. For practical purposes it is useful to choose selected directions in $\vec{k}$ space. In particular, for

$\vec{k} = (o,o,k)$, all matrices are diagonal and the dynamic equations are greatly simplified. As an example, we consider the translational relaxation function. For $\vec{k}$ in z-direction, Eq. (3.12) reads (i fixed):

$$[z^2 - \Omega_i^2 - z\sigma_i(z)] \phi_{ss}^{ii}(z) = [z - \sigma_i(z)] \Omega_i^{-2} \tag{4.10}$$

with

$$\sigma_i(z) = \beta_i'^2 / (z + i\lambda_i) \tag{4.11}$$

Here $\Omega_i^2 = D_{ii}$ with

$$\Omega_{11}^2 = \Omega_{22}^2 = M_{11}(1 - y\delta/T) = (V_z/m) k^2 c_{44} \tag{4.12a}$$

$$\Omega_{33}^2 = M_{33}(1 - x\delta/T) = (V_z/m) k^2 c_{11} \tag{4.12b}$$

where $\delta = 4a^2 B^2 / V_z c_{44}^\circ$, $\gamma = 16a^2 A^2 / V_z c_{11}^\circ$, $y = R_{33}$, $x = R_{11}$, $M_{11} = (V_z/m) k^2 c_{44}^\circ$ and $M_{33} = (V_z/m) k^2 c_{11}^\circ$. We note that at $T_c = y\delta$, c_{44} vanishes. The temperature dependence of the single-particle susceptibilities x and y has been discussed in ref. [11]. In Eq. (4.11), $\beta_i'^2 = M_{ii} - D_{ii}$, $\lambda_1 = \lambda_2 = \Lambda_{11} X_{11}$, $\lambda_3 = \Lambda_{44} X_{44}$, with $X_{11} = 16k^2 a^2 A^2 / (M_{33} - D_{33})m$, $X_{44} = 4k^2 a^2 B^2 / (M_{11} - D_{11})m$. We remark that at T_c when c_{44} vanishes, X_{ii}^{-1} stays finite and therefore λ_i does not vanish.

The resonances of $\phi_{ss}^{ii}(z)$ are obtained by solving the equation

$$\omega^2 - \Omega_i^2 - \omega\sigma_i(\omega) = o \tag{4.13}$$

We can discuss by hand two extreme cases. a) <u>Fast relaxation</u>,

$\lambda_i > \omega \approx \sqrt{M_{ii}}$. Then Eq. (4.13) reduces to $\omega^2 - \Omega_i^2 + i\omega(\beta_i'^2/\lambda_i) = o$ with the two roots

$$\omega_\pm^i = \pm \, \Omega_i - (1/2)\beta_i'^2/\lambda_i \tag{4.14}$$

For $i = 1,2$ one has a soft mode doublet with frequency $\propto \sqrt{c_{44}}$ as was measured by neutron [6] and Brillouin [7] scattering. We note that λ_i does not tend to zero for $T \to T_c$. Due to the high value of λ_i, the width of the central resonance due to the pole at $\omega = -i\lambda_i$ in $\sigma_i(\omega)$ is so large that this resonance disappears in the flat background. Therefore one sees only a two-peak structure [20]. Consider now case b), slow relaxation, $\lambda_i < \omega \approx \sqrt{M_{ii}}$. Then Eq. (4.13) has three roots for fixed i:

$$\omega_\pm^i = \pm \, \omega_i - (1/2)\lambda_i \alpha_i^2 \tag{4.15a}$$

$$\omega_o^i = - \, i\lambda_i(1-\alpha_i^2) \tag{4.15b}$$

where $\alpha_i^2 = \beta_i'^2/\omega_i^2$, with $\omega_i^2 = M_{ii}$. Near T_c, $\Omega_1 = \Omega_2 \to o$ and therefore $\alpha_1 = \alpha_2 \to 1$ and $\omega_o^i \to o$. Consequently, the central peak exhibits critical slowing-down but the damping of the Brillouin doublet remains normal as is also the case for the fast-relaxation regime. These results are in agreement with neutron and Brillouin scattering experiments [6], [20], [7]. Finally, we have plotted $-\text{Im}\phi_{ss}^{ii}(\omega) = -\phi_{ss}^{ii''}(\omega)$ taken from Eq. (4.10) as a function of ω for case a) (Fig. 1) and case b) (Fig. 2). By inelastic neutron scattering, one is able

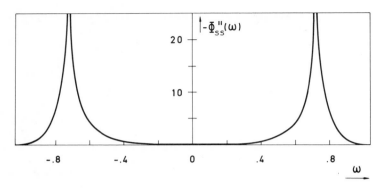

FIG.1.   Displacement-displacement correlation function, $\Omega = 0.7$, $\beta' = 0.55$, $\lambda = 5.3$ (meV).

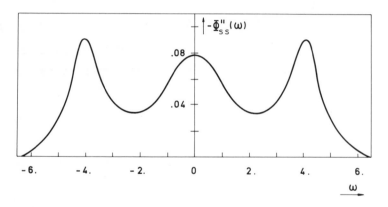

FIG.2.   Displacement-displacement correlation function, $\Omega = 2.6$, $\beta' = 2.8$, $\lambda = 2.0$ (meV).

to cover both the frequency regimes of fast and slow relaxation in KCN [20] .   There is agreement between the present
theory and experiment.

Acknowledgements

The autors acknowledge most useful discus-
sions with J.M. Rowe and J.J. Rush.   Financial support has

been obtained by the project "Neutron Scattering", Interuni-
versitary Institute for Nuclear Research, Belgium and the
Sonderforschungsbereich "Ferroelektrika", Deutsche Forschungs-
gemeinschaft.

REFERENCES

[1] See, e.g. Berne, B.J., and Pecora, R., <u>Dynamic Light</u>
      <u>Scattering</u>, Wiley-Interscience, New York (1976)

[2] Leontovich, M.A., Izv. Akad. Nauk SSR, Ser. Fiz. $\underline{5}$,
      (1941); Bull. Acad. Sc. USSR, Phys. Ser. $\underline{4}$, 499 (1941);
      Rytov, S.M., Zh. Eksp. Theor. Fiz. $\underline{33}$, 166, 514, 671
      (1957), Engl. Transl. Soviet Phys. JETP $\underline{6}$, 130, 401,
      513 (1958)

[3] Starunov, V.S., Tiganov, E.V., and Fabelinski, I.L.,
      Zh. Eksp. Teor. Fiz. Pisma Redakt. $\underline{5}$, 317 (1967); Engl.
      Transl. JETP Letters. $\underline{5}$, 260 (1967); Stegeman G. I.A.,
      and Stoicheff, B.P., Phys. Rev. Lett. $\underline{21}$, 202 (1968)
      and Phys. Rev. $\underline{7A}$, 1160 (1973)

[4] Courtens, E.J. de Physique-Lettres, $\underline{37}$, L21 (1976);
      Bischofberger, T. and Courtens, E., Phys. Rev. Lett.
      $\underline{35}$, 1451 (1975)

[5] Haussühl, S., Solid State Comm. $\underline{13}$, 147 (1973), and
      Acta Crist. in press

[6] Rowe, J.M., Rush, J.J., Vagelatos, N., Price, D.L.,
      Hinks, D.G., and Susman, S., J. Chem. Phys. $\underline{62}$, 4551
      (1975)

[7] Krasser, W., Buchenau, U., and Haussühl, S., Solid State
     Comm. 18, 287 (1976); Boissier, M., Vacher, R., Fontaine,
     D., and Pick, R.M., J. de Physique, in press

[8] Anselm, A.I., and Porfireva, N.N., Zh. Eksp. Theor. Fiz.
     19, 438 (1949)

[9] Van Kranendonk, J., and Sears, V.F., Canad. J. Phys. 44,
     313 (1966)

[10] Michel, K.H., and De Raedt, H., J. Chem. Phys. 65, 977
     (1976)

[11] Michel, K.H., and Naudts, J., Phys. Rev. Lett. 39, 212
     (1977); and J. Chem. Phys. 67, 547 (1977)

[12] Suga, H., Matsuo, T., and Seki, S., Bull. Chem. Soc.
     Japan 38, 1115 (1965)

[13] Rehwald, W., Sandercock, J.R., and Rossinelli, M., preprint

[14] Kadanoff, L.P., and Martin, P.C., Ann. Phys. (N.Y.), 24,
     419 (1963)

[15] Mori, H., Progr. Theor. Phys. 23, 423 (1965); Zwanzig,
     R.W., J. Chem. Phys. 33, 1388 (1960)

[16] Götze, W., and Michel, K.H., in Dynamical Properties of
     Solids, edited by G.K. Horton and A.A. Maradudin, North-
     Holland; Amsterdam, (1974)

[17] Michel, K.H., and Naudts, J., J. Chem. Phys., in press

[18] Van Hove, L., Phys. Rev. 95, 1374 (1954)

[19] Sears, V.F., Canad. J. Phys. 44, 1279, 1299 (1966); idem
     45, 237 (1967)

[20] Rowe, J.M., Rush, J.J. and Chesser, N.J., to be published

DISCUSSION

R.E. LECHNER: You have obtained rotation-translation interference terms in the coherent scattering cross-section taking into account the coupling between rotational and translational motions.

Would you get similar terms for incoherent scattering and if so would they make a significant contribution to the scattered intensity in the quasi-elastic region?

K.H. MICHEL: In theory, yes. I think the practical importance of these interference terms depends on the properties of the system, for instance the shape of the molecules. For incoherent scattering, however, the primary problem is to improve the formulation of the reorientational motion. Bart de Raedt and I are preparing a publication on this subject.

H. HAHN: You mentioned that Mr. Rowe fitted the experimental spectra to your theory. What parameters had to be adjusted in this fit?

K.H. MICHEL: Perhaps Mr. Rowe would like to answer this.

J.M. ROWE: We fitted the values of Λ (a transport coefficient) and Ω at each temperature. The value of Λ was not particularly temperature-dependent.

R.M. PICK: I agree with the general form of your equations, but I should like to ask to what values of J you have to go in your expansion. Our own Raman measurements show that: (a) in both KCN and NaCN, the time of residence of a CN^- ion in its own well is 50.6 times a typical libration period, which means that there is a fair degree of localization, and large values of J are needed to describe the pseudo-libration regime; and (b) in KCN, the phase transition at 168 K cannot be explained by the $J = 2$ F_{2j} third-order harmonics — one needs to go at least to the $J = 4$ F_{2j} third-order harmonics.

Did you in fact take such large values of J into account in your calculation and experiment fit?

K.H. MICHEL: Comparing our theory with Haussühl's results on the elastic constants for KCN and NaCN, we concluded that, for KCN, the $J = 4$ term is negligible in the bilinear coupling of rotations to translations, while for NaCN the bilinear coupling itself is less important for all values of J. We have no detailed knowledge of your particular experiments, but as far as we know there is no evidence from other experiments that in KCN the $J = 4$ terms are important in the bilinear coupling.

LATTICE DYNAMICS
OF COPPER-BASED ALLOYS

N.A. CHERNOPLEKOV, P.P. PARSHIN,
A.Yu. RUMYANTSEV, M.G. ZEMLYANOV
Kurchatov Atomic Energy Institute,
Moscow,
Union of Soviet Socialist Republics

N. KROÓ, L. ROSTA, I. VIZI,
Central Research Institute for Physics,
Budapest,
Hungary

Abstract

LATTICE DYNAMICS OF COPPER-BASED ALLOYS.
    Phonon dispersion curves have been measured in solid solutions of disordered Cu-Ge
and Cu-Ga alloys by inelastic neutron scattering on tripple-axis spectrometers. The analysis
of experimental data shows that the dispersion curves of different alloys, having the same valency
electron concentration per atom, are the same. This is in good agreement with the thermodynamical and elastic properties of the studied alloys. The empirical dependence of phonon
frequencies on the concentration of impurity atoms is formulated, and the results are interpreted
in terms of the Born-von Kármán model as well as by use of a phenomenological electron-shell
model.

1. Introduction

    It has been shown in several theoretical papers [1,2,3,4]
and later experimentally confirmed [5,6] that small concentrations of impurity atoms in the host lattice give rise not only
to local and virtual phonon states but also to considerable deformation of the spectral distribution of host lattice vibrations. To clear the influence of electrons on phonon spectral
deformations the dispersion curves of copper alloyed with germanium and gallium atoms were studied. The dispersion curves
were measured by coherent inelastic neutron scattering on
triple-axis spectrometers.

481

CHERNOPLEKOV et al.

TABLE I. CHARACTERISTICS OF THE SAMPLES STUDIED

Alloy	Mosaic spread /minutes/	Lattice parameter			Impurity concentration /% at./	
		X-ray data	neutron data	[7]	top	bottom
$Cu_{0.875}Ga_{0.125}$	25	3.645 ± 0.003	3.648 ± 0.005	3.648	12.2 ± 0.2	12.3 ± 0.2
$Cu_{0.955}Ga_{0.045}$	39	-	3.630 ± 0.005	3.626	4.25 ± 0.03	4.39 ± 0.03
$Cu_{0.917}Ge_{0.083}$	23	3.650 ± 0.003	3.653 ± 0.006	3.643	-	-
$Cu_{0.96}Ge_{0.04}$	35	-	3.633 ± 0.005	3.627	3.7 ± 0.2	-

Copper has a fully occupied d-electron shell; therefore, one should expect a rather big influence of the change in free electron concentration on the formation of the phonon spectra for the alloy system. The atomic masses of gallium and germanium are not appreciably different from that of copper, thus the influence of the parameter of mass difference does not play an important role. Gallium and germanium have a continuous series of solid solutions with copper in a wide range of concentrations. This enables one to grow single-crystal alloy specimens with different concentrations of valency electrons. Furthermore, the copper-based alloys are well suitable for neutron scattering experiments, since they have small absorption and incoherent scattering cross-sections.

2. Sample preparation

The single crystals $Cu_{0.875}$ $Ga_{0.125}$, $Cu_{0.955}$ $Ga_{0.045}$ $Cu_{0.917}$ $Ge_{0.083}$, $Cu_{0.96}$ $Ge_{0.04}$ having dimensions of 25 mm in diameter and 55 mm in length were grown by the Bridgeman-method. X-ray analysis showed all samples to be disordered solid solutions, the lattice parameters fit the reported data [7]. The quality of the single-crystal samples was checked by measuring the rocking curves of different reflections.

A chemical analysis was carried out to control the homogeneity of the samples which established the impurity concentration of small pieces taken from the bottom and top of the cylindrical specimens. Furthermore, the lattice parameter as well as the homogeneity of the single crystals were checked by the neutron scattering method described in [8]. Results of the quality check of the specimens are summarized in Table I.

3. Experiments

The dispersion curves of copper and its Ge- and Ga-alloys were measured on the triple-axis spectrometers in Budapest and Moscow. Both spectrometers have the same construction and very similar geometry, their technical details are described in [9] and [10].

The dispersion curves for $Cu_{0,875} Ga_{0.125}$ and Cu crystals were measured in the Kurchatov Institute, the remaining samples and some of the phonon branches in $Cu_{0.875} Ga_{0.125}$ crystal were studied in the Central Research Institute for Physics. Results obtained on the different spectrometers are in good agreement with each other and the dispersion curves of Cu agree within experimental errors with data published in [11] and [12].

Measurements were carried out by constant-Q method except for scans for low-energy phonons ($q/q_{max} = 0.15$) where the use of constant energy transfer was more convenient. Depending on the phonon energies and on the focusing conditions the wavelength of the incident neutron beam was varied between 1.2 and 1.7 Å.

The phonon energies were determined from the centre of the Gaussians fitted to the measured neutron groups. Accuracy connected with the statistical errors was calculated on the analogy of [13].

To estimate the experimental resolution we measured the cross-sections of the resolution ellipse corresponding to the transversal as well as to the longitudinal scans using a perfect germanium single crystal. Since the resolution function can be experimentally determined only near the reciprocal lattice points, the resolution function of the spectrometers was calculated by a Monte Carlo simulation. The dimensions of the resolution ellipses were used to estimate the maximum of the experimental errors which can be much less because of the focusing effects in the case of the transversal branches.

The dispersion curves $\omega_s(\vec{q})$ were measured in the main symmetry directions for the $Cu_{0.875} Ga_{0.125}$ sample /Fig. 1 / The [$\xi 00$] T_1 and T_2 [$0\xi\xi$] branches were determined for the $Cu_{0.917} Ga_{0.083}$ alloys /Fig. 1 / and phonons were measured only in the [$\xi 00$] direction for the $Cu_{0.955} Ga_{0.045}$ and $Cu_{0.96} Ge_{0.04}$ samples /Fig. 2 /.

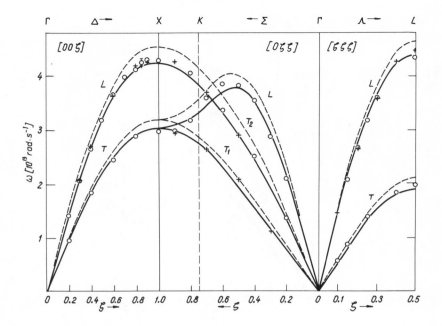

FIG.1. Dispersion curves of copper [11] and its alloys with Zn, Ga and Ge:
--- Cu; —— $Cu_{0.75}$ $Zn_{0.25}$ [8]; ○ $Cu_{0.875}$ $Ga_{0.125}$; + $Cu_{0.917}$ $Ge_{0.083}$

4. Results and discussion

The special feature of the copper alloys with Ga, Ge Zn
[8] is the nearly complete coincidence of their phonon spectra
when the concentration of the valency electrons per atom (e/a)
is the same /Fig. 1 /. This is in good agreement with the results of the lattice specific-heat studies as well as with the
experimental data on elastic constants [14,15]. It is very
convenient to compare the spectra in ion plasma frequencies
$\omega_p^2 = \frac{4\pi Z^2 e^2}{M\Omega_O}$ /Fig. 3 / as the mass (M) dependence of the frequency
does not play any role and the difference in unit cell volumes
Ω_O is also approximately taken into account.

Considering the measured data, it can be concluded that
the energy change of the lattice vibrations spectrum in the

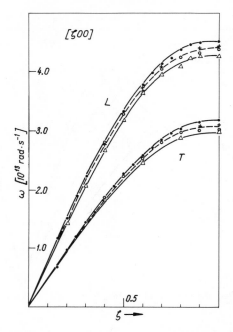

FIG.2. *Dispersion curves of copper and its alloys with Ga and Ge in direction* [ξ00]
● *Cu*; + *Cu*$_{0.955}$ *Ga*$_{0.045}$; ○ *Cu*$_{0.96}$ *Ge*$_{0.04}$; △ *Cu*$_{0.875}$ *Ga*$_{0.125}$
The curves have been drawn through the measured points.

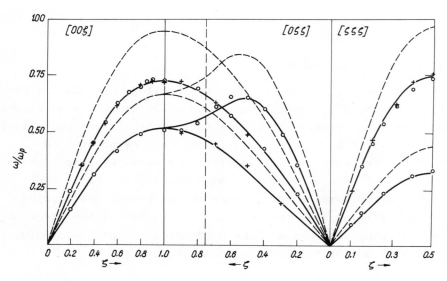

FIG.3. *Phonon spectra of copper and its alloys in scale of ion plasma frequencies.*
--- *Cu*; —— *Cu*$_{0.75}$ *Zn*$_{0.25}$ [8]; ○ *Cu*$_{0.875}$ *Ga*$_{0.125}$; + *Cu*$_{0.917}$ *Ge*$_{0.083}$

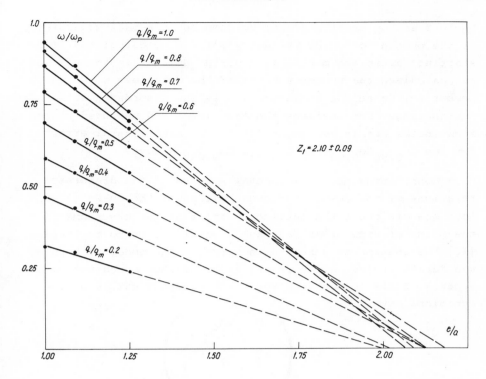

FIG.4.   *Variation of phonon frequency of copper-based alloys as a function of electron concentration e/a for different wave vectors in the [ξ00] direction of transversal propagation.*

studied alloys is determined by the changes in electron concentration. The phonon frequencies decrease linearly with increasing e/a as it turns out from the comparison of the dispersion curves for the copper and the $Cu_{0.875}$ $Ga_{0.125}$, $Cu_{0.955}$
$Ga_{0.045}$ alloys in the [ξ00] direction /Fig. 4./. Extrapolation
of the lines in Fig. 4 gives a fixed point of intersection z_1
with the abscissa which shoes the proportional decreasing in
phonon frequencies corresponding to the different phonon wave
vectors. In this way the phonon frequencies of all the series
of Zn, Ga and Ge alloys can be described by the expression:

$$\omega = \omega_0 \frac{z_1 - z}{z_1 - z_0} \cdot \frac{\omega_p}{\omega_{p_0}}$$

where Z and ω_p are the proper valence and plasma frequencies of the phonon for which frequency ω is to be calculated. The starting values are marked by index O. Using this formula one can calculate the phonon spectra of the Cu alloys with the proper Zn, Ga and Ge concentration in the disordered solid solution range. For instance, the calculated and measured phonon frequencies are in agreement within the experimental errors for the $Cu_{0.96}Ge_{0.04}$ and $Cu_{0.917}Ge_{0.083}$ alloys.

Considering the experimental results on the dispersion relations of the Cu-Ga, Cu-Ge as well as of the Cu-Zn [8] alloys one can treat the lattice dynamics of these systems from the point of view of an "average crystal" as proposed in paper [16]. We interpret our data in terms of the model of Born - von Kármán including the interactions of four coordination spheres. Table II contains the force-constant values of the dynamical matrix

$$\phi = \begin{pmatrix} \alpha_1^n & \beta_3^n & \beta_2^n \\ \beta_3^n & \alpha_2^n & \beta_1^n \\ \beta_2^n & \beta_1^n & \alpha_3^n \end{pmatrix}$$

/n is the number of coordination spheres/ of the Cu-Zn and Cu-Ga alloys with electron concentration e/a = 1.25. The good agreement /$\sim$2% deviation/ of the measured with the computed dispersion curves must be pointed out. It can be also seen that the limitation of the interaction to four instead of six coordination spheres [8,12] does not change considerably the value of the force constants /see Table II /.

We also calculated the dispersion curves of Cu-Zn, Cu-Ga, Cu-Ge alloys (e/a = 1.25) in terms of the electron shell model developed in [17,18] for the lattice dynamics of noble and transition metals. In this model interactions between the ion cores are supposed to be of central type and to be caracterized by the force constants α_1 and α_2 of the first and second coordination spheres. The interaction between the ion cores and the compact d-electron shell is considered by a constant K_1,

TABLE II.   INTERATOM FORCE CONSTANTS IN 10^4 dyn·cm^{-1} UNITS
CALCULATED BY THE BORN-VON KÁRMÁN MODEL FOR COPPER
AND ITS ALLOYS WITH Zn AND Ga

Nearest atom	Force const.	4 coordination spheres			6 coordination spheres	
		Cu	Cu-Zn	Cu-Ga	Cu [12]	Cu-Zn [8]
110	α_1^1	1.313	1.166	1.187	1.312	1.135±0.014
	α_3^1	-0.140	-0.111	-0.133	-0.150	-0.161±0.019
	β_3^1	1.492	1.372	1.345	1.463	1.377±0.028
200	α_1^2	0.010	-0.010	-0.009	0.053	0.057±0.026
	α_2^2	-0.061	-0.098	-0.066	-0.027	-0.055±0.017
211	α_1^3	0.067	0.063	0.040	0.087	0.092±0.011
	α_2^3	0.034	0.035	0.038	0.038	0.041±0.008
	β_1^3	0.005	0.015	0.021	0.016	0.005±0.014
	β_2^3	0.028	0.040	0.037	0.033	0.062±0.008
220	α_1^4	-0.002	-0.006	0.001	0.024	-0.021±0.009
	α_3^4	-0.037	-0.008	-0.010	-0.037	0.004±0.013
	β_3^4	0.040	-0.005	-0.003	0.061	-0.017±0.028

and the interaction of the nearest d-electron shells by a constant S. Contribution from the conduction electrons to the deformation of phonon spectra is taken into account by the analogy of the Krebs model [19] where, to describe the conduction
electron scattering on the ion cores and s-shell, a parameter P
and, to take into account long-range-order-effects, a parameter
A' is introduced. We have used a simplified version of this

TABLE III.   PARAMETERS OF THE ELECTRON SHELL MODEL
DESCRIBING THE LATTICE DYNAMICS OF COPPER AND ITS ALLOYS

	Force constants in 10^4 dyn·cm^{-1} units				
	α_1	α_2	K	S	A
Cu	5.11	2.57	-3976.0	-32.4	66.7
Cu-Zn Cu-Ga Cu-Ge	11.30	3.09	-2271.0	-37.4	62.09

electron-shell model [17],where only the scattering of the conduction electrons on the d-shell is considered corresponding
to P=1 and in this case A' can be expressed in terms of the
elastic constants. Constants K and S are determined from the
frequency values of the transversal vibrations in the [ξ00]
direction at the Brillouin-zone boundary, and α_1 and α_2 from
the elastic constants. In the calculations we used the Bohm-
-Pines screening parameter. The force-constant values are
given in Table III and the calculated dispersion curves for
copper and its alloys are shown in Fig. 5. One can see that
the transversal branches are much better described than the
longitudinal ones and that the largest deviation of the experimental from the computed curves can be observed in directions
[ξξξ] and [ξ00] /5-7%/. The α_1, K and S values indicated in
Table III are different from those of [17] which can be explained by the strong dependence of these parameters on the zone
boundary frequencies.

From the results one can conclude that within the shell
model a better coincidence of the experimental and calculated
results can be reached if the scattering of electrons on the
ion cores is taken into account. Parameters K and S have to
be determined by fitting the vibration frequency spectrum as
it has been done for the dispersion curves of copper in [18].

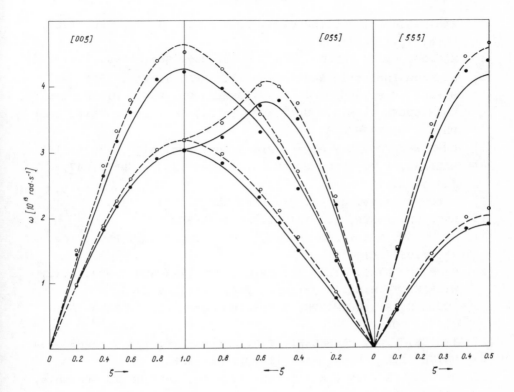

FIG.5. *Comparison of experimental and calculated dispersion curves for copper and its alloys with Zn, Ga and Ge.*

--- ⎱ *calculation by the electron*　　　　⎰ *Cu*
——— ⎰ *shell model for*　　　　　　　　　⎱ *the alloys*
○ *Cu* [11];　● *Average frequency values of alloys*

Finally, we should like to thank W.A. Somenkov for valuable discussions, A.P. Zhernov for his help in the model construction as well as Ye.W. Melnikov., N.T. Bezobrazov and L. Zámbo for growing the crystals and for their chemical analysis.

R E F E R E N C E S

[1]   LIFSHIZ, I.M., Nuovo Cimento, Suppl. vol. 3,ser X. /1956/716
[2]   KRIVOGLAZ, M.A., Sov. Journ. Exp. Teor. Phys. 40,/1961/567

[3] KAGAN, Yu.M., IOSZILEVSZKI, Ya.A., Sov. Journ. Exp. Teor.
     Phys. 42,/1962/ 259

[4] ELLIOT, R.J., TAYLOR, D.W., Proc. Roy. Soc. A296,/1967/161

[5] Neutron Inelastic Scattering vl, IAEA, Vienna, 1968

[6] SIRICH, G.F., ZHERNOV, A.P., ZEMLJANOV, M.G., MIRONOV, S.P.,
     CHERNOPLEKOV, N.A., SHITIKOV, Yu.L., Sov. Journ. Exp. Teor.
     Phys. 70,/1976/ 353

[7] HUME,W. - ROTHERY et al. Proc. Roy. Soc. A157, /1936/ 167

[8] HALLMAN, E.D., BROCKHOUSE, B.N., Can. Journ. Phys. 47,
     /1969/ 1117

[9] GOLOVIN, A.Ye. at al, Preprint IAE No. 2445 /1974/

[10] KROO, N. ROSTA, L. VIZI, I. KFKI-73-35

[11] SVENSSON, E.C., BROCKHOUSE, B.N., ROW, J.M. , Phys. Rev.
     155,/1967/ 619

[12] NICKLOW, R.M., GILAT, G., SMITH, H.G., RAUBENHEIMER, L.T.,
     WILKINSON, M.K., Phys. Rev. 164, /1967/ 922

[13] STEDMAN, R., WEYMOUTH, T., Brit. Journ. Appl. Phys. D2,
     /1969/ 904

[14] ISAACS, L.L., MASSALSKI, T.B., Phys. Rev. 138A, /1965/ 134

[15] RAYNE, I.A., Phys. Rev. 110, /1958/ 606

[16] BROCKHOUSE, B.N., KAMITAKAHAZA, W.A., IAEA SYMP. Grenoble,
     /1972/ 73

[17] FIELEK, B.L., Journ. Phys. F. 5, /1975/ 17

[18] FIELEK, B.L., Journ. Phys. F. 5, /1975/ 1451

[19] KREBS, K., Phys. Rev. 138A, /1965/ 143

MOLECULAR CONFORMATION OF POLYPROPYLENE IN THE MOLTEN AND CRYSTALLINE STATES

J. SCHELTEN, W. SCHMATZ
Institut für Festkörperforschung der
    Kernforschungsanlage Jülich GmbH,
Jülich,
Federal Republic of Germany

D.G.H. BALLARD
ICI Corporate Laboratory,
Runcorn, The Heath,
United Kingdom

Abstract

MOLECULAR CONFORMATION OF POLYPROPYLENE IN THE MOLTEN AND
CRYSTALLINE STATES.

Small-angle neutron scattering studies have been made of molten and crystalline
polypropylene by using samples containing small amounts of deuterated polypropylene in
a protonated polypropylene matrix. The specimens were characterized by small- and wide-
angle X-ray scattering to determine the d-spacing and the degree of crystallinity x and by gel
permeation chromatography to determine molecular weights M_w and molecular weight
distributions. The degree of crystallinity was varied from 0.5 to 0.7, the d-spacing from
120 Å to 250 Å and the molecular weight from 34 000 to 1 540 000. Clustering effects were
not observed. The radii of gyration $\langle s^2 \rangle_w^{1/2}$ of the tagged molecules varied approximately
proportional to $M_w^{1/2}$ and were almost independent of d and x. In the melt, similar values
were obtained which are within experimental uncertainties equal to those in θ-solution. For
$\langle s^2 \rangle_w \kappa^2 \gg 1$, the scattering law approaches a κ^{-2} dependence. A chain molecule model for
the crystalline state is introduced which takes into account experimental results concerning
the morphology of the polypropylene specimens as well as conformational parameters of the
polypropylene molecules.

INTRODUCTION

Classical diffraction technique making use of X-rays, electrons and neutrons
as applied to polymers in their molten and solid states provides information on
the arrangement of atoms and small atomic groups. From such diffraction
experiments, the strongest evidence was obtained for the existence of different
polymer states. However, little, if any information can be deduced from these

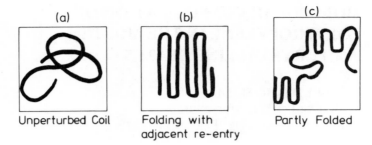

(a)   (b)   (c)

Unperturbed Coil   Folding with   Partly Folded
                       adjacent re-entry

FIG.1. (a–c). Various chain molecule conformations.

diffraction results on the conformation of the long chain molecules. Knowledge of conformation is of fundamental interest because it is generally accepted that the large variety of mechanical and thermal properties of polymer solids is coupled to considerable conformation changes of the chain molecules. In Fig. 1 a–c, a few conformations are sketched which are, today, believed to be realized in polymer solids or melts.

About seven years ago, independently at three different places, the idea of how conformation parameters could be measured very directly was born. By blending normal protonated polymers with a small fraction of deuterated polymer molecules, a contrast is achieved in neutron scattering experiments as is indicated in Fig. 2. The contrast is based on the property that the nuclear coherent scattering lengths of H and D are very different, $- 0.374$ and $+ 0.667$ in units of 10^{-12} cm, respectively. For electrons and X-rays, the corresponding lengths are the same. The neutron scattering from the small fraction of tagged chain molecules occurs mainly at small scattering angles ϑ of the order of $\lambda/\langle s^2 \rangle_W^{1/2}$, where $\langle s^2 \rangle_W^{1/2}$ is the mean radius of gyration of the tagged chain molecules. This quantity is a measure of the mean square displacements of D atoms, at a long chain molecule, from its centre of mass. Thus, experimental data of chain conformations are measured by neutron small-angle scattering (SAS) facilities. This specialized neutron scattering technique was developed up to a very high performance at very few reactor stations [1, 2]. In this paper, we shall present SAS results achieved by the SAS facility at FRJ-2 of Jülich [3].

For the study of chain conformations of polymers in the partially crystallized state, it would be quite natural to start with the best known polymer polyethylene. Earlier scattering experiments with polyethylene over several years have revealed some serious difficulties which are described elsewhere [4, 5] and which we are still trying to overcome. As an alternative approach to the problem of obtaining

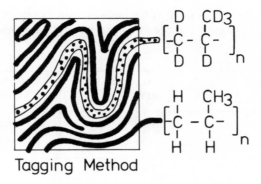

Tagging Method

FIG.2.   Polypropylene molecule tagging by deuteration.

reliable information on chain molecule conformations, we have changed the polymer from polyethylene $(CH_2)_n$ to the similar polymer polypropylene $(CH_2\text{-}CH\text{-}CH_3)_n$. The experiments with polyethylene had left unanswered the question of whether polyolefins crystallize with chain folding when the polymer is slowly cooled from the melt or annealed at temperatures below the melting point. It is essentially this question which was pursued by the very recent first scattering experiment with polypropylene. Here, the clustering problems we were facing with polyethylene were either absent or much less severe — for reasons we do not know yet.

It is the purpose of this paper, first, to describe the preparation of poly-propylene specimens and their characterization by various methods. Second, we shall discuss the obtained conformation parameters determined from the neutron scattering experiments in view of our morphological insight into molten and crystallized polypropylene. Third, a confirmation model will be introduced which can be made consistent with all experimental results.

EXPERIMENTS AND RESULTS

Protopolypropylene (PPH) and deuteropolypropylene (PPD) were synthesized by using organometallic polymerization catalysts with special features yielding polymers with very high tacticities as compared with conventional Ziegler systems. The polymers were freed from catalyst impurities and atactic material by conventional means.

The tacticity of the protopolymer was determined by C13 NMR and found to be 97—99% isotactic in all cases. It was fractionated into five fractions with molecular weights (M_w) 46 000 to 1 135 000 and melting points of 163 to

TABLE I. CRYSTALLINE FRACTIONS (x) AND D-SPACINGS OF
POLYPROPYLENE SPECIMENS (AVERAGE VALUES OF SIX
SPECIMENS)

	Quenched (PPQ)	Annealed (PPA)	Crystallized (PPC)
x	0.56	0.63	0.68
d	122 Å	200 Å	250 Å

$166.5°C$ measured at $5°C \cdot min^{-1}$. Hot orthodichlorobenzene (ODCB) was used
as a solvent for the fractionation by the coercevation technique with triethylene
glycol as non-solvent. Molecular weights were measured by gel permeation
chromatography in ODCB as solvent and National Physical Laboratory Standard
polypropylene samples were used for calibration. The molecular weight polydispersity can be described well by a log-normal distribution function with
M_W/M_N values as given in Table II. According to this distribution function,
weight average values were calculated from measured z average radii of gyration.

The level of deuteration in deuteropolypropylene was obtained by integrating the NMR trace obtained on a 220 Mc/s machine for the protopolymer
and comparing this with a PPD solution of the same concentration run under
the same conditions. The fractions examined were, at least, 95% deuterated.
The same fractionation procedure was used to give fractions with values of M_W
between 34 000 to 1 540 200 and melting points for $5°C \cdot min^{-1}$ between 161°
and 164°. The melting temperatures of PPD and PPH measured at $0.62° \cdot min^{-1}$
with a Perkin Elmer DSC-2 show no observable difference. In this respect,
polypropylene differs from linear polyethylene where a 6° difference in melting
temperature was detected between deuterated and protopolymers.

The components of blends were chosen so as to match crystallization
temperature and molecular weight as closely as possible from the available
fractions. Components were mixed as powders, and the mixture was dissolved
in ODCB and precipitated in methanol washed and dried in a vacuum oven.
Samples were compression-moulded to give plaques 1 mm in thickness and
quenched into cold water; these samples are identified as quenched samples in
the tables. Some of these were annealed by heating to 137°C and maintaining
this temperature for 24 hours; these samples are identified as annealed samples
in the tables. Finally, quenched samples were heated well above the melting
point and then cooled at 139°C to be crystallized slowly. They are identified
as crystallized in the tables. (Table I).

TABLE II. DATA FOR POLYPROPYLENE WITH PPH MATRIX AND PPD TAGGED MOLECULES. THE CONCENTRATION OF THE LATTER IS 0.03 g·g⁻¹. MEASUREMENTS ARE TAKEN AT 23°C.

Sample No.	PPH $10^{-3}M_w$	PPD $10^{-3}M_w$	$\dfrac{M_w}{M_N}$	$10^{-3}(M_w)_{app}$	$\dfrac{(M_w)_{app}}{M_w}$	$\langle s^2\rangle_z^{1/2}$ (Å)	$\langle s^2\rangle_w^{1/2}$ (Å)	$\dfrac{\langle s^2\rangle_w^{1/2}}{M_w^{1/2}}$ (Å·g$^{-1/2}$)	Q
Quenched									
PPQ1	46	34	2.52	64	1.88	180	113	0.61	4.1
PPQ2	46	140	1.68	118	0.84	180	139	0.37	
PPQ3	56	340	2.02	299	0.88	255	179	0.31	2.17
PPQ4	105	575	1.56	529	0.92	320	256	0.34	
PPQ6	114	1540	1.48	1480	0.96	503	413	0.39	1.7
Annealed									
PPA1	46	34	2.52	74	2.17	180	113	0.61	3.3
PPA2	46	140	1.68	122	0.87	190	147	0.39	
PPA3	56	340	2.02	299	0.88	265	186	0.32	2.4
PPA4	105	575	1.56	587	1.02	347	278	0.37	
PPA6	114	1540	1.48	1509	0.98	514	423	0.40	1.7
Crystallized									
PPC1	46	34	2.52	240	7.1	235	148	0.8	1.7
PPC2	46	140	1.68	185	1.32	235	181	0.48	
PPC3	56	340	2.02	347	1.02	290	218	0.37	2.5
PPC4	105	575	1.56	667	1.16	368	296	0.39	
PPC6	114	1540	1.48	2002	1.30	580	477	0.38	1.8

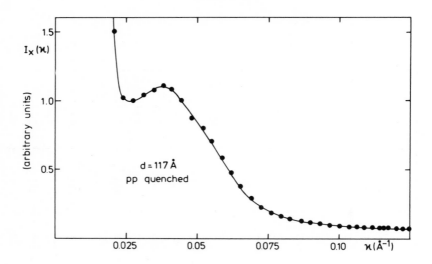

FIG.3. Small X-ray scattering I(κ) *versus scattering vector* κ *for quenched polypropylene* (PPQ 2).

Crystallinities were derived from relative areas under the Bragg peaks obtained with a Philips diffractometer used in the transmission mode (Cu K_α radiation). Measurements of lamellar stacking periods (d-spacing) were carried out with a Kratky camera. The intensity data were corrected for resolution errors by using standard computer techniques. The small angle X-ray scattering of $I(\kappa)\kappa^2$ versus κ with $\kappa = 4\pi \sin\Theta/\lambda$ was used to determine d-spacing from the diffraction peaks. A typical small-angle scattering pattern is shown in Fig. 3.

The extrapolated forward neutron scattering cross-section $d\Sigma(0)/d\Omega$, measured in absolute units, is a very sensitive indicator as to whether the PPD molecules are clustered or distributed statistically. Only for statistical distribution, the following relation holds

$$\frac{1}{cK_N}\frac{d\Sigma}{d\Omega}(0) = \frac{1}{M_w} \tag{1}$$

where c is the concentration of tagged molecules and K_N is a constant given by

$$K_N = \rho N_L \left(\frac{\nu\gamma(b_D - b_H)}{M_0}\right)^2 \tag{2}$$

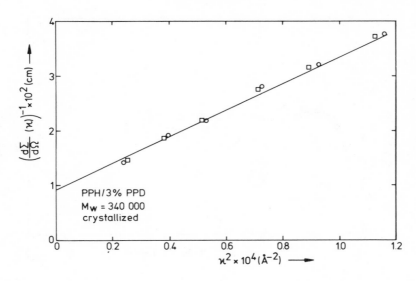

FIG.4. *Reciprocal neutron scattering cross-section versus κ^2 for specimen PPC 3. From slope and intercept of the straight line $\langle s^2 \rangle_z^{1/2}$ is obtained.*

Here, ρ is the mass density, N_L the Avagadro number, $\nu = 6$ is the number of H sites of a tagged segment $C_3 D_{6\gamma} H_{6(1-\gamma)}$, where γ is the degree of deuteration and M_0 the molecular weight of the chain segment. The contrast is provided by the scattering lengths b_D and b_H. The extrapolated forward scattering cross-section is obtained from the usual linear plots $1/(d\Sigma/d\Omega)$ versus κ^2. Where there is no clustering, M_w determined from neutron measurements (Eq. (1)) should equal the well known molecular weight of the tagged molecules which was determined previously by other means before blending was carried out. Where clustering does occur, curves obtained by plotting $(d\Sigma/d\Omega)^{-1}$ against κ^2 are still linear [4], but the value of the intercept now gives the apparent molecular weight of the cluster $(M_w)_{app}$. The ratio $(M_w)_{app}/M_w$ is a measure of the number of molecules in the cluster and has been used diagnostically to determine the absence of clustering. A typical plot of the scattering data used to obtain values of M_w and the radius of gyration $\langle s^2 \rangle_w^{1/2}$ is shown in Fig. 4. The results of this analysis are given in Table II.

Measurements were also carried out at higher angles. A typical curve obtained for all molecular weights, except for the lowest, is shown in Fig. 5.

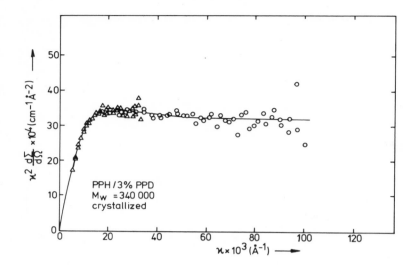

FIG.5. *Kratky plot of the scattering from 3% PPD in isothermally crystallized polypropylene* (PPC 3).

It is similar to those obtained with the quenched and annealed samples. At higher values the quantity Q defined by

$$Q = \frac{\kappa^2 \langle s^2 \rangle_w}{C M_w K_N} \frac{d\Sigma}{d\Omega}(\kappa) = \kappa^2 \langle s^2 \rangle_w |F(\kappa)|^2 \tag{3}$$

becomes a molecule parameter where $|F(\kappa)|^2$ is the form factor of the polymer molecules, normalized to 1 at $\kappa = 0$. From the Kratky plots (see Fig. 5) it is indicated that the scattering function approaches a κ^{-2} dependence, i.e. the values of Q as given in Table II are independent of κ, provided $\kappa > 0.025$ A. For a Gaussian chain, we obtain a κ^{-2}-dependence with Q = 2. The values of Q as given in Table II are close to 2.

In Fig. 6, measured radii of gyration are shown as a function of molecular weight. The Gaussian chain is represented by a straight line as indicated in Fig. 6. It is evident from this figure that the data for solid PP generally fit the model of Gaussian distribution of scattering segments. For the specimen with smallest M_w, the determination of M_w from GPC is somewhat uncertain. If $\langle s^2 \rangle_w$ had been plotted against the apparent M_w, then the solid line in Fig. 6

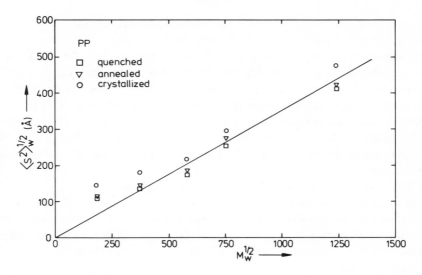

FIG.6.   Radius of gyration $\langle s^2 \rangle_w^{1/2}$ of chain molecules as a function of GPC molecular weight
for the quenched, annealed and crystallized polypropylene specimens.

would have been approached much better. The quenched and annealed samples
give almost identical radii of gyration, although there is a major increase in
d-spacing as a result of different thermal treatments. For the crystallized samples,
the values are slightly larger than for the other two samples. A particularly
important feature of all the results in Table II is the fact that although the
d-spacing has increased by more than a factor of two by crystallizing the samples,
the values of $\langle s^2 \rangle_w^{1/2}$ for a particular molecular weight are similar. Furthermore,
the values of Q are of the order of 2, and there is no significant difference
between quenched, annealed or crystallized samples.

After the scattering experiments with polypropylene in the crystalline state
the specimens PP Q 1–6 were heated up to temperatures of 200°C and 220°C,
which are beyond the melting point, and were measured at these temperatures
for several hours in the molten state. During this treatment, about 50% of the
sample material evaporated. This effect caused uncertainties as to how corrections
for the background should be performed. In addition, because of this disappear-
ance of sample material during the measurement, it was not possible to determine
the forward-scattering cross-section in absolute units, and, therefore, nothing
could be said about clustering in the melt. Furthermore, it was virtually impossible
to obtain reliable scattering data in the higher-κ region, where data must be
collected for a very long time and where precise background data are absolutely

necessary. The scattering patterns in the molten state were similar to the patterns in the crystalline state. The radii of gyration, $\langle s^2 \rangle_w^{1/2}$, as measured in the molten state and, thereafter, in the crystalline state at 150°C and 23°C are plotted versus M_w in Fig. 6. Within the experimental uncertainty the radii of gyration do not depend on temperature and obey the $M_w^{1/2}$ law. The experimental uncertainties are, to a large extent, caused by the uncertainty of the background correction because of the losses of sample material mentioned. In Fig. 6, the straight line $\langle s^2 \rangle_w^{1/2} = 0.34 \, M_w^{1/2}$ is drawn, which describes the molecular weight dependence of the radius of gyration for isotactic polypropylene in Θ-solution.

Thus, the results of these neutron scattering experiments are: (i) In the molten state and in Θ-solution the radii of gyration are the same. (ii) The radii of gyration are only slightly affected by going from the molten to the crystalline state. Both results have been deduced from various experiments with polyethylene [3] and (i) is in accordance with the results for amorphous polymethylmetacrylate [6] and polystyrene [7, 8].

DISCUSSION

The simplicity of these results enables some rather obvious conclusions to be drawn on the relationship between the morphology of isotactic polypropylene and the conformation of the chain. It is evident that the different thermal treatments which cause a change in the long spacing from 120 to 250 Å have no significant effect on the conformation of the chain as a whole. Moreover, random coil statistics is able to describe the disposition of chain segments around the centre of mass, independent of the degree of crystallinity and d-spacing. Trying to reconcile these observations with models postulating the presence of crystalline regions with thicknesses comparable with the measured d-spacing is a challenging task.

Let ℓ_c be the stem length of the polymer chain in the crystalline region of a lamella and ℓ_a the average length per fold of polymer chain in the amorphous regions. Then, the total length L is given by

$$L = \ell_c n_L n_s + \ell_a n_L \tag{4}$$

where n_L is the mean number of lamellas traversed by a chain molecule, and n_s is the mean number of chain stems per lamella.

In addition, the relations

$$\ell_a = d(1 - x) \qquad \text{and} \qquad \ell_c = dx \tag{5}$$

hold, where x is the degree of crystallinity.

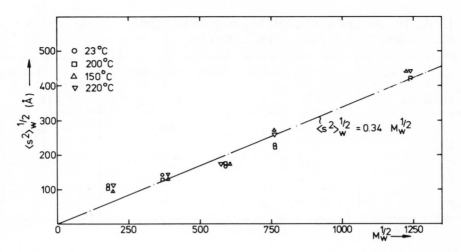

FIG.7.   Radius of gyration $\langle s^2 \rangle_w^{1/2}$ of chain molecules as a function of molecular weight M_w
for the polypropylene specimens PPQ1–6 measured in the melt at $200°C$ and $220°C$ and then
in the solid at $150°C$ and $23°C$.

In an idealised way, we may imagine that, after n_s foldings, the chain
molecules perform a one-dimensional random walk with a step length d in the
direction of the stems.

A view of a molecule conformation according to a more specified model is shown
in Fig. 7. Furthermore, it is assumed that the contribution of a group of n_s stems
to the radius of gyration of a chain molecule can be neglected.

In this case the radius of gyration is solely determined by the random walk
and is given by

$$\langle s^2 \rangle = \frac{1}{6} \, n_L \, d^2 \tag{6}$$

If we describe the molecular weight dependence of $\langle s^2 \rangle$ and L by the following
relations:

$$\langle s^2 \rangle^{1/2} = \beta M_w^{1/2} \tag{7}$$

and

$$L = \eta M_w \tag{8}$$

TABLE III. NUMBER OF LAMELLAS n_L OF OCCUPIED SINGLE CHAIN AND NUMBER OF STEMS n_s PER LAMELLA

n_s Sample No.	Quenched 9	Annealed 14	Crystallized 18
1	1.5	0.2	0.5
2	7	3	1.5
3	17	6	4
4	28	11	7
6	76	28	18

with η independent and β almost independent of M_w, the model parameters n_L and n_s can be expressed in terms of the experimental parameters β, η, d and x measured for the quenched, annealed and crystallized specimens. We calculate

$$n_s = \frac{\eta d}{6\beta^2} \qquad (9)$$

and

$$n_L = \frac{6\beta^2 M_w}{d^2} \qquad (10)$$

Numerical values are calculated for the experimental results for d and x, using for $\eta = 0.0517$ Å·g^{-1} and for $\beta = 0.35$ Å·g$^{-1/2}$; they are given in Table III. As can be seen from this table, reasonable model parameters were obtained in accounting for experimental facts concerning morphology and conformation. The only exception is the case of the lowest molecular weight where n_L values less than 1 are calculated. In addition, it turns out that the number of stems is independent of the molecular weight and that n_s increases with increasing degree of crystallinity and increasing d spacing.

A specification of the model is necessary to account for the κ^{-2} behaviour of the scattering law indicated by the measurements in the region of higher κ values. The simplest way to do this is to imagine the molecule folded n_s times along a plane so that a platelet of height ℓ_c and width w is formed, consisting of n_s equally spaced stems. Such platelets within the lamellas are again interconnected

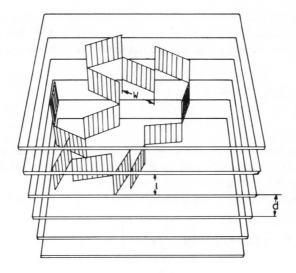

FIG.8.   *Three-dimensional view of a particular chain molecule conformation according to the fold-and-jump model within a stack of crystalline and amorphous regions. The amorphous region is suppressed to a large extent for the sake of clarity.*

according to a one-dimensional random walk in the stem direction, with a step size d as was discussed above. Furthermore, it is assumed that there is no orientation correlation between consecutive platelets which would not necessarily mean random orientation but could also be realized by randomly choosing one of a few equivalent crystallographic planes as the folding plane. According to this rule, Fig. 7 was drawn to illustrate the model.

For $w \ll \ell_c$ the same n_s and n_L values are obtained as listed in Table III. For $w \cong \ell_c$ the n_L values are lowered by 25% while n_s is increased by about the same amount. For a molecule folding with an adjacent or nearly adjacent re-entry the spacing between two consecutive stems is less than 10 Å. With the n_s values of Table III, this leads to dimensions of the plates of up to 90 Å, 140 Å and 180 Å for the quenched, annealed and crystallized specimens, respectively, which implies the relation $w \leqslant \ell_c$.

In the following, the scattering law for the high-κ region is investigated. The scattering function of platelets of dimensions ℓ_c and w with random·orientation approaches a κ^{-2} dependence if $\kappa\ell_c$ and κw become larger than one. This situation is realized in our platelet model since coherent interference of the scattering from plates belonging to the same chain molecules and to different chain molecules both do not exist. The reasons are, first, that orientation correlations do not exist between platelets belonging to the same chain and, second, that the tagged molecules are statistically distributed. For the scattering cross-section of the tagged molecules we obtain in the high-κ region for this model

$$\frac{d\Sigma}{d\Omega}(\kappa) = N_T\, n_L\, (n_s\, \ell_c\, \Delta b)^2\ \frac{k}{\frac{1}{12}(\ell_c^2 + w^2)}\ \kappa^{-2} \tag{11}$$

where N_T is the number of tagged molecules per unit volume, Δb is the scattering contrast per unit length of a tagged molecule and k is a numerical value lying around one depending essentially on the ratio w/ℓ_c (see Fig. 9, in Ref. [4]). In the low-κ region, the scattering cross-section of the tagged molecules is given by

$$\frac{d\Sigma}{d\Omega}(\kappa) = N_T\, n_L^2\, (n_s\, \ell_c\, \Delta b)^2 \left[1 - \frac{1}{3}\kappa^2\langle s^2\rangle \right] \tag{12}$$

with $\langle s^2\rangle$ given by formula (6).

With Eqs (6), (11) and (12), we obtain for the quantity Q defined in Eq. (3):

$$Q = \frac{2d^2}{\ell_c^2 + w^2}\, k = \frac{2k}{x^2}\ \frac{\ell_c^2}{\ell_c^2 + w^2} \tag{13}$$

Inserting here x = 0.65, w = ℓ_c and k = 1, the model value of Q is 2.4 which compares well with the experimental Q-values given in Table II.

In summary, for large molecular weights, all experimental facts concerning morphology and conformation are consistent with this chain molecule model. For low-molecular-weight molecules, this model fails because the obtained values of $n_L < 1$ are unrealistic.

Scattering experiments with polypropylene are in progress to explore the low-molecular-weight region where very few foldings are expected.

ACKNOWLEDGEMENT

The assistance of T. Crowley in doing the scattering experiments is appreciated.

REFERENCES

[1] SCHMATZ, W., SPRINGER, T., SCHELTEN, J., IBEL, K., J. Appl. Crystallogr. 7 (1974) 96.
[2] IBEL, K., J. Appl. Crystallogr. 9 (1976) 630.
[3] SCHELTEN, J., Kerntechnik 14 (1978) to appear.

[4]   SCHELTEN, J., BALLARD, D.G.H., WIGNALL, G.D., SCHMATZ, W., Polymer 17
      (1976) 751.
[5]   SCHELTEN, J., WIGNALL, G.D., BALLARD, D.G.H., LONGMAN, G., Polymer (1977)
      (in press).
[6]   KIRSTE, R.G., KRUSE, W.A., SCHELTEN, J., Macromol. Chem. 162 (1972) 299.
[7]   BENOIT, H., COTTON, J.P., DECKER, D., FARNOUX, B., HIGGINS, J.S., JANNINK, G.,
      OBER, R., PICOT, C., Nature 245 (1973) 13.
[8]   WIGNALL, G.D., BALLARD, D.G.H., SCHELTEN, J., Eur. Polym. J. 10 (1974) 861.

DISCUSSION

H. HAHN: From Schelten's large-scale type of random walk for the single chain, and from Flory's single-segment random walk model, you should be able to calculate the constant for the high-κ behaviour of the function $s(\kappa)$. Should there not be a difference between the measured and calculated values in view of the fact that the step length is different?

W. SCHMATZ: Actually, this was done. In the fold and jump model the constant is a function of the ratio w/ℓ (width/length of the folding plane). By comparing the measured and calculated constants the result $w \approx \ell$ was obtained.

D. RICHTER: As far as I remember, the results of earlier experiments on molten polymers were interpreted as indicating a random coil conformation. For instance, the meander model of Pechhold, which considers extended segments in the melt, was ruled out by these experiments. However, you are saying that the extended chain segments in the crystalline parts of the polymer will not show up in the scattering law, which remains indistinguishable from that of a random coil. Is there not a contradiction here?

W. SCHMATZ: For a needle gas, the κ^{-2} dependence of the scattering function turns into a κ^{-1} dependence for $\kappa > 2/a$, where a is the persistence length. Such behaviour was not found in the amorphous state and this model was therefore rejected. On the other hand, for polymers in the crystalline state we have good evidence for the presence of straight stems but again just a κ^{-2} dependence. The fold and jump model is in accordance with both results. Straight polymer segments are present and the κ^{-2} dependence is ensured by the platelets formed by a folding molecule. It is worth mentioning that the meander model must be modified by introducing refolding in order to be consistent with experimental findings.

Session V

LIQUID CRYSTALS AND POLYMERS

Chairman

S. YIP
United States of America

Invited Review Paper

HYDRODYNAMIC INSTABILITIES
AND NEUTRON SCATTERING

T. RISTE, K. OTNES
Institutt for Atomenergi,
Kjeller,
Norway

H. BJERRUM MØLLER
Risø Research Establishment,
Roskilde,
Denmark

Abstract

HYDRODYNAMIC INSTABILITIES AND NEUTRON SCATTERING.

The flow pattern in a liquid layer heated from below changes character as the vertical
temperature gradient is increased. A review is given for the sequence of instabilities connected
with the different flow regimes, with emphasis on their phase-transition aspects. Utilizing the
coupling that exists between the molecular orientation and flow in a liquid crystal, we have
used neutron scattering to explore these phenomena. The special features of liquid crystals in
this respect are pointed out. Experiments near the lowest lying instability, the Rayleigh-
Bénard transition, verify the mean-field predictions for the change of the threshold gradient
with the applied magnetic field, the behaviour of the order parameter (the fluid velocity)
versus ϵ (the reduced gradient scale), the time-dependent growth and the critical slowing down
of the growth rate of the order parameter. A pre-transitional tail of intensity is analysed within
the same formalism and it is suggested that it arises from hydrodynamic fluctuations driven by
the microscopic fluctuations of the liquid. Experiments at higher gradients reveal a timeperiodic flow regime with frequencies down to cycles per hour. These observations lend support
to modern theories for the transition to turbulence.

1. INTRODUCTION

Four years ago, when studying the phase transition from the nematic to
the isotropic liquid state by neutron scattering, we were intrigued by a
strong intensity component of a transient character each time we changed the
sample temperature. At first it was a matter of curiosity to find out what
the origin of it was, later it became the subject of serious study. The kind
of hydrodynamic instability that we observe is often referred to as the
Rayleigh-Bénard instability. To explain what it is, consider a liquid in a
vessel subjected to a vertical temperature gradient. At a a small gradient
heat is transported by conduction and the liquid remains quiescent. When the
gradient exceeds a well-defined threshold value, convection sets in and regu-
larly shaped convection cells are observed. The cell pattern and its formation has been widely studied both experimentally [1] and theoretically [2],

and we can actually often see the phenomenon when we look at the cumulus clouds on the sky. To "see" such a flow pattern with neutrons we have to use liquid crystals. Here the elongated molecules are oriented by the flow and the orientation in its turn strongly influences the intensity of the liquid diffraction peaks. Hence we in principle can deduce information about the onset of convective flow at the Rayleigh-Bénard instability from neutron data.

By further increase of the temperature gradient, and thus of the Rayleigh number R, one ultimately reaches the turbulent region where an irregular, timedependent pattern of eddies replaces the regular, static pattern of convection rolls. The possible ways in which turbulence may develop has, following the classical work of Landau [3], been the subject of much theoretical work [4,5]. There is possibly a difference in behaviour among liquids of different Prandtl number P, a parameter measuring the ratio between the viscosity and the thermal conductivity. At least in liquids of low P's, the time-independent laminar flow regime at low R's and the timedependent turbulent-flow regimes are separated by a timeperiodic flow regime that may involve one or several instabilities as R is changed.

The growing interest among physicists in these phenomena stems from the phase transition analogies of such instabilities and from the manifestation they give of non-equilibrium phenomena [6]. Physics has given a new dimension to the hydrodynamic problems by allowing for fluctuations. Fluctuations originate on the microscopic level of the system under study, but couple with and influence the macroscopic behaviour of the system. For hydrodynamic instabilities there is, to our knowledge, no experimental observation of the fluctuations and their possible critical enhancement [7] near the critical Rayleigh number.

A nematic liquid crystal seems particularly well suited for a study of these phenomena. As shown by the Orsay group [8], both theoretically and experimentally, the critical Rayleigh number R_c can be reached at much smaller gradient values than in isotropic liquids. Hence one can reach higher values of R than in isotropic liquids. Secondly both R and P can be drastically changed through the application of a magnetic field, which in principle allows a test of scaling and the possible dependence of higher instabilities on P. Thirdly, in liquid crystals, thermal fluctuations of orientations are enormous. They couple with the flow and thus may create a chance for observing fluctuactions near R_c.

There are, unfortunately, no other neutron experiments on these phenomena than ours. After reviewing the qualitative features of the theory and our experiments in the next two sections, we shall in the last section compare our results with experiments and theory.

2. THEORY

In the Boussinesq approximation of the hydrodynamic equations all material constants except the density are considered constant. Consider a liquid contained in a vessel and heated from below. The solution for the different flow regimes can be given in the space of the dimensionless parameters R and P defined by

$$R = \frac{\beta g \ell^3 \Delta T}{\nu \varkappa} \qquad\qquad P = \frac{\nu}{\varkappa} \qquad\qquad (1)$$

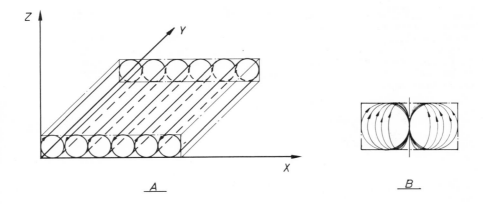

FIG.1.   *Schematic view of convection rolls in two sample cells heated from below. (a) Rectangular cell, (b) cylindrical cell, cut-away view.*

β: volume thermal expansion coefficient
g: gravitational acceleration
ℓ: the vertical layer thickness of the liquid
ΔT: the vertical temperature difference
ν: the kinematic viscosity
κ: the heat diffusivity

The calculated critical value R_c for the onset of convection is, for
rigid boundaries, found equal to 1708 and the critical wavenumber for the
mode that starts the convection is approximately π/ℓ.   A stability analysis
shows a strong preference for two-dimensional rolls of this wavenumber.   In
a rectangular box the roll axis is horizontal and along the shorter horizontal
dimension, see Fig. 1a. In a cylindrical vessel the pattern is one of toroidal rolls, the roll axis is a circle orientated perpendicular to the axis
of the cylinder. See Fig. 1b. Most theoretical papers are for high aspect
(width to depth) ratios of the vessel. The effect of decreasing the aspect
ratio is to reduce the number of rolls and to increase R_c [9].

As mentioned above the Rayleigh-Bénard instability may be treated as
a phase-transition problem. The order parameter v is the velocity in the
roll of the critical wavenumber. Landau theory [2] predicts

$$v \propto \epsilon^{\frac{1}{2}} \qquad\qquad \epsilon = \frac{R - R_c}{R_c} \qquad\qquad (2)$$

Observe that ϵ is essentially a reduced temperature gradient scale.   An n-th
order harmonic of the critical mode is predicted to behave as $\epsilon^{n/2}$.   Landau
theory also gives prediction for the time behaviour of the order parameters
as the system evolves from one stationary state to another. The initial
growth rate is exponential and the rate is proportional to ϵ, i.e. there is
critical slowing down. These predictions for the static and the dynamic
behaviour of the order parameter are the same as for an equilibrium phase

transition in more than four spatial dimensions. The effect of fluctuations
has been treated in linear [10,11] and in nonlinear theory [12]. Linear
theory predicts for the inverse correlation length ξ^{-1} a proportionality
with $\epsilon^{\frac{1}{2}}$. The corrections from non-linear effects, as calculated by Graham
[12], are important only within a narrow range $\epsilon \ll 10^{-6}$ and thus not likely
to be seen. In a scattering experiment he predicts for the intensity in the
conduction regime

$$I(q) \propto \frac{Q}{(\frac{q^2 - q_c^2}{q_c})^2 + 4\xi^{-2}} \tag{3}$$

Q is a quantity related to the initial microscopic state of the system, and
will be defined below for a liquid crystal. For ξ he finds

$$\xi^{-1} = (q_\ell \sqrt{3}/2) |\epsilon|^{\frac{1}{2}} \tag{4}$$

where $q_\ell = \pi/\ell$. The first term in the denominator in (3) is for the equilibrium phase transition problem simply q^2. In (3) the factor corresponds
to a preferential selection of fluctuations of wavenumber close to q_c, which
again is very close to q_ℓ. Physically this means that out of the spectrum
of convection rolls set up by the fluctuations, only those of dimension
corresponding to q_ℓ adapt to the vessel and are selected.

Theory suggests several possible ways for the development from
laminar convection to turbulence. At $R > R_c$ and increasing R, higher instabilities may involve

a)   transition to a new stable point in phase space, i.e. to another
     time-independent structure. This would be analogous to structural
     transition in solids.

b)   transition to a time-dependent structure, an oscillatory state,
     in which the system rotates in an orbit in phase space. The
     orbit is often referred to as a "limit cycle".

c)   transition to an asymptotic, strange attracting orbit in phase
     space, a mechanism first introduced by Lorenz [13].

Landau [3] and Hopf [14] introduce subsequent transitions of type
(b) to explain turbulence. Each transition adds a new period, incommensurate with the previous one, and in the end a white chaotic spectrum is
obtained after a large number of transitions.

Ruelle and Takens [15] find that turbulence itself is a strange-
attractor state that is reached after a limited (2-3) number of transitions
of the oscillatory type. The Lorenz [13] model gives one single transition
from the laminar to the strange-attractor, turbulent state.

Neither of the three mechanisms seem possible to rule out, and systems
may possibly belong to certain universality classes in their behaviour [5].
The Prandtl number, which is low for highly thermal-conducting liquids, is
an important parameter. Transitions between two stationary states, (i.e.
type (a) above), of mutually parallel rolls seems possible when $P < 1.1$ [2].
Detailed calculations by Mc Laughlin and Martin [16] indicate that the
Lorenz mechanism, i.e. type (c) above, may occur only for $P > 11/3$. At

smaller values of P they find qualitatively the same picture as Ruelle and Takens [15], a sharp transition to an aperiodic state preceded by a periodic regime with a maximum of three time-dependent states.

Clever and Busse [17] have performed calculations of the oscillatory state. They find that the oscillations are waves travelling along the axis of a two-dimensional roll. They also calculate the critical Rayleigh number for the onset of the oscillatory instability versus Prandtl number and wavenumber q, and find that the distance from R_c increases with P and q. Also the frequency increases with P and q.

At present greatest attention is attached to what happens as $R \rightarrow \infty$, i.e. in isotropic, homogeneous turbulence. Renormalization group theory and other phase-transition methods have been applied to calculate different properties such as critical dimensionality, fluctuation spectrum etc. Useful reviews are given by de Gennes [5] and by Martin [4].

When comparing our experiments below with theory, a modification of the formulas to liquid crystals [8,12] is necessary. Nematic liquid crystals are anistotropic liquids [18] whose molecules may be coherently aligned by the application of an external magnetic field, provided that the field exceeds a critical value H_c. If we introduce $q_\ell = \pi/\ell$ in (1), we have

$$R = \frac{\beta g \, \Delta T \, \pi^4}{(\nu q_\ell^2)(\kappa q_\ell^2)\ell} \tag{5}$$

where the expressions in parentheses may be identified as inverse relaxation times for velocity and temperature, respectively. In a nematic this formula gets slightly more complicated [12] by the presence of the anisotropic thermal conductivity $\kappa_a = \kappa_{||} - \kappa_{\perp}$ ($||$ and $\perp$ denoting parallel and perpendicular to the optical axis), and the very long relaxation time for orientation. Its inverse is

$$\gamma_3 = q_\ell^2 \, (K/\rho\gamma_1) \, [1 + H^2/H_c^2] \tag{6}$$

γ_1 is an effective kinematic viscosity and K is an elastic constant. It follows that

$$R = \frac{\beta g \, \kappa_a \, \Delta T}{\gamma_{th}\gamma_3\eta\ell} \qquad\qquad P = \frac{\gamma_3}{\gamma_{th}} \tag{7}$$

where $\gamma_{th} = \kappa_{||} q^2$ and η is a viscosity coefficient. Comparing (1) and (7) we see that P and ΔT_c, the threshold temperature, are both reduced by a factor $\gamma_3/\nu q_\ell^2$ from the isotropic-liquid values. This reduction factor is typically $10^{-3} - 10^{-5}$. We have tacitly assumed that H is horizontal and that heating is from below.

The effect of the convective flow is to turn the molecular axes by an angle θ from the horizontal direction of H. θ is determined by two counteracting torques, a magnetic torque due to the diamagnetic anisotropy χ_a and a viscous torque proportional to the velocity gradient [18]. At equilibrium

$$\sin \theta \sim \frac{\eta \, (\nabla v)}{\chi_a H^2} \tag{8}$$

In formula (3) the intensity of thermal fluctuations is measured by a quantity Q. According to Graham [12] Q is given by P and two other dimensionless numbers Q_1 and Q_2:

$$Q_1 = k_B T^2 \beta g / (\rho c_v \eta \mu_a \Delta T) \qquad (9)$$

$$Q_2 = k_B T / \{ \ell K [1 + H^2 / H_c^2] \} \qquad (10)$$

$$Q = \pi^2 (Q_1 + Q_2) / [2(1 + P)] \qquad (11)$$

c_v is the heat capacity at constant volume. The dominant source is due to the orientational fluctuations, contained in Q_2. This term makes liquid crystals the best candidate for observing hydrodynamic fluctuations near the convective instability. Also the possibility to reduce the effect of fluctuations by the application of an external field is very convenient.

3. EXPERIMENTS

Some of the experiments reviewed here have been briefly reported before [19-21]. All the experiments have been performed on deuterated samples of the nematic liquid crystal para-azoxyanisole (PAA). Physical constants for this substance are listed [18,22], except $\varkappa$, for which we use the value for the nematic substance MBBA. PAA is nematic in the range 119-135 °C, but by supercooling this temperature range can easily be extended to about 100 °C.

In the investigation of the convective, Rayleigh-Bénard instability the sample cell was a vertical slab, as in Fig. 2a. The inner dimensions a, b, and c were respectively 38, 38 and 5 mm. The container walls were all made of aluminium, which gives good heat conductivity and a possibility to apply small gradients. Heating was made by electrical heating elements attached to the top and the bottom. A steady temperature difference ΔT could be applied while keeping the mean temperature constant. Three thermocouples placed at bottom, top and half-height were used for measurement and control. In Fig. 2a the applied field H is along the horizontal direction, but the setup had provision for changing its direction by an angle θ towards the vertical direction. All experiments were done in the double-axis mode of the neutron spectrometer, and the incident wavelength was mostly 1.28Å. By always observing at momentum transfer 1.8 Å^{-1} one could take advantage of the strong orientational dependence of the intensity of the first diffraction peak. In Fig. 3 we see the effect on the intensity when changing θ under conditions when there is no convection. The intensity I follows quite closely a $\sin^4 \theta$ behaviour [23]. The field applied (240 Ørsted) was sufficient to align the optical axis along the field direction. This is shown by Fig. 4, which is used for determining H_c, the critical field for alignment. An approximate value $H_c = 25$ Ørsted will be used in the further analysis of data taken in this geometry. A value of H_c measured in this way, with a thick cell and with no special precaution in securing well-defined boundary conditions (i.e. anchoring) for molecular alignment, should only be accepted as an order-of-magnitude value. In the geometry of Fig. 2a one expects [19] $H_c = (\pi/c)(K/\chi_a)^{\frac{1}{2}}$. Order of magnitude one has $K \sim 10^{-6}$ and $\chi_a \sim 10^{-7}$, which for c = 0.5 cm gives an expected value $H_c \sim 20$ Ørsted. To further characterize the sample in the given geometry we have measured the relaxation from the fully aligned to the randomly aligned state, i.e. observed the relaxation from the top to the bottom of Fig. 4. The observed relaxation time derived from Fig. 5 is 16200 s. Assuming a splay mode, and inserting the appropriate viscosity coefficient, one finds a wavelength of 2.5 cm for the decaying mode. This shows that modes given by the size of the sample are active.

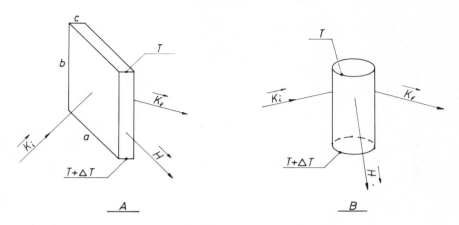

FIG.2.   Scattering geometry for (a) slab cell, (b) cylindrical cell. k_i and k_f denote incident and outgoing neutron wave vectors, magnetic field H is along scattering vector.

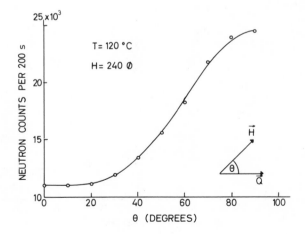

FIG.3.   Neutron intensity versus θ, the vertical angular distance between scattering vector and magnetic field.

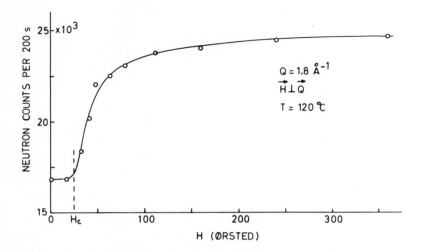

FIG.4. Measurement of critical field for vertical alignment of molecules.

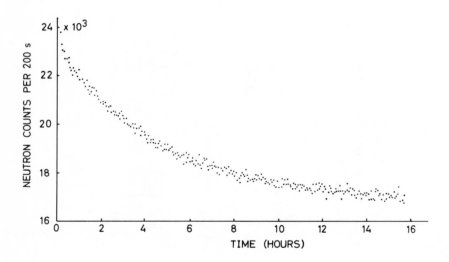

FIG.5. Relaxation from fully aligned to randomly aligned state. At time zero 240 Ø field was switched off.

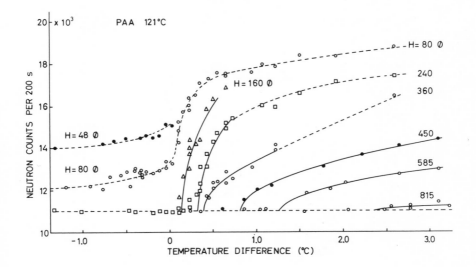

FIG.6. *Average neutron intensity as a function of vertical temperature difference with slab aluminium container. Values of horizontal magnetic field are given, fully drawn parabolic curves are least-square fitted to data. For clarity many points are left out.*

We now have sufficient knowledge of the sample in the chosen geometry to actually start the convection experiment. By measuring the intensity in the first diffraction peak as a function of the applied gradient, and at different values of the applied horizontal field, the curves of Fig. 6 were obtained. Each point represents an average of a sequence of about a hundred measured points. At sufficiently strong fields the intensity observed below the convective instability saturates at a value representing the fully aligned, quiescent state where heat is transported by conduction. Above the threshold gradient (ΔT_c) a viscous torque induces an alignment towards the vertical direction, hence the intensity starts climbing up the curve of Fig. 3. At first glance the curves for $\Delta T > \Delta T_c$ do not seem to reflect a universal behaviour, in particular we see that the curvature decreases at stonger fields Our first goal is to see if some kind of data collapse is possible in this gradient range. Inserting the material constants for PAA in the formulas above, assuming only twist deformations, we arrive at the following values for the dimensionless parameters at the actual temperature:

$$R = 7 \times 10^7 \ \Delta T [1 + H^2/H_c^2]^{-1} \tag{12}$$

$$P = 4 \times 10^{-3} [1 + H^2/H_c^2] \tag{13}$$

$$Q_1 = 7.09 \times 10^{-14} / \Delta T \tag{14}$$

$$Q_2 = 4.9 \times 10^{-8} [1 + H^2/H_c^2]^{-1} \tag{15}$$

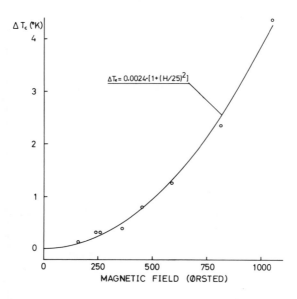

FIG.7. Critical gradient for onset of convection, deduced from Fig. 6, as a function of applied field.

inserting further $R_c = 1708$ we obtain from (12) for the threshold gradient as a function of field an expected behaviour

$$\Delta T_c(H) = 2.4 \times 10^{-5}[1 + H^2/H_c^2] \qquad (16)$$

In Fig. 7 we have fitted the observed threshold gradients for $H \geq 160$ Ørsted to an expression $\Delta T_c(H) = \Delta T_c(0)[1 + H^2/H_c^2]$ in which we have inserted $H_c = 25$ Ørsted. The data give $\Delta T_c(0) = 2.4 \times 10^{-3}$ K, which is a factor 100 higher than predicted. Most of this difference can be accounted for by the low aspect ratio of the cell, as discussed later.

From the fitted expression we can now plot all data versus the reduced parameter ϵ. This is done in Fig. 8 which shows that the data scale reasonably well to a universal behaviour. The plotted curve is of the form $\epsilon^{0.5}$. Another series of more accurate data [20] for a single value of H gave an exponent $0.52 \pm .02$. If we assume $v \propto \nabla v$ at small velocities in laminar flow, then equation (8) and Fig. 3 together would imply that the relation between the order parameter v and the neutron intensity I should be $I \propto v^4$. Hence the observed static exponent for the order parameter should be $\beta = 0.52/4 = 0.13$, i.e. as for a 2-dimensional system [20,21]. Preliminary calculations [24] show, however, that the indicated relation between order parameter and neutron intensity breaks down at extremely small values of v. Integration of the flow-induced alignment over the expected convection pattern [9] for our geometry, and invoking Fig. 3, leads to an approximately linear relation between I and v. Hence our data suggest $\beta \sim 0.5$, but a more exact value must await further progress in the calculations [24].

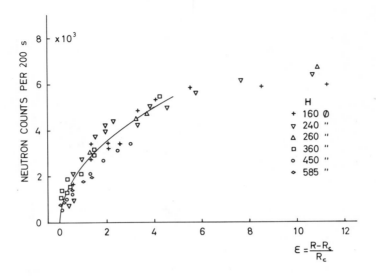

FIG.8.   Data collapse for convection regime (from Fig.6) when plotted versus reduced parameter ε.   Constant high-field background is subtracted.   A parabolic curve is drawn as a guide to the eye.

Next we turn to data for $\Delta T < \Delta T_c$.   At $H \le 160$ Ørsted the intensity above the high-field level mostly reflects the effect of incomplete alignment.   The pretransitional slope is possibly the effect of fluctuation enhancement when approaching ΔT_c.   Orientational fluctuations definitely affect our data at low values of H: Slow, long-wavelength fluctuations make the intensity fluctuate in time more than allowed for by statistics. The crucial point is whether the hydrodynamic fluctuations, to which orientational fluctuations are coupled, are amplified when approaching ΔT_c.   In an attempt to parametrize our data we fit the sloping part of our pretransitional data to the mean-field expression (3).   Unfortunately we cannot test for the dependence on $(q^2-q_c^2)/q_c$.   Our data are affected by this intense, long wavelength part of the fluctuation spectrum and very little by the q-value corresponding to the momentum transfer for the scattering and thus we have no control of the effective q's involved.   If we insert $Q = Q_2$ and (4) in (3), and guess $q_c = q_\ell$, we can write (3) approximately as

$$I \propto \frac{1}{[1+H^2/H_c^2](1+r^2|\epsilon|)} \tag{17}$$

with

$$r = \frac{2}{(q/q_\ell)^2-1} \tag{18}$$

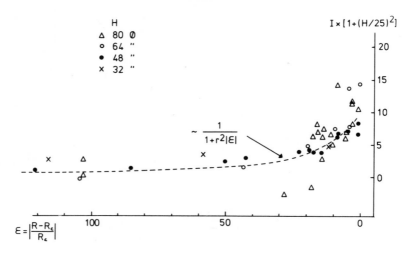

FIG.9.   *Attempt at data collapse for conduction regime. Asymptotic background values have been subtracted, residual intensity is multiplied with factor in square brackets. Indicated curve is Lorentzian with $r^2 = 0.1$.*

The data points that we have fitted to this formula represent averages measured over several hours.   Also we have taken care to include only data where we let the system drift from a horizontally aligned state towards its final value, in order to minimize the uncertainty when subtracting the non-fluctuating part on the intensity.   For the fluctuating part we finally arrive at the points given in Fig. 9.   For comparison we have drawn a curve from formula (17) with $r^2 = 0.1$.   The scattering of points is considerable, but the reasonable value of r and the approximate fit to the curve probably reflects the mean field behaviour of the correlation-length when approaching T_c.

We have so far not been able to study the time-dependence of the fluctuations for $\Delta T < \Delta T_c$.   The initial growth rate of the order parameter at $\Delta T > \Delta T_c$ is of the predicted exponential form, as seen from Fig. 10.   The inset of the same figure shows that thermodynamical slowing-down is observed.   To fix the ϵ-scale we needed ΔT_c, which was taken from Fig. 7

To investigate the onset of higher instabilities we built another slab-geometry cell, as in Fig. 2a, but with stainless steel side walls in order to reach higher values of ΔT and R.   The cell dimension c was now 4 mm, otherwise the dimensions were the same as in the aluminium cell used previously.   The data that we obtained are shown in Fig. 11.   After an initial part that reflects the onset of convection, the curves now attain a second increase around $\Delta T = 12°$ indicative of a higher instability.   The change in the intensity level probably reflects a change in the spatial roll pattern.   In the gradient range where the intensity shows a sudden change the intensity oscillates between an upper and a lower level, and data points giving the mean values would have little meaning.   The long periods involved, and an awkward operational schedule of the reactor, prevented us from investigating this

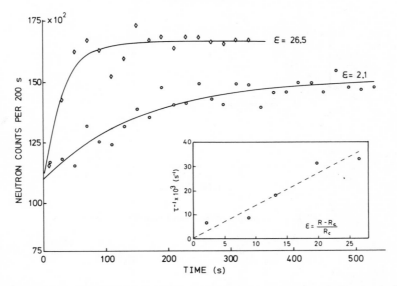

FIG.10. *Neutron intensity as a function of time after lowering of applied magnetic field from ~ 300 to 48 Ø. Initial field was sufficient to quench convection, with final field value the growth of convective flow follows fitted exponential curve. Inset shows inverse time constant τ versus reduced parameter ε.*

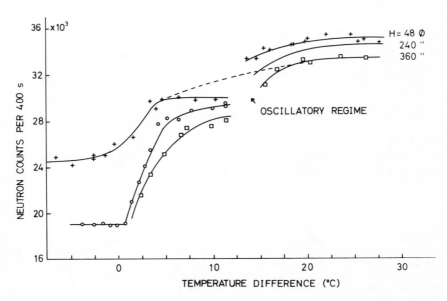

FIG.11. *Average neutron intensity as a function of vertical temperature difference with slab stainless-steel container. Data points in oscillatory regime are left out. Broken-line curve shows alternative branch for development of convection from low gradients, only 48 Ø curve shown.*

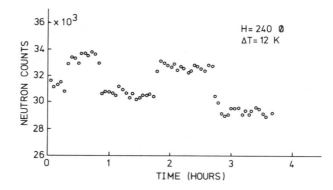

FIG.12. *Example of data in oscillatory regime.*

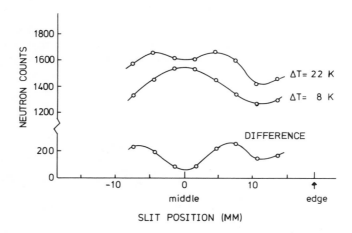

FIG.13. *Horizontal profile of scattered beam measured with (5 X 5) mm² slit at half-height of sample cell. Non-uniformity of incident beam has been corrected for. Lower curve is difference between upper two.*

oscillatory region more closely. An example of the oscillations is shown in Fig. 12. There is, however, an alternative path for the development of the flow pattern at higher gradients. This is indicated by the broken curve without data points. Each path represents a stable state of the system since one could spend several weeks on a path without interference of the other.

The roll geometry on the broken curve path was recently investigated by scanning with a narrow slit (5x5)mm² horizontally across the convection cell. The profiles are shown in Fig. 13. Remembering that the alignment

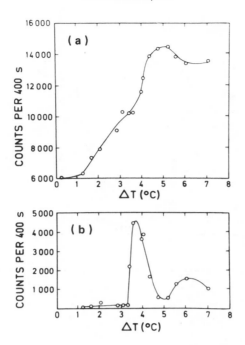

FIG.14. (a) Average neutron intensity (I_0) observed with cylindrical aluminium container, as a function of vertical temperature difference ΔT. (b) Variance $\langle \Delta I^2 \rangle = \langle (I - I_0)^2 \rangle$, i.e. mean square of fluctuations of intensity about the time average, versus ΔT.

is induced by the velocity gradient, the profiles and their difference suggest a single convection roll with a growing contribution of higher harmonics along the horizontal axis as the gradient is increased. Unfortunately we have no such measurements yet for the other path.

Further evidence for a time-dependent flow pattern was obtained in experiments [19] which actually were made before those reported above. The sample container was cylindrical with inner diameter 5 mm and height 25 mm. Controlled heating from above and below made it possible to keep a mean temperature and a chosen gradient constant within ± 0.02 °C for days. A field of 50 Ørsted was applied along the scattering vector. This was well above the critical field H_c, but we unfortunately do not have sufficient data on this cell to present data on an R- or ε-scale. Fig. 14a shows average intensities (I_0) recorded for several values of the gradient. In Fig. 14b is plotted the mean square fluctuations $\langle \Delta I^2 \rangle = \langle (I - I_0)^2 \rangle$ about the time average. The curve suggests two higher instabilities above the Rayleigh-Bénard point. Fig. 15 gives in more detail raw and processed intensity data for seven selected values of the gradient. For each value we give (on the top two lines) the directly recorded time dependence I(t) of the intensity, the autocorrelation function $\langle \Delta I(0) \Delta I(t) \rangle$ of the fluctuations, and the spectral function obtained by taking the Fourier transform of the latter function. (The spectral lines have been relabelled from that of ref. 20).

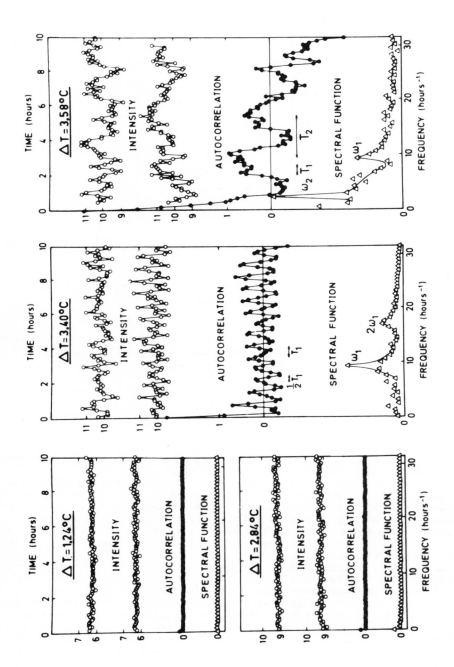

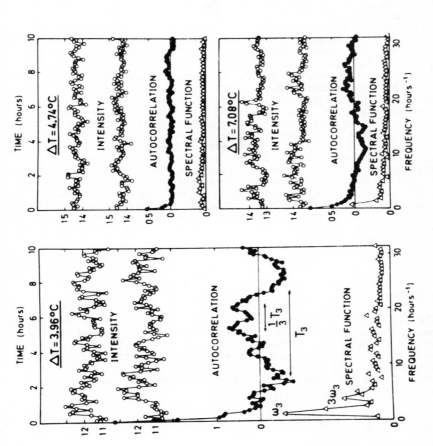

FIG.15. For seven different values of ΔT are shown (1) time variation of neutron intensity I(t) on two lines, (2) autocorrelation function of fluctuations $\langle \Delta I(0)\,\Delta I(t)\rangle$, and (3) spectral function $|\int e^{i\omega t}\,\langle \Delta I(0)\times\Delta I(t)\rangle\,dt|$. Some characteristic frequencies and corresponding periods are indicated.

The following tendency is seen: The increase in $\langle \Delta I^2 \rangle$ marks the passage to time-dependence of the fluctuations. In the first maximum the spectral function develops from a single line with its second harmonic at $\Delta T = 3.40°$ to one with two and perhaps three lines at 3.58 °C. The second maximum marks the passage to a time-dependent and less periodic regime. In Fig.14a a continuous curve is drawn through the data points. In the region of strong oscillations the use of average values has restricted meaning, and one might as well have drawn a discontinuous curve as in Fig. 11.

The last set of experiments that we want to report is an attempt at visual observation of the flow pattern. The sample cell was made of quartz side walls and metallic top and bottom. The geometry was close to that of Fig. 1a; x, y and z dimensions were 25, 7.5, and 4 mm, respectively. The mean temperature was at about 136 °C, such that the upper half of the liquid was isotropic and the lower part nematic. Only the isotropic part is transparent, and the flow pattern is made visible by isotropic droplets mixing into and marking the convection rolls. A magnetic field was applied parallel to the long horizontal dimension. The critical field should scale with the short horizontal dimension, hence from Fig. 4 we expect $H_c \sim 40$ Ørsted. In the convection region the flow pattern was always one of two-dimensional rolls parallel to the short horizontal edge. For $H \sim H_c$ two rolls appeared at $\Delta T \sim 0°$. At $\Delta T = 6°$ the pattern suddenly changed to four rolls and at $\Delta T = 12°$ rolls appeared and disappeared with time constants of the order of 10 s. Possible oscillations at lower gradients must have been considerably shorter or longer to evade visual observation. The visual observations were supplemented by neutron experiments on the same cell . Distinct changes in the intensity level could be observed at the gradients mentioned. The critical gradients behaved with the applied field qualitatively as in Fig. 7. Further neutron experiments on this cell were stopped, however, due to the short time constants involved and the rather awkward geometry for neutron experiments.

4. DISCUSSION

The first question we shall ask is whether a consistent picture of the hydrodynamic instabilities appears from the experiments quoted above, and whether this picture agrees with other experiments and with theory. The other experiments we shall compare with are either on similar convective instabilities or on the closely related Taylor instability. In the latter one studies the radial flow of a liquid contained between an inner rotating cylinder and an outer stationary one.

The Rayleigh-Bénard instability

Most of our experiments were on a slab cell whose aspect ratio (width/height) is rather unconventional. Theory [9] predicts only one roll in a cell of our geometry, and this seems to be borne out by our experiments. Theory [9] also predicts R_c to be increased by a factor 10 - 100 from its normal value of 1708. This factor, together with the arbitrary choice that we have made for the material constants, the uncertainty in measuring such small temperature gradients etc., probably accounts for the discrepancy between the predicted and observed values for ΔT_c. The predicted behaviour of ΔT_c versus H is, however, verified with considerable accuracy. The universal behaviour of the order parameter borne out by Fig. 8 is gratifying and demonstrates the usefulness of phase-transition analogies for this phenomenon.

Also it shows the insensitivity of the first instability to changes in P. The exponential growth of the order parameter versus time and the critical slowing down of the growth rate as $\epsilon \to 0$, both predicted by mean-field theory, are verified. The same phenomena have earlier been demonstrated with high precision by Gollub and Freihlich [25] and by Behringer and Ahlers [26] in Taylor- and Rayleigh-Bénard instability measurements, respectively.

Our search for pretransitional fluctuations gave the data of Fig. 9. There is quite some scatter in the data, which largely represents the difficulty in subtracting two large numbers. The constant number to be subtracted at each value of the field, the non-fluctuating part, is also difficult to determine and adds to the uncertainty. The fact that data fit reasonably well to a mean-field formula, and with reasonable values for the wavevectors involved and for the correlation range, makes us believe that we really see pretransitional fluctuations and their reduction by an external field. The sharpness of the transitions at higher fields seems to exclude an explanation in terms of poorly defined applied gradients. One possibility that cannot be excluded is perhaps a spectrum of transition gradients at low fields, because of the poorly aligned intial state. It is hard to understand though that this could produce a tail at negative gradients.

Higher instabilities

Using formula (12) and (13), which are valid for the slab geometry, we see that our experiments cover Rayleigh numbers up to 10^9 and Prandtl numbers in the range 10^{-2} - 10. This is wider than previously reported and demonstrates the possibilities offered by liquid crystals for such studies. Experiments on the stainless-steel cell (Fig. 11) show that rolls are stable to high R's. The intensity values point definitely to ordered vertical alignment of molecules, i.e. to ordered flow, even at the highest R-values. A break-down into smaller eddies would be easy to detect, since we know the isotropic-liquid intensity at high temperatures. Fig. 11 suggests two possible paths for the development of high-gradient flow. Along one path we have so far not detected any high instabilities. The gradual build-up of higher harmonics agrees with the more accurate light-scattering data on silicon oil by Bergé and Dubois [27]. The other path involves an oscillatory regime with one or more instabilities. This is almost certainly the same region that we studied in greater detail on the cylindrical sample (Figs. 14 and 15). In both geometries do the experimental data indicate a new roll pattern. Guided by the visual observations with the quartz cell, we guess that this is a sudden change to a pattern where the number of rolls has been doubled. In the oscillatory regime Fig. 15 reveals a sequence where new frequencies are added before a transition to time-dependent but less periodic regime is reached. We definitely see two and possibly three frequencies simultaneously at $\Delta T = 3.58$ °C, thus lending some support to the theory of Ruelle and Takens [15,16]. One expects low frequencies for a liquid of such low P-values [17], but the calculations do not cover the actual P-range of our experiments. According to Fig. 11 the Rayleigh numbers for the periodic instabilities and the Rayleigh-Bénard instability are in ratios 3 and 5. These ratios are higher than calculated [16,17]. Our experiments on the slab cell give, however, much higher ratios. This is physically reasonable, since it seems easier to rearrange the flow pattern in the cylindrical geometry. Recently Gollub and Swinney [28] have reported light-scattering observations on a rotating fluid where data reveal a sequence of three instabilities, each adding a new frequency to the velocity spectrum. At a higher instabilty all spectral lines seem to disappear. We know of no other observations by microscopic methods where data similar to this, and to our Fig. 15, have been reported for a convective system.

Future experiments

The high-gradient data obtained with the cylindrical cell and with the quartz cell indicate that we had entered an aperiodic, time-dependent regime. It seems worthwhile to persue this phenomenon further to see if fully developed turbulence could be reached, a regime for which quite a few theoretical predictions have been made. Also the effect of varying the Prandtl number through the applied field, and the effect on the periodic regime, seems worth investigating further. We want to stress, however, that experiments on hydrodynamic instabilities are very difficult and time-consuming, and not rewarding in terms of the speed with which one can produce papers. Notice that the frequencies that we have observed are down to cycles per hour, corresponding to energy changes of 10^{-18} eV of the neutrons scattered. This is probably a good measure of the patience that the experimenter should have.

ACKNOWLEDGEMENTS

We have benefitted much from discussions with a number of colleagues in our laboratories and with P.G. de Gennes, J. Feder, O. Kvernvold, S.W. Lovesey, E. Palm and H. Thomas.

REFERENCES

[1] Whitehead, J.A.Jr., in Fluctuations, Instabilties, and Phase Transitions, edited by T. Riste (Plenum, N.Y.,1957) p. 153.
[2] Palm, E., Annual Review of Fluid Mechanics 7 (1975) 39.
[3] Landau, L.D. and Lifshitz, E.M., Fluid Mechanics (Pergamon, London, 1959).
[4] Martin, P.C., J. de Phys., Colloq. 37 (1976) C 1
[5] de Gennes, P.G., in Fluctuations, Instabilities, and Phase Transitions, edited by T. Riste (Plenum, N.Y. 1975) p. 1.
[6] Haken, H., Rev.Mod.Phys. 47 (1975) 67.
[7] Graham, R., Phys.Rev. A10, (1974) 1762.
[8] Guyon, E. and Pieranski, P., Physica 73 (1974) 184 and references therein.
[9] Cotton, I., Int. J. Heat Mass Transfer 15 (1972) 665, quoted in Rogers, R.M., Rep.Progr.Phys. 39 (1976) 1.
[10] Zeitsev,V.W. and Shliomis, M.I., Zh.Eksp.Teor.Fiz. 59 (1970) 1583, Sov.Phys.JETP 32 (1971) 866.
[11] Lekkerkerker, H.N.W. and Boon, J.P., Phys.Rev. A10 (1974) 1355.
[12] Graham, R.,in Fluctuations, Instabilities and Phase Transitions, edited by T. Riste (Plenum, N.Y., 1975) p. 215.
[13] Lorenz, E.N., J.Atmos.Sci. 20 (1963) 130.
[14] Hopf, E., Commun. Pure Appl. Math. 1 (1948) 303.
[15] Ruelle, D. and Takens, F., Commun. Math. Phys. 20 (1971) 167.
[16] Mc Laughlin, J.B. and Martin, P.C., Phys. Rev. A12 (1975) 186.
[17] Clever, R.M. and Busse, F.H., J. Fluid Mech. 65 (1974) 625.
[18] de Gennes, P.G., The Physics of Liquid Crystals (Clarendon Press, Oxford, England 1974).
[19] Møller, H.B., and Riste, T., Phys.Rev.Lett. 34 (1975) 996.
[20] Møller, H.B., Riste, T. and Otnes, K.,in Fluctuations, Instabilities, and Phase Transitions, edited by T. Riste (Plenum, N.Y., 1975) p. 313
[21] Riste, T., Proc.Conf.Neutron Scattering, Conf. 760601-P2 (Oak Ridge, 1976) p.379.
[22] Stephen, M.J. and Straley, J.P., Rev.Mod.Phys. 46 (1974) 617.

[23] Similar curves have been used in deriving the orientational order
      parameter. See Kohli, M., Otnes, K., Pynn, R. and Riste, T., Z.Phys.
      B24 (1976)147.
[24] Feder, J. (private communication).
[25] Gollub, J.B. and Freihlich, M.H., in Fluctuations, Instabilities, and
      Phase Transitions, edited by T. Riste (Plenum, N.Y., 1975) p. 195 and
      Phys.Rev.Lett. 33 (1974) 1465.
[26] Behringer, R.P. and Ahlers, G. (to be published)
[27] Bergé, P. and Dubois, M., Phys. Rev. Lett. 32 (1974) 1041 and in
      Fluctuations, Instabilities, and Phase Transitions, edited by T. Riste
      (Plenum, N.Y., 1975) p. 323.
[28] Gollub, J.P. and Swinney, H.L., Phys.Rev.Lett. 35 (1975 927.

DISCUSSION

N. KROÓ: In your paper you have considered the fluctuations in liquid
crystals with thermal gradients. Would you expect similar behaviour if external
fields, for instance electric fields, were applied?

T. RISTE: In our experiment the sample was strained out of equilibrium
by thermal effects. The same could have been achieved with an alternating electric
field. The light scattering from a liquid crystal that has been perturbed in this
way is called dynamical scattering.

N. KROÓ: Your slide showed the spectral function of fluctuations with
maxima at frequencies ω_1 and $2\omega_2$. What type of parameters, e.g. geometry or
material characteristics, determine the position and height of these maxima?
Can higher harmonics ($3\omega_1$, $4\omega_1$, etc.) also be seen?

T. RISTE: Frequencies are determined by the dimensions of the vessel and
by the Prandtl number. Frequencies incommensurate with ω_1 are in fact observed.
Concerning the amplitudes, I would refer you to the work of McLaughlin and
Martin cited as our Ref. [16].

S. YIP (*Chairman*): I think one can draw a useful analogy between your
hydrodynamic instabilities and the instabilities in chemically reacting systems.
In particular, the oscillations you showed remind one of transitions between
different states in a chemically reacting system with multiple steady state
solutions; these transitions are driven by fluctuations which in general cannot
be properly described by mean field theories.

T. RISTE: In my presentation I gave examples of instabilities leading to
transitions between the space- and time-dependent dissipative structures first
introduced by Prigogine and co-workers. You are quite right that it is all part of
a wider picture in which chemical reactions, biological evolution and even
sociological phenomena such as the formation of opinion are interrelated.
Synergetics is a new science, introduced by H. Haken, that aims at revealing
common features of these seemingly unrelated disciplines.

P. ZIESCHE: Is it possible to extend such measurements to study the instability of a laminar flow between parallel planes or in a tube, i.e. the onset of turbulence at a critical Reynolds number?

T. RISTE: In principle, it should be possible. However, since the flow in the case you mention would have less regularity, neutron experiments might not be easy.

W. SCHMATZ: How does H_c depend on the relevant dimension of the vessel?

T. RISTE: H_c is inversely proportional to the linear dimension of the vessel.

W. SCHMATZ: Your equations contained the ratio q/q_c, where q_c is the reciprocal length of the relevant vessel dimension. What is q?

T. RISTE: q is a wave vector of the orientation fluctuations in the liquid crystal that couple with and drive the hydrodynamic fluctuations. The value of q is limited at the low-frequency end by the size (ℓ) of the vessel and at the high-frequency end by the length of the molecules. The position of the peaks that we look at with neutrons is always at $Q = 1.8$ Å^{-1}, which bears no relation to q. The intensity of the peak is modulated by fluctuations of the wave vector q, which are most abundant for $q \sim q\ell$.

S. LOVESEY: I should just like to comment that the self-diffusion constant of a simple liquid will display anomalous behaviour at the onset of convective instability, for a sample in slab geometry, and this behaviour can, in principle, be studied with neutron scattering.

E. FRIKKEE: For observations in the vicinity of the transition to the convection regime, an accurate knowledge of the temperature difference ΔT will be required. How is the stabilization of ΔT achieved in your experiment?

T. RISTE: We control ΔT by varying the heating power that we apply to the top and bottom of the vessel.

E. FRIKKEE: If the transition to the convection regime is preceded by fluctuations, it seems to me that the non-ordering field in this fluctuation regime would be the local gradient $\partial T/\partial z$ rather than ΔT across the sample cell. Could you comment on this?

T. RISTE: The sharpness of the transitions in high magnetic fields indicates that ΔT is well defined. With a lower field the fluctuations also imply local gradients but these are intrinsic parts of the physical phenomenon that we are studying.

MOLECULAR ORDER AND DYNAMICS IN LIQUID CRYSTALS
Contribution from high resolution neutron scattering

A.J. DIANOUX
Institut Laue-Langevin,
Grenoble

F. VOLINO
Groupe de dynamique des
    phases condensées,
Laboratoire de cristallographie,
Montpellier,
France

Abstract

MOLECULAR ORDER AND DYNAMICS IN LIQUID CRYSTALS. CONTRIBUTION FROM
HIGH RESOLUTION NEUTRON SCATTERING.

In the past few years, the study of molecular motions in liquid crystals has made significant
progress owing to the existence of novel high resolution instruments at the high flux reactor of
the Institut Laue-Langevin in Grenoble. The aim of the present paper is to show, on a particular
example, which kind of results can be and have been obtained. Neutron quasi-elastic spectra
have been interpreted in terms of incoherent scattering and analysed with models permitting
both translational and rotational motions of the molecules. These results have been compared
with similar ones obtained from other spectroscopic techniques, and we could draw clear
conclusions concerning the nature of molecular order in liquid crystals. In particular the
Meyer-McMillan microscopic theory, which predicts an orientational ordering around the long
axis in the tilted smectic phases, can be ruled out.

1. INTRODUCTION

Liquid crystalline systems usually present a number of different
mesophases which are characterized by the existence of a long range
molecular ordering [1] , superimposed on the short range order which
already exists in the isotropic phase. The study of such ordering and of
the microscopic dynamics in these phases, has been the subject of considerable work, both theoretical and experimental. Microscopic theories for
the nematic phase and the various smectic phases have been developed
and predict the values of suitable translational and orientational order parameters. On the other hand several experimental techniques are available
to study this problem : light scattering, X-ray or neutron diffraction,
infrared absorption or Raman scattering, magnetic resonances (NMR, ESR,
NQR)...

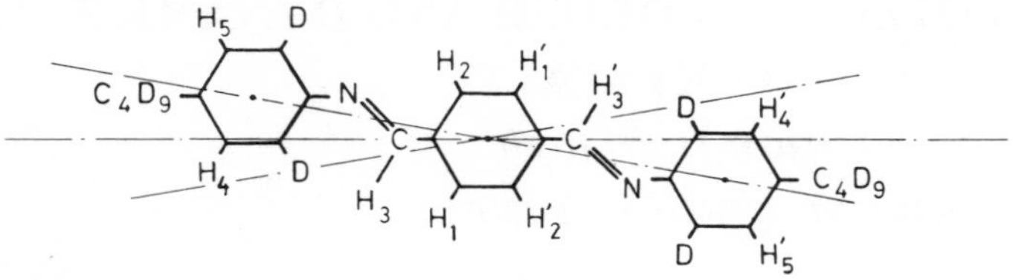

FIG.1. Sketch of the partially deuterated TBBA molecule in its trans-conformation. The new body axis after a trans-trans isomerization is also shown.

The aim of this paper is to show, on a particular substance, that high resolution incoherent neutron quasielastic scattering (NQES) presents an alternative approach to tackle the problem of molecular order and dynamics of liquid crystals. More than ten years ago, incoherent NQES has already been used to study liquid crystals. However, due to the relatively bad experimental conditions (low neutron flux and poor energy resolution), the results were not accurate and the analysis sometimes incorrect. In the past few years these studies have made significant progress owing to the existence of novel high resolution instruments at the high flux reactor of the Institut Laue-Langevin in Grenoble.

We will report here some of the results that we have obtained on an exemplary material, namely terephtal-bis-butyl aniline (TBBA)(Fig.1). This compound exhibits not less than eight phases and mesophases between room temperature and 236°C, including tilted smectic C, H and VI phases.

The various transitions are depicted below :

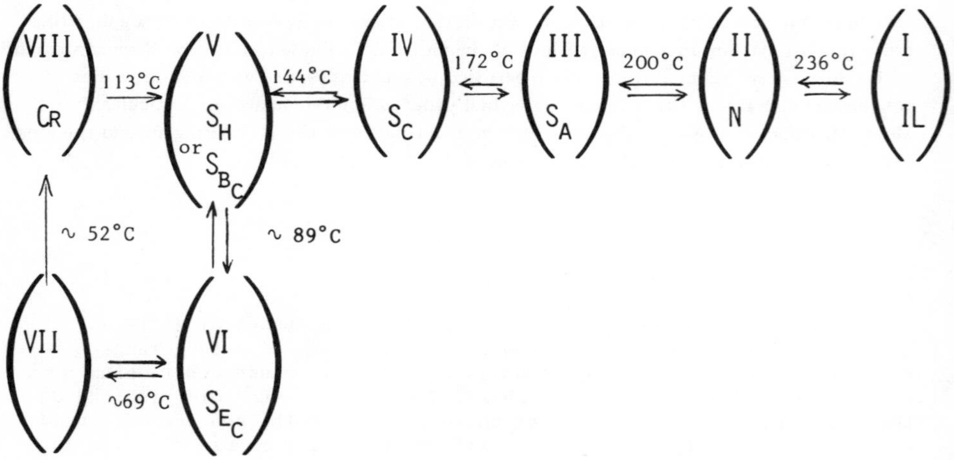

The paper will be organized as follows. First we present the basic concepts of incoherent NQES, aimed at the study of molecular ordering and dynamics in liquid crystals. Then we present results on translational motion in the tilted and non tilted smectic phases. There follows the description of the rotational motions (time scale $\sim 10^{-10} - 10^{-11}s$) in these phases. In each section we will correlate the NQES results with results obtained by other techniques mainly NMR and NQR.

2. BASIC CONCEPTS OF INCOHERENT NEUTRON QUASIELASTIC SCATTERING

We will only present here the main results of incoherent NQES which are relevant for the study of molecular motions in liquid crystals. For more details the reader is referred to standard textbooks [2] ; another presentation of the method has been done by us [3].

We consider the idealized case of a hydrogeneous substance containing only one proton per molecule. Such substance scatters neutrons almost entirely incoherently. Due to the molecular motions, the position $\underset{\sim}{r}$ of the proton varies with time. The self-correlation function pertinent to incoherent NQES is the so-called intermediate (incoherent) scattering law [2] $I_s(\underset{\sim}{Q},t)$ defined by :

$$I_s(\underset{\sim}{Q},t) = \ll e^{i\underset{\sim}{Q}[\underset{\sim}{r}(t)-\underset{\sim}{r}(0)]} \gg_{r_o} \tag{1}$$

where Q is the neutron momentum transfer, $\underset{\sim}{r}(t)$ and $\underset{\sim}{r}(0)$ are the position vectors of the proton at time t and time 0, respectively. In Eq. (1), the inner brackets indicate a suitable ensemble average, while the outer brackets indicate an average over all the possible initial positions. The intensity of scattered neutrons is then directly proportional to the (incoherent) scattering law $S_s(\underset{\sim}{Q},\omega)$ given by :

$$S_s(\underset{\sim}{Q},\omega) = \frac{1}{2\pi} \int I_s(\underset{\sim}{Q},t) \, e^{-i\omega t} \, dt \tag{2}$$

Note that from the definitions (1) and (2) one has :

$$\int S_s(\underset{\sim}{Q},\omega)d\omega = I_s(\underset{\sim}{Q},0) = 1 \tag{3}$$

The overall molecular motion can generally be decomposed into translational, rotational and vibrational parts. Assuming that these motions are dynamically uncoupled, one can write, with obvious notations :

$$I_s(\underset{\sim}{Q}, t) = I_s^{trans} \cdot I_s^{rot} \cdot I_s^{vib} \tag{4}$$

In the quasielastic region, the vibrational contribution is only a Debye-Waller factor :

$$I_s^{vib} = e^{-Q^2<u^2>} \tag{5}$$

where $<u^2>$ is some mean-square amplitude of vibration. The incoherent scattering law in the quasielastic region will thus be a convolution of the translational and rotational parts, multiplied by a Debye-Waller factor :

$$S_s(\underset{\sim}{Q},\omega) = S_s^{trans} \otimes S_s^{rot} \times e^{-Q^2<u^2>} \tag{6}$$

For simple (Fick's law) translational diffusion in an isotropic medium, one obtains :

$$S_s^{trans}(Q,\omega) = \frac{1}{\pi} \frac{DQ^2}{(DQ^2)^2 + \omega^2} \tag{7}$$

The case of anisotropic translational diffusion has been treated in [4].
        Concerning the rotational motions, several models have been
put forward; some of them, which are aimed at describing the rotational
motion in liquid crystals, are reported in [4]. We will only introduce
here the concept of Elastic Incoherent Structure Factor. For purely
rotational motion, the proton always stays at the surface of a sphere
of radius r. This implies that the intermediate scattering law does not
decay to zero for infinite time [2], but to some finite value $A_o(Q)$. One
can write :

$$I_s^{rot}(Q,t) = A_o(Q) + [I_s^{rot}(Q,t) - A_o(Q)] \tag{8}$$

The quantity in brackets now decays to zero, generally as a sum of
exponential functions for stochastic processes [5] . From Eq. (2),
the rotational scattering law can be written as :

$$S_s^{rot}(Q,\omega) = A_o(Q) \, \delta(\omega) + \frac{1}{\pi} \sum_{n>0} A_n(Q) \; L_n(\omega) \tag{9}$$

when $L_n(\omega)$ are Lorentzian functions. Consequently the scattering law is the
sum of a sharp $\delta(\omega)$ function and a broad component whose width is simply
related to the average rotational correlation time. Using (3), one sees
that :

$$A_o(Q) + \sum_{n>0} A_n(Q) = 1 \tag{10}$$

which shows that $A_o(Q)$ is the fraction of the total (quasielastic)
intensity contained in the purely elastic term. $A_o(Q)$ is called the
Elastic Incoherent Structure Factor (EISF) of the model. Since the initial
and final distributions of the protons are the same, one obtains from
Eq. (1)

$$A_o(Q) = |< e^{iQ \cdot r} >|^2 \tag{11}$$

Let θ be the angle between Q and r . Expanding the exponential one can
write :

$$A_o(Q) = \left| \sum_{\ell=0}^{\infty} (2\ell+1) \, i^\ell \, j_\ell(Q \, r) < P_\ell(\cos \theta)> \right|^2 \tag{12}$$

where the j_ℓ are spherical Bessel functions [1].
        One can see that by measuring the EISF, one gets information
on the quantities $<P_\ell>$. If there are several, dynamically non-equivalent,
protons on the molecule, the right hand sides of Eq. (11) or (12) should
be averaged over the motion of these protons.
        When self-diffusion is present, one can still extract the EISF
from the measured spectra [3]. Of course, one needs to know by a separate
experiment, the self-diffusion tensor. Assuming, for example, isotropic
simple diffusion, characterized by a self-diffusion coefficient D, the
only difference in identifying the intensity of the sharp component is

---

[1] Please note the error in formula (8) of reference [33].

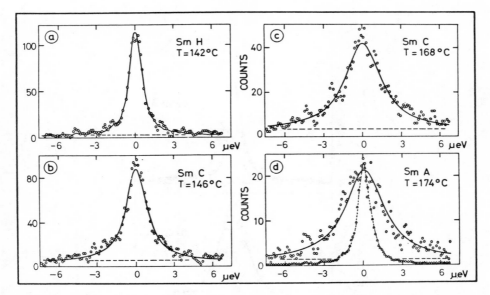

FIG.2. *Typical very high resolution neutron quasi-elastic spectra of D-TBBA in the smectic H, C and A phases for $Q = 0.28$ Å^{-1}, together with the experimental resolution shown on spectrum d. The spectra are taken with the backscattering spectrometer IN10 of the ILL using an incident wavelength of 6.28 Å and a resolution of about 1 μeV FWHM. The full curves are the best fit of a Lorentzian function convoluted with the resolution, together with a flat background shown in dashed line.*

to replace the measured resolution function R(ω) by an effective resolution function R'(ω) = R(ω) ⊗ T(ω), where T(ω) is the Lorentzian function given by Eq. (7) and where the symbol ⊗ represents a convolution product.

3. TRANSLATIONAL MOTIONS IN THE SMECTIC PHASES OF TBBA

Our first study of molecular motions in TBBA at high resolution [6] showed that the NQES spectra were composed of a sharp peak superimposed on a broader component, as expected for rotational motion. The width of the broad component in the Sm H phase was of the order of 100 μeV FWHM; it is even greater in the C and A phases. Using the very high resolution backscattering technique [7,8], we have then been able to measure the broadening of the sharp peak, due to translational motions, the rotational contribution being merely a flat background. This method is in fact commonly used to study translational diffusion in liquid crystals [9, 10].

3.1. Powder sample

Fig. 2 gives examples of four spectra measured in the H, C and A phases of a powdered form sample of D-TBBA (completely deuterated on the butyl chains). The apparent self-diffusion coefficient D_{ap} which has been extracted from these spectra by assuming a theoretical Lorentzian lineshape of width $\Delta E = 2h\, D_{ap}\, Q^2$, turns out to be very small in the H phase

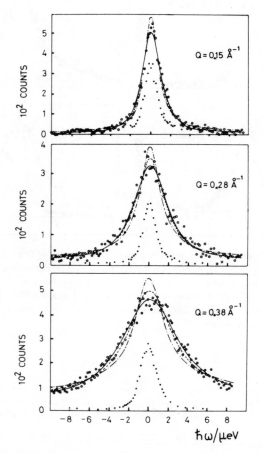

FIG.3. *NQES spectra of SmA TBBA at 184°C obtained in the $Q_{\parallel}H_0$ geometry, for three scattering angles. (a)* ——— : *best fit of a single Lorentzian curve convoluted with the resolution function, yielding $D_{\parallel} = 2.8 \times 10^{-6}$ cm²/s; (b)* – – – : *fit with a theoretical expression taking into account the influence of possible undulation modes and with $D_{\parallel} = 1.8 \times 10^{-6}$ cm²/s; (c)* – · – · – : *similar fit with $D_{\parallel} = 0.46 \times 10^{-6}$ cm²/s; (d)* .... : *shape of the corresponding resolution function. The flat background fitted in each case is not shown for clarity. It is seen that the quality of the fit is good when only self-diffusion is considered. The quality deteriorates with increasing contribution of the undulation modes (and correlatively decreasing influence of self-diffusion) and with the scattering angle.*

TABLE I. SELF-DIFFUSION COEFFICIENTS OF SMECTIC A TBBA AT 184°C

D $10^{-6} cm^2/s$	N M R multipulse method (a)	N M R two-pulse method (b)	Neutron back-scattering method (c)
$D_{\parallel}$	0.46 ± 0.05	2.6 ± 0.4	2.8 ± 0.2
$D_{\perp}$	1.4 ± 0.2	2.5 ± 0.4	2.8 ± 0.2
$\overline{D}$	1.1 ± 0.2	2.5 ± 0.4	2.7 ± 0.5 (d)
			2.8 ± 0.2

a) from ref. [12] ; errors are estimated from their figure 2 ;
b) from ref. [15] ; errors are estimated from their figure 6 ;
c) this work ;
d) extrapolation from figure 2 of ref. [11].

($D_{ap} < 6 \times 10^{-8}$ cm²/s) and measurable in the C and A phases ($D_{ap} \simeq 1-3 \times 10^{-6}$ cm²/s) [11]. These findings are in agreement with the plastic crystalline picture for the H phase, and the liquid like nature of the C and A phases. However, it was impossible to draw further conclusions, since the experiment was performed on a powder sample.

At that time NMR data obtained by means of a multipulse method [12] were available, from which the two components $D_{//}$ and $D_{\perp}$ (parallel and perpendicular to the average molecular direction) of the self-diffusion tensor were deduced. The average coefficient $\overline{D}$ turned out to be nearly a factor of three smaller than our D_{ap}. Consequently it was suggested [11] that the difference could be attributed to the undulation modes which are predicted for smectics [13], [14]. Later, another NMR experiment using a simpler two pulse method [15], yielded $\overline{D}$ values which were consistent with the one found using neutron scattering. To clarify the situation, we decided to perform NQES experiments on an aligned Sm A sample of TBBA at a temperature common to the two above-mentioned NMR experiments namely 184°C.

3.2. Oriented sample

The $30 \times 30 \times 0.8$ mm³ sample is oriented by cooling it slowly from the nematic phase under a 1.7 kG magnetic field produced by a permanent magnet. The perfection of the alignment is of the order of 10° as can be measured by following the amplitude of the first diffraction peak versus the angle of the flat sample with respect to the beam. This alignment is worse than the one measured on a similarly aligned TBBA sample by neutron diffraction [16], due to the fact that the illuminated area was much bigger (9 cm² versus 0.3 cm² in [16]). Two geometries were used, namely Q parallel or perpendicular to the magnetic field, for three scattering angles (see fig. 3).

Assuming anisotropic simple diffusion, one can extract the components of the self-diffusion tensor, which are compared in table I with the one obtained by the NMR methods. One sees that the results in the $Q \perp H_0$

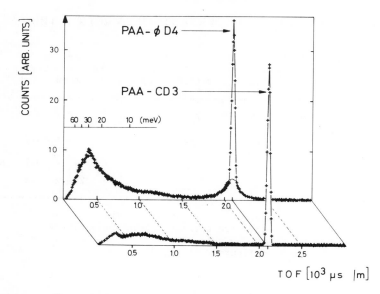

*FIG.4. Time-of-flight spectra for the two partially deuterated analogs of PAA at 100°C.
Elastic momentum transfer Q = 1.45 Å⁻¹ with an incident wavelength of 8.25 Å. The spectra
are taken with the multichopper spectrometer IN5 running at 10 000 rev/min; elastic
resolution ≅ 48 μeV FWHM.*

geometry suggest that the data of reference [15] are preferable. Very
recently the multi-pulse NMR technique for the determination of self-diffusion constant has been reexamined [17] and it has been shown that one
has to be careful in extracting information about the diffusion from this
technique. Consequently the contribution of undulation modes is not needed
to explain the $Q /\!/ H_0$ results. The corresponding data analysis is detailed
in reference [18] and some fits are shown in fig. 3.

   Another alternative for the interpretation of the neutron spectra in
the $Q /\!/ H_0$ geometry is to consider the diffusion of the molecules in the presence of the potential which is responsible for the existence of the smectic planes. We show in ref. [19] that the NMR data of ref. [15] and the
neutron data of ref. [18] are also consistent with one another if one
assumes that this potential is less than or around the thermal energy $k_B T$.

4.   ROTATIONAL MOTIONS IN THE SMECTIC AND SOLID PHASES OF TBBA

4.1. Introduction

   Our incoherent NQES results have shown that in all the normal smectic
phases of TBBA, there exists some kind of rotational motion of the molecules
around their long molecular axis. Another kind of rotational motion has to
be considered, namely the fluctuations of this long molecular axis. These
fluctuations are expected to be isotropic in the uniaxial smectic A phase
and anisotropic in the biaxial C and H phases.

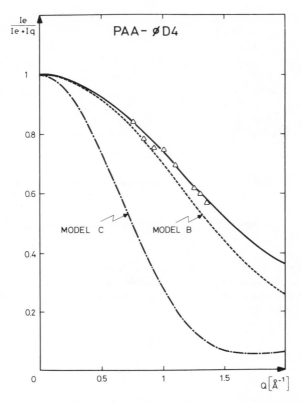

FIG.5. Experimental EISF as a function of Q extracted from the spectra of PAA−ϕD4 at 100°C (triangles). It is compared with two models; - - - : model B (rotation of the methyl groups alone); ····-·-: model C (simultaneous rotation of methyl and methyl groups). —— : best fit of model B taking into account the non-perfect deuteration (95%). The radius of gyration of the methyl protons has been taken as 1.032 Å.

A very controversial question is to decide whether or not there exists an orientational ordering of the molecules around their long axis in the tilted smectic phases. The microscopic mean-field theories of Meyer and McMillan [20] for the smectic C and H phases and that of Meyer [21] for the smectic H and VI phases contain such orientational ordering as a fundamental feature. In these theories, this ordering is linked to the existence of a strong intermolecular dipole-dipole interaction which is responsible for the tilted character of these phases. We will show that in accordance with other results, the NQES data do not agree with the existence of such ordering, at least in the normal smectic phases. Furthermore the only published data, claiming such ordering, obtained by using Nuclear Quadrupole Resonance (NQR), have been reanalyzed and we have shown that they can agree with the neutron results.

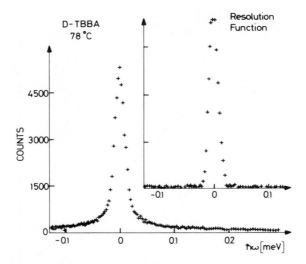

FIG.6.   Typical high resolution NQES spectrum of D-TBBA in the smectic VI phase of
Q = 1.03 Å⁻¹, together with the experimental resolution function.   The instrument used is the
multichopper IN5 running at 10 000 rev/min with an incident wavelength of 11.0 Å; elastic
resolution ≅ μeV FWHM.

4.2.   Reorientations in the solid phase

By comparing the neutron spectra of TBBA in its solid phase, with its
partially deuterated analog, we have been able to show [22] that there do
not exist large amplitude notions of the body in this phase. However, the
extremities of the butyl chains reorient rapidly (last methylene and methyl
group) with correlation times varying from 1.5×10^{-11} s to 0.8×10^{-11} s
between room temperature and the transition crystal – Sm H at 113°C. This
finding is in agreement with a recent structural determination using X-ray
diffraction [23] , where the authors could not localize the last carbon
atom of the butyl chains. Later we have shown [24] that the same freezing
out of the body motion exists in the metastable Sm–VII phase, whose nature
has to be elucidated further.

To conclude this investigation of the rotational motion which exists
in the solid phase of mesogenic materials, we wish to mention the study of
methyl groups rotation in solid para-azoxyanisole (PAA) [25]. Fig. 4 shows
the time-of-flight spectra for two partially deuterated analogs of PAA,
one of which is deuterated on the methyl groups, the others on the benzene
rings. These two spectra exhibit striking differences, showing that the
methyl groups are not only involved in a random rotational motion (quasi-
elastic scattering) but also perform some kind of periodic motion
(inelastic peak around 30 meV). By extraction of the EISF from the
quasielastic spectra, one sees immediately (fig. 5) that the only
possible motion of the methyl group is around its C_3 axis.

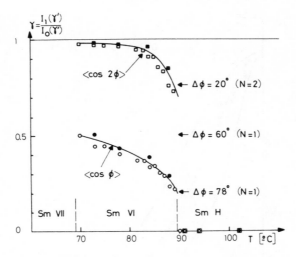

FIG.7.   Values of the order parameters extracted from the NQES spectra in the supercooled H
and VI phases of D-TBBA, as a function of temperature. N = 1 corresponds to a polar ordering;
N = 2 corresponds to a bipolar ordering (jump by π plus fluctuations around the two equilibrium
positions).   The corresponding mean angular fluctuation amplitude Δφ is indicated for each case.

4.3.   Reorientations in the H and VI phases

Preliminary experiments in the H phase [6],[26] of TBBA had revealed
that the neutron spectra were not in accordance with the Meyer-McMillan
theory [20] for this phase, by failing to detect any orientational
ordering for the rotational motion around the long molecular axis.
Furthermore, the data in the normal H phase [27] (at 119°C and 137°C) showed
that the motion had to be more "isotropic" than uniaxial rotation, implying
an additional motion that we attributed to (anisotropic) axis fluctuations.

Later on, we presented a more detailed NQES study of the supercooled
H and of the VI phase of TBBA [24]. The EISF and the lineshapes were
analyzed in terms of models permitting orientational ordering around the
long axis [28]. An example of the spectra obtained in the VI phase at
78°C is shown in fig. 6. It clearly shows a sharp peak reproducing the
resolution function superimposed on a broad component. This result is at
variance with deuteron NMR [29] and Raman scattering [30] works, where it
is suggested that the motion freezes out on cooling to the VI phase.

Using the calculations developed in ref. [28], we could extract
values for the orientational parameters <cos φ> for a polar ordering and
< cos 2φ > for a bipolar ordering. This is depicted in fig. 7. In accordance
with our previous results [6, 26, 27] we found that < cos φ >= <cos 2 φ> =0
for the normal and supercooled H phases. For the VI phase the neutron data
cannot discriminate between the two models. The reasons why we prefer the
model with 2 sites, where the molecules are allowed to flip by π around
the long axis, is discussed in length in ref. [24].

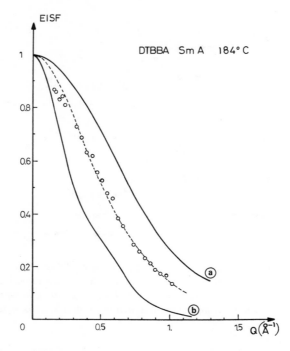

FIG.8.   Experimental EISF as a function of Q for a powder sample of D-TBBA at 184° in the smectic A phase, and extracted from the quasi-elastic spectra assuming that the sharp component is broadened by translational self-diffusion with diffusion coefficient of 2.8×10^{-6} cm^2/s. This EISF is compared with a model permitting uniform rotation around the long axis and fluctuations of this axis. The only parameter of the problem is the amplitude of the fluctuations, i.e. the order parameter $\langle P_2 \rangle$.   Curves (a) and (b) are for $\langle P_2 \rangle = 1$ and 0, corresponding to purely uniaxial motion and spherical motion, respectively. The dotted curve fitting the experimental points corresponds to $\langle P_2 \rangle \cong 0.70$.

These results were challenged by recent ^{14}N nuclear quadrupole resonance (NQR) data [31] , where it was concluded that there exists a polar orientational ordering around the long axis in accordance with the Meyer–McMillan theory [21]. From a critical analysis of these various results, we have shown [32] that the models suggested by the NQES data are also consistent with these NQR data. The average amplitude of the anisotropic fluctuations of the long axis in the H phase is found to be of the order of 20° at 139°C, in accordance with our NQES results [27]. For the VI phase, the two sets of data are quite consistent with one another, but do not allow discrimination between a polar or a bipolar ordering.

4.4.   Reorientations in the C and A phases

The same kind of rotational motion as in the H phase is occurring in the C phase of TBBA, with larger amplitudes of the axis fluctuations and shorter correlation times [27].

In the A phase, the variation of the EISF with the momentum transfer Q reveals that the order parameter $< P_2 >$ describing the fluctuations of the long molecular axis, is of the order of 0.7 [33]. (Fig. 8). This result is fully consistent with the NQR data [31]. Since in the A phase, the electric field gradient (EFG) tensor appears as axially symmetric, one obtains the result that the resonance frequency is directly related to the resonance frequency in the solid phase and to $<P_2>$. Using the NQR data, one has $< P_2 > = 0.7$, when the angle between the largest principal axis of the ^{14}N EFG tensor in the solid and the long axis, is 62°. This value is very near the value that the authors of ref. [31] believe it to be.

5. CONCLUSION

In this paper we have shown, by recalling some of our results, that high resolution incoherent NQES on liquid crystals has brought valuable complementary information, when compared with the information obtained by the other spectroscopic techniques. This is particularly clear for the low temperature smectic phases of TBBA, where translational freedom of the molecules is small. In particular we have shown that, in the H and C phases of TBBA, there is no orientational ordering around the long axis, as predicted by the microscopic theories, where the dipole-dipole inter-action is the dominant one. It thus appears that the tilted or non-tilted smectic phases should be characterized by a criterion other than the existence or non-existence of a strong dipolar interaction between the molecules. It is worthwhile mentioning that this result has received recently a "chemical" confirmation, since a mesogen having no dipole moment on the body has been synthetized and which, "in spite of this", presents a tilted smectic C phase [34] . It appears from this study that the occurrence of a smectic C phase is strongly dependent upon the length of the hydrocarbon chains.

It is clear that the information obtained by incoherent NQES is not so direct in the more fluid phases of liquid crystals, mainly the smectic A and the nematic phases, where the translational freedom blurs the information one could get on the orientational order. It is still possible to study this order, if one has complementary data about the translational motion at high Q values, where the models are more sensitive. However, one is limited experimentally by the existence of broad diffuse scattering lines in the neutron diffraction pattern which reduce the Q range where the scattering is purely incoherent.

REFERENCES

[1]   For a general review on liquid crystals, see for example, de GENNES, P.G., "The Physics of Liquid Crystals", Clarendon Press (1974).

[2]   SPRINGER, T., "Quasielastic Neutron Scattering for the Investigation of Diffuse Motions in Solids and Liquids". Springer-Verlag (1972).

[3]   VOLINO, F., and DIANOUX, A.J., Proceedings EUCHEM Conference - Schloss-Elmau (April 1976).

[4]   DIANOUX, A.J., VOLINO, F., and HERVET,H., Mol. Phys. 30 (1975) 1181.

[5]   THIBAUDIER, C., and VOLINO, F., Mol. Phys. 26 (1973) 1281; 30 (1975) 1159.

[6]   HERVET, H., VOLINO, F., DIANOUX, A.J., and LECHNER, R.E.,J. Physique Lett. 35 (1974) L151.

[7]   BIRR, M., HEIDEMANN, A., and ALEFELD, B., Nucl. Instrum. Methods, 95 (1971) 435.

[8]   ALEFELD, B., Kerntechnik, 14 (1972) 15.

[9]   TÖPLER, J., ALEFELD, B., and SPRINGER, T., Mol. Cryst. Liq. Cryst.
       26 (1974) 297.

[10]   LEADBETTER, A.J., TEMME, F.P., HEIDEMANN, A., and HOWELLS, W.S.
       Chem. Phys. Lett. 34 (1975) 363.

[11]   DIANOUX, A.J., VOLINO, F., HEIDEMANN, A., and HERVET, H., J. Physique
       Lett. 36 (1975) L-275.

[12]   BLINC, R., BURGAR, M., PIRŠ, J., ZUPANČIČ, I., and ŽUMMER, S., Phys.
       Rev. Lett. 33 (1974) 1192.

[13]   de GENNES, P.G., J. Physique, Coll. 30 (1969) C4-65.

[14]   MARTIN, P.C., PARODI, O., and PERSHAN, P.S., Phys. Rev. A6 (1972)
       2401.

[15]   KRÜGER, G.J., SPIESECKE, H., and Van STEENWINKEL, R., J. Physique Coll.
       37 (1976) C3-123.

[16]   HERVET, H., LAGOMARSINO, S., RUSTICHELLI, F., and VOLINO, F., Acta
       Cryst. A32 (1976) 166.

[17]   STEPIŠNIK, J., Proc. 3rd European Experimental NMR Conference,
       Helsingör (Denmark) April 1977.

[18]   DIANOUX, A.J., HEIDEMANN, A., VOLINO, F., and HERVET, H., Mol. Phys.
       32 (1976) 1521.

[19]   VOLINO, F., and DIANOUX, A.J., to be published.

[20]   MEYER, R.J., and McMILLAN, W.L., Phys. Rev. A9 (1974) 899.

[21]   MEYER, R.J., Phys. Rev., A12 (1975) 1066.

[22]   VOLINO, F., DIANOUX, A.J., LECHNER, R.E., and HERVET, H., J. Physique
       Coll. 36, (1975) C1-84.

[23]   DOUCET, J., MORNON, J.P., CHEVALIER, R., and LIFCHITZ, A., Acta
       Cryst. B33 (1977) 1701.

[24]   DIANOUX, A.J., HERVET, H., and VOLINO, F., J. Physique 38 (1977) 809.

[25]   HERVET, H., DIANOUX, A.J., LECHNER, R.E. and VOLINO, F., J. Physique
       37 (1976) 587.

[26]   HERVET, H., VOLINO, F., DIANOUX, A.J., and LECHNER, R.E., Phys. Rev.
       Lett. 34 (1975) 451.

[27]   VOLINO, F., DIANOUX, A.J., and HERVET, H., J. Physique Coll. 37
       (1976) C3-55.

[28]   DIANOUX, A.J., and VOLINO, F., Mol. Phys. (1977) in print.

[29]   DELOCHE, B., CHARVOLIN, J., LIEBERT, L., and STRZELECKI, L.,
       J. Physique Coll. 36 (1975) C1-21.

[30]   DVORJETSKI, D., VOLTERRA, V., and WIENER-AVNEAR, E., Phys. Rev. A12
       (1975) 681.

[31]   SELIGER, J., OSREDKAR, R., ŽAGAR V., and BLINC, R., Phys. Rev.
       Lett. 38 (1977) 411.

[32]   VOLINO, F., and DIANOUX, A.J., Phys. Rev. Lett. 39 (1977) 763.

[33]   VOLINO, F., DIANOUX, A.J., and HERVET, H., Mol. Cryst. Liq. Cryst.
       38 (1977) 125.

[34]   GRAY, G.W., and GOODBY, J.W., Mol. Cryst. Liq. Cryst. 37 (1976) 157.

DISCUSSION

M. LAMBERT: What is the characteristic time for the molecular rotations in the Sm B_c modification?

A.J. DIANOUX: It is within the range $(1 - 3) \times 10^{-11}$ s.

T. SPRINGER: All the quasi-elastic scattering work carried out so far has assumed that rotations and translations are independent, and the results tend to support this. Could you comment on the physical justification for this assumption?

A.J. DIANOUX: It is certainly justified in the case of diffusion in liquid crystals. The relationship between the diffusion coefficient and the characteristic time for translation is $D = \ell^2/2\tau_D$. For translation perpendicular to the smectic planes, we have

$$D \cong 3 \times 10^{-6} \text{ cm}^2/\text{s and } \ell \cong 25 \text{ Å}$$

so that we get $\tau_D \cong 10^{-8}$ s. This has to be compared with the characteristic time for rotation, which is $\tau_R \cong 10^{-11}$ s. It can be said that translation and rotation are not dynamically coupled. Of course, one can think of certain types of motion having complete coupling between rotation and translation — screw motion for example.

J.W. WHITE: Have any systematic differences been encountered between the NMR and neutron scattering techniques employed for translational diffusion measurements on liquid-crystal phases? If so, can these differences be attributed to differences in the time scales of observation associated with the two techniques?

A.J. DIANOUX: Earlier quasi-elastic neutron scattering results for nematics have been attributed solely to a translational contribution, even for fairly high values of Q, and this apparent diffusion coefficient was greater than the one measured by NMR. Since that time, the back-scattering technique used by Springer and co-workers has shown that the two methods can give identical results, if one measures at sufficiently low Q. For smectics, as far as I know, the only measurements of D by NMR are the two that I quoted in my talk. An interesting situation arises if one has obtained reliable D values with NMR (long-range diffusion), since it is then possible to determine the potential holding the smectic planes by fitting the neutron spectra, obtained with the back-scattering technique, to the theoretical expressions that I mentioned in my presentation.

C.J. WRIGHT: Do I understand from the scattering law you quoted for undulation modes that there is no theoretical reason to expect inelastic scattering from such phenomena?

A.J. DIANOUX: Not for the *incoherent* scattering. In this connection I would refer you to a paper by Dr. Gennes (J. Phys. 36 (1975) 603).

DYNAMIQUE DES PHASES CRISTALLINE ET SMECTIQUES ORDONNEES DE TBBA

B. DORNER
Institut Laue-Langevin,
Grenoble

J. DOUCET, M. LAMBERT, A.M. LEVELUT, P. PORQUET
Laboratoire de physique des solides,
Orsay,
France

Abstract–Résumé

DYNAMICS OF THE CRYSTALLINE PHASE AND THE ORDERED SMECTIC PHASES OF TBBA.

The dynamics of the crystalline phase and of the ordered smectic phases of terephthal bis-butyl aniline (TBBA) were studied using coherent neutron inelastic scattering. The experiments were carried out on a hydrogenated single-domain sample using the IN2 spectrometer at the Institut Laue-Langevin. The study proved the existence of both longitudinal and transverse modes propagated parallel to the molecular layers for the three phases studied. On the other hand, the shearing mode, which is propagated perpendicular to the molecular layers, was observed only for the crystalline phase: however, the spectral distribution of the scattered neutrons is modified — at least for the smectic B_c phase — and this modification will have to be studied further later on. Thus, the crystal-smectic B phase transition does not bring about an important change in the lattice dynamics (phonons of wave vectors perpendicular to the molecular direction); in particular, the sound velocity values are changed only slightly. The mobilization of the molecules around their principal axis causes at most a slightly increased damping of the collective modes. The two ordered smectic modes studied thus behave like ordered solids; they can be regarded as plastic crystals.

DYNAMIQUE DES PHASES CRISTALLINE ET SMECTIQUES ORDONNEES DE TBBA.

La dynamique des phases cristalline et smectiques ordonnées du téréphtal bis-butyle aniline (TBBA) a été étudiée par diffusion inélastique cohérente des neutrons thermiques. Les expériences ont été effectuées sur un échantillon monodomaine hydrogéné en utilisant le spectromètre IN2 de l'Institut Laue-Langevin. Les résultats prouvent l'existence à la fois des modes longitudinaux et transverses se propageant parallèlement aux couches moléculaires, et ceci pour les trois phases étudiées. Par contre, le mode de cisaillement se propageant perpendiculairement aux couches moléculaires n'a été observé que pour la phase cristalline: on observe cependant, au moins pour la phase smectique B_c, une modification de la répartition spectrale des neutrons diffusés, dont l'étude devra être reprise ultérieurement. La transition de phase cristal-smectique B n'entraîne donc pas de modification importante de la dynamique du réseau (phonons de vecteurs d'onde perpendiculaire à la direction moléculaire); en particulier les valeurs de la vitesse du son ne sont que faiblement modifiées. La mise en mouvement des molécules autour de leur grand axe n'entraîne tout au plus qu'une faible augmentation de l'amortissement des modes collectifs. Les deux phases smectiques ordonnées étudiées se comportent donc comme des solides ordonnés; elles peuvent être considérées comme des cristaux plastiques.

Le téréphtal bis-butyle aniline (TBBA) existe sous 9 formes différentes : 2 phases solides, 5 phases mésomorphes, 1 phase liquide et une
phase pseudocristalline dont la structure est mal connue [1] :

IX   VIII   V   IV   III   II   I

$\overset{-33°C}{\underset{}{Cr_1 \longrightarrow}}$ $\overset{113°C}{Cr_2 \longrightarrow}$ $\overset{144°C}{Sm\ B_C \longleftrightarrow}$ $Sm\ C \longleftrightarrow Sm\ A \longleftrightarrow N \longleftrightarrow L\ I$

$\overset{52°C}{\uparrow}$ $\overset{}{\underset{84°C}{\downarrow}}$

VII $\leftarrow$ $Sm\ E_C$

$\underset{VI}{68°C}$

Nous nous sommes plus particulièrement intéressés à la phase
Cr_2(VIII) qui est la phase stable à la température ambiante et aux phases
smectiques ordonnées (V,VI) obtenues par chauffage et refroidissement du
cristal. La structure de ces différentes phases est en effet connue [2]
[3] [4] , elle a été déterminée par diffraction et diffusion de rayons X:
les phases smectiques V et VI sont des phases relativement ordonnées, dif-
ficiles à distinguer de cristaux plastiques à molécules très anisotropes.
Une étude de la dynamique de réseau par diffusion cohérente inélastique de
neutrons a donc été entreprise afin de rechercher si le comportement thermique de ces phases pouvait être décrit de la même manière que celui d'un
cristal et en particulier détecter l'existence de modes transverses.

Les expériences se sont heurtées à deux types de difficultés :
- Obtenir un gros échantillon monodomaine : ceci est possible si on part
d'un monocristal de la phase cristalline. Par chauffage et refroidissement
successifs il se transforme en monodomaine des deux phases smectiques,
l'orientation des grands axes moléculaires étant peu modifiée. Par contre,
lors du retour à la phase cristalline, l'échantillon est devenu polycris-
tallin et donc inutilisable pour une expérience ultérieure. Toutes les mesures doivent donc avoir lieu au cours du même cycle thermique. Nous avons
disposé d'assez grands monocristaux (10 x 20 x 2 mm^3) obtenus par croissan-
ce à partir d'une solution de TBBA dans le chloroforme (Laboratoire de
Physique Cristalline - Orsay).

- Travailler avec un échantillon hydrogéné. Les seuls monocristaux dont nous
avons disposé étaient hydrogénés ; néanmoins les spectres de neutrons ont
pu être obtenus pour chacune des trois phases.

Structure des différentes phases

Dans les trois cas, les molécules sont disposées en couches et leur
grand axe est incliné par rapport à la normale aux couches ; le réseau est
monoclinique, les paramètres cristallins et les groupes d'espace sont don-
nés dans le tableau suivant :

Phase	a $\overset{\circ}{A}$	b $\overset{\circ}{A}$	c $\overset{\circ}{A}$	β	groupe
Cr_2	17,57	5,75	53,2	115°5	A $2/_a$
Sm B_c	10,15	5,18	28,6	119°	C $2/_m$
Sm E_c	10,38	5,24	28,31	123,6°	Pa

b est l'axe binaire, l'axe c a été choisi dans les 3 cas parallèle à l'axe moléculaire : les molécules sont disposées dans des couches parallèles au plan a,b. Rappelons que la molécule de TBBA, de formule :

$$C_4 H_9 \langle O \rangle - N = CH - \langle O \rangle - CH = N - \langle O \rangle - C_4 H_9$$

a une longueur maximale de 29 Å lorsque les chaînes terminales sont étirées.

La structure de la phase cristalline est relativement complexe [4], elle a été déterminée par les méthodes classiques utilisant un grand nombre de taches de diffraction avec, cependant, une difficulté particulière liée à l'existence d'un mouvement déjà important des atomes de carbone terminaux.

La structure des deux phases smectiques est plus simple : le paramètre c correspond toujours à une longueur moléculaire, il n'y a pas ou peu d'interpénétration des molécules d'une couche à la suivante. La fig.1 représente les deux mailles cristallines correspondant au cristal et la phase Sm B_C ; elle donne également leur orientation respective (il n'y a que peu de changement au passage à la phase Sm E_C). Si on compare les deux phases smectiques :

1°/ Dans la phase smectique B_C, la distance entre axes moléculaires est sensiblement la même, quelle que soit la direction des molécules proche-voisines ; d'autre part, les positions moléculaires sont équivalentes dans la structure. Ces résultats sont compatibles avec la mise en évidence d'un mouvement des molécules autour de leur grand axe [5] [6], conduisant à cette "isotropie" de la structure (fig.2).

2°/ Dans la phase smectique E_C, il existe une déformation de la structure liée au fait que les molécules ne sont plus équivalentes (fig.3): le seul mouvement orientationnel possible est alors un retournement de 180° des molécules.

Les réseaux réciproques diffèrent donc dans les deux cas : si on compare les figures 2 et 3, on voit qu'il existe des taches de diffraction supplémentaires pour la phase Sm E_C, taches qui apparaissent lors de la transition Sm B_C → Sm E_C.

Ces deux phases smectiques ont donc des structures très ordonnées qui sont voisines de celles des cristaux plastiques et diffèrent notablement du cas des couches lipidiques. En effet :
- Il existe des taches de diffraction hkℓ pour lesquelles h ou k et ℓ ne sont pas nuls simultanément, c'est-à-dire qu'il existe des corrélations

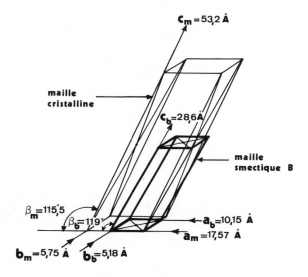

FIG.1.   *Maille élémentaire de la phase cristalline à 20°C et de la phase Sm B$_c$ à 125°C du TBBA.*

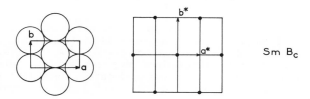

FIG.2.   *Représentation de la maille élémentaire dans le plan des couches smectiques pour la phase Sm B$_c$ et maille réciproque correspondante. Les positions des molécules sont équivalentes.*

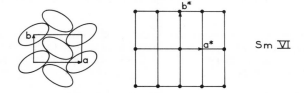

FIG.3.   *Représentation de la maille élémentaire dans le plan des couches smectiques pour la phase Sm E$_c$ et maille réciproque correspondante. Les positions des molécules ne sont plus équivalentes.*

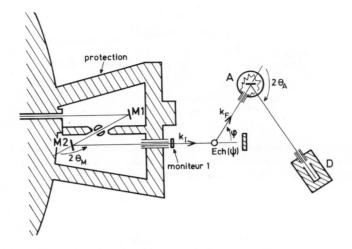

FIG.4.   *Schéma du spectromètre à 3 axes IN2. M₁ et M₂ = cristaux monochromateurs,*
A = cristal analyseur, D = détecteur. k_I et k_F sont les vecteurs d'onde, $2\theta_M$, φ et $2\theta_A$ les
angles de diffusion et ψ est l'angle d'orientation de l'échantillon.

de position entre molécules appartenant à des couches différentes.
- Les taches de diffraction sont fines. Il y en a peu, elles sont limitées
aux petites valeurs de h,k,ℓ : le réseau moyen est bien défini, le facteur
de Debye-Waller est important, dû à une amplitude grande des déplacements
des molécules autour de leur position moyenne.

Il était donc intéressant, en présence de ce mouvement moléculaire
de grande amplitude, d'essayer de caractériser la dynamique de réseau en
distinguant en particulier les modes se propageant parallèlement et perpendiculairement au plan des couches.

Dynamique de réseau

Les expériences ont été effectuées au moyen du spectromètre à trois
axes IN2, de l'Institut Laue Langevin (fig.4). Pour obtenir des résultats
significatifs en utilisant un échantillon hydrogéné [7], nous avons dû opé-
rer avec une bonne résolution et travailler à basse énergie E_O = 1,20 THz
(λ = 4,05 Å) en utilisant un filtre de Be pour réduire la contamination
due aux longueurs d'onde harmoniques. Monochromateur et analyseur étaient
en graphite pyrolitique.

1°/ Excitations de vecteur d'onde perpendiculaire aux grands axes moléculaires

Ce sont les excitations de vecteur d'onde q parallèle au plan réciproque hko. L'image de ce plan réciproque, obtenue par diffraction de
rayons X [2], est représentée figure 5 ; elle montre l'existence autour des
noeuds hko de taches diffuses (b - fig.5) relativement intenses. Ces taches

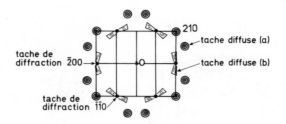

FIG.5. *Représentation schématique du cliché de diffraction de rayons X. Les taches diffuses (a) traduisent un ordre local de symétrie moins élevée, tandis que les taches diffuses (b) rendent compte des mouvements des molécules autour de leur position moyenne.*

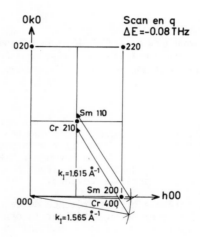

FIG.6. *Exemple d'un enregistrement à énergie constante et Q variable en phase smectique pour la recherche du mode Lb*. (Plan de diffusion (a*, b*)).*

diffuses, d'intensité décroissant en $1/q^2$, sont dues au déplacement des molécules autour de leurs positions d'équilibre : elles indiquent donc que les mouvements sont de grande amplitude, donc de fréquence faible, ce qu'on pouvait attendre des phonons acoustiques pour ce composé.

L'étude des phonons acoustiques longitudinaux et transverses a donc été menée en utilisant les taches de diffraction intenses 200 et 110 du plan hko (400 et 211 pour la phase cristalline). Un exemple d'enregistrement effectué pour la recherche des modes longitudinaux se propageant suivant b est décrit schématiquement figure 6. Tous les modes, longitudinaux et transverses, se propageant suivant les directions réciproques a* ou b* et polarisés dans le plan réciproque a*, b* ont pu être observés. Il faut

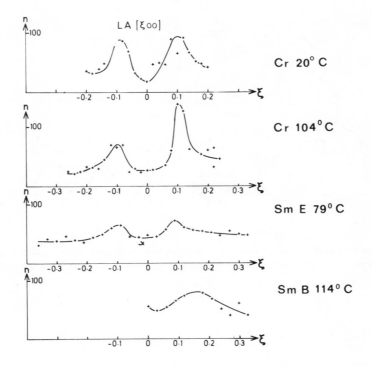

FIG.7. Pics de phonon relevés à énergie constante pour le mode longitudinal polarisé a* dans les trois phases cristal, Sm E_c et Sm B_c. Q = (400). Temps de mesure par point ~ 20 min.

remarquer que, la symétrie du cristal étant faible, ces modes ne sont en général pas purement transverses ou longitudinaux, seule la direction de l'axe binaire ayant des propriétés particulières (la description des mouvements moléculaires faite ultérieurement (fig. 8 - fig.11) n'est donc qu'approximative).

La figure 7 reporte les groupes de neutrons obtenus pour les trois phases lors de la recherche du mode longitudinal polarisé suivant a* (mouvements moléculaires décrits fig.8) : même s'ils sont élargis pour les phases smectiques, ils restent bien définis tant que la longueur du vecteur d'onde reste limitée par rapport aux dimensions de la zone de Brillouin. Pour des vecteurs d'onde plus grands, le signal devient faible et se trouve noyé dans le bruit de fond incohérent. Les courbes de dispersion n'ont donc pas pu être déterminées dans toute la zone de Brillouin ; elles sont reproduites figure 8 et fig.9 et ne sont pas très différentes lorsqu'on passe d'une phase à l'autre.

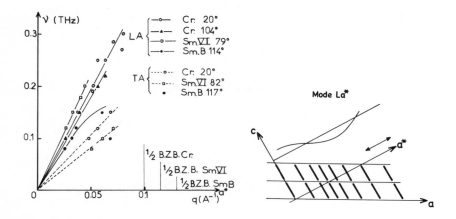

FIG.8. *Courbes de dispersion des modes se propageant dans la direction a* (polarisation a* et b*) et représentation schématique du déplacement des molécules pour le mode longitudinal.*

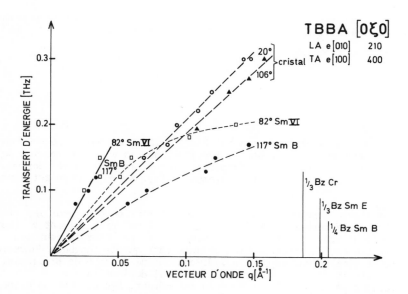

FIG.9. *Courbes de dispersion des modes se propageant dans la direction b* (polarisation a* et b*).*

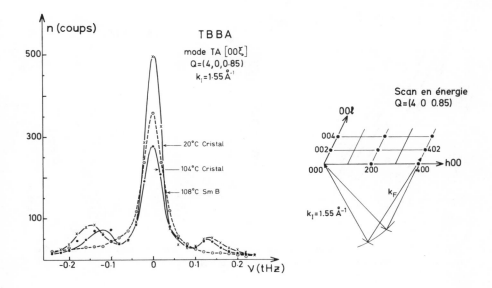

FIG.10. Enregistrement à Q constant et énergie variable pour la recherche du mode T_c^* polarisé a* (plan de diffusion (a*, c*)).

On peut cependant faire les remarques suivantes :
- Dans le cas des modes transverses, les branches de dispersion sont toujours plus basses pour la phase smectique B_C et, par conséquent, la vitesse du son plus faible. Ce résultat n'est pas surprenant étant donné la nature de cette phase qui est la plus "fluide" des trois phases étudiées.

- Dans le cas des modes longitudinaux, si la vitesse du son est la même pour les deux phases smectiques lorsque la polarisation est parallèle à b (nous n'avons pas de résultats pour la phase cristalline), elle devient légèrement supérieure pour la phase Sm E_C lorsque la polarisation est selon a* : elle est alors même supérieure à la vitesse du son correspondante pour le cristal. Ces résultats pourraient être une conséquence du type d'empilement relativement compact des molécules dans cette phase et décrit figure 3.

Lorsque le vecteur d'onde a une composante importante dans le plan des couches smectiques, les modes acoustiques transverses existent donc et sont aussi bien définis que pour un cristal plastique.

2°/ Excitations de vecteur d'onde perpendiculaire aux couches moléculaires

Cette fois le vecteur d'onde est dirigé perpendiculairement au plan des couches a,b, c'est-à-dire parallèlement à la direction réciproque c*. La géométrie de l'expérience sera donc différente, le plan de diffusion utilisé étant le plan réciproque hoℓ (fig.10).

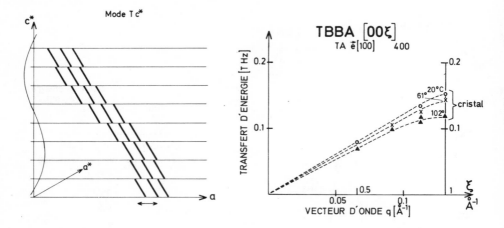

FIG.11. *Courbe de dispersion des modes transverses se propageant dans la direction c* et représentation schématique du déplacement des molécules pour ce mode.*

L'étude de ces excitations est particulièrement intéressante car les déplacements moléculaires correspondants peuvent être décrits (fig.11.b), dans un modèle de molécules rigides, comme un cisaillement des couches moléculaires les unes par rapport aux autres. L'existence d'un mode transverse acoustique se propageant perpendiculairement aux couches est liée à la nature des interactions inter-couches : si la fusion des chaînes alphatiques était responsable de la transition cristal → smectique B, le mode devrait devenir visqueux, les couches glissant alors les unes sur les autres [8].

De fait, les résultats obtenus ne sont pas concluants. En effet les groupes de neutrons correspondant à ce type d'excitation ne sont clairement visibles que dans le cas du cristal (20° - 104° : courbes de la fig.10). Ils correspondent alors à des excitations d'énergie très faible : 0,15 THz en bordure de zone de Brillouin pour le cristal à 20°C. Les courbes de dispersion correspondantes sont reportées figure 11.a. Bien que les atomes de carbone terminaux de la molécule de TBBA soient animés de mouvements de grande amplitude dans la phase solide [4], les modes étudiés ici restent bien définis.

Lors du passage à la phase smectique B_C la situation devient plus confuse ; en effet, des groupes de neutrons à énergie définie ne sont plus visibles (fig.10). Par contre, si on compare les deux répartitions spectrales obtenues pour le cristal et la phase smectique B_C à sensiblement la même température, on voit que l'intensité quasi-élastique a augmenté pour la phase smectique : ceci ne peut être un effet de diffusion incohérente. Cependant, dû au pic incohérent important, il est difficile, dans l'état actuel des expériences, d'apprécier l'origine de cette augmentation d'intensité : diminution d'énergie d'excitations encore bien définies, suramortissement de ce type d'excitations ou pic quasi-élastique dû au glissement des couches avec temps de relaxation.

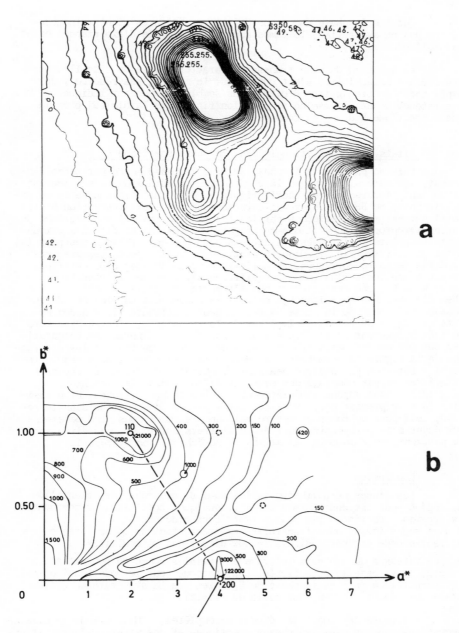

FIG.12. a) Enregistrement densitométrique d'un cliché de diffraction aux rayons X du TBBA en phase Sm B (T = 128°C) avec le faisceau incident parallèle à la direction d'allongement des molécules. (Le cliché est une image peu déformée du plan réciproque (a*, b*)). b) Carte montrant les valeurs de l'intensité incohérente et cohérente élastique des neutrons dans le plan réciproque (a*, b*). T = 117°C, k = 2,662 Å^{-1}. Les lignes joignent des points d'égale intensité.

Quant à la phase smectique E_C, les expériences n'ont malheureusement pas pu avoir lieu, le temps accordé à ce cycle d'expériences étant naturellement limité.

La question du mode transverse caractéristique du cisaillement des couches moléculaires n'est donc, pour le moment, pas résolue ; des expériences de propagation d'ultra-sons semblent cependant indiquer l'existence d'une vitesse de propagation finie mais faible [9] pour la phase smectique B d'autres composés.

Effets pré-transitionnels dans la phase smectique B_C

Lors du passage de la phase Sm B_C à la phase Sm E_C par refroidissement, les molécules, jusque là en désordre orientationnel, s'orientent en donnant l'ordre latéral décrit figure 3. Bien que désordonnée en moyenne, la phase Sm B_C est cependant caractérisée par l'existence d'un ordre local qui est mis en évidence par les taches diffuses (a) du diagramme de rayons X reproduit schématiquement figure 5 : les taches diffuses entourent les points réciproques qui deviennent des noeuds réciproques pour la phase Sm E_C (210, fig.5). D'autre part, elles sont reproduites avec une symétrie ternaire correspondant à l'existence de 3 types d'orientations de cet ordre local [10] (domaines différents). Lors de la transition Sm B_C → Sm E_C, une des orientations l'emporte, et seule la série de taches diffuses hko à indices h,k entiers se condensent sur les noeuds du réseau réciproque de la phase Sm E_C. On peut s'attendre alors à des effets critiques au voisinage immédiat de la transition, c'est-à-dire lors de l'établissement de l'ordre à grande portée. Des expériences comparatives ont été menées par diffusion de rayons X et de neutrons : les diagrammes de la figure 12 permettent la comparaison des courbes de niveau d'intensité obtenues par analyse densitométrique d'un diagramme de rayons X (fig.12.a) et par comptage des neutrons diffusés dans le plan hko (fig.12.b). Nous voyons immédiatement que les taches diffuses, bien visibles dans le premier cas, ne se détachent pas du fond continu dans le second, ceci pour un temps de mesure raisonnable. Ceci nous rend pessimistes quant à la perspective de l'étude d'effets critiques, par diffusion de neutrons, tout au moins en utilisant un échantillon hydrogéné.

Conclusion

Les études de diffusion inélastique de neutrons sur échantillon hydrogéné nous ont donc permis de tirer quelques conclusions concernant la dynamique de réseau des phases smectiques ordonnées :
- Les modes acoustiques transverses existent, tout au moins lorsque leur vecteur d'onde est perpendiculaire aux directions moléculaires.

- Les vitesses du son sont relativement faibles comme on pouvait s'y attendre, la vitesse la plus élevée étant obtenue pour le mode longitudinal (q parallèle à a^*) de la phase Sm E_C, bien que la structure de cette phase soit moins dense que celle du cristal.

Il reste cependant des études incomplètes, celles du mode de cisaillement des couches dans les phases smectiques et des effets pré-transitionnels accompagnant la transition Sm B_C → Sm E_C. Les expériences vont être reprises en utilisant des monocristaux complètement deutériés qui existent maintenant grâce à la coopération de l'équipe de Chimie du Laboratoire de Physique des Solides et du Laboratoire de Physique Cristalline d'Orsay. Une étude préliminaire menée à Saclay [11] pour le cristal à 20°C a déjà

permis de prolonger les courbes de dispersion des modes acoustiques longitudinaux et transverses, de vecteur d'onde parallèle à a$^{\prime\prime}$ (fig.8) jusqu'en
bordure de zone de Brillouin ; elle a également mis en évidence l'existence d'un autre type d'excitations non encore identifié.

REFERENCES

[1] DOUCET, J., LEVELUT, A.M., LAMBERT, M., Phys. Rev. Lett. **32** (1974) 301.

[2] LEVELUT, A.M., LAMBERT, M., C.R. Acad. Sci., Paris **272 B** (1971) 1016.

[3] LAMBERT, M., LEVELUT, A.M., Anharmonic Lattices, Structural Transitions and
     Melting (Riste, T., Ed.), Noordhoff, Leiden (1974) 375.

[4] DOUCET, J., MORNON, J.P., CHEVALIER, R., LIFSCHITZ, A., Acta Crystallogr.,
     Sect. **B 33** (1977) 1701;
     DOUCET, J., LEVELUT, A.M., LAMBERT, M., Ibid. 1710.

[5] HERVET, H., VOLINO, F., DIANOUX, A.J., LECHNER, R.E., J. Phys. (Paris), Lett. **35**
     (1974) L. 151.

[6] CHARVOLIN, J., DELOCHE, B., J. Phys. (Paris) **37** (1976) C3-69.

[7] DOUCET, J., DORNER, B., LAMBERT, M., LEVELUT, A.M., PORQUET, Ph., Soumis
     au J. de Phys.

[8] De GENNES, P.G., SARMA, G., Phys. Lett. A **38** (1972) 219.

[9] UNAL, H., BACRI, J.C., J. Phys. (Paris), Lett. **38** (1977) L. 111.

[10] LEVELUT, A.M., J. Phys. (Paris) **37** (1976) C3-51.

[11] MOUSSA, F., LEVELUT, A.M., Communication personnelle.

DISCUSSION

J.W. WHITE: Have you any evidence of low-frequency optic branches
cutting the longitudinal and transverse acoustic modes you have observed?
I should think that these branches must be present in the frequency range
covered by your experiments and that the recent Saclay results on fully deuterated
material could perhaps be interpreted as a TA optic mode mixing.

M. LAMBERT: In the case of the H sample, an attempt was made to find
the 0.65 TH mode visible in Raman spectroscopy. The failure to see this mode
may be due to damping of the mode, which only appears as a well-resolved thin
line in the Raman spectrum of the low-temperature crystalline phase. Since only
a few crystals were available, we did not cool the sample in the low-temperature
phase.

The fully deuterated crystals have been available for a short time only. We
hope to observe some optic branches and interactions between the rotational
motion of the molecules and the collective modes propagating parallel to the
layers. Further experiments will be carried out at ILL in Grenoble and at Saclay.

N. KROÓ: Some acoustic phonons are harder in one of the smectic phases
than in the solid phase. Is this change properly reflected in the macroscopic
parameters, for example in the density?

M. LAMBERT: No. The density of Sm E_c is less than the crystal density. The higher value of the sound velocity may perhaps be associated with the 'herring-bone' structure.

N. KROÓ: Has your sample been oriented in the LIX phases?

M. LAMBERT: The monoclinic axes are nearly parallel in the three phases. A single crystal transforms in single domains of Sm B_c and Sm E_c. It was only necessary to reorient the sample slightly, just a few degrees.

N. KROÓ: The origin of one of the phonon branches you showed on your last slide is not clear. How does the phonon resonance width in this branch compare with that of the others? I should think that broader lines here could be explained by 'hybrid' modes.

M. LAMBERT: The line corresponding to the supplementary branch is in fact broader. We have to be cautious as regards the interpretation until further experiments have been performed with the deuterated sample. Complex results may be due to the low crystal symmetry..

H. HAHN: The transition from the 'herring-bone' structure to the hexagonal smectic phase in TBBA is strongly reminiscent of the transition from α-gel to smectic in lipid bilayer systems. I know it is very difficult to prepare sufficiently big samples for scattering neutrons in these bi-layer systems, and I should therefore like to ask whether any recent progress has been made in this direction.

M. LAMBERT: I am not aware of any work on *oriented* bi-layer systems. We are now studying lecithine crystals by means of X-ray diffraction and diffuse scattering, but the sample size is only about 0.2 mm, which is too small for further coherent neutron inelastic scattering studies.

A.J. DIANOUX: What happens to the phonons in the higher Brillouin zones for the smectic B_c phase? In incoherent scattering, we have a reasonable quasi-elastic intensity due to random rotational motion for $Q > 0.5$ Å^{-1} only. It would be interesting to have some means of evaluating the possible interaction between the phonons and this rotational motion, whose time-scale is $\cong 10^{-11}$ s.

M. LAMBERT: We hope to see some interaction between the molecular rotational motion and the translation collective modes in triple-axis experiments on deuterated single domains. It would, of course, also be interesting to perform experiments like the ones that you performed on IN5, but with fully deuterated powder, in order to see whether any coherent inelastic scattering is superimposed on the incoherent scattering. No measurements were made in the higher Brillouin zones, because we were looking for acoustic modes close to the intense Bragg spots. Large-angle Bragg spots do not exist for the Sm B_c and Sm E_c phases (Debye-Waller factor). It might be interesting to make observations farther in the reciprocal space.

DEUTERATION AS APPLIED TO SMALL-ANGLE NEUTRON SCATTERING FOR THE STUDY OF POLYMERS
Methods, results and prospects

F. BOUE, M. DAOUD, M. NIERLICH,
C. WILLIAMS, J.P. COTTON, B. FARNOUX,
G. JANNINK
Laboratoire Léon Brillouin,
CEA, Centre d'études nucléaires de Saclay,
Gif-sur-Yvette

H. BENOÎT, R. DUPPLESSIX†, C. PICOT
CRM,
Strassburg,
France

Abstract

DEUTERATION AS APPLIED TO SMALL-ANGLE NEUTRON SCATTERING FOR THE STUDY OF POLYMERS: METHODS, RESULTS AND PROSPECTS.

The possibilities of small-angle neutron scattering (SANS) are discussed by way of three actual problems of polymer research: (1) The effect of excluded volume on the conformation of neutron polymers in solution; (2) the relation between conformation and relaxation for usual polymers in hot stretched bulk; (3) the effect of electrostatic charges on linear polyelectrolytes in solution. For each of these problems, the contribution of SANS is set forth and new experimental results are presented.

INTRODUCTION

In order to show why Small-Angle Neutron Scattering (SANS) technique is so extensively used for studies in the field of polymer research, we begin by describing what a polymer chain is.

A polymer chain is obtained from the repetition of N identical molecules (the monomer) linearly connected by a chemical bond. The essential parameter is this number N of links (or the molecular weight M). Typical values for N lie between 10^2 and 10^4, thus a polymer chain is characterized by the statistical nature of its conformation (which is the average of all the configurations that can be adopted by the chain) and its corresponding large size R.

---

† Present address: Institut Laue-Langevin, Grenoble, France.

Here two types of polymers will be considered :

i) Neutral polymers - A prototype of these is the polystyrene $(C_8H_8)_N$. A typical value of its size, in dilute solution, is about 350 Å for $N = 500$ ($M \sim 5.10^5$).

ii) Polyelectrolytes - These are polymers with one (more or less) ioni- zable group per monomer. An example is the sulfonated polystyrene (PSS) whose chemical formula is $(C_8H_7SO_3Na)_N$; in water, it is dissociated in polyions $(C_8H_7SO_3^-)_N$ and counterions Na^+ and a typical value of its size in dilute solution is about 1300 Å for $N=500$ ($M_W \sim 10^6$).

The fundamental problem in this field is yet to determine the conforma- tion of a polymer chain in different environments (dilute solutions, semi- dilute solutions and in the bulk state). It is an experimental problem and also a theoretical one [1,2,3] since the conformation will be perfectly known if the probability $P(\vec{r})$ of having two links of the chains at a distance $\vec{r}$ is determined.

Here we discuss the importance of SANS for these problems by describing the technique as a labelling one (section 1) and how it can solve some typical polymers problems (described in section 2) using different methods : Increasing of the contrast (section 3) , selective labelling (section 4) and using chains all partially labelled (section 5).

All the data shown here are registered using the experimental SANS fa- cilities of the HFR reactor of the Laue Langevin Institut (ILL) at Grenoble and these of the Leon Brillouin Laboratory (L.L.B) at Saclay.

1. SMALL-ANGLE NEUTRON SCATTERING

In polymer problems, one is essentially concerned with the determination of positions of monomers, i.e in the long-distance range $r \gg \ell$ (where ℓ is the length of a link ~ 10Å). The scattering techniques of interest are those which involve scattering vectors q ($q = (4\pi/\lambda) \sin \theta/2$, where λ is the wave length and θ the scattering angle) smaller than ℓ^{-1}. This is the case for light, X-rays and neutron radiations.

In particular, with SANS [4,5] it is possible to reach q values above about 8.10^{-4} Å^{-1}. This range is better matched to characteristic lengths of polymers than that obtained from the two other techniques mentioned above. But the best possibility of SANS derives from the contrast notion which is connected [6,7] with the hypothesis of incompressibility of the system. Let us insist on this point in a simple case.

We assume that the system observed is only composed of two types of elementary scatterers of small size (< ℓ) : *monomers* of density $\rho_1(\vec{r})$; partial molar volume v_1 and its coherent scattering length a_1 (which is, at this q scale, the sum of the scattering length of its atoms) and "*solvent*" *molecules* (with corresponding parameters $\rho_o(\vec{r})$, v_o and a_o).

The number of scatterers $n(\vec{r})$ and the scattering length density $a(\vec{r})$ at a point $\vec{r}$ of the system are defined by

$$n(\vec{r}) = v_1\rho_1(\vec{r}) + v_o\rho_o(\vec{r})$$
$$a(\vec{r}) = a_1\rho_1(\vec{r}) + a_o\rho_o(\vec{r})$$

(1a)

or

$$a(\vec{r}) = \left(a_1 - a_o\frac{v_1}{v_o}\right)\rho_1(\vec{r}) + \frac{a_o}{v_o}n(\vec{r})$$

(1b)

This function is introduced because the amplitude of scattering $A(q)$ is the Fourier transform of $a(\vec{r})$. If we neglect the fluctuations of the number of scatterers at $\vec{r}$ (it is the incompressibility hypothesis) we can write $n(\vec{r}) = 1$

$$A(\vec{q}) = \left(a_1 - a_o \frac{v_1}{v_o} \right) \rho_1(\vec{q}) \; ; \; q \neq 0 \tag{2}$$

where $\rho_1(\vec{q})$ is the Fourier transform of $\rho_1(\vec{r})$. In fact, the hypothesis of incompressibility is reasonable only in the q range concerned here : $q\ell \ll 1$; since in this range the density fluctuations are negligeable with respect to the concentration fluctuations, this is not the case for $q\ell > 1$.

For polymers, in different monomolecular environments, the scattered intensity $I(q)$ is thus given by the relation

$$I(\vec{q}) = K^2 S(\vec{q}) \tag{3}$$

It is the product of two terms : a technical term K^2, the scattering power, due only to the weight given by the radiation to the monomer in the medium; a physical term $S(q)$, the scattering function, which is a function of the position of monomers in the system only. We will now discuss briefly these two terms.

1.1. The scattering function $S(q)$

The scattering function $S(q)$ is given by the following relations :

$$S(q) = \sum_{ij} < e^{i\vec{q}(\vec{r}_i - \vec{r}_j)} > \sim \int e^{i\vec{q} \cdot \vec{r}} P(\vec{r}) \, d_3 r \tag{4}$$

where $\vec{r}_i$ is the position of the ith monomer and the brackets correspond to thermal average of observables inside them. $S(q)$ is the Fourier transform of the probability $P(\vec{r})$ of having two monomers at a distance $\vec{r}$.

Let us consider, for instance, the function $S(q)$ obtained from a solution of n polymers. Three domains of q ($q\ell \lesssim 1$) are of particular interest :

i) In the Guinier range ($qR \lesssim 1$). The long-range correlations between monomers are observed. For dilute solutions, the data of $S(q)$ are interpreted in terms of the Guinier approximation [8]:

$$S(q) = n N^2 \left(1 - \frac{q^2 R^2}{3} \right) \tag{5}$$

Thus the measurements give a value for the radius of gyration R. R is the global size of the polymer.

ii) In the intermediate range $R^{-1} < q \lesssim \ell^{-1}$, the correlations at short distances between monomers inside a chain are observed. The $S(q)$ variation gives the detail or the form of the chain. Typical variations of $S(q)$ are q^{-2} for a gaussian polymer, q^{-1} for a rigid-rod polymer.

Extrapolation at q=0 . In this range ($qR \ll 1$), the fluctuations of the number of polymers in a volume q^{-3} are obtained. In fact, the extrapolated value $S(o)$ is the quadratic mean square of n, $(\overline{n^2} - \overline{n}^2)$ and from this value one has access to the thermodynamical properties of the solution. If μ is the chemical potential we can write [9]

$$S(q)_{q \to 0} = S(o) = N^2 kT \left(\frac{\partial \mu}{\partial \overline{n}} \right)^{-1} \tag{6}$$

where T is the temperature and k the Boltzmann constant. For solutions, relation (6) becomes

$$S(o) = kTC \left(\frac{\partial \pi}{\partial C} \right)^{-1}$$ (7)

where π is the osmotic pressure of the solution and C the monomer concentration (C $\sim$ nN). These limit relations are a good meeting point for theoreticians and experimentalists.

1.2. The scattering power K^2

For polymer solutions Eq.(3) is valid for all radiations. But K is a function of the nature of the radiation-matter interaction.

For neutrons, K is an apparent coherent scattering length of the monomer in the medium

$$K = a_1 - a_o \frac{v_1}{v_o}$$ (8)

Only the nuclei of the atoms are concerned here and a_o can have positive or negative values. This reflects the nature of the nuclear interaction of neutron matter. So using a judicious pair solvent-solute, it is possible to have a_1 positive and a_o negative and thus obtain   a very large scattering power.

For photons, however, K is given by a difference between the absolute values of the corresponding parameters (the polarizability of elementary scatterers for light, their electron number for X rays). These quantities are only dependent on the electron shells of the atoms and reflect a property of the electromagnetic interaction between photons and matter. Then the values of the scattering power are small compared with those obtained with neutrons.

This difference will be the main feature of a labelling method. This method is essential to follow the conformation of a polymer in different environments (like other chains) as function of parameters such as temperature, concentration or charge. It consists in a change of the scattering power of a type of scatterer, the rest being unchanged. In photon techniques, this is only possible by changing the electron shells (i.e. by a chemical change of the polymer). But mixing polymers of different chemical species leads to a phase separation. Thus such method is not adequate. While in neutron scattering, isotopic substitution gives a labelling method which keeps the chemical properties unchanged.

For organic compounds the easiest method is the substitution of protons by deuterons. Deuteration has two advantages :On the one hand, this method has been applied for a long time in NMR experiments and as a result deuterated products are often easy to obtain. On the other hand, the change H-D leads to a large variation in the scattering power since the coherent scattering length of an hydrogen atom has a definite negative value ($a_H = -0.374 \times 10^{-12}$ cm) while it is positive for a deuteron ($a_D = +0.667 \times 10^{-12}$ cm).

Let us give an example : for a hydrogeneous polystyrene chain (PSH) in a good solvent CS_2 , the value of the scattering power K^2 is about 0.1, while for the same polymer deuterated (PSD) in the same solvent this value becomes about 70. Deuteration only has changed the intensity by a factor 700 !

So, with SANS, it is possible to observe the conformation of a PSD chain in very dilute solutions ($\sim 10^{-3}$ g cm^{-3}) , in semi-dilute solution for a PSD chain dispersed in a mixture of PSH and CS_2 and also in the bulk state of PSH chains.

This is why deuteration associated with SANS is now very often used in the field of polymer research. The first experiments were made with some D-polymers dispersed in a matrix of H-polymers (or the inverse). The data [10-14] are consistent with the predictions (see ref.1, for instance) of the random walk character of the conformation of a chain in the bulk state.

We will now illustrate the different labelling methods by some examples taken from actual polymer problems.

2. ACTUAL PHYSICAL PROBLEMS

In this section, we discuss some problems encountered in three domains of polymer research : for neutral polymers, one is interested in the determination of the conformation of the chain as a function of concentration and temperature. We emphasize about these studies since they serve as a reference for current polymer work. For hot stretched polymers the problem is a dynamical one : it raises the question of the correspondence between conformation and relaxation. For polyelectrolytes in solution, it is the influence of electrostatic interactions on polyelectrolyte conformations in solution is unknown.

Most of these old problems have not been solved yet because of the failure of classical techniques to observe a chain among other ones. There is no doubt that SANS will make an important contribution to their solutions.

2.1. Neutral polymer solutions

A well-known problem in polymer physics is the excluded-volume problem [1] (or self-avoiding walk problem [15] in the case of a single polymer chain). This is as follows:

The interaction potential between two monomers has a hard core at small distances, which prevents two segments from being at the same position. Let $V(r)$ be this potential. One can define a pseudo-potential [2] $v\,\delta(r)$ to describe this interaction :

$$v(T) \equiv \int (e^{-V(r)/kT} - 1)\ \ddot{d}_3 r \qquad (9)$$

$v(T)$ is the excluded-volume parameter and is temperature-dependent. For high temperatures, v is positive and the net interaction is repulsive. It has been shown that, apart from a narrow region around a special temperature Θ [1] defined by $v(\Theta) = 0$, this interaction cannot be treated as a perturbation [16]. For instance, it has been shown that the mean squared end-to-end distance [1,2] R^2 varies as

$$<R^2> \ \sim \ N^{2\nu}\,\ell^2 \qquad \text{(single coil)} \qquad (10)$$

where $\nu = 0.6$ rather than $\nu_G = 0.5$ for a gaussian, non-interacting coil, so that it is largely swollen. The corresponding solutions are said to be in a "good solvent" for this reason. As examples, carbon disulfide (CS_2) and benzene (C_6H_6) are good solvent of benzene since the room temperature is largely above Θ , while cyclohexane at 35°C is a theta solvent.

It has been proved recently that there is a strict analogy [17,18] between this problem (when N is very large) and the n-vector model [19] of critical phenomena, in the limit when n goes to zero.

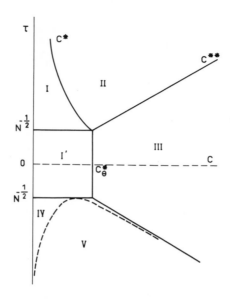

FIG.1.   *Temperature concentration diagram for neutral flexible polymer solutions.* $\tau = (T - \theta)/\theta$
*is the reduced temperature and c the monomer concentration. This diagram can be drawn by
applying the analogy between polymer solutions and critical phenomena. The different regions,
as discussed in the text, are: I, I' and IV: dilute solution; II and III: semi-dilute regions;
V: coexistence region.*

When the temperature is decreased, one finds that there is a narrow domain, around the Θ temperature, where the chain behaves as if it were
Gaussian [1]

$$<R^2> ~ N ~ \ell^2 \tag{11}$$

The solvent is said to be a theta solvent for these solutions. If we let N
go to infinity, this domain reduces to a point (T = 0 , C = 0) called the
theta point. In   analogy with critical phenomena, the theta point has
been related to a tricritical point [20].

If temperature is still lowered, the coil contracts into a dense sphere
[21]

$$<R^2> ~ N^{2/3} ~ \ell^2 \tag{12}$$

where the solvent is called a bad solvent, before a phase separation takes
place.

The very important property of the theta point allowed us to draw a diagram in a (τ,C) plane [22] (τ is the reduced temperature τ = (T-Θ)/Θ and
C is the monomer concentration). This diagram is shown in Fig.1. The lines

C^* and C^*_Θ separate the dilute region, which was discussed above and where the coils are far apart from the semi-dilute region where they overlap : one can define C^* by the condition that the radius of a chain is of the same order as the distance between the centers of gravity [23]

$$C^* \sim \frac{N}{R^3} \sim N^{1-3\nu} \, \ell^{-3} \tag{13}$$

In the following, we will be concerned with the evolution of the conformation of a coil both when temperature is varied (section 3) and when concentration is increased beyond C^* (section 4).

2.2. Polymers in stretched bulk

All the physical problems about stretched-bulk polystyrene have to deal with two concepts : conformation and relaxation. The problem is : at this point we know the conformation of chains in the bulk at rest [14] ; it is an isotropic three-dimension random walk of step ℓ (i.e. $\nu = 1/2$ in Eq.(10)). What will be the conformation when we stretch the polymer ?

Let us speak first about the technique of stretching. Sheets of polystyrene ($M \sim 10^5$) of $0.1 \times 2 \times 6$ cm^3 initial dimensions are uniaxially stretched above the glass transition temperature ($Tg \sim 100°C$) ; from the initial length L_o we obtain a length $L = \lambda L_o$ (where λ is the extension ratio) ; it is a rather big elongation ($\lambda \sim 3$ here but can reach 7) and an elastic deformation. If, after cooling, the sample is heated again above Tg without any strain, it reverses to its first length L_o and shape.

Under these conditions conformation is always the result of stretching and relaxation during the time of stretching. But we can get information about relaxation if, starting from the state of the sample cooled just after stretching, we let it relax by heating the sample again above Tg during various lengths of time. So the exploration of monomer correlation in a large range of distances - from ℓ to the length of the extended chain - should correspond to an exploration of the range of time of the relaxation spectrum. The basic theory of deformation is the affine (or homogeneous) one : each vector joining two links of the chain is deformed as a macroscopic vector, even for short distances between links. So, starting from the bulk, we obtain a three-dimensional random walk with a step $\ell_\perp = \ell/\sqrt{\lambda}$ in the perpendicular direction and $\ell_{//} = \lambda\ell$ in the parallel direction.

Already in 1942, Kuhn and Grün had observed [24] that the birefringence results could not be explained by an affine deformation down to the scale of the statistical segment, which would give an orientation, thus a birefringence much larger than observed. The response function of a chain stretched by the ends gives a very weak orientation [25,26]. From another point of view, a chain taken in a network will be affinely deformed down to the scale of the mesh of the network, and for shorter distances deformed with a weak orientation ; in our problem the other chains could play the role of the network.

So the question is : if the affine theory is not verified at all distances, at what distance does it fail ? By SANS this distance would appear to us as a scattering vector q^* of the corresponding cross-over of $S(q)$.

In conclusion, we will try to observe the shape of $S(q)$ in the intermediate range and the existence of a cross-over. The variation of q^* with relaxation by effect of temperature or time would give information about dynamical effects in these samples.

2.3. Polyelectrolytes

For linear polyelectrolytes, the situation is very different from that of neutral polymers. The dissociation of the ionizable groups in water leads to long-range electrostatic interactions between monomers, and the excluded-volume effects are usually neglected. This dissociation has two main consequences :

a) In dilute solutions (C<C*), linear polyions have been known [3] to have large overall dimensions and a fairly rigid conformation. This is an effect of the long-range interactions. However, in semi-dilute solutions, organization is still unknown and two models have been proposed :

- the lattice model of Lifson and Katchalsky [27] in which the chains, visualized as infinitely long rigid rods, are aligned and form a lattice ;
- the isotropic model of De Gennes et al. [28] of partially flexible chains. Each chain behaves as a succession of rigid segments of size ξ ; inside a segment the electrostatic forces are predominant while they are screened out between segments by the small counterions. At large scale each chain has an ideal behaviour.

So SANS should be a useful tool to differentiate between the models by studying the conformation and rigidity of the chains (both in Guinier and intermediate range) and their organization in semi-dilute solutions.

The presence of counterions in the solution leads to a high osmotic pressure, characteristic of polyelectrolyte solutions [29,30]. This osmotic incompressibility results from the electrical neutrality of the solution. The osmotic pressure can be written simply :

$$\Pi = \Pi_{polyions} + \Pi_{counterions} \tag{14}$$

or
$$\Pi = kT(n_p + n_p \nu \phi_p) \tag{15}$$

where n_p is the number of polyions per unit volume, ν the number of ionized groups and ϕ_p , an osmotic coefficient ; $\nu \phi_p$ is of the order of N , the degree of polymerization of the polyelectrolyte, so that

$$\Pi_{polyelectrolyte} \sim N \, \Pi_{neutral \, polymer} \tag{16}$$

The measured osmotic pressure of a polyelectrolyte solution is always large compared to that of a neutral polymer. Furthermore, when a simple electrolyte is added to the solution, the chains are progressively neutralized and the osmotic pressure falls rapidly. In scattering experiments the osmotic compressibility is directly observable from the scattered intensity extrapolated at zero angle (see Eq.(7)). So that, independently of the two models, S(q) should be small, at small q^s , and should increase when salt is added [3,35].

This second effect is well known of all experimentalists [29] ; however, no definite experiment has established the conformation of the chains or the organization of the solution yet.

3. IMPROVED CONTRAST

Here one wants to make the best choice of solvent-solute system for the greatest value of the apparent coherent scattering length K (see Eq.(3)), i.e. a good intensity. This is often obtained by deuteration of all solvent molecules or all polymer chain molecules. Since isotopic substitution does not change the properties of the system, it is not different from the one

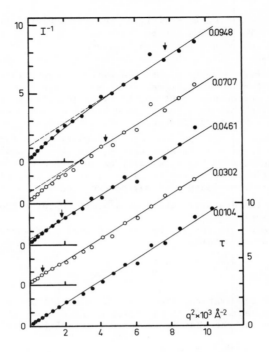

FIG.2. Inverse scattered intensity versus q^2 for dilute solutions at different values of the reduced temperature in region I. One can see a departure from linearity for low values of q, corresponding to the excluded-volume behaviour (see Section 3). The q^2 behaviour can only be interpreted with the criticality analogy. These data were recorded at Saclay.

studied by light or X-rays. Nevertheless, with the gain in contrast one can work with more dilute solutions than it is possible with X-rays and further-more explore a larger q range than is accessible by light scattering.

These are the advantages of SANS with the method of improved contrast. Let us apply it to polymer problems.

3.1. Neutral polymers

As a first example of this method, let us focus on the dilute regimes of polymer solutions. As has been said in section 2, the different coils are far apart from each other in these regions (I, I' and IV in the diagram, Fig.1). So, in what follows, all the experiments are done at a fixed value of the concentration and by varying the temperature. The system which is studied is a solution of (hydrogenated) polystyrene dissolved in a good sol-vent, the deuterated benzene C_6D_6, with a concentration $C = 0.4 \times 10^{-2}$ g cm^{-3}, lower than the overlap concentration C^* (the molecular weight of the chains is 3.8×10^6).

The inverse scattered intensity, $S^{-1}(q)$ is displayed in Fig.2 as a function of q^2 . Two domains can be observed :
- for high values of q , the curve is linear,
- for lower values of q , there is a departure from linearity.

The different curves have been obtained with different values of the reduced temperature. For the first time, it is shown experimentally that even for one polymer chain in a solution, the behaviour is not uniform, and one has to distinguish between a large-scale behaviour and a small-scale behaviour. Each one is quite different.

This q^2 dependence of the scattered intensity needs further explanations. In order to give an interpretation, let us give some basic properties of the diagram [22], Fig.1. We will be concerned with regions II and III in next section. Let us now focus on dilute regimes. As temperature is varied, different behaviours [31] may be expected :

At very low temperatures, there is a "demixion" curve (domain V is a coexistence region).

When temperature is raised, we get into region IV where the coils collapsed into dense spheres

$$<R^2> ~ \left(\frac{N}{\tau} \right)^{2/3} \tag{17}$$

Around the $\cap$ temperature, there is a domain (I') where the behaviour is called "theta behaviour". It is nearly Gaussian, but if one looks at the analogy, one can see that it is in fact tricritical :

$$<R^2> ~ N \ell^2 \tag{11}$$

$$S(q) ~ q^{-2} \tag{18}$$

Notice that this region extends both above and below C .

For high temperatures, the behaviour is critical [17]:

$$<R^2> ~ N^{2\nu} \tau^{2(2\nu-1)} \ell^2 \tag{19}$$

It was believed that in the intermediate range $(R^{-1} < q < \ell^{-1})$ the scattered intensity should be [32] :

$$S(q) ~ q^{-1/\nu} \tag{20}$$

This is region I in the diagram. The experiments shown in Fig.3 were performed in this region. Their results are in contradiction to this last relation. This apparent contradiction can be solved if we interpret the experiments with the help of the relationship between the theta point and a tricritical point. We can give a scaling approach to the function S(q) :

$$S(q,\tau,N^{-1}) = \tau^{-2} f \left(\frac{1}{N\tau^2} , \frac{q}{\tau} \right) \tag{21}$$

In region (I), the first variable in the function f is much less than unity. Then the behaviour of the intensity depends only on the value of the second variable. This introduces naturally a cross-over value for the momentum transfer:

$$q^* ~ \tau ~ \xi^{-1} \tag{22}$$

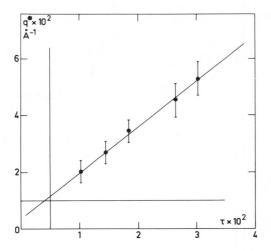

FIG.3. *Cross-over q* versus temperature. q* corresponds to the cross-over between typical*
q^2 *and* $q^{5/3}$ *behaviour of* $S^{-1}(q)$ *(see Fig. 2) occurring in dilute solutions in a good solvent.*

For high values of q (q >> τ) one is led to

$$S(q,\tau,N^{-1}) \sim q^{-2} \tag{23}$$

whereas for low values (q<<τ) one has to make a change of variables [33]:

$$\left.\begin{array}{l} N' = N\tau^2 \\[4pt] q' = \dfrac{q}{\tau} \end{array}\right\} \tag{24}$$

and introduce the critical exponents :

$$S\left(\frac{1}{N\tau^2}, \frac{q}{\tau}\right) = \bar{S}\left(\frac{1}{N'}, q'\right)$$

$$\sim q'^{-1/\nu} f\left(\frac{1}{N'q'^{1/\nu}}\right)$$

and, by using Eq.(24) and Eq.(21),

$$S(q,\tau,N^{-1}) = q^{-1/\nu} \tau^{-2+1/\nu} g\left(\frac{\tau^{-2+1/\nu}}{N q^{1/\nu}}\right) \tag{25}$$

which in turn leads to the variations of the radius of gyration of a chain
(cf. ref.[22]) and to the behaviour of the scattered intensity in the
intermediate range $(R^{-1} << q << \xi^{-1})$:

$$S \sim q^{-1/\nu} \tau^{-2+1/\nu} \tag{26}$$

The curves shown in Fig.2 are in good agreement with Eqs (23) and (26).
Moreover, one can determine the experimental values of the cross-over q^*
from one of these regimes to the other. This is shown on Fig.3 and is in

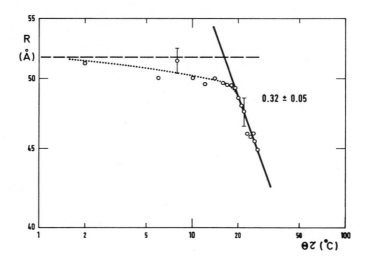

FIG.4. Log-log plot of radius of gyration R of a small hydrogenous polystyrene chain as a function of the temperature θ. The solvent used in deuterated cyclohexane (θ = 38°C). The cross-over is clearly seen when passing from region I' to region IV of the diagram Fig. 1. The corresponding cross-over temperature θ = 19°C is in good agreement with previous experimental results [31].

agreement with Eq.(22). So these curves strongly confirm the equivalence which has been established between flexible polymer solutions and critical phenomena [17].

In order to complete the study of these dilute regimes, we have plotted in Fig.4 the results of an experiment which has been performed at lower temperatures and shows a cross-over between regions (I') and (IV) of the diagram. This experiment has been done with polystyrene dispersed in deuterated cyclqhexane (Θ = 38°C). In order to have larger regions, the molecular weight chosen for the polymer chains were small (M_W = 25 500). More experimental details of this study, made at Saclay using the set-up described in ref.[14], will be published elsewhere.

Fig.4 shows the variation of the radius of gyration of a chain versus temperature. (This experiment has been done in the Guinier range, qR << 1). It allows an experimental check of the passage from relation (11) to relation (17). Let us note that this is the first time that relation (17) is checked experimentally and that this experiment can be performed only by SANS because one has to use lower molecular weights to have larger regions, which can be reached experimentally ; this implies a lower radius of gyration, which can be measured by SANS only.

3.2. Polymers in stretched bulk

In that case we observed pure polystyrene in the bulk state and all the monomers have the same coherent scattering length. In the concerned

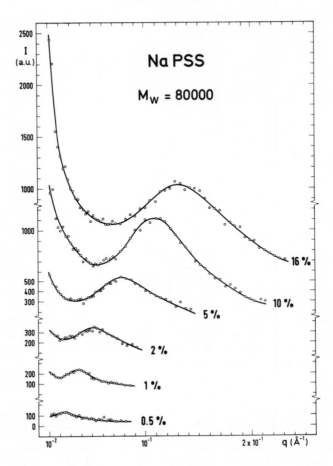

FIG.5. Scattered intensity per monomer of a solution of hydrogenated sulphonated polystyrene (NaPSS_H of molecular weight 80 000) in D_2O versus concentration for monomer concentrations ranging from $5 \times 10^{-3}\,g\cdot cm^{-3}$ to $1.6 \times 10^{-1}\,g\cdot cm^{-3}$. Notice the central scattering which is not observed, Fig.6. These data were recorded at Saclay ($\lambda = 4.7\,\overset{\circ}{A}$, $\Delta\lambda/\lambda = 5 \times 10^{-3}$).

q range ($q\ell \lesssim 1$) , there are no fluctuations of density because of the incompressibility of the bulk. So the probability $P(r)$ (see Eq.(4)) is reduced to a constant proportional to the bulk density ; then $S(q) = 0$ for $0 < q \lesssim \ell^{-1}$. The only possibility of obtaining a non-zero intensity lies in the labelling of monomers among the other ones (see sections 4 and 5).

3.3. Polyelectrolytes

The experiments described here have been performed at Saclay and at ILL in the intermediate range (3×10^{-3} to 10^{-1} Å^{-1}) with sulfonated polystyrene (sodium salt). Two systems have been studied : hydrogenated chains (PSS$_H$) dissolved in D_2O and deuterated chains (PSS$_D$) dissolved in H_2O .

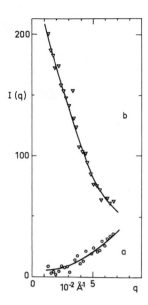

FIG.6.   Intensity scattered by a solution of $3 \times 10^{-2} g \cdot cm^{-3}$ of deuterated sulphonated polystyrene (NaPSS$_D$ of molecular weight 72 000) in H_2O as a function of q; (a) without added salt and (b) with salt added to the same solution. On the lower curve, the maximum is not seen since the q range studied is too small.

The scattered intensity $I(q)$ is shown in Fig.5 for the system PSS$_H$ + D$_2$O   at different polymer concentrations. Its characteristics are a broad maximum and a surprising high value for $I(q \to 0)$. The latter was a puzzle until great care was taken that the solution contained no foreign small ions. Deuterated sulfonated polystyrene dissolved in ultrapure H$_2$O (electrical resistivity of 1.8×10^7 Ω/cm) and contained in quartz cells only yields a very small intensity at small q-values. Fig.6 shows the scattered intensity $I(q)$ as a function of q for a salt-free solution (a) and when salt has been purposely added (b). In salt-free solutions the very small intensity extrapolated at zero angle shows the high osmotic pressure of the solution which disappears with addition of salt. Therefore, the absence of added ions is an essential factor for observing the real response function of a solution of polyelectrolyte.

The broad maximum mentioned above had been observed by SANS for another polyelectrolyte of small molecular weight only [34] ; it appears here for all molecular weights and concentrations. Its behaviour has been studied as a function of polymer concentration (5×10^{-3} g·cm^{-3} < c < 1.6×10^{-1} g·cm^{-3}) , molecular weight M (30 000 to 800 000) and ionic strength of the solution. It shows that :
 - the position of the peak varies as $c^{1/2}$, where c is the monomer concentration (Fig.7)[1]:

---

[1]   If it is M-dependent, this dependence is rather weak and has to be verified by other experiments.

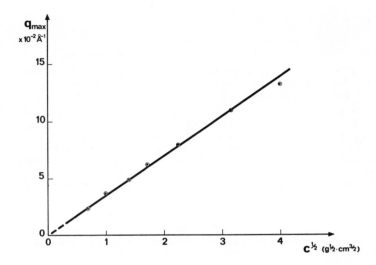

FIG. 7.   Plot of q_{max}-value at which the maximum in $I(q)$ occurs at different concentrations c as a function of the square root of c.

   - it disappears when the electrostatic forces are screened out by addition of a simple electrolyte (salt) ;
   - on the high-q side of the peak and far from it, I(q) varies as l/q , showing the rigidity of the chains at short distances ;
   - no other peak is visible at different q's.

   Although the possibility of a rigid lattice seems ruled out, these results don't allow us to choose a model, and further experiments using a few labelled chains in an unlabelled matrix, both in the intermediate and Guinier range, will give more information on the conformation of the chains and their organization in the solution. This requires other techniques which will be discussed in the next section.

4. SELECTIVE LABELLING

   This is the method used to observe the conformation of a polymer in different environments. In fact, two possibilities are open :

   The first one corresponds to the deuteration of a few chains among analogous hydrogenous chains. It is the method used for studies in the bulk state where Eq.(3) is still valid. The situation is more complex if one wants to determine the conformation of one chain among the other ones and the solvent. Even if we label a few chains, Eq.(3) has to be generalized. This is easy [7], following the treatment given in section 1. In the simple case of two types of scatterers in the solvent, Eq.(3) becomes

$$I(q) = K_D^2 S_D(q) + K_H^2 S_H(q) + 2 K_H K_D S_{DH}(q) \qquad (27)$$

where K_D^2 and $S_D(q)$ are the scattering power and the scattering functions of deuterated polymers, K_H^2 and $S_H(q)$ those of hydrogenous one. $S_{DH}(q)$ is the interference term. The problem here is to obtain the response function of one type of polymer chain only, $S_D(q)$ for instance.

If we are lucky, it is possible to find a solvent, of physical interest, such that the K_H value would be zero. It is the case for PSD in a mixture of PSH dispersed in a good solvent, carbon disulfide CS_2 .

But, in most cases, this is not possible and then the problem of the separation of conformational terms $S_D(q)$, $S_H(q)$ and $S_{HD}(q)$ from technical ones K_H and K_D in Eq.(27) is raised. A powerful tool is provided by the "contrast variation" method which may be viewed as a generalization of the preceding one. It consists in varying the coherent scattering length of the solvent molecules by mixing, at concentration x , natural (a_H) and deuterated (a_D) molecules. Thus the mean coherent scattering length of the solvent is given by :

$$a_o(x) \; = \; x \; a_H \; + \; (1-x) \; a_D$$

The simple variation of x leads to a linear change of values of the apparent scattering length $K_H(x)$ and $K_D(x)$. Following this method it is now possible to separate in Eq.(27) the conformational and the technical terms. This technique has been used for a long time in light [36] and X-ray [37] experiments. It is now useful for structural studies of biological molecules [5,38] by neutron scattering. For this last case, mixtures of heavy and light water are easy to obtain and lead , from x = 0 to 1 , to a wide range of contrast variation. The preservation of the chemical properties of the solvent is here also a great advantage of SANS. The method has been also tested [39] with success in order to separate the conformation of the two sequences of a copolymer in solution.

4.1. Neutral polymer solutions

In order to illustrate the first selective deuteration technique, let us come back to our polymer solutions. If we start from the dilute solutions (regions I or I' in diagram, Fig.1) and increase the concentration, the different molecules overlap (regions II and III) because of their flexibility. It is then very interesting to know the behaviour of one chain in this kind of solutions. This can be done by labelling a small proportion of the chains in solution by deuteration.

The following experiments lead to measurement of the radius of gyration of a chain in the semi-dilute region II [23]. They have been performed in the Guinier range (qR<<1). The results were obtained by the usual Zimm plot technique. The system consists in some totally deuterated polystyrene (PSD) chains dissolved in a mixture of hydrogenated polystyrene (PSH) in CS_2 . The total concentration C is larger than the overlap concentration C^* while the concentration C_D of labelled chains is much less than C^*. Two different molecular weights were used (1.14×10^5 and 5×10^5). The results are displayed on Fig.5. They show that the squared radius of gyration is proportional to the molecular weight and varies with concentration as a power law :

$$R^2 \; \sim \; N \; C^x$$

$$x \; = \; - \; 0.25 \pm 0.02 \tag{28}$$

Here again these results are in contradiction with the usual predictions [1] that the radius of gyration of a chain should be proportional to the

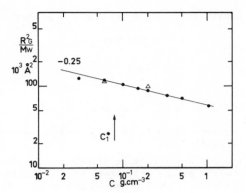

FIG.8. *Squared radius of gyration divided by molecular weight as a function of monomer concentration c in a log-log plot. These data were recorded on the D11 SANS apparatus of ILL (Grenoble). These values have been obtained in the Guinier range from samples of PSD dissolved in a mixture of PSH and CS$_2$. The R values have been obtained from zero extrapolation of the PSD concentration. They were done twice, using two different molecular weights (●: M = 114 000; △: M = 500 000). Obviously, there is no dependence on molecular weight and a power law dependence on c prevails.*

square root of the molecular weight (which is satisfied) and independent of concentration (which is not satisfied). So another interpretation has to be given to these experimental results. The magnetic analogy used for dilute solutions [17] has been extended to this end [18] : it has been shown that the polymer concentration $C_p \equiv C/N$ is related to an applied (external) magnetic field in this analogy [18].

Thus we can apply scaling arguments to find the different lengths, as has been done for dilute solutions. One can show that the radius of gyration may be put into the scaled form [23] :

$$R \sim N^\nu \ell \, f\left(\frac{C}{C^*}\right) \tag{29}$$

where $C^* \sim N^{1-3\nu} \ell^{-3}$ is the overlap concentration.

In semi-dilute solutions, where $C \gg C^*$, the function f(x) has a power law behaviour

$$f(x) \sim x^a \tag{30}$$

leading to

$$R \sim N^{\nu-a(1-3\nu)} \, C^a$$

If we now impose a Gaussian variation for the N dependence of R , we find

$$\frac{1}{2} = \nu - a(1-3\nu)$$

i.e.

$$a = \frac{2\nu - 1}{2(1-3\nu)}$$

and

$$<R^2> \sim N \, C^{\frac{2\nu-1}{1-3\nu}} \approx N \, C^{-1/4} \qquad (31)$$

Thus we recover an exponent which is in very good agreement with what has been observed experimentally.

A physical interpretation of this behaviour may be given as follows : One may consider the chain as the trajectory of a particle. This particle has a large number of contacts with other chains (i.e. other particles) in the solution. At each contact, it is scattered in a random direction. So after a certain number of contacts (i.e. if we consider a distance much bigger than its mean free path), it has completely forgotten its original path. This leads to a Gaussian behaviour for the N dependence of R (N plays the role of time in the analogy). As we just said, one is also led to introduce another length ξ in the problem (associated to the mean free path of our particle). For lengths less than ξ our picture leads to a free particle, i.e. a chain with excluded volume, whereas if we take ξ as an elementary step, the behaviour is Gaussian. All these features have indeed been checked experimentally by SANS associated with total deuteration technique (cf. section 3).

Let us finally quote that all the domains of the diagram in Fig. 1 have been observed [40] by SANS, including region III. The latter is a region where [41] the coils overlap, but have locally (for $r \ll \xi$) the same behaviour as in region I' (see section 3).

4.2. Polymers in stretched bulk

The main part of the results have been obtained by selective deuteration [42]. The samples consist of some C_D ($C_D = 0.75\%$ to 6%) completely deuterated chains and $1-C_D$ protonated chains. If $C_D < C_D^*$, where C_D^* is the overlapping concentration beyond which two deuterated chains overlap - $C_D \sim 7\%$ for $M = 10^5$ - we observe the signal of a chain among the other chains.
First we have verified there is no influence of the value of C_D (if $C_D < C_D^*$).

In Guinier range, we have obtained the size of $R_\perp$ in perpendicular direction which are written in Table I. For any temperature, they are equal to $R = R_0/\sqrt{\lambda}$: the affine theory is verified at the scale above and near $R_\perp \sim 50 \text{Å}$.

In the intermediate range we obtain the variation of the intensity versus the scattering vector : we use the representation $1/I$ versus q^2 because :
1) the bulk at rest gives [14] a straight line, the slope is proportional to the square of the step-length ℓ^2 ;
2) if the deformation is affine, we should have in perpendicular and parallel directions two straight lines of slope ℓ^2/λ and $\lambda^2\ell^2$.

The affine theory is roughly verified for an unrelaxed sample stretched at 110°C, Fig. 9.

TABLE I. VARIATION OF R IN THE PERPENDICULAR
DIRECTION FOR DIFFERENT TEMPERATURES OF
STRETCHING.

We always find $R \cong R_0/\sqrt{\lambda}$; since $R_0 \cong 95$ Å, the affinity is verified.
The values are extracted from the results of diffusion on the ILL, D11 spectrometer.

Temperature of stretching	115 [°C]	120 [°C]	130 [°C]	140 [°C]
$R \sqrt{\lambda_L}$ [Å]	100	95	98	102

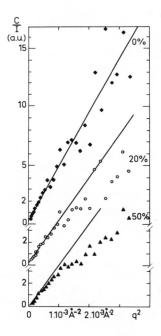

FIG.9. Inverse intensity versus q^2, for the sample stretched at $110°C$ and not relaxed. The
linear q^2 dependence is characteristic for an affine deformation. On the contrary, for the two
relaxed samples (20% and 50% of relative stress decreasing), we observe a departure from the
straight line. These data where obtained at ILL on the D17 spectrometer ($\lambda = 9.9$ Å,
$\Delta\lambda/\lambda = 10\%$).

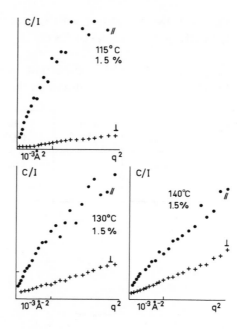

FIG.10.   From the same set of data, observed influence of stretching temperature and
comparison with the $110°C$ stretched sample.   There is a "loss of affinity" increasing with
stretching temperature.

For higher temperatures, it is not verified. A cross-over appears :
there is a departure from linearity of C/I versus q^2 (Fig.10) ; this leads
to a value of q^*. In this case, it is difficult to distinguish between
the effects of different temperature-dependent phenomena (see section 2).

A cross-over can also be observed for samples stretched at 110°C, quenched, heated again and relaxed ; in contradistinction to the uniform behaviour of the unrelaxed sample, we get a cross-over which is here clearly
related to relaxation.

Finally, Fig.11 shows the results for a completely relaxed sample :
it has reverted to isotropic bulk conformation. The comparison with a sample stretched at 180°C is striking. The parallel (//) and perpendicular (⊥)
response functions become parallel for high q value ; thus small-distance
behaviour is still isotropic while orientational effects appear only for
large distances.

The treatment of such data in order to obtain quantitative results is
still going on.

4.3. Polyelectrolytes

An original example of the contrast variation technique is provided
by polyelectrolyte solutions. The problem was whether the central peak

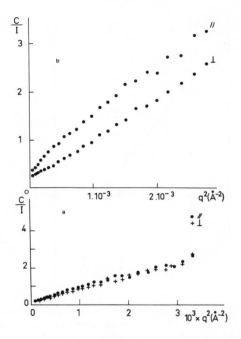

FIG.11. Effect of time during which the sample relaxes: (a) completely relaxed sample;
(b) temperature effect: the sample has again been heated up to 180°C.

(see section 3) is due to the chains (i.e. is the system homogeneous) or
to some sort of unknown impurity X (dust, for instance) forming a two-
component solute (NaPSS + X) . In the presence of such impurities, the
scattering intensity would be

$$I(q) = K_P^2 S_P(q) + K_X^2 S_X(q) + 2 K_X K_P S_{PX}(q) \tag{32}$$

and not

$$I(q) = K_P^2 S_P(q) \tag{33}$$

as expected. Here P and X are indexes which characterize the functions of
polyelectrolytes and impurities, respectively.

In order to solve this problem, we used mixture of x percent of heavy
water and (1-x) percent of light water. The calculated value of x which
gives a zero value of $K_P(x)$ is about 30% . In the experiments, x was varied from zero to one. The resulting intensity of the central peak was
varying in the same way as that of the rest of the signal and was about
zero for x = 0.3 (Fig.12). Therefore the signal observed at small q values
was only due to the polyions, thus Eq.(33) is valid.

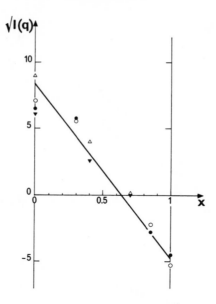

FIG.12. Square root of intensity measured at different q values as a function of solvent composition $xH_2O + (1 - x)D_2O$. The $K_p(x)$ value is extinguished for an x value very close to 0.7, the calculated value. The dots correspond to $NaPSS_H$ of a molecular weight of 8×10^4 measured at $q = 2.9 \times 10^{-2} \text{ Å}^{-1}$ ($\bullet$) and $q = 5.8 \times 10^{-2} \text{ Å}^{-1}$ ($\circ$); triangles to $NaPSS_H$ of a molecular weight of 8×10^5 measured at q values of $2.4 \times 10^{-2} \text{ Å}^{-1}$ ($\blacktriangledown$) and $1.4 \times 10^{-2} \text{Å}^{-1}$ ($\triangle$).

5. PARTIAL LABELLING OF ALL CHAINS

In this last section we enter in the perspective part of this paper. Let us develop it with the help of examples.

5.1. Neutral polymer chains

A point of interest is the following : are the polymer chains in the bulk state totally interpenetrated ? i.e. do the centers of mass of chains behave as a perfect gas ?

The experimental answer will be given using a bulk polymer with some labelled monomers at the center of each chain. If we assume that the central deuterated monomers of a chain are never far away from its center of mass, we have materialized this last one. The pseudo-copolymer used PSH-PSD-PSH (sample HDH 1) is composed of three sequences of the same molecular weight (13 000). From a chemical point of view it is a homopolymer. From SANS, the bulk of such chains is a solution of little PSD chains inside a medium of PSH monomers.

Fig.13 shows the scattering intensity obtained with this sample. The set-up used at Saclay is described in ref.[14]. The most striking result of Fig.13 is the presence of a peak (or a bump) of intensity. A similar result is obtained with an analogous pseudo-copolymer (HDH 2) composed of the same deuterated central part but with wings nine times longer.

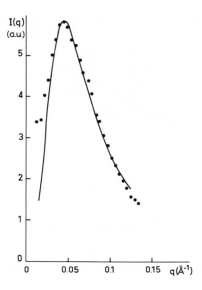

FIG.13. Plot of I(q) versus scattering vector q. These data have been obtained with the sample HDH1 where all chains have a deuterated central part. The full line is a curve calculated by using Eq.(34). Obviously, the fit is rather good.

In order to interpret this peak, we use the theoretical prediction [6] of de Gennes. In his paper, the intensity scattered by a solid sample of chains all partially labelled is given. The impossibility of having two monomers at the same point is taken into account by a mean interaction deduced from a random-phase approximation associated with the incompressibility of the bulk state.

Following this treatment we obtain :

$$S(X) = \frac{2n\ N_D^2}{\mu^2\ X^2} \left\{ [e^{-\mu X} - 1 + \mu X] - \frac{\left[\mu X + e^{-\frac{1-\mu}{2}X}(e^{-\mu X} - 1) \right]^2}{e^{-\mu X} - 1 + X} \right\} \quad (34)$$

where $X = q^2 R^2$ and $\mu = N_D/N$, R is the radius of gyration of one pseudo-copolymer of N links which contain N_D deuterated links.

The data are fitted with this expression where the only parameter of the fit is R . The result is the full line drawn on Fig.13. The R value deduced from the fit is 56 Å. This value is in good agreement with the value of 60 Å for such a polystyrene chain (M = 39 000) in the bulk [14]. For the other sample (HDH 2), the fit is not good, the calculated bump is narrower than the experimental one. This poor agreement can be explained from the polydispersity (i.e. the weight distribution) of the wings since strong effects of polydispersity have been seen [43] on bisequential copolymers in solution.

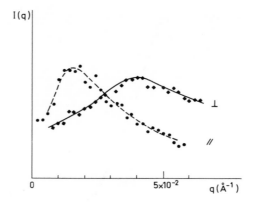

FIG.14. Scattering intensity by the sample HDH₂ where all chains are all-partially labelled versus the scattering vector q. The strong effect of the stretching on the peak is clearly seen. The parallel (‖) and perpendicular (⊥) response functions are very different. The treatment of all curves has not yet been carried out; full lines are eye guides only.

Thus the peak indicates a repulsion of the labelled monomers in the bulk state. This phenomenon has been predicted and discussed in terms of "correlation hole" in refs.[6] and [23].

A practical consequence of these experiments is the possibility of determining the radius of gyration of a chain from the position of a peak of intensity. It is relatively easy since the great number of labelled monomers leads to a good intensity. Another advantage derives from the peak position which is a more accessible q range because the q position of the maximum is, in fact, matched to the size of the labelled part of the chain. If these remarks are of rather poor interest for neutral polymers, at rest, this is not the case for stretched polymers and polyelectrolytes.

5.2. Polymers in stretched bulk

For these samples, the selective labelling method requires both a very long time of exposure in the neutron beam and a very small q range. The first requirement is necessary to reduce the dispersion of the data. It is a consequence of the anisotropy of stretched samples since different parallel and perpendicular response functions are found. The second one derives from the large value of the radius of gyration (∼ 300 Å) in the direction of extension.

From the experimental point of view, the method of all partially labelled chains is already of greater interest than the last one because of advantages cited at the beginning of this section.

From a theoretical point of view it would be possible to observe just a part of the chains and to vary the labelled length with respect to other characteristic distances : such as mean distance between two entanglements or distances related to a characteristic relaxation time.

Until now just a test experiment has been done using the SANS facilities of D17 (ILL). The sample used is the long wing pseudo-copolymer (HDH 2) because a great molecular weight is necessary to a good extension. The value of the extension ratio $\lambda = L/L_o$ is three. It was obtained with a stretching temperature of 120°C.

Fig.14 shows the variation of intensity along the perpendicular and parallel directions. One can notice the great differences between their behaviours. The locus of the maxima, in the XY plane of the multidetector used at D17, is an ellipse which confirms the affinity at this distance range. The whole variation of the intensity raises a problem of interpretation which is not yet solved.

6. CONCLUDING REMARKS

In order to conclude it is perhaps not necessary to insist again on the interest of SANS in the field of polymer physics but a few remarks have to be made:

i) In this brief review the important studies of crystallized polymers (such as polyethylene) have not been mentioned since they are discussed at this conference [44].

ii) Only few experimental details have been given. The reason is that the experimental curves have been shown here only as examples of the technique. Moreover, most of them are recent and will be the subject of more detailed publications.

iii) For the all partially labelled chains, it is important to insist on the necessity of taking into account the polydispersity of each sequence of the pseudo-copolymer. This is the feature that makes application of this method difficult.

Acknowledgments

We wish to thank Dr. D. Sadler for fruitful discussions about Fig.13, Drs. M. Roth and R. Gosh for their help in the acquisition and treatment of the data at ILL, A. Bousquet and C. Etter for their assistance at Saclay and Strasbourg.

REFERENCES

[1]   FLORY, P.J., "Principles of Polymer Chemistry" Cornell. Univ. Press New York (1966)
[2]   EDWARDS, S.F., Proc. Phys. Soc. 85 (1965) 613
[3]   OOSAWA, F., "Poly-electrolyter" M. Dekker, Inc. N.Y. (1971)
      TANFORD C., "Physical Chemistry of Macromolecules" Wiley N.Y. (1969)
[4]   SCHMATZ, W. et al., J. Appl. Cryst. 7 (1974) 96
[5]   JACROT, B., Rep. Progr. Physics, 39 (1976) 911
[6]   de GENNES, P.G., J. de Physique, 31 (1970) 235
[7]   COTTON J.P., BENOIT, H., J. de Phys. 36 (1975) 905
[8]   GUINIER, A., "Théorie et Technique de la Radiocristallographie", Dunod (1964)
[9]   EGELSTAFF, P.A., "An Introduction to the Liquid State", Academic Press (1967)
[10] KIRSTE, R.G. et al., Makromol. Chem. 162 (1973) 299
[11] BALLARD, D.G. et al., Eur. Polym. J. 9 (1973) 965
[12] LIESER, D.G. et al., Polymer letters, 13 (1975) 39
[13] ALLEN, G., in "Structural Studies of Macromolecules by Spectroscopic Methods", K.J. Ivin Ed. Wiley (1974)

[14] COTTON, J.P. et al., Macromolecules, 7 (1974) 863
[15] FISHER, M.E., J. Chem. Phys. 44 (1966) 616
[16] FIXMAN, M. J. Chem. Phys. 23 (1955) 1656
[17] de GENNES, P.G., Phys. Lett. 38A (1972) 339
[18] des CLOIZEAUX, J., J. de Phys. 36 (1975) 281
[19] STANLEY, H.E., "Introduction to Phase Transitions and Critical Pheno-
     mena", Clarendon Press (1971)
[20] de GENNES, P.G., J. de Phys. Letters, 36 (1975) p.55
[21] MOORE, M.A., J. Phys. A, 10 (1977) 305
[22] DAOUD, M., JANNINK, G., J. de Phys. 37 (1976) 973
[23] DAOUD, M. et al., Macromolecules, 8 (1975) 804
[24] KUHN, V.W., GRÜN , F., Kolloid Zeit. (1942) 248
[25] ROE, R.J., KRIGBAUM, W.R., J. Appl. Phys. 35 (1961) 2215
[26] de VRIES, A.J., BONNEBAT, C., private communication
[27] LIFSON, S., KATCHALSKY, A., J. Polym. Sc. 13 (1954) 43
[28] de GENNES, P.G., PINCUS, P., VELASCO, R.M., BROCHARD, F., J. de Phys.
     37 (1976) 1461
[29] KATCHALSKY, A., ALEXANDROWICZ, Z., KEDEM, O., "Chemical Physics of
     Ionic Solutions", Conway and Barradas, Ed. Wiley (1966)
[30] TAKAHASHI, A., KATO, N., NAGASAWA, M., J. Phys. Chem. 14 (1970) 944
[31] COTTON, J.P. et al., J. Chem. Phys. 65 (1976) 1101
[32] EDWARDS, S.F., Proc. Phys. Soc. 88 (1966) 265
[33] HANKEY, A., STANLEY, H.E., Phys. Rev. 36 (1972) 3515
[34] MOAN, M., Thesis - Brest (1976)
     COTTON, J.P., MOAN, M., J. de Physique Letters, 37 (1976) L75
[35] PFEUTY, P., J. de Physique, Colloque de Poitier in press.
[36] For example : STRAZIELLE, C., "Light Scattering from Polymer Solutions"
     HUGLIN M.B., Ed. Acad. Press p.635 (1972)
[37] STUHRMANN, H.B., KIRSTE, R.G., Z. Phys. Chem. 56 (1967) 335
[38] LUZZATTI, V. et al., Mol. Biol. 101 (1976) 115
[39] DUVAL, M., et al., Polymer letters 14 (1976) 586
[40] FARNOUX, B., Thesis, Ann. de Phys. 1 (1976) 73
[41] DAOUD, M., Thesis, Paris VI, University (1977)
[42] BOUE, F., University Thesis, University of L. Pasteur, Strasbourg (1977)
[43] IONESCU, L., Thesis, University of L. Pasteur, Strasbourg (1977)
[44] SCHELTEN, J., SCHMATZ, W., BALLARD, D.G.H, This Conference.

DISCUSSION

T. SPRINGER: An essential factor in the method of partial deuteration
is the assumption that non-deuterated and deuterated polymer chains have the
same physical behaviour. How far is this assumption justified?

J.P. COTTON: In the case of low molecular weight ($M \lesssim 10^6$) similar
behaviour has been observed for deuterated polystyrene inside a hydrogenous
matrix and also for the converse system. For long chains, of molecular weight
above 2 or 3 million, one can calculate from the mixing enthalpy, which is
M-dependent, that segregation should occur. However, we have not done any
experiments with such high molecular weights.

NON-PERIODIC MOLECULAR MOTIONS
IN THE MODIFICATIONS C AND D
OF UNIAXIALLY ORIENTED n-C$_{33}$H$_{68}$

D. RICHTER
Institut für Festkörperforschung der
  Kernforschungsanlage Jülich GmbH,
Jülich

B. EWEN
Institut für physikalische Chemie,
Universität Mainz,
Mainz,
Federal Republic of Germany

Abstract

NON-PERIODIC MOLECULAR MOTIONS IN THE MODIFICATIONS C AND D OF
UNIAXIALLY ORIENTED n-C$_{33}$H$_{68}$.
    The paraffin n-C$_{33}$H$_{68}$ undergoes three solid-solid phase transitions between room
temperature and the melting point. Each of these phases is considered to be the response
of the crystal lattice to the onset of specific types of molecular motions. In the two highest
phases, called C and D, the molecular motions have been investigated by quasi-elastic neutron
scattering using uniaxially oriented samples. The following results have been obtained: In
the C-phase, translational jumps over one CH$_2$-unit and rotational 180° jumps take place
independently. The jump rates at T = 67°C are $v_{rot} = 4 \pm 2 \times 10^7 \, s^{-1}$ and $v_{trans} = 2.1 \pm 0.4$
$\times 10^8 \, s^{-1}$. In the D-phase, the chains perform rigid rod-like rotations with $D_{rot} = 6.0 \times 10^{10} \, s^{-1}$.
In addition, translational diffusion with a diffusion constant of $D_{trans} = 1.0 \times 10^{-5} \, cm^2 \cdot s^{-1}$
was found. This translational diffusion is limited to a spatial extension of $\pm 4.5 \pm 0.5$ Å.

1.   INTRODUCTION

    Considerable effort has been spent in the investigation of
the complex solid phase behaviour exhibited by the paraffines
/1-6/. The relation between structure and molecular reorientation
in n-alkane crystals was analyzed in detail in the case of
n-C$_{33}$H$_{68}$ /3-6/. This n-alkane exhibits four stable modifications
(A, B,C,D) between room temperature and the melting point T$_m$ =
71.8 C . The phases are charaterized by different types of molecular disorder and can be regarded as the response of the
crystal lattice to the onset of specific types of molecular motion.

589

In the A-phase, the paraffin crystals have a well ordered orthorhombic structure containing neither interfacial nor intra-chain defects in detectable quantities /5/. NMR-investigations /6/ of the second moment as a function of γ, the angle between the texture axis and the direction of the static magnetic field, indicate, together with dielectric measurements on polar deriva-tives where a similar NMR behaviour is observed /7/, that 90° jumps of the chains around their axes are active.

The phase transition from the A-phase to the B-phase (at T = 54.5°C) is accompanied by a sudden drop of the second moment. The angular dependence of the second moment suggests the onset of 180° jumps around the chain axes /6, 9/. X-ray investigations /5/ show that the lamellar structure remains perfect in this phase, while the orientational long-range order of the chain planes is lost. In order to understand the observed rotational short range order it was assumed that the 180° jumps occur in a cooperative manner.

Passing from B to C (T = 65.5°C) the lamellar structure becomes distorted. A region of interfacial defects with a thick-ness of 7.5 Å appears, indicating longitudinal disorder of the chains. The extended zig-zag structure of the chains and the ro-tational short-range order are preserved. NMR

measurements /6/ show that there is no sudden change in the rotational behaviour of the molecules at this phase transi-tion. It was proposed /5,6/ that flip-flop screw jumps, that is: 180° rotations coupled with longitudinal shifts over one CH_2-group, are the mechanism leading to the observed defect struc-ture.

Finally, in the D-phase (phase transition at T = 68°C) the crystal structure is highly distorted. The subcell changes from an orthorhombic to a nearly hexagonal structure indicating rotational disorder. The chain axes are tilted with respect to the surface normal of the lamellae by an angle of 19.5°. The region of interfacial defects has now an extension of about 10 Å and the chains contract /5/. Hence, in addition to the longitu-dinal and rotational disorder, intra-chain defects are present. This is also supported by the occurrence of a new band in the IR spectrum /6/, which is assigned to be the local mode of a gauche-trans-gauche sequence in an otherwise stretched paraffin

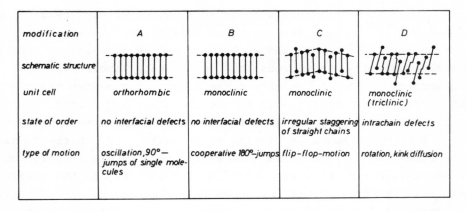

FIG.1. *Schematic representation of the structural properties of the n-alkane* $C_{33}H_{68}$ *in the solid phases A, B, C and D* [4–6], *together with the proposed motional mechanisms active in these phases.*

chain /10/. The second-moment NMR observations in the D-phase /6,8,9/can be roughly interpreted by a rigid-rod rotation of the chains around their axes. Improvements may be possible by including the influence of the diffusion of intra-chain defects and torsional oscillations of the chains.

A summary of the structural properties of the n-alkane $C_{33}H_{68}$ in the different phases, together with the proposed molecular motions, is given schematically in fig. 1. This complex picture has been developed on the basis of experiments which were sensitive to the molecular behaviour either in space or in time. Hence, it seems to be worthwhile to prove this conception by quasielastic neutron scattering, a technique combining both sensitivities. Two earlier neutron experiments /11,12/ on molecular relaxation in paraffins have been reported. Both experiments suffered from poor energy resolution and could only . detect motions in the so-called rotator phase which corresponds to the D-phase in our case. While Barnes /11/ interpreted his results on $C_{19}H_{40}$ by purely rotational motion, Windsor et al./12/ concluded that in addition to the rotational diffusion the molecules in $C_{23}H_{48}$ perform long-range diffusion in the chain direction as well as perpendicular to it.

The aim of this work was the application of high-resolution
quasielectric neutron scattering to investigate the types of
motion active in the C- and D-phase of $n-C_{33}H_{68}$. Using uniaxially
oriented samples, it was possible to separate longitudinal and
rotational motions by orienting the vector of momentum transfer
$\hbar\vec{Q}$ parallel or perpendicular to the chain axes. The small jump
rates in the C-phase required the use of a backscattering spectrometer, which has a resolution of a few 10^{-7} eV. In the D-phase
the time scale of motion is more rapid. Here, a high-resolution
time-of-flight machine was sufficient to investigate the quasielectric spectra. As will be shown below, in the case of spatially restricted motions, there appears always an elastic contribution in the quasielastic spectrum, which reflects the space distribution of a proton in the lattice for $t \to \infty$. In the D-phase,
this elastic component was investigated separately using a back-
scattering spectrometer.

2.   DYNAMICAL MODELS AND SCATTERING LAW

The scattering of slow neutrons by molecules containing protons is nearly entirely determined by the large incoherent scattering cross-section of the protons. The intensity of the scattered neutrons is proportional to the incoherent scattering law.
According to van Hove /13/, it can be written as the Fourier
transform of the self correlation function of the proton:

$$S_{inc}(\vec{Q},\omega) = \frac{1}{(2\pi)^3} \int d\vec{r} \, dt \, e^{i(\vec{Q}\cdot\vec{r}-\omega t)} \, G_s(\vec{r},t) \qquad (1)$$

where $\hbar\vec{Q}=\hbar(\vec{k}_o-\vec{k}_1)$ and $\hbar\omega = E_o-E_1$ are the change of momentum and
energy during the scattering process. $\vec{k}_o$ and $\vec{k}_1$, and E_o, E_1 are
wave vectors and energies before and after scattering, respec-
tively.

In calculating the self-correlation function the oscillatory
motions of the proton will be neglected. In the energy region of
interest they only enter the scattering law in the form of a
Debye-Waller factor. Under the further assumption of instantaneous, uncorrelated jumps with negligible jump times, the time

evolution of $G_s(\vec{r}, t)$ can be calculated from rate equations and, in the limiting case of continuous diffusion, from the diffusion equation.

Assuming that each proton can occupy N different sites, the probability $P_n(t)$ of finding a proton at a site $\vec{r}_n$ at a time t obeys the differential equation

$$\frac{\partial}{\partial t} P_n(t) = \sum_{m=0}^{N-1} M_{nm} P_m(t) \tag{2}$$

where M_{nm} is the probability per unit time that a jump takes place from a site m to a site n. The general solution for $P_n(t)$ is given by:

$$P_n(t) = \sum_{k=0}^{N-1} E_n^k e^{-t/\tau_K} \tag{3}$$

$1/\tau_K$ being the eigenvalues and E_n^k the eigenvectors of the jump matrix M. Introducing $P_{nm}(t)$ by the initial condition

$$P_{nm}(0) = \delta(\vec{r}_n - \vec{r}_m) \tag{4}$$

and assuming an equal distribution over the accessible sites, one gets:

$$P_{nm}(t) = \sum_{k=0}^{N-1} E_n^k E_m^k e^{-t/\tau_K} \tag{5}$$

The self-correlation function is obtained by performing the thermal average:

$$G_s(\vec{r}, t) = \sum_{k=0}^{N-1} \sum_{\substack{m=0 \\ n=0}}^{N-1} \frac{1}{N} E_n^k E_m^k e^{-t/\tau_K} \delta(\vec{r} - (\vec{r}_n - \vec{r}_m)) \tag{6}$$

Fourier transformation in space leads to the intermediate scattering law

$$I(\vec{Q}, t) = \sum_{n,m,k=0}^{N-1} \frac{1}{N} E_n^k E_m^k e^{i\vec{Q} \cdot (\vec{r}_n - \vec{r}_m)} e^{-t/\tau_K}$$

$$= \sum_{k=0}^{N-1} I_K(\vec{Q}) e^{-t/\tau_K} \tag{7}$$

In the case of spatially restricted motions the smallest eigen-
value $1/\tau_O$ is always zero. The corresponding $I_O(\vec{Q})$ is called incoherent structure factor and represents the Fourier transform of
the asymptotic proton distribution for $t \to \infty$. In the incoherent
scattering law, which is obtained after Fourier transformation in
time, it contributes as an elastic line:

$$S_{inc}(\vec{Q},\omega) = I_O(\vec{Q})\ \delta(\omega) + \sum_{k=1}^{N-1} I_K(\vec{Q})\ \frac{1}{\pi}\ \frac{1/\tau_K}{(1/\tau_K)^2 + \omega^2} \qquad (8)$$

Neglecting the effect of the CH_3-endgroup rotations, three
different jump mechanisms will be discussed for the C-phase. In
model A, the flip-flop mechanisms, which were proposed on the basis
of structural and NMR investigations, are considered. In the flip-
flop-model, translational and rotational motions are strongly
correlated and described by one jump rate v_f. Diagonalizing the
corresponding jump matrix yields the eigenvalues:

$$\frac{1}{\tau_K} = 2v_f(1 - \cos\frac{k\pi}{N}) \qquad k = 0,\ 1,\ 2,\ \ldots,\ N-1 \qquad (9)$$

and normalized eigenvectors

$$E_n^O = \frac{1}{\sqrt{N}}$$
$$E_n^K = \sqrt{\frac{2}{N}}\ \cos(\frac{2n+1}{2}\ \frac{k\pi}{N}) \qquad k = 0,\ 1,\ 2,\ \ldots,\ N-1 \qquad (10)$$

In the models B and C two possibilities for independent
translational and rotational motion are examined. In model B,
the flip-flop model is extended by an additional translational
jump mechanism (jump rate v_t) over two CH_2-groups which seems
to be possible according to potential calculations of Mc Cullough
/14/. As the flip-flop mechanism, this translational jump preserves the short-range order and fits, therefore, into the concept
of non-cooperative jumps in the C-phase. In this case, there is
no general anlytic solution of the rate equations. For N = 5,
which is most probable in view of the observed thickness of interfacial disorder /5/, the eigenvalues are:

$$\frac{1}{\tau_0} = 0$$

$$\frac{1}{\tau_{1/2}} = \frac{3}{2} v_t + \frac{5}{2} v_f \pm \frac{1}{2} \sqrt{9v_t^2 - 10v_t v_f + 5v_f^2} \tag{11}$$

$$\frac{1}{\tau_{3/4}} = \frac{3}{2}(v_t + v_f) \pm \frac{1}{2} \sqrt{(v_t + v_f)^2 + 4v_f^2}$$

The eigenvectors are rather complicated expressions and depend explicitly on the two jump rates of the system. They will not be given here in detail.

Model C assumes the opposite to the flip-flop mechanism, namely no coupling between translational and rotational motion. In order to establish the observed short-range order, the jumps would have to take place in some way cooperatively. Under the assumption of completely independent rotational and translational motions, the intermediate scattering law is given by the product of the translational $(I^{trans}(\vec{Q},t))$ and the rotational $(I^{rot}(\vec{Q},t))$ one. $I^{trans}(\vec{Q},t)$ is equivalent to the intermediate scattering law of the flip-flop-model if the jump vectors, $\vec{r}_m$, are exchanged in the proper way. The rotational part is very simple /11/ and has the form

$$I(Q,t)^{rot} = \frac{1}{2}(1 + \cos \vec{Q} \cdot \vec{r}_{rot}) + \frac{1}{2}(1 - \cos \vec{Q} \cdot \vec{r}_{rot}) e^{-2v_{rot}t} \tag{12}$$

where v_{rot} is the rotational jump rate and $\vec{r}_{rot}$ is the corresponding jump vector.

For the D-phase, the dynamical model is constructed on the basis of the earlier structural /5/ and dynamical /6,11/ investigations. The pseudo-hexagonal subcell structure together with the NMR and neutron data on $C_{19}H_{40}$ show that there are no well-defined equilibrium orientations in this phase. Consequently, rotational diffusion around the chain axes (radius a) is considered. In spite of the relatively large region of interfacial defects, the lamellar structure is retained in the D-phase. Therefore, it is assumed that translational diffusion of the chains occurs mainly within the lamellae. The spatial extension b of this translational diffusion process should then be correlated

to the thickness of the defect region. Assuming no correlation
between the translational and rotational components, the intermediate scattering law is given by a product of the translational
and rotational parts as mentioned before. The rotational part
is well-known /15/ and has the form

$$I^{rot}(\vec{Q},t) = J_0^2(\vec{Q}\cdot\vec{a}) + 2 \sum_{n=1}^{\infty} J_n^2(\vec{Q}\cdot\vec{a}) \, e^{-n^2 D_r t}$$

$$= \sum_{n=0}^{\infty} I_n^{rot}(\vec{Q}\cdot\vec{a}) \, e^{-n^2 D_r t} \tag{13}$$

where J_i are Bessel functions of the i-th order and D_r is the
rotational diffusion constant. In order to calculate $I^{trans}(\vec{Q},t)$
the appropriate Langevin equation would have to be solved. Here
it is approximated by using the corresponding diffusion equation

$$\frac{\partial}{\partial t} G(z,t) = - D_{trans} \frac{\partial^2}{\partial z^2} G(z,t) \tag{14}$$

with the boundary conditions of vanishing particle flux through
the borders of the cage at $z = \pm b$ and the initial condition

$$G_{z_0}(z,t=0) = \delta(z-z_0) \tag{15}$$

$I^{trans}(\vec{Q},t)$ yields

$$I^{trans}(\vec{Q},t) = \frac{1}{2(\vec{b}\cdot\vec{Q})^2} (1-\cos(2\vec{b}\cdot\vec{Q})) + \sum_{n=1}^{\infty} \frac{2(\vec{Q}\cdot\vec{b})^2 \sin^2(\vec{Q}\cdot\vec{b})}{((n\pi)^2 - (\vec{Q}\cdot\vec{b})^2)^2} e^{-(n\pi/b)^2 D_{tra}}$$

$$= \sum_{n=0}^{\infty} I_n^{trans}(\vec{Q}\cdot\vec{b}) \, e^{-(n\pi/b)^2 D_{trans} t} \tag{16}$$

Finally, the intermediate scattering law becomes

$$I(\vec{Q},t) = \sum_{n,m=0}^{\infty} I_n^{trans}(\vec{Q}\cdot\vec{b}) \, I_m^{rot}(\vec{Q}\cdot\vec{a}) \, e^{-(m^2 D_{rot} + (n\pi/b)^2 D_{trans})t} \tag{17}$$

So far, the scattering law has been calculated for single
crystals. In the next step, the structure of the actual samples

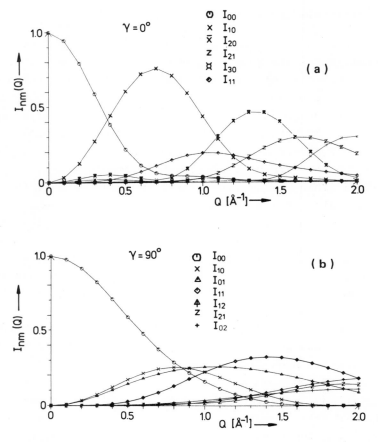

FIG.2.   Coefficients $I_{nm}(Q,\gamma)$ in the scattering law for the D-phase as a function of Q for
(a) $\gamma = 0$, (b) $\gamma = 90°$.

has to be taken into account. The paraffin crystals used are uniaxially oriented. The misorientation may be characterized by a
Gaussian distribution of the lamellar surfaces with respect to the
texture axis with a width of about $25°$ /7/. The geometrical considerations underlying this necessary averaging process have been
proposed by Olf and Peterlin /9/. As the final result, the coeffi-
cients $I_\ell(\vec{Q})$ are obtained as a function of $|\vec{Q}|$ and the angle γ be-
tween the orientation of momentum transfer and texture axis of the
sample. As an example, fig. 2 presents some of the coefficients
$I_\ell(\vec{Q},\gamma)$ valid for the D-phase as a function of Q for two different
angles γ.

3.   EXPERIMENTS AND RESULTS

The n-alkane n-$C_{33}H_{68}$ of extreme high purity /5/ was obtained
from Prof. Heitz (Marburg). It exhibited the same transition and
melting behaviour, with respect to temperature and enthalpy, as
the material used for the former investigations /4,5,6,7/. The
samples were prepared in the following way: Small, flat crystals,
precipitated by methanol from dilute tetrahydrofurane solution,
were rapidly strained through a fine porous glass filter of 5o mm
diameter. After carefully drying, the loosely packed mat was
compressed. This yielded an uniaxially oriented mat, the chain
directions distributed in a narrow range around the texture axis
/7/, which was parallel to the normal of the pressed surface.
Square pieces of 40x40 mm were cut out of such mats and stacked
up so that a total thickness of approximately 0.4 mm was gained.
The sample was filled into a flat Al-container, the desired
temperatures could be kept constant within $\pm 0.3^{\circ}C$ during the
measuring time of a spectrum.

Except for preliminary measurements, which have been undertaken at the Jülich Dido reactor, the experiments were performed
at the Grenoble high-flux reactor using the backscattering spectrometer IN10 and the multichopper time-of-flight machine IN5.
In the C-phase the experiments were carried out at the IN10,
measuring spectra simultaneously for 7 approximately equidistant
Q values in   the Q-range $0.15 \leq Q \leq 1.9$ $Å^{-1}$. Owing to the shape
of the sample, it was possible to orient the momentum transfer
parallel or perpendicular to the chain axes for one detector
only. For all other detectors, the angle γ had a value somewhere
between 0 and 90°. Altogether 6 measurements with different
orientations of the sample have been performed, 4 at T = 67°C
and two at T = 66°C . The instrumental resolution was determined
from measurements at 150 K, where the scattering is practically
elastic, yielding values between 0.24 and 0.57 µeV (HWHM) depending on the analyzer crystal and the Q value. The energy range
covered by the instrumental (energy window) ΔE was ± 2.7 µeV.

The incoherent structure factor in D-phase was investigated
also at the IN10 in a Q-range 0.07 $Å^{-1}$ $\leq Q \leq 1.9$ $Å^{-1}$ using an
energy window of $\Delta E =$ 10 µeV and an energy resolution of about
0.8 µeV (HWHM). The temperature was 70°C. During each of the 6

measurements, 8 different Q values were investigated simultaneously. As a reference, the intensity at T = 65 C was measured
in each case.

Finally, the quasielastic spectra in the D-phase (T=69.5°C)
were investigated at the IN5 spectrometer with incident wavelengths of 6.08 Å and 10.6 Å yielding a resolution of 40 μeV and
8 μeV (HWHM), respectively. The Q-range covered was $0.2 \leq Q \leq 1.9$ $Å^{-1}$
in the case of λ = 6.08 Å and $0.1 \leq Q \leq 1.1$ $Å^{-1}$ for λ = 10.6 Å.
Always 6 Q-values were investigated at one time, two sets of
spectra for Q ∥ and two for Q ⊥ for λ = 6.08 Å. For the longer
wavelength, one run was performed, for Q oriented parallel to
the chain axis.

In the C -phase, the observed quasielastic line broadening
was small, rendering it impossible to separate the elastic and
quasielastic contributions in the spectra without assumptions.
In order to discriminate the different models a very careful
analysis of the data was necessary. The following procedure was
applied: In a first step, all the spectra at one temperature
were fitted with the theoretical scattering laws corresponding
to the different models with a common variation of the parameters.
To this purpose, these laws were convoluted with the experimentally obtained resolution function. Parameters were the intensities and the jump rates of the models under consideration. In
a second step, each single spectrum was fitted with the resolu-
tion-broadened scattering law, in order to check if there were
systematic deviations from the jump rates as obtained by the
common fit in step 1. In addition, the sum of weighted mean
square deviations was used as a criterion comparing the results
for one model with those for another.

Performing single spectrum fits for the flip-flop model-
systematic deviations of the flip-flop rate v_f to lower values
compared to the results of the combined fit were found for
spectra with Q-oriented perpendicular to the chain axes. This
led to the conclusion that the rotational component in the scattering law is smaller than required by the rigid coupling of
rotation and translation assumed in the flip-flop model.

Model B which introduces an additional translational jump
rate v_t for jumps with a jump length over 2 CH_2-units could
account for the smaller line broadening for Q perpendicular to

the chain axes. But the jumplength of two CH_2-units does not reproduce the experimental Q dependence of the results. The results
of the single spectra fits deviate strongly in both directions
from the values at the combined fit.

Assuming independent rotational and translational jumps
(model C) the best agreement between the results of the common
fit and the single spectra fits is obtained. Moreover, the sum
of squares gains a value which is nearest to the expectation
value of χ^2 for these fits. It results a small rotational component just on the border of resolution of the instrument. The
observed line broadening for Q⊥ is nearly entirely due to the
misorientation of the chain axes with respect to the texture
axis. The numbers are:

T	66°C	67°C
$v_{rot} [s^{-1}]$	$\sim 2\times10^7$	$4 \pm 2\times10^7$
$v_{trans} [s^{-1}]$	$1.8 \pm 0.3\times10^8$	$2.1 \pm 0.4\times10^8$

In all cases, the measurements were not sensitive enough to distinguish between different spatial extensions of the translational
diffusion. Therefore, according to the thickness of the interfacial defect region an extension by two CH_2-units in each direction was assumed. The intensity profiles obtained, in order
to determine the incoherent structure factor in the D-phase,
were corrected with respect to the instrumental and empty scan
background. In addition, the contributions of the quasielastic
lines, which appear within the energy window of the IN10 as an
extra background, were subtracted. The remaining intensity was
normalized in dividing by the intensity obtained at 65°C . The
influence of the Debye-Waller factor, which may change at the
phase transition, was assumed to be small and neglected. The
results are shown in fig. 3.

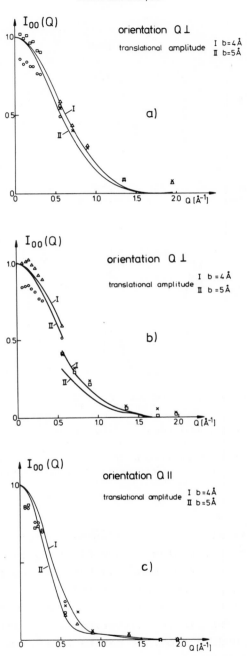

FIG.3.   *Experimental results for the incoherent structure factor in D-phase. (a) and (b) Q oriented mainly perpendicular, (c) mainly parallel to the chain axes. ○, x experimental points before, and □, △ after multiple-scattering corrections. Solid lines: theoretical curves (see text).*

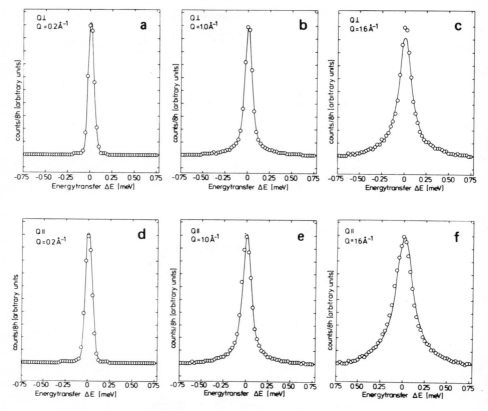

FIG. 4.   *Experimental spectra after converting into energy scale*
(a), (b), (c) Q ⊥ to the chain axes for Q = 1.6 Å⁻¹
(d), (e), (f) Q ∥ to the chain axes for Q = 1.9 Å⁻¹
Solid lines: theoretical curves obtained by the combined fitting procedure.

In the next step of data refinement, multiple-scattering corrections were calculated by the DISCUS-program of the Harwell library, which allows calculation of the corrections for the polycrystalline case. (For a single crystal until now no program is available.) The calculations were made using the scattering law for single scattering with a uniaxial crystal in the considered Q-direction. As can be seen from fig. 3, the largest shifts of the data points occurred at small Q values. For Q ⊥, the contribution of multiple-scattered neutrons seems to be overestimated whereas for Q ∥ the corrections are too small.

The solid lines in fig. 3 give the theoretical curves for a rotational radius of a = 1.4 Å which corresponds to a rigid rod-like rotation and for a translational diffusion length of 4 and 5 Å. The experimental points fall predominatly between these two lines.

The time-of-flight spectra, obtained at the IN5, were corrected with respect to background and detector efficiency and transferred to energy scale using the program IN5DAX supplied by the ILL. Thereafter, a similar procedure as in the C-phase was applied. All 23 spectra for λ = 6.08 Å were fitted with common variation of the parameters with the theoretical scattering law, which was convoluted with the corresponding experimental resolution functions. For a and b the values obtained from the structure factor determination were used. Serious deviations from the values of the common fit appeared neither by performing single spectra fits nor in the evaluation of the spectra obtained during the 10.6 Å measurement. In fig. 4, 6 typical spectra are shown together with the result of the common fit (solid line). In all cases, there is very good agreement between theory and experiment. For the rotational diffusion constant a value of D_{rot} = 6.0x10^{10} sec^{-1} was found. The translational diffusion constant was determined to D_{trans} = 1.0x10^{-5} cm^2/sec.

4. DISCUSSION AND CONCLUSION

According to structural and NMR investigations /4,5,6/ the phase transition from B to C was related to the onset of the so-called flip-flop mechanism. This mode had the property of preserving the short-range order by introducing longitudinal disorder without the need of cooperativity. In view of the experiments reported here, another picture about the motions in the C-phase is proposed. The experimental results show that there is no rigid coupling between translational and rotational motion. The assumption of an additional translational jump process which for itself preserves short-range order (model B) cannot account for the observed Q-dependence of the quasielastic broadening. According to model C , which is in best agreement with the experimental data, the C -phase is characterized by the onset of

translational jumps over one CH_2-unit. They occur more or less
independently from the rotational $180°$ jumps, which were already
active in the B-phase. The obtained rotational jump rate is in
good agreement with results of dielectric measurements. In order
to get more detailed information on the motional mechanism active
in the C-phase, additional measurements with higher resolution,
which may be provided by the spin-echo spectrometer /16/, or on
shorter chains, where the time scale of motion is expected to be
faster, would be required.

Following Strobl et al. /5/, the D-phase is characterized by
rotational and longitudinal disorder as well as intrachain defects. On the basis of their data, rotational-, translational- and
kink-diffusion seemed to be possible. These experiments establish
the following picture: The structure factor measurements support
very much a rigid~rod-like rotation around the chain axes. In the
case of kink diffusion (a = 1.9 Å instead of a = 1.4 Å) the
structure factor should have been steeper. The rotation of kinked
chains, however, would presumably cause an only slightly changed
structure factor, because most of the hydrogen would still rotate with a radius given by the geometry of the extended molecule.
So there is no discrepancy between this result and the structural
investigations of Strobl et al., who stated that about 50% of the
chains should be kinked. There is, however, no indication of
long-range diffusion perpendicular to the chain axes, as stated
by Windsor et al./12/. The good agreement of the measured quasi-
elastic spectra with the scattering law for rotational diffusion
again makes kink diffusion very unlikely because in that case
only a few distinct sites would be occupied by the H-atom, giving
rise to a quite different Q-dependence of linewidth. The smaller
rotational diffusion constant $D_{rot} = 6.0 \times 10^{10}$ sec^{-1} compared to
the values obtained by Barnes /11/ (5.7×10^{11} sec^{-1}) and Windsor
et.al ($2 \times 10^{11} sec^{-1}$) might arise from an increasing amount of
defects with increasing chain length, as proposed by Windsor et
al. /12/ by comparing their data with those of Barnes. Another
explanation would be an increasing activation energy for rotational jumps with an increasing number of CH_2-units as proposed
by Stohrer /17/.

Concerning the translational diffusion, the diffusion con-
stant $D_{trans} = 1.0 \times 10^{-5}$ cm^2/sec is in good agreement with the

value given by Windsor et al. (D_{trans} = 9±2$\times$10^{-6} cm^2/sec). However, in contrast to Windsor et al., who stated long-range diffusion in chain direction, the structure factor determination
clearly shows the spatial restriction of this diffusion process.
Its spatial extension of 4.5 Å has to be compared with the width
of 10 Å found for the region of interfacial defects. Evidently,
the fast diffusion process takes place over about half this length.

ACKNOWLEDGEMENTS

The authors are grateful to Prof. W. Heitz for supplying the
high-purity n-alkane $C_{33}H_{68}$, to Prof. E.W. Fischer and Prof.
T. Springer for many stimulating discussions and suggestions.
They wish to thank A. Heidemann and R. Lechner for their advice
during the experiments. The support given by the Institut Laue-
Langevin to this work is gratefully acknowledged. Finally, one
of the authors (B.E.) thanks for the financial support by the
"Bundesministerium für Forschung und Technologie".

REFERENCES

/1/   MÜLLER, A., Proc. R. Soc. A127   (1930) 417

/2/   MÜLLER, A., Proc. R. Soc. A138   (1932) 514

/3/   BROODHURST, M., J. Res. Natl. Bur. Stand. A66   (1962) 241

/4/   PIESCZEK, W.,   STROBL, G.R., MALZAHN, K., Acta Cryst. B30
        (1974) 1278

/5/   STROBL, G., EWEN, B., FISCHER, E.W., PIESCZEK, W.,   J. Chem.
        Phys. 61   (1974) 5257

/6/   EWEN, B., FISCHER, E.W., PIESCZEK, W.,   STROBL, G., J. Chem.
        Phys. 61   (1974) 5265

/7/   EWEN, B., Thesis, Mainz (1972)

/8/   ANDREW, E.R., J. Chem. Phys. 18   (1950) 607

/9/   OLF, H.G., PETERLIN, A., J. Polym. Sci. A2 8 (1970) 771

/10/   SNYDER, R.G., J. Mol. Spectrosc. 7   (1961) 116

/11/   BARNES, J.D., J. Chem. Phys. 58   (1973) 5193

/12/   WINDSOR, G.G., BLOOR, D., BONSOR, D.H., BATCHELDER, D.N.,
        Internal Report MPD/NBS/38, AERE, Harwell (1977)

/13/   VAN HOVE, L., Phys. Rev. <u>95</u>   (1954) 249

/14/   McCULLOUGH, R.L., J. Macromol. Sci.-Phys. <u>B9</u>   (1974) 97

/15/   DIANOUX, A., VOLINO, F., HERVET, H., Mol. Phys. <u>30</u>
        (1975) 1181

/16/   MEZEI, F., Z. Physik <u>255</u>   (1972) 146

/17/   STOHRER, M., Thesis, Stuttgart (1975)

DISCUSSION

A.J. DIANOUX: In the D-phase, you assume that, in addition to rotational motion, there is some translation of the protons along the chain axis, which has spatial limitations. For the translational motion do you use a diffusive type of model with an infinite repulsive potential at the limits?

D. RICHTER: Yes. We assumed translational diffusion within a cage of length $2b \sim 10$ Å.

A.J. DIANOUX: In the D-phase, could your spectra for Q, parallel or perpendicular to the average chain axis, be regarded as due to a combination of rotational motion around the chain axis and a certain deformation of the chains (represented for example by axis fluctuation)?

D. RICHTER: No, I don't think so, because the rather steep structure factor for Q $\parallel$ indicates a proton translational amplitude of about 5 Å. This can hardly be attributed to axis fluctuation of a molecule with a length of ~ 44 Å.

C.G. WINDSOR: Did you observe any deviations from a Q^2 law for the quasi-elastic width in the high-temperature phase?

D. RICHTER: For small Q-values the intensity profile is elastic within the energy resolution of the high-resolution back-scattering spectrometer. At intermediate Q-values quasi-elastic lines appear. The Q-dependence of the line width is very similar to the case of rotational diffusion, and in the Q-range of interest we did not observe a Q^2 law. However, I think that, in the Q-range you have investigated, any deviation of the effective width from a Q^2 law will be slight.

W. SCHMATZ: Can you correlate the change in the incoherent structure factor parallel to the chain axis at the phase transition with other observations?

D. RICHTER: We know from small-angle X-ray experiments that, at the phase-transition from C to D, a region of interfacial defects with a thickness of ~ 10 Å appears. This must be correlated with the spatial extension (± 5 Å) of the longitudinal diffusion as obtained from the structure factor determination.

EFFECT OF INTERCHAIN FORCES ON ACOUSTIC PHONON BRANCHES IN DEUTERATED UNIAXIAL POLYETHYLENE

G. PEPY
Laboratoire Léon Brillouin,
CEA, Centre d'études nucléaires de Saclay,
Gif-sur-Yvette,
France

H. GRIMM
Institut für Festkörperforschung der
        Kernforschungsanlage Jülich GmbH,
Jülich,
Federal Republic of Germany

Abstract

EFFECT OF INTERCHAIN FORCES ON ACOUSTIC PHONON BRANCHES IN DEUTERATED UNIAXIAL POLYETHYLENE.

A mapping of the intensity of neutrons scattered by the phonon branches ν_5^a, ν_9^a along the c* axis, in uniaxial deuterated polyethylene, has been measured in the anticrossing region, at nitrogen and room temperatures. The predicted gap between the phonon dispersion curves has been proven at both temperatures. It is smaller than has been foreseen. Only the ν_9^a branch is well described by a theoretical model. The ν_5^a branch seems to be rather sensitive to temperature.

1. INTRODUCTION

A polymer as simple as polyethylene has for a long time been attracting the attention of experimenters as well as theoreticians. Models were first proposed for the isolated chain, but soon calculations were made which incorporated H-H interactions in the orthorhombic crystalline material [1, 2, 6]. As soon as a perdeuterated crystal was available, acoustic phonon measurements were performed by neutron spectroscopy [3, 4]. For crystals having been aligned by stretching along the c* axis, only longitudinal phonons in this direction could be observed. These early measurements and theoretical work emphasized the interest of the neighbouring region of branches ν_5^a and ν_9^a, to evaluate the interchain forces [4, 5].

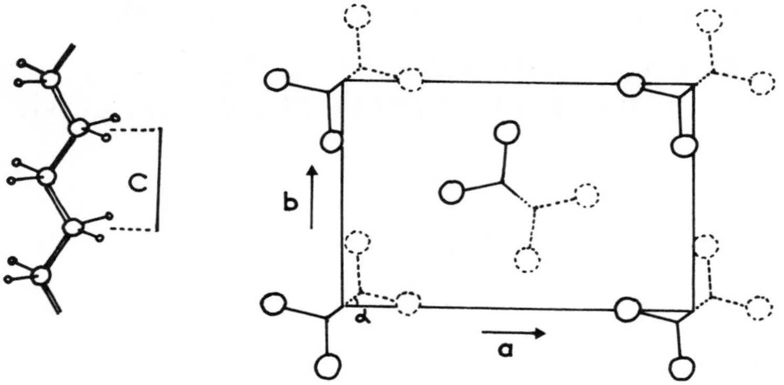

FIG.1.   *Structure of polyethylene. After Refs [4, 6].*

2.   EXPERIMENTAL DETAILS

Owing to the high symmetry of the basis in the unit cell (Fig.1), along the
c* axis, all structure factors exhibit a periodicity twice as large as the lattice
periodicity. This makes the structure factor of all [0, 0, 2n+1] Bragg peaks
vanish, and reduces to zero the intensity scattered by half of the phonon branches
in each Brillouin zone. This has brought some confusion in the numbering of
BZ, and about the folding or unfolding of phonon branches. Here, we shall
start from the unit cell as is shown in Fig.1, and follow Kitagawa's presentation [6]. Indeed, the ν_9^a branch exhibits an intensity identically zero along the
c* axis, but a small anticrossing region with ν_5^a, where interchain forces restore
some intensity [4], only in the vicinity of the odd Brillouin zone centres. Owing
to the small incoming neutron wave vector, $k_i = 2.665$ Å^{-1} (chosen and kept
fixed for filtering purposes), the only possibility was to work by the [0,0,1]
reciprocal lattice point. The small incoming-neutron energy made it necessary to
work with energy gain. We had about the same sample size (2 × 4 × 0.1 cm^3)
as early work [4], but the signal-to-background ratio and the intensity itself
were improved by using the triple-axis spectrometer at Dido reactor (Jülich):
this facility benefits of a double graphite monochromator (low background)
and a vertically bent analyser. Owing to the unusually broad mosaic of the
sample, 9°, it was very efficient to loosen the horizontal divergences to the crude
values of 2°, 0.75°, 1.6°, 1.6°. Therefore, we were able to do a mapping versus
momentum and frequency of the region where the curves are close.

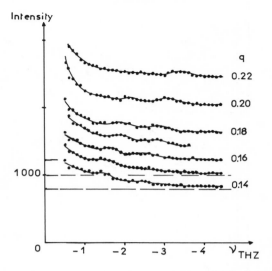

FIG.2. *Mapping versus q and v of the intensity scattered at 77 K. Full lines were adjusted.*

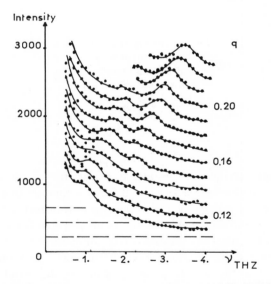

FIG.3. *Mapping versus q and v of the intensity scattered at 300 K. Full lines were adjusted.*

3.   MEASUREMENTS

The phonon branches ν_5^a and ν_9^a have been measured along the c* direction in the small anticrossing region beyond the [0, 0, 1] reciprocal lattice point, at nitrogen and room temperatures (Figs 2 and 3). Owing to the poor scattered

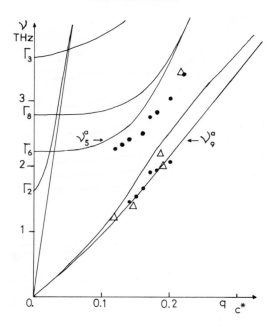

FIG.4. *Phonon dispersion curves*
●   *this experiment at 77 K*
△   *Feldkamp's measures* [4]
—— *Kitagawa's model* [6].

intensity, it is not a straightforward task to extract the background. For each constant-Q scan, the background has been fitted separately to a four-parameter law $c_1/(c_2^2 + \nu^2) + c_3 + c_4\nu$ (where ν is the energy transfer), while the peaks were adjusted to Gaussians. Later on, taking an averaged law for the background, we checked that the fit of the Gaussians was not disturbed.

The positions of the phonon peaks were compared to Kitagawa's model [6]. It is clearly seen that the branch ν_9^a (group symmetry Δ_4, bending perpendicular to the plane of the chain) seems well described by this model, at nitrogen and higher temperatures (Figs 4–6). Indeed, this branch does not move significantly as a function of temperature. On the other hand, the branch ν_5^a (group symmetry Δ_4, bending inside the plane of the chain) is sensitive to temperature. At 77 K the measured points are not too far from the calculated curve and seem to follow it accordingly. At 300 K, the frequency of ν_5^a phonons decreases linearly versus $\vec{q}$, much lower anyway than the calculated curve. One must consider that these points are merely the fitted position of the Gaussian peaks:

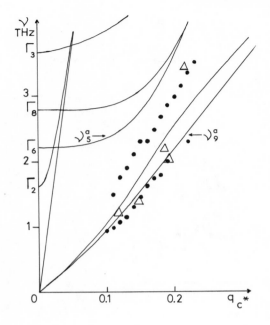

FIG.5. Phonon dispersion curves
●   this experiment at 300 K
△   Feldkamp's measures [4]
—— Kitagawa's model [6].

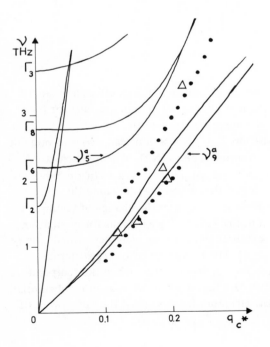

FIG. 6. Phonon dispersion curves
●   this experiment at 370 K
△   Feldkamp's measures [4]
—— Kitagawa's model [6].

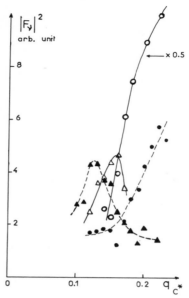

FIG.7.   Structure factor
○ ν_5^a branch 77 K;   △ ν_9^a branch 77 K;
● ν_5^a branch 300 K;   ▲ ν_9^a branch 300 K;
Lines are only to guide.

they should be corrected for resolution. Nevertheless, this effect is small, of the same order of magnitude as the uncertainty. It cannot account for the qualitative discrepancy between the measurement and the model.

The intensity of neutrons scattered by the phonons can also give valuable information on their generalized structure factors (N.B. to write "structure factor" is short but improper; in fact, we consider the square of the modulus of the component of the eigenvector of the phonon mode, along the c* axis). Preliminary results corrected for Bose statistics and the change of volume of the resolution ellipsoid are shown in Fig.7. (We have reasons for comparing nitrogen and room temperature measurements as they were performed closely in time and with the same geometry.) The maximum of the ν_9^a structure factor is slightly displaced towards smaller wave vectors when the temperature is raised. On the contrary, the structure factor of the ν_5^a branch is substantially reduced. Let us point out that the structure factors are of the same order of magnitude, while the predicted ratio $|F_{\nu_5^a}/F_{\nu_9^a}|^2$ was 20.

4.   DISCUSSION

The room temperature measurements do not show the ν_5^a branch flattening at 2.43 THz for $\vec{q} = 0$ which was deduced from infra-red spectroscopy [7], although at nitrogen temperature the flattening may be real.

Three processes may be invoked to explain the changes with temperature:

(a)   The expansion of the unit cell along the $\vec{a}$ and $\vec{b}$ axes together with a possible change of the angle α of the plane of the chain inside the cell. This process would change gradually the four interchain forces considered in the theoretical model [6]. Therefore, it should not introduce any qualitative change with T. It could be the main process only if, finally, it were shown that ν_5^a flattens to a finite value.

(b)   Renormalization of phonons. Its effect is unknown; it is a guess to suggest that ν_5^a would be much disturbed.

(c)   Erratic rotation of large parts of the chains around the c^* axis [8]. This process would average to zero the effects of the surroundings (i.e. the interchain forces). Then we are back to the isolated polymer chain. It is well known that in such a case ν_5^a has to collapse to the origin [4, 6].

Unfortunately, it is rather difficult to appreciate which of the processes, (b) or (c), is the most likely since both are enhanced by temperature.

One must also point out that the Lorentzian part of the background was much lowered at nitrogen temperature (this fact allowed us to save a significant signal-to-background ratio notwithstanding the energy gain geometry). Owing to the lack of detailed measurements of this effect, we could not clarify its physical meaning.

5.   CONCLUSION

The existence of the gap between ν_5^a and ν_9^a phonon branches is proven. Mainly at room temperature, there are large discrepancies between neutron scattering measurements and theory concerning the frequency and intensity of these phonon branches in their anticrossing region.

ACKNOWLEDGEMENTS

We wish to thank Professor J.S. King for the deuterated polyethylene sample and Professor G.C. Summerfield for suggesting the investigation of the ν_5^a, ν_9^a gap.

One of us (G.P.) is very grateful to Prof. H. Stiller for the kind invitation, which allowed him to perform these measurements successfully, as well as for valuable discussions.

REFERENCES

[1]   TASUMI, M., KRIMM, S., J. Chem. Phys. **46** 2 (1967) 755.
[2]   TASUMI, M., KRIMM, S., J. Polymer Sci. P **A2** 6 (1968) 955.
[3]   LYNCH, J.E., SUMMERFIELD, G.C., FELDKAMP, L.A., KING, J.S., J. Chem.
      Phys. **48** 2 (1968) 912.
[4]   FELDKAMP, L.A., VENKATARAMAN, G., KING, J.S., "Dispersion relation for
      skeletal vibrations in deuterated polyethylene", Neutron Inelastic Scattering (Proc.
      Symp. Copenhagen, 1968) 2, IAEA, Vienna (1968) 159.
[5]   LYNCH, J.E., Doctoral Thesis, University of Michigan (1968).
[6]   KITAGAWA, T., MIYAZAWA, T., Adv. Polymer Sci. **9** (1972) 335.
[7]   BERTIE, J.E., WHALLEY, E., J. Chem. Phys. **41** (1964) 575.
[8]   RICHTER, D., Private communication.

DISCUSSION

W.J.L. BUYERS: At all temperatures, the major part of the scattering
is a smooth continuum falling monotonically with frequency and the 'phonon'
peaks appear as small perturbations on this. In anharmonic solids, such as
quantum crystals, the peaks in the spectrum are not single-phonon peaks, but
involve multiple-peaked one-phonon scattering coupled to the two- and higher-
phonon continuum. What is your explanation of the continuous spectrum in
deuterated polyethylene?

G. PEPY: In order to gain intensity we were obliged to relax the collimation and the background is therefore large, even far from the elastic lines. For
some Q values there is also contamination by a Debye-Scherrer line from the
holder. However, we made sure that the statistics were adequate to extract the
peaks sitting on this 'background'.

W.J.L. BUYERS: You have mentioned only difficulties of an experimental
nature. Even a temperature of 77 K could well be above the value at which one
or more structural or orientational transitions could have taken place to produce
the observed structure. This could possibly produce quasi-elastic scattering
from overdamped modes. Do you think the continuum scattering arises from
this or some other physical phenomenon?

G. PEPY: We had not enough time to measure the quasi-elastic scattering
in detail. We only did some scans in order to check whether the shape was
Lorentzian. Actually, the shape changes very much with temperature. A
physical process might be the reason, but to decide this would require a special
study of the background with better resolution.

J.W. WHITE: In connection with the question raised by Mr. Buyers,
perhaps I can suggest that one possible contribution to the underlying intensity
in scattering from deuterated polyethylene lies in the variability of the crystal
lamella thickness along the C* direction. The 2.5 Å repeat thus gives only a

basis for a type of extended zone if one regards the crystal as an extended sand-wich of lamellae. The variability in the lamella size could give density of state at low frequencies.

In another connection I should also like to ask a question. For the theoretical curves you showed in comparison with your experiments, could you say what 'setting angle' was used for the chains and how the theoretical curves vary with the setting angle?

G. PEPY: The setting angle for the chains is not well known. The calcu-lated curves are taken from Kitagawa's work [6]. The setting angle was 45°. It would of course be very interesting to know the quantitative influence of the setting angle on the theoretical phonon branches.

N. KROÓ: Are your experimental data good enough to determine line widths and their dependence on temperature and momentum transfer? If so, do they support any particular one of the conclusions you formulated at the end of your talk?

G. PEPY: I have started to compare the measured neutron groups with data computed from the resolution function of the triple axis and from assumed dispersion curves. Small corrections are necessary for the frequencies, but the widths of the groups agree. The resolution is so relaxed that it is impossible to extract any intrinsic width of the phonon modes.

DYNAMICS OF INTERLAMELLAR WATER IN DIVALENT CATION EXCHANGED EXPANDING LATTICE CLAYS*

P.L. HALL, D.K. ROSS, J.J. TUCK, M.H.B. HAYES
Departments of Chemistry and of Physics[†],
University of Birmingham,
Birmingham,
United Kingdom

Abstract

DYNAMICS OF INTERLAMELLAR WATER IN DIVALENT CATION EXCHANGED EXPANDING LATTICE CLAYS.

Quasi-elastic neutron scattering measurements have been made on various samples of montmorillonite and vermiculite containing two or three layers of water between each silicate layer with the objective of measuring the diffusive motions of the water. For all samples, if the broadened peaks are fitted on the assumption that the interlamellar water contributes to the quasi-elastic component only, kinked broadening curves are obtained that change with the instrumental resolution. If, however, the quasi-elastic fraction, X, is allowed to vary, a reasonably smooth broadening curve is obtained along with reduced values of X which show some Q dependence. Moreover, the extra elastic scattering at high Q can be correlated with the fraction of water that is coordinated to the ions. This is interpreted to indicate that the broadening is due to basically rotational diffusion of the non-shell water and elastic scattering from the shell-water. High resolution measurements of IN10 indicate that this extra 'elastic' component is in fact slightly broadened.

1. Introduction

Montmorillonite and vermiculite are expanding lattice clay minerals, having structures which are essentially mica-like silicate units about 9.6Å thick. These minerals may expand to accommodate one or more layers of water between the silicate layers. The interlamellar space also contains exchangeable cations which balance the negative charges on the silicate layers that arise from isomorphous substitutions. Montmorillonite and vermiculite differ in the magnitude and location of the negative charge on the layers. Both minerals, however, expand in a stepwise manner giving a discrete series of 001 plane spacings corresponding to integral numbers

* This work has been supported by a post doctoral fellowship (P.L.H.) and a research studentship (J.J.T.) awarded by the Science Research Council of the United Kingdom.

† Messrs Hall, Tuck and Hayes are in the Department of Chemistry, and Mr. Ross is in the Department of Physics.

of molecular layers of water, depending on the relative humidity and the nature of the exchangeable cation [1]. Thus these minerals provide a unique system for investigations of the dynamics and structure of thin electrolyte films, apart from the particular significance of the water-cation-clay system to soil chemistry, agronomy and catalysis [2].

The influence of the silicate surface on the mobility of interlamellar water has been widely studied by macroscopic techniques, and more recently by quasi-elastic neutron scattering [3-5] and NMR spectroscopy [6-8]. Though these studies have not yet provided a completely comprehensive description of the dynamics of interlamellar water in clays, they lead to the general consensus that such water is more highly structured and less mobile than bulk water. However, it exhibits a range of properties intermediate between crystalline hydrates and ionic solutions depending on the interlamellar separation, i.e. the number of molecular layers present. Hougardy and co-workers [6] have shown that the NMR spectra of the interlamellar water in a two-layer hydrate of Na^+ vermiculite $(d_{001} = 14.8Å)$ can be interpreted in terms of rotational diffusion of water molecules coordinated to the Na^+ ions about C_2 axes with a correlation time corresponding to a diffusion coefficient of $\sim 10^{-6}$ $cm^2 \cdot s^{-1}$ at ambient temperature, together with slower diffusion of the entire cation hydration shell.

The pioneering work in this field by quasi-elastic neutron scattering is that of Olejnik, White and co-workers [3-5] on monovalent [Li^+ and Na^+] montmorillonite and vermiculite systems containing a wide range of interlamellar water thicknesses. They showed that the effective diffusion coefficients in these systems increase rapidly with increasing water layer thickness, tending to approach the value of the bulk water diffusion coefficients [$D = 2.3 \times 10^{-5}$ $cm^2 \cdot s^{-1}$] at higher plane spacings. Thus the silicate surface appears to strongly influence only the nearest few water layers. Their data showed a linear dependence of log D upon the inverse water layer thickness, which could be explained in terms of macroscopic thermodynamic properties.

Their significant contribution was, however, restricted to an energy resolution of ca. 200 μeV, and quasi-elastic broadenings were derived merely from linewidth measurements; moreover, no data were reported regarding the degree of platelet orientation and possible anisotropy of diffusion in these systems.

The advent of higher resolution spectrometers, such as the IN5 and IN10 spectrometer at ILL, Grenoble, together with the development of more sophisticated quasi-elastic data analysis procedures, has opened the possibility of deriving more detailed information on the dynamics of water in clays. We have therefore made measurements on a range of divalent [Ca^{2+} and Mg^{2+}] montmorillonite and vermiculite systems using spectrometers covering a range of energy resolutions, and using samples prepared in a manner so as to exploit the plate-like nature of the clay particles in maximizing the degree of orientation. In this way both the range of cationic species investigated by the neutron technique has been extended, and further details of the dynamic processes in clay-water systems have been elucidated.

2.   Experimental

2.1   Sample Preparation and Neutron Diffraction Studies

Montmorillonite [API No 26, Wyoming, U.S.A.] and vermiculite [Libby, Montana, U.S.A.] were initially converted to their sodium exchange forms by standard techniques [9]. Suspensions of the sodium clays, of particle size range 0.2 - 2.0 μm e.s.d., were then deposited in the form of thixotropic gels by suction of water through 'Sartorius' cellulose nitrate membranes [pore size 0.02 μm]. After conversion to the Ca^{2+} or Mg^{2+} exchange forms the gels were dried to produce self-supporting films of dimensions approximately 50 x 50 x 2 mm. The indirect route to the preparation of the divalent cation exchanged clays is necessary in order to maximize the preferential orientation of the crystallites, since it avoids the 'edge-to-face' settling likely to occur in a direct preparation due to the higher charges at particle surfaces and edges. The samples were then equilibrated at constant known water vapour partial pressures p/p_0 to obtain specimens containing up to three layers of interlamellar water. The samples were sealed in aluminium casettes, and examined by neutron diffraction to check the homogeneity of expansion and degree of platelet orientation.

The neutron diffraction measurements were made using the long-wavelength Guide Tube Diffractometer at AERE Harwell, U.K., and the D16 diffractometer at ILL, Grenoble [Incident wavelength 4.7Å and 4.6Å, respectively]. The results, which are summarised in Table 1, indicate that homogeneous expansion had been achieved giving a relatively strong single d_{001} spacing in all cases. However, the (001) reflections become rapidly less intense beyond the first order, typically only the first 3 or 4 orders being discernible. This result is no doubt attributable to the combined effect of low structure factors, the breadth of the peak in $\sin \theta / \lambda$ due to some lack of uniformity of the c-axis spacing, and imperfect particle orientation.

The degree of platelet orientation can be deduced from ω rocking curves, illustrated in Fig. 1a for a Mg^{2+} montmorillonite slab sample containing two interlamellar water layers [d_{001} = 15.6Å]. The corresponding (001) Bragg peak is illustrated in Fig. 1b. The rocking curve illustrated is typical of that obtained for all samples investigated. The minima A and C are separated by an angle of $2 \sin^{-1} \lambda/2d$, and can therefore be attributed to maximum attenuation of incident and diffracted beams by the plane of the sample. After correction of these curves for one-component incoherent filtering corrections, assuming rectangular slab geometry, mosaic spreads were estimated from the resultant full widths at half maxima. These were found to be in the range $35°$ - $40°$ for all samples examined, irrespective of cation or

TABLE 1

Diffraction Data

SAMPLE	d_{001} SPACING $\overset{\circ}{A}$	NO. OF WATER LAYERS
Ca^{2+} montmorillonite	15.5	2
Ca^{2+} mont "	18.5	3
Mg^{2+} mont "	15.6	2
Mg^{2+} mont "	18.5	3
Na^+ mont "	15.5	2
Ca^{2+} vermiculite	14.9	2
Mg^{2+} vermiculite	11.8	1

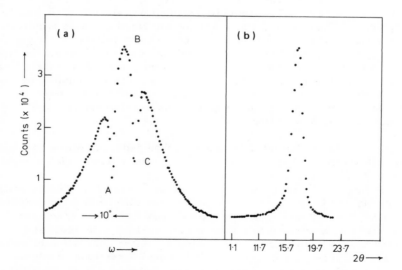

FIG.1. (a) Rocking curve for Mg^{2+} montmorillonite 2 layer hydrate and (b) 001 reflection for the same sample.

clay type. There is, however, always more intensity in the wings of the clay-water rocking curves than can be attributed to incoherent or diffuse scattering. More detailed examination of the rocking curve shapes indicates that the coherent component is not well represented by the assumption of a Gaussian distribution of platelet orientations. Though the distribution of plane normals does peak strongly normal to the plane of the slabs, its angular dependence is probably more closely described by an ellipsoidal [12] or Maier-Saupe [13] distribution, or perhaps by an admixture of highly preferentially and randomly orientated components. The mosaic spreads quoted are therefore not strictly comparable with values obtained for more perfectly orientated systems where a Gaussian distribution is conventionally assumed.

Further characterization of the particle orientation distribution in these systems is being undertaken, as well as experiments which will attempt to improve the degree of orientation. The results obtained are, however, comparable with results obtained by other workers [10] on clay-water specimens prepared by a pressure-plate technique [11] which suggests that the limit to the attributable orientation may be imposed by the particle morphology.

2.2   Quasi-elastic Neutron Scattering Studies

Preliminary quasi-elastic measurements were made using the RXS spectrometer at AWRE, Aldermaston, U.K., on the two- and three-layer hydrates of Ca^{2+} montmorillonite. This instrument, which has been described elsewhere [14], is of relatively low energy resolution, and has a single pair of detectors, orientated to give a series of points for which Q lay either parallel or perpendicular to the sample plane. Later measurements were made using the IN5 and IN10 spectrometers at ILL Grenoble. With the multiple counter banks of the latter instruments inevitably a range of Q directions with respect to the sample normal were obtained. In these runs, samples were normally positioned at 45° or 135° to the incident beam direction, so that Q lay either perpendicular or parallel to the sample normal for the 90° detectors only, but relatively close to $Q_{//}$ or $Q_{\perp}$ for a number of other detectors, as illustrated in Fig. 2. The experiments at different sample orientations were performed in order to determine any anisotopy of diffusion. Table 2 summarizes the incident wavelengths, maximum Q values and energy resolutions for the spectrometers used.

The time-of-flight quasi-elastic data were analysed using a computer programme 'Quelda' developed at Birmingham. The basis of this method, to be described elsewhere, is to fit the raw time-of-flight data (by minimization of χ^2) to a model consisting of the sum of a broadened Lorentzian converted from an energy to a time-of-flight scale and an elastic component. In this model both the full width and weighting factor (quasi-elastic fraction, X) of the Lorentzian are adjustable parameters. All corrections such as filtering and detector efficiency factors are incorporated in the model rather than used to correct the raw data.

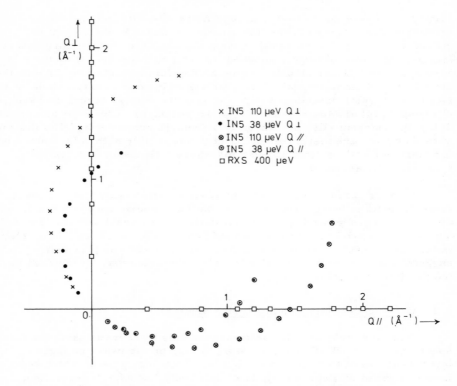

FIG.2. Diagram illustrating Q vectors measured with the various instruments. For IN5, vectors are given for incident wavelengths of 8.5 and 6 Å.

TABLE 2

Instrumental Parameters

INSTRUMENT	WAVELENGTH (Å) (Å)	RESOLUTION FWHM (µeV)	MAXIMUM (Å⁻¹)
RXS	4.0	400	2.20
IN5	6.0	110	1.93
IN5	8.5	38.5	1.36
IN10	6.3	1.5	1.41

TABLE 3

Montmorillonite Samples

NO. OF WATER LAYERS	COMPOSITION gH_2O/g CLAY	THEORETICAL QUASI-ELASTIC FRACTION X
1	0.095	0.66
2	0.19	0.79
3	0.28	0.85

Preliminary experiments had verified that the elastic peak profile from anhydrous clays was identical in shape to the instrumental resolution provided the $\underline{Q}$ values did not overlap with coherent (001) reflections.

The data were analysed in two ways. In the first method, the quasi-elastic fraction, X, was fixed at a theoretical value representing the fraction of the total incoherent cross section attributable to the interlamellar water. The data obtained in this way should be comparable with those obtained from previous measurements, yielding effective or averaged diffusion coefficients on the assumption that all the interlamellar water contributes to the quasi-elastic peak intensity.

In the second method, the quasi-elastic fraction was also used as an adjustable parameter, in order to permit the separation of components of the interlamellar water undergoing different diffusive processes, or possibly the separation of rotational from translational motions.

Table 3 summarizes the composition and calculated X values for the mono-, bi- and trilayer hydrates of montmorillonite and vermiculite which were investigated. Figure 3 shows the broadening curves obtained from IN5 measurements at two different resolutions (110 μeV and 180 μeV) on the same sample (Ca^{2+} - montmorillonite three water layer system) at the same orientation (yielding a set of $\underline{Q}$ vectors labelled $Q_{//}$ in Fig.2). Both spectra show an inflexion at approximately 2.0$\overset{o}{A}^{-2}$, but quasi-elastic broadenings of apparently different magnitudes, the lower resolution run yielding lower broadenings.

The inflexions in the broadening curves are common to the majority of samples examined, and occur in each case at approximately the same momentum transfer. These shapes suggest a component nature for the broadening curves, i.e. two or more Lorentzian components possibly

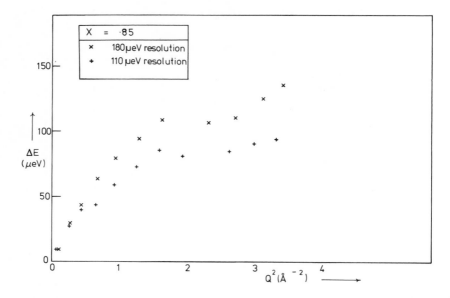

FIG.3. Broadening curves for Ca^{2+} montmorillonite 3 layer hydrate measured on IN5 for two instrumental resolutions, with the quasi-elastic fraction, X, fixed at 0.85.

exhibiting a different Q-dependence [15]. However, the fact that the magnitude of the quasi-elastic broadenings is apparently dependent on the instrument resolution suggests the further possibility that the data are not accurately described by a quasi-elastic fraction of 0.85. Figure 4a illustrates the corresponding broadening curves for the same data when X is allowed to vary, the corresponding fitted values of X being plotted in Figure 4b. These data show greater statistical fluctuations than the fixed X fits. This is because there is some correlation between these parameters. The ΔE curve could be improved using a smooth curve drawn through the X values. In the majority of cases the data analysed this way gave a good fit at a lower value of χ^2 than in the cases where X was constrained to its theoretical value. Furthermore, significant systematic deviations from the fitted function were normally apparent in the broadening curves for fixed X, but were eliminated when X was allowed to vary, as illustrated in Fig. 5 [data at 110 µeV for a Q^2 of 1.580 $Å^{-2}$]. It is seen from Fig. 4 that the quasi-elastic broadenings for different resolutions now lie essentially on the same curve, exhibiting greater quasi-elastic broadening but correspondingly reduced values of X in all cases. The fitted values of X show some Q dependence, tending to increase from relatively low values at low Q and flatten out at approximately 0.65 ± 0.05. The

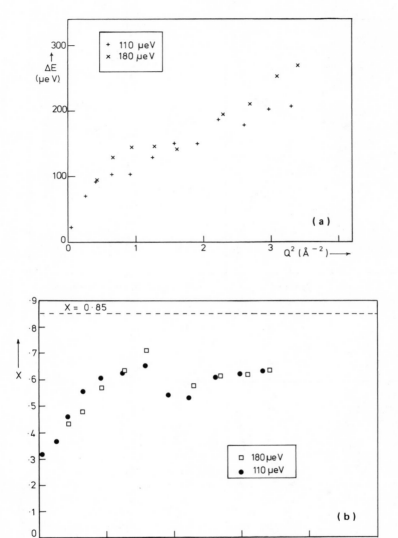

FIG.4.   (a) Broadening curve for Ca²⁺ montmorillonite 3 layer hydrate measured on IN5 for
two instrumental resolutions for variable X. (b) Fitted value of X for each resolution.

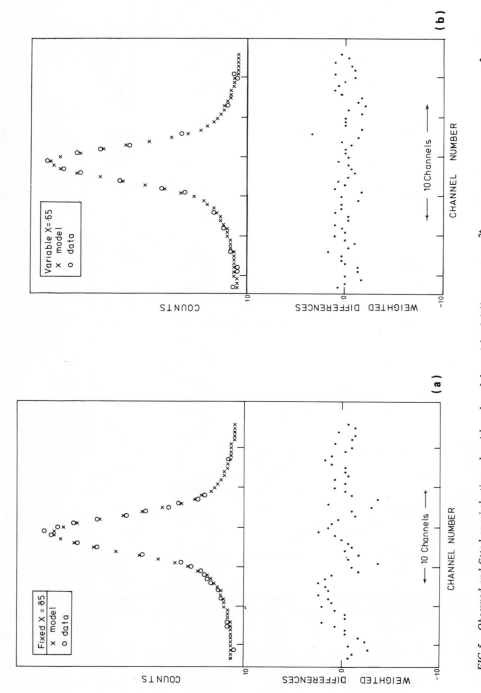

FIG.5.   Observed and fitted quasi-elastic peaks with a plot of the weighted differences for Ca²⁺ montmorillonite 3 layer hydrate, $Q^2 = 1.58$, resolution = 110 μeV (a) fixed X. (b) variable X.

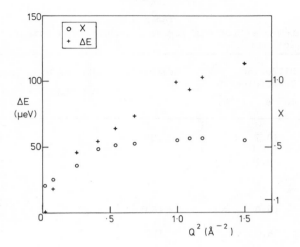

FIG.6. Broadening and X plots for Ca²⁺ montmorillonite 2 layer hydrate measured on IN5 at an instrumental resolution of 38 µeV.

diffusion coefficient as estimated from the variable X fits is approximately 1.6×10^{-5} $cm^2 \cdot s^{-1}$ compared to values of 7.8×10^{-6} or 7.2×10^{-6} from the data at X = 0.85 for high and low resolution, respectively. Qualitatively these results are typical of those obtained for the entire range of samples studied. We will discuss below their implications in terms of models for the interlamellar water dynamics, after considering their dependence on sample orientation and discussing the results obtained at higher energy resolutions, including those obtained on the backscattering spectrometer IN10.

Preliminary results obtained using the low resolution RXS spectrometer show little anisotropy in the quasi-elastic broadenings for Q directions parallel and perpendicular to the sample plane. This finding has been confirmed in measurements on IN5 for the three water layer Ca^{2+} montmorillonite at 110 µeV for sample orientations 90° apart. The anisotropy in the quasi-elastic broadenings are invariably less than about 10%. This is too small a value to be explained on the basis that the broadenings arise solely from macroscopic diffusion parallel to the interlamellar plane, even when allowance is made for spatial averaging over the large mosaic spreads involved. Any model for the water dynamics in clays should therefore incorporate components of the motion both parallel and normal to the layers.

The data for the two layer Ca^{2+} montmorillonite system, recorded on IN5 at 38 µeV resolution illustrated in Fig. 6, show, in addition to little or no anisotropy, the other features referred to above, i.e. the

TABLE 4

Effective diffusion coefficients for each sample from both fixed and variable quasi-elastic fractions, X.

Sample	Diffusion Coefficient D cm^2 s^{-1} x 10^{-6}	Resolution μeV	No. of H_2O Layers	Instrument	X
Ca^{2+} Mont	13.7	38	2	IN5	VAR
	4.7	38	2	IN5	FIXED
Ca^{2+} Mont	3.4	1	2	IN10	VAR
Ca^{2+} Mont	15.0	180	2	IN5	VAR
	6.0	180	2	IN5	FIXED
Ca^{2+} Mont	16.0	180	3	IN5	VAR
	7.8	180	3	IN5	FIXED
Ca^{2+} Mont	16.0	110	3	IN5	VAR
	7.2	110	3	IN5	FIXED
Mg^{2+} Mont	15.0	180	2	IN5	VAR
	4.9	180	2	IN5	FIXED
Mg^{2+} Mont	3.4	1	2	IN10	VAR
Mg^{2+} Mont	13.7	110	3	IN5	VAR
	5.86	110	3	IN5	FIXED
Na^{+} Mont	9.4	110	2	IN5	FIXED
Ca^{2+} Verm	10.3	110	2	IN5	VAR
	2.1	110	2	IN5	FIXED

optimum fits occur at higher broadenings and lower (but somewhat Q dependent) X values. In the case of the two layer system, the limiting value of X at higher $\underline{Q}$ is somewhat lower (0.55 $\pm$ 0.05). For these data we find a diffusion coefficient of approximately D = 1.3 x 10^{-5} cm^2. s^{-1} for the two layer Ca^{2+} montmorillonite. In Table 4 the calculated diffusion coefficients are listed for each sample at the various energy resolutions, using data fitted with both theoretical and optimum quasi-elastic fractions.

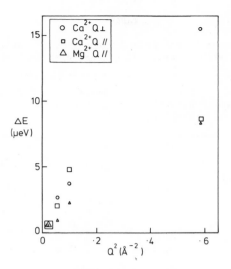

FIG. 7. Broadening curve for Ca²⁺ and Mg²⁺ montmorillonite 2 layer hydrates obtained from the high resolution backscattering spectrometer IN10.

We turn now to the IN10 data for the two layer Ca^{2+}-montmorillonite system (energy resolution 1.0 - 1.5 μeV). Here, we find an approximately linear dependence, also isotropic, of ΔE on Q^2 out to $Q^2 = 0.6$ $Å^{-2}$, but showing quasi-elastic broadenings some 4 - 5 times lower than IN5 data for the same system. A two layer Mg^{2+} montmorillonite exhibited broadenings of closely similar magnitude, though measurements on this sample were made at one orientation only. From the IN10 data one obtains, for both Ca^{2+} and Mg^{2+} exchange forms, a diffusion coefficient of 3.4 x 10^{-6} $cm^2 \cdot s^{-1}$. The IN10 broadening curves for these two samples are illustrated in Figure 7. The data will be discussed more fully elsewhere, but here we will remark that for the intermediate Q values the quasi-elastic fraction indicated by the analysis programme 'SAND' [21] was of the order of 0.5.

3.   Discussion and Conclusions

The layer charge deficiency in aluminosilicate minerals determines the concentration of exchange cations occupying the interlamellar space. This is normally referred to as the 'cation exchange capacity', and values of approximately 95 and 140 milliequivalents per 100 grams have been measured for the API No. 26 montmorillonite and the Libby vermiculite, respectively [9, 16]. For divalent cation exchanged montmorillonites, this defines a composition of the type

$$M^{2+}_{0.17} \, (Al, \, Mg)_2 \, Si_4 \, O_{10} \, (OH)_2 \, n \, H_2O$$

TABLE 5

Relative population of hydration and non-hydration shell water in montmorillonite, with corresponding quasi-elastic fractions.

Exchange Cation Valency	No. of waterlayers	Non-hydration shell n_2	Hydration shell (n_1)	X Total	X non-shell
1	2	5	6	0.79	0.36
1	3	10	6	0.85	0.53
2	2	16	6	0.79	0.57
2	3	27	6	0.85	0.69

From the known water/clay ratios for particular numbers of interlamellar water layers, one can deduce the value of n and hence the number of water molecules per exchange cation. Assuming that there are 6 molecules directly coordinated to the cations in inner hydration shells when two or more interlamellar water layers are present [17] one may calculate the relative populations of hydration-shell (n_1) and non hydration-shell (n_2) water molecules. The values obtained in montmorillonite are listed in Table 5.

X ray diffraction studies on the two layer Mg^{2+} vermiculite hydrate [17] has indicated that the arrangement of the two layer of water oxygen atoms forms octahedral groups, about half of the octahedral cavities being occupied by the exchange cations, i.e. the ratio of hydration to non-hydration shell water is approximately 0.5.

Table 5 also shows the quasi-elastic fraction calculated for the non-hydration shell water only. It can be seen that the values of $X_{non-shell}$ for the two- and three-layer divalent montmorillonite, (0.57 and 0.69, respectively) are in good agreement with the limiting values of X obtained at higher Q values from the IN5 data for the two- and three-layer Ca^{2+} montmorillonite. We suggest,therefore, the following interpretation for the IN5 and IN10 data taken together:

(a)   The larger broadening observed on IN5 arises from the water molecules not directly coordinated to the interlamellar exchange cations. This fraction exhibits higher diffusion coefficients [1.3×10^{-5} and 1.6×10^{-5} $cm^2 \cdot s^{-1}$ for the two- and three-layer cases] than average values obtained previously, though somewhat less than bulk water.

(b)   The smaller broadenings observed on IN10 arise from water molecules of lower mobility in the cation hydration shell. On IN10, the IN5 broadenings will be fairly flat at all except the lowest Q-values, and probably indistinguishable from the background. The observed IN10 quasi-elastic fraction of ~0.5 can therefore be interpreted as the ratio of the remaining quasi-elastic intensity $[0.79 - 0.57 = 0.22]$ to the total remaining scattering $[0.22 + (1.0 - 0.79)] = 0.43$. Some variations with Q were observed in the fitted quasi-elastic fraction for the IN10 data. These can be attributed both to contributions from the broader component [at low Q] and at high Q to the fact that even the narrower quasi-elastic component begins to become too broad for the IN10 energy window. The IN5 results for the other cationic forms of montmorillonite, as well as the two-layer Ca^{2+}-vermiculite, are also consistent with this hypothesis in that they show a limiting value of the quasi-elastic fraction at high Q values which correlated quite well with the non-hydration shell water fraction. Further measurements, both at fairly high resolution on IN5, and on IN10, are necessary in order to confirm these suggestions.

Turning now to the low Q behaviour of the quasi-elastic fraction, its increase with increasing Q is identical to the behaviour of an elastic incoherent structure factor (EISF) arising from some rotational diffusion model [18]:

$$A_o(\underline{Q}) = I(\underline{Q}, t = \infty) = \int G_s(\underline{r}, t = \infty) \exp(i\underline{Q}.\underline{r}) \, d\underline{r}$$

Such a result would be obtained if the motions of the water molecules giving rise to the broader quasi-elastic component are bounded in space for $t = \infty$. For continuous rotational diffusion on a sphere of radius a, one finds that the self-correlation function satisfies the diffusion equation.

$$\frac{\partial G_s}{\partial t} = D_r \nabla^2 G_s$$

which may be solved [19] to obtain an EISF corresponding to a zeroth order Bessel function

$$A_o(Q) = j_o^2(Qa)$$

An alternative motion might be that of rotational jump motion about N sites on a circle of radius a, i.e. the Barnes model [20] :

$$S(\underline{Q}, \omega) = A_o(\underline{Q}) \delta(\omega) + \frac{1}{\pi} \sum_{\ell=1}^{N-1} A_\ell(Q) \frac{\tau_\ell}{1 + \omega^2 \tau_\ell^2}$$

where the EISF is given by

$$A_o(Q) = \frac{1}{N} \sum_{P=1}^{N} j_o\left(2a \sin \frac{\pi P}{N}\right) \cos\left(2\pi P \over N\right)$$

In both cases the EISF decreases with increasing Q from a value of 1 at Q = 0. No detailed attempt to fit our data to a particular rotational diffusion model has yet been made, but certain features are immediately apparent:

(a)   Though the broader diffusion component appears to be dominated by rotational diffusion, the quasi-elastic broadenings obtained with variable X still increase with increasing Q when fitted to a single Lorentzian plus elastic component. This implies that either some macroscopic diffusion also occurs, or that the rotational model contains several Lorentzian terms which effectively gives a net ΔE increasing with Q. This could arise from either the spherical diffusion model, or from the Barnes model for $N > 2$.

(b)   The lack of anisotropy in the values of D can be explained on the basis that (i) macroscopic diffusion is relatively limited and/or is coupled to proton motions normal to the layers; and (ii) that if uniaxial rotational reorientations occur, they probably occur about axes not closely parallel or perpendicular to the interlamellar plane. Both these conclusions are consistent with macroscopic diffusion and NMR measurements [6, 8] and X-ray structural determinations on the water - Mg^{2+} vermiculite system [17].

(c)   If one recalculates X as an EISF, assuming that the saturation of its value with increasing Q corresponds to the minimum of an EISF of Bessel function type, one may estimate an effective radius of gyration of ca. $3\overset{\circ}{A}$, which corresponds to the mean molecular diameter for H_2O. Thus the rotational diffusion revealed is inconsistent with a 'propeller' motion of H_2O molecules about a C_2 axis, as found by Hougardy and co-workers for the hydration-shell water in Na^+-vermiculite [6], but could perhaps be consistent with interchange of water molecules between the layers in the presence of molecular voids, or perhaps to rotational jump motion of water molecules about a fixed hydrogen bond.

(d)   The diffusive component of lower mobility, which has been tentatively assigned to the water molecules in the hydration shell of the exchange cations, might also incorporate a contribution from centre-of-mass diffusion of non-hydration shell water molecules. One might tentatively imagine motion of this type as following a fairly tortuous path between the larger relatively static hydrated cations.

For the two layer Ca^{2+} vermiculite case, IN5 data fitted with variable X give virtually the same broadenings as in the montmorillonite case, although with a smaller limiting value of X of approximately 0.4, which is consistent with the smaller fraction of non-hydration shell cations in this case. The average broadenings obtained for fixed X (= 0.79) are considerably lower than in the montmorillonite case, as previous data indicates [5].

Further high-resolution quasi-elastic measurements are planned which it is hoped will enable the construction of somewhat more definitive models for the mobility of the two distinct populations of interlam ellar water, and also permit the differences between the silicate surfaces in montmorillonite and vermiculite to be more accurately defined.

Acknowledgements

We are indebted Dr. A. J. Dianoux and Dr. W. S. Howells of the Institut Laue Langevin, Grenoble, for advice and help in performing the IN5 and IN10 measurements, respectively.

References

[1]   NORRISH, K, Disc. Faraday Soc., 18 (1954) 120.
[2]   FARMER, V.C., in "The Chemistry of Soil Constituents", Ed.
        D. Greenland and M.H.B. Hayes, Wiley, London (to be published).
[3]   OLEJNIK, S., STIRLING, G.C. and WHITE, J.W., Special Disc.
        Faraday Soc., 1 (1970) 194.
[4]   HUNTER, R.J., STIRLING, G.C. and WHITE, J.W., Nature Phys.
        Sci., 230 (1971) 192.
[5]   OLEJNIK, S. and WHITE, J.W., Nature Phys. Sci., 236 (1972) 15.
[6]   HOUGARDY, J., STONE, W.E.E. and FRIPIAT, J.J., J. Chem.
        Phys., 64 (1976) 3840.
[7]   WOESSNER, D.E., SNOWDEN B.S. and MEYER, G.H., J. Coll.
        Interface Sci., 34 (1970), 43.
[8]   HECHT, A.M. and GEISSLER, F., J. Coll. Interface Sci., 44
        (1973) 1.
[9]   POSNER, A.M. and QUIRK, J.P., Proc. Roy. Soc., 275A (1964) 35.
[10]   THOMAS, R.K. and CEBULA, D., Private Communication.
[11]   (a) BARCLAY, L.M. and OTTEWILL, R.H. (1970) Special Disc.
        Faraday Soc., 1, 138; (b) CALLAGHAN, I.C., and OTTEWILL,
        R.H. (1974) Faraday Disc. Chem. Soc., 57, 110.
[12]   TCHALENKO, J.S., BURNETT, A.D., and HUNG, J.J. (1971)
        Clay Minerals, 9 47.
[13]   MAIER, W. and SAUPE, A., (1958) Z. Naturf. A, 13 564.
[14]   CARLILE, C.J. and ROSS, D.K. (1975). J. Appl. Cryst., 8, 292.
[15]   SPRINGER, T., "Quasi-elastic Neutron Scattering for the
        Investigation of Diffusive Motions in Solids and Liquids, Springer-
        verlag. (1971).
[16]   PICK, M.E. (1973) Ph.D. Thesis, University of Birmingham.
[17]   SHIROZU, H. and BAILEY, S.W. (1966) Am. Mineralogist, 51
        1124.
[18]   DIANOUX, A.J., VOLINO, F, and HERVET, H. (1975). Mol.
        Phys. 30 1181.
[19]   SEARS, V.F., (1966) Can. J. Phys. 44, 1299.
[20]   BARNES, J.D., (1973) J. Chem. Phys. 58 5193.
[21]   HOWELLS, W.S. (1975-76) I.L.L. Report No. 75H130T and
        76H122T.

DISCUSSION

C.J. WRIGHT: Have you attempted to fit your data using Stockmeyer's scattering law for two-dimensional diffusion? For your 1—3 monolayer films this law would not only be more appropriate than the three-dimensional scattering law, but might also give you part of the extra elastic contribution which you needed to invoke and which you explained by the hypothesis of restricted diffusion of water molecules in the hydration spheres of the ions.

P.L. HALL: We have not yet attempted to fit our data to a two-dimensional scattering law. We have made preliminary calculations which suggest that a model with $D_{||} \gg D_{\perp}$ would lead to much greater anisotropy than we have observed in the quasi-elastic broadening. The broader component is clearly dominated by rotational motions, with the translational diffusion coefficients at least $4 - 5$ times smaller. The latter component may be anisotropic, however, but we have no clear-cut data on this as yet.

C.J. WRIGHT: Do you have any details regarding the separation between the edges of your clay lamellae, and, if so, are you able to set a limit on the fraction of water in your sample that is not in the intervening space between the basal planes of the lamellae, but in the pores between their edges?

P.L. HALL: We have no accurate data on the separation between platelet edges. However, surface area measurements for these systems suggest a total — interlamellar plus external — surface area of about $750 \ m^2 \cdot g^{-1}$. Nitrogen adsorption data indicate a variable external surface area between 40 and $70 \ m^2 \cdot g^{-1}$, so that a pessimistic estimate of the external surface water would be around 10%. At first sight, one might expect this water to contribute to the broader quasi-elastic component, but the situation is complicated because there may be external cations present, giving the possibility of two types of external surface water.

J.W. WHITE: I should like to mention that my colleagues Thomas, Cebula and Parry at Oxford have just finished a long series of experiments on water and rain mobility in monovalent cation clay and lamellar liquid crystal systems. In these two different classes of compound the general conclusion of weak anisotropy for water diffusion is supported, but we have found cases where the slow and fast scattering from the Stern and diffuse double-layer water are clearly separated, on the neutron time scale, and also cases where — as was just suggested by Mr. Wright — a 2-dimensional scattering law gives a better fit to the quasi-elastic scattering than the Lorentzian approximation. It is clear that further work is needed to separate out the contribution of rotational scattering. Furthermore, at low water-layer thicknesses, it is difficult to imagine how translational diffusion of whole water molecules can be so rapid, and I wonder whether the idea of proton mobility should not be revived. Could you comment on this?

P.L. HALL: The systems which you and your colleagues are investigating are somewhat different from ours, in that monovalent cation-exchanged clays can expand to include many interlamellar water layers. In the divalent cation forms, expansion is limited to three layers of water, and we are seeing a separation into two components of water molecules, differing in mobility, within the Stern layer itself.

While I agree that further experiments and the development of a comprehensive model for water dynamics in clays is necessary, it is difficult to see how our results could be interpreted in terms of two-dimensional diffusion. In the preferentially oriented systems we have investigated, the situation would be more or less intermediate between the single crystal case — which predicts a Lorentzian whose width is a function of the direction of Q — and the powder average which Mr. Wright's comment implies. In the intermediate case, the scattering law is not analytic, and must be evaluated numerically. This subject has been discussed by Dianoux and co-workers [18].

In the low water-thickness limit, proton mobility is certainly higher than in bulk solution, but data obtained by Mortland and Fripiat some time ago suggest that the degree of dissociation is less than $\sim 1\%$, so it is difficult to explain the quasi-elastic data on this basis.

COHERENT INELASTIC SCATTERING IN INHOMOGENEOUS MEDIA

P. SCHOFIELD
Materials Physics Division,
Atomic Energy Research Establishment,
Harwell, Didcot, Oxfordshire,
United Kingdom

Abstract

COHERENT INELASTIC SCATTERING IN INHOMOGENEOUS MEDIA.

Taking as an example a set of spherical particles in a fluid medium, this paper outlines the theory of the scattering law for inhomogeneous media, in the case when the inhomogeneities are regions of uniform material of dimension large compared to interatomic distances and the wavelength is comparable to the size of the inhomogeneities. The scattering law can be written as the sum of two terms: (i) *contrast* scattering, proportional to differences in scattering power of the regions, depending on their macroscopic motion and (ii) *fluctuation* scattering from the density fluctuations within each region. The fluctuation scattering, in turn, can be represented as a sum of two terms for each region: (a) *bulk* scattering, proportional to the scattering law for an infinite medium of the material of that region, and (b) *boundary* scattering, from the free oscillations of the regions, which can be expressed in terms of the surfaces of the regions. The paper concludes with a brief discussion of the long wavelength hydrodynamic regime (wavelength long compared to the size of inhomogeneities) where the present theory breaks down.

1. INTRODUCTION

In a previous paper [1] we gave the theory of inelastic neutron scattering from isolated small spherical particles for scattering vectors, κ, small compared to the interatomic spacing within the particle. It was assumed that the particles consisted of a fluid core surrounded by an elastic shell, and that the density fluctuations within these regions could be treated by continuum theory.

In this work the theory is generalised to include interaction with the medium in which the particles are embedded. The calculation is illustrated by carrying through in detail the case where the particles are contained within a thin skin represented by a surface tension μ. However, the results are obtained in a rather more closed form than in [1] and an interesting feature of the final expression for the scattering law is that it can be expressed as the sum of terms of the scattering from the solvent and particle material in proportion to their volume plus terms relating to the boundary between them. This is a general result, which we feel may be of value in the use of inelastic scattering to study the dynamics of, for example, biological material, colloidal suspensions and solutions of polymers.

Although we have neutron scattering in mind in developing this theory, it would apply also to unpolarised light scattering (with suitable modification of the scattering amplitude and refractive index). The detailed theory is, however, at present restricted to scattering by longitudinal fluctuations for scattering vectors satisfying

$$L^{-1} \ll \kappa \ll \ell^{-1}$$

where L is the interparticle spacing and ℓ the intermolecular spacing in solvent and particle. That is, we do not consider in detail the true 'hydrodynamic' regime of the system ($\kappa L \ll 1$) in which sound can propagate with velocity depending on size and concentration of the particles (see section 6); we are concerned with an intermediate regime where the sound waves propagated within and outside the particle are modified by the surface between them.

In section 2, the general form of the scattering law is discussed. It is shown that this can be represented as the sum of two parts, which we call the 'contrast' scattering, which depends on the difference of the scattering amplitude density of particle and solvent, well-known from diffraction studies of such systems, and the 'fluctuation' scattering which arises from the dynamical fluctuations in the two media, and which is the main concern of the paper. In section 3, we develop the hydrodynamic model of the system. In order to solve the equations, it is necessary to obtain the amplitudes of the surface fluctuations of the particle. This is treated by standard theory [2].

In section 5, we show how the scattering law may be expressed in terms of the solutions of the linearised hydrodynamic equations, in the form above-mentioned, in terms of the boundary of the system.

2.   THE NEUTRON SCATTERING LAW

In considering the scattering of long wavelength neutrons from chemically inhomogeneous systems, we wish to consider the definition of a new scattering law, $B(\underset{\sim}{\kappa},\omega)$ in place of the conventional Van Hove function $S(\vec{\kappa},\omega)$ [3]. Whereas $S(\vec{\kappa},\omega)$ is defined independent of scattering amplitude, it is more convenient in this context to include the amplitude in the definition. We define a scattering amplitude per unit mass, $b(\vec{R},t)$, at point $\vec{R}$ and the mass density at point $\vec{R}, \rho(\vec{R},t)$, such that

$$b\,(\vec{R},t)\,\rho(\vec{R},t) = \Sigma\, a_i\, \delta\,(\vec{R} - r_i(t)\,) \qquad (2.1)$$

$$\rho(\vec{R},t) = \Sigma\, M_i\, \delta\,(\vec{R} - r_i(t)\,) \qquad (2.2)$$

where a_i is the conventional coherent scattering length of nucleus i at $\vec{r}_i(t)$. We chose to use mass rather than number density since mass density is the macroscopic physical quantity.

The Fourier components of the scattering density are given then by

$$b_{\underset{\sim}{\kappa}}\,(t) = \int d^3\vec{R}\, b(\vec{R},t)\, \rho(\vec{R},t)\, e^{i\,\vec{\kappa}.\vec{R}} \qquad (2.3)$$

and we define the 'material scattering law' in contrast to the 'particle scattering law', $S(\vec{\kappa},\omega)$, as

$$B\ (\vec{\kappa},\omega)\ =\ \frac{1}{2\pi}\ \int\ dt\ <\ b_{-\vec{\kappa}}(o)\ b_{\vec{\kappa}}(t)\ >\ e^{-i\omega t} \qquad (2.4)$$

(For a monatomic coherent ·scattering medium, for example $B(\vec{\kappa},\omega)$ is just $<a>^2\ S(\vec{\kappa},\omega)$.)

The convenience of this notation is illustrated by the subject of this paper, the scattering from spherical particles of mean radius a, with mean density $\bar{\rho}$. and scattering amplitude per unit mass b, in a medium with mean properties $\bar{\rho}_0$, b_0. We suppose the particle at time t to have its centre of mass at $R_1(t)$ and to be bound by a fluctuating surface given by

$$F\ (\vec{R}\ t)\ =\ R\ -\ a\ -\ r\ (\vec{u},t)\ =\ 0 \qquad (2.5)$$

where $r\ (\vec{u},t)$ is the fluctuation in the radius in the direction given by the unit vector $\vec{u}$. R now denotes position relative to the centre of mass. If $\rho_1(\vec{R},t)$ and $\rho_0(\vec{R},t)$ represent the fluctuation in density, then (2.3) gives

$$b_{\kappa}(t)\ =\ e^{i\vec{\kappa}.\vec{R}_1(t)}\ [b_1\ \int_{F<o}\ d^3\vec{R}\ e^{i\vec{\kappa}.\vec{R}}(\bar{\rho}_1\ +\ \rho_1(\vec{R},t)\ )$$

$$+\ b_o\ \int_{F>o}\ d^3\vec{R}\ e^{i\vec{\kappa}.\vec{R}}\ (\bar{\rho}_o\ +\ \rho_o\ (\vec{R},t)\ )] \qquad (2.6)$$

We shall consider in this paper nearly rigid particles, for which the relative fluctuation in the radius, $r(\vec{u},t)/a$, is much less than unity. In this case we may expand (2.6) to first order in $r(\vec{u},t)$ to obtain:

$$b_{\vec{\kappa}}(t)\ =\ e^{i\vec{\kappa}.\vec{R}_1(t)}\ [b_1\ \{\ \bar{\rho}\ 4\pi a^2\ \frac{j_1(\kappa a)}{\kappa a}\ +\ \int_{R<a}\ d^3\vec{R}\ \rho_1(\vec{R},t)e^{i\vec{\kappa}.\vec{R}}$$

$$+\ \bar{\rho}_1\ a^2\ \int\ d\vec{u}\ r(\vec{u},t)e^{i\vec{\kappa}.\vec{u}a}\}$$

$$+\ b_o\ \{\ -\ \bar{\rho}_o\ 4\pi a^2\ \frac{j_1(\kappa a)}{\kappa a}\ +\ \int_{R>a}\ d^3\vec{R}\ \rho_o(\vec{R},t)e^{i\vec{\kappa}.\vec{R}}$$

$$\bar{\rho}_o\ a^2\ \int d\vec{u}\ r(\vec{u},t)e^{i\vec{\kappa}.\vec{u}a}\}] \qquad (2.7)$$

for $\vec{\kappa}\ \neq\ o$. $j_i\ (q)$ is the Bessel function [4].

To a good approximation, the motion of the centre of mass will be uncorrelated with the internal fluctuations, so that we can write the scattering law as the sum of two parts: 'contrast' scattering denoted by c arising from the difference in mean scattering density and 'fluctuation' scattering, denoted by f. For particles of the size we are considering (a>100Å) it is known from light scattering studies that the centre of mass executes Brownian motion, so that the contrast scattering is given by

$$<b_{-\vec{\kappa}}(o)\ b_{\vec{\kappa}}(t)>_c\ =\ (b_i\bar{\rho}_1\ -\ b_o\bar{\rho}_2)^2\ [4\pi\ a^3\ \frac{j_i(\kappa a)}{\kappa a}\ ]^2\ \exp\ \{\ -D_s\ \kappa^2\ |t|\} \qquad (2.8)$$

where D_s is the self-diffusion coefficient of the particle. This represents the Rayleigh scattering from a diffusing sphere [5].

Denoting the fluctuation terms in the square brackets in (2.7) by
$\tilde{b}_{\vec{\kappa}}(t)$, the scattering from the fluctuations is given by

$$< b_{-\vec{\kappa}}(o) \; b_{\vec{\kappa}}(t)>_f = \exp \{ -D_s \; \kappa^2 \; |t|\}< \tilde{b}_{-\vec{\kappa}}(o) \; \tilde{b}_{\vec{\kappa}}(t)> \qquad (2.9)$$

and the fluctuation part of the scattering law $B_f(\vec{\kappa},\omega)$ by the Fourier
transform.

In the following we calculate the Laplace transform of the correlation
function of $\tilde{b}_{\vec{\kappa}}(t)$:

$$\tilde{B}(\vec{\kappa},z) = \int_o^\infty dt < \tilde{b}_{-\vec{\kappa}}(o) \; \tilde{b}_{\vec{\kappa}}(t) > e^{-zt} \qquad (2.10)$$

in terms of which, for a classical system

$$B_f(\vec{\kappa},\omega) = \frac{1}{\pi} \int_0^\infty dt < b_{-\vec{\kappa}}(o) \; b_{\vec{\kappa}}(t) > \cos \omega t \; e^{-D_s \kappa^2 |t|}$$

$$= \frac{1}{\pi} \; \mathrm{Re} \; \tilde{B} \; (\vec{\kappa}, \; D_s \; \kappa^2 + i\omega) \qquad (2.11)$$

Thus the diffusive broadening due to the motion of the particle is
incorporated as a shift in the axis of integration.

In the following sections, it will be important to bear in mind that
we are considering the fluctuations within a particle of fixed mass, relative
to the centre of motion. To first order in surface fluctuation, this
implies the constraints:

$$\int_{R<a} d^3\vec{R} \; \rho_1 \; (\vec{R},t) + \bar{\rho}_1 \; a^2 \int d\vec{u} \; r(\vec{u},t) = 0 \qquad (2.12)$$

$$\int_{R<a} d^3\vec{R} \; \vec{R} \; \rho_1 \; (\vec{R},t) + \bar{\rho}_1 \; a^3 \int d\vec{u} \; \vec{u} \; r(\vec{u},t) = 0 \qquad (2.13)$$

3.   THE EQUATIONS OF MOTION

As in [1], we now consider linearised hydrodynamic equations of motion
for the fluctuations in density, $\rho_1(\vec{R},t)$ and in the surface $r(\vec{u},t)$. In
order to incorporate the t = 0 initial values of the correlation functions,
we write equations of motion for correlation functions $\rho_1(\vec{R},t)$, $\tilde{\rho}_2(\vec{R},t)$ and
$r(\vec{u},t)$ of the quantities with $b_{-\kappa}(o)$. Thus

$$\tilde{x}(t) = b_1 \int_{R'<a} d^3\vec{R}' < \rho_1 \; (\vec{R}',o) \; x(t) > e^{-i \; \vec{\kappa}.\vec{R}'}$$

$$+ b_o \int_{R'>a} d^3\vec{R}' < \rho_o(R',o) \; x(t) > e^{-i\vec{\kappa}.\vec{R}'}$$

$$+ (b_1\bar{\rho}_1 - b_o\bar{\rho}_o) \; a^2 \int d\vec{u}' < r(\vec{u}',o)x(t) > e^{-i\vec{\kappa}.\vec{u}'a}$$

$$(3.1)$$

where x stands for ρ_1, ρ_2 or r, etc.

The equations of motion for the variables are as follows (see [1]). Since we are interested here only in the longitudinal fluctuations, the velocity field in medium i may be represented as the gradient of a potential $\Phi_i(\vec{R},t)$, for R < a(i = 1), R > a (i = 0)

$$\vec{V}_i \ (\vec{R},t) = -\vec{\nabla} \ \tilde{\Phi}_i \ (\vec{R},t) \tag{3.2}$$

The equations are:

(i) Continuity within each region:

$$\tilde{\rho}_i \ (\vec{R},t) - \bar{\rho}_i \ \nabla^2 \ \tilde{\Phi}_i \ (\vec{R},t) = 0 \tag{3.3}$$

(ii) Continuity at the interface - the fluid on each side moves with the speed of the surface:

$$\tilde{r} \ (\vec{u},t) = -\frac{\partial}{\partial a} \ \tilde{\Phi}_i \ (a \ \vec{u},t) \tag{3.4}$$

(iii) The linearised Navier-Stokes equation, in which we replace the pressure $\tilde{p}_i(\vec{R},t)$ by $c_i^2 \ \tilde{\rho}_i(\vec{R},t)$, using the compressibility relation between pressure and density fluctuation, and writing the result in terms of the speed of sound, c_i:

$$\nabla^2 \ \{\bar{\rho}_i \ \dot{\tilde{\Phi}}_i \ (\vec{R},t) - c_i^2 \ \tilde{\rho}_i \ (\vec{R},t) - D_i \ \dot{\tilde{\rho}}_i \ (\vec{R},t)\} = 0 \tag{3.5}$$

where D_i is the kinematic viscosity.

(iv) Pressure balance at the surface [6] which gives the pressure difference across the skin is given by Laplace's formula as the surface tension, μ, times the curvature. For small fluctuations about a sphere this gives:

$$c_0^2 \ \tilde{\rho}_0 \ (a\vec{u},t) - c_1^2 \ \tilde{\rho}_1 \ (a\vec{u},t) = \mu \ (\frac{2}{a^2} + \nabla^2) \ \tilde{r} \ (\vec{u},t) \tag{3.6}$$

where ∇^2 is the angular part of the Laplacian operator at radius a.

To calculate $B(\kappa,z)$, the Laplace transforms of the equation are taken, and the potential eliminated in favour of the variables $\tilde{\rho}$ and $\tilde{r}$. Defining, for each variable, the Laplace transform

$$x(z) = \int_0^\infty \tilde{x}(t) \ e^{-zt} \ dt \tag{3.7}$$

the transformed equations are the wave equation in each medium (i = 1,2)

$$z^2 \ \rho_i \ (\vec{R},z) - (c_i^2 + D_i z) \ \nabla^2 \ \rho_i \ (\vec{R},z) = (z - D_i \nabla^2) \ \tilde{\rho}_i \ (\vec{R},0) \tag{3.8}$$

with the boundary conditions

$$z^2 \ \bar{\rho}_i \ r(\vec{u},z) + (c_i^2 + D_i z) \ [\frac{\partial}{\partial R} \ \rho_i \ (R\vec{u},z) \ ]_{R \ = \ a}$$

$$= z \ \bar{\rho}_i \ \tilde{r} \ (\vec{u},o) + D_i \ [\frac{\partial}{\partial R} \ \tilde{\rho}_i \ (R\vec{u},o) \ ]_{R \ = \ a} \tag{3.9}$$

$$c_0^2 \ \rho_0 \ (a\vec{u},z) - c_1^2 \ \rho_1 \ (a\vec{u},z) = \mu \ (\frac{2}{a^2} + \nabla^2) \ r \ (\vec{u},z) \tag{3.10}$$

In deriving these equations, note that $\dot{\tilde{\rho}}_i(\vec{\kappa},o) = \dot{\tilde{r}}(\vec{u},o) = 0$ by time reversal symmetry.

In order to solve these equations, we first calculate the initial values $\tilde{\rho}_i(\vec{\kappa},o)$ and $\tilde{r}(\vec{u},o)$.

4.   EQUILIBRIUM FLUCTUATIONS

The initial values required for the solutions of equations (3.8-10) are given by the equilibrium correlation functions of the fluctuations in density and in the surface. This is done by the standard procedure [2] using the general principle that the probability distribution of the fluctuations is given by exp $\{-\beta W\}$ where W is the work required to produce the fluctuation from equilibrium. This presents certain difficulties in the present case because of the constraints (2.12-14).

First we calculate the work done specifically by the surface. This is given by the functional

$$W_s(r(\vec{u})) = \int d\vec{u} \int_o^{r(\vec{u})} a^2 \, \delta r'(\vec{u}) \, (p \, (r'(\vec{u})) - p \, (r'(\vec{u}))$$

$$= - \int d\vec{u} \int_o^{r(\vec{u})} a^2 \, \delta r'(\vec{u}) \, \mu \, (\frac{2}{a^2} + \nabla^2) \, r'(\vec{u}) \qquad (4.1)$$

by Laplace.

Writing

$$r(\vec{u}) = \sum_\ell (2\ell + 1) \, r_\ell \, P_\ell \, (\vec{\kappa}.\vec{u}) \qquad (4.2)$$

where $\vec{\kappa}$ is the direction of the scattering vector (note that we are only interested in fluctuations with a longitudinal component), one finds -

$$W_s(r(\vec{u})) = 4\pi\mu \sum_\ell (2\ell + 1) \, (\ell - 1) \, (\ell + 2). \frac{1}{2} r_\ell^2 \qquad (4.3)$$

For $\ell = 1$ this vanishes so that the fluctuation appears unbounded. However, $\ell = 1$ corresponds to a shift of the centre of mass (cf 2.13) which we have treated self consistently by separating the centre of mass motion. Hence the $\ell = 1$ term should be excluded.

For $\ell = 0$, the contribution to W is negative, showing that the particle is unstable under surface forces alone. The collapse of the particle is prevented by the resistance of the material within and outside it.

We must add to W, therefore, a volume term

$$W_v = \frac{1}{2} \, (\frac{\partial \rho_1}{\partial V_1} + \frac{\partial \rho_0}{\partial V_0}) \, \Delta V^2 \qquad (4.4)$$

which, in our notation reduces to

$$W_v = \frac{1}{2} \, (\frac{1}{V_1} \, \bar{\rho}_1 \, c_1^2 + \frac{1}{V_0} \, \bar{\rho}_0 \, c_0^2)(4\pi a^2)^2 \, r_0^2 \qquad (4.5)$$

where

$$V_1 = \frac{4}{3} \pi a^3 \quad , \quad V_o = V - V_1 \tag{4.6}$$

where V is the free volume per particle (see § 1).

The fluctuations in the surface amplitudes are therefore given by

$$< r_o^2 > = \frac{kT}{(4\pi a^2)^2 \, (\frac{1}{V_1} \, \bar{\rho}_1 \, c_1^2 + \frac{1}{V_o} \, \bar{\rho}_o \, c_o^2) - 8\pi\mu} \tag{4.7}$$

and for $\ell > 1$, for which there is no change in volume.

$$< r_\ell^2 > = \frac{kT}{4\pi\mu \, (2 \, \ell + 1) \, (\ell - 1) \, (\ell + 2)} \tag{4.8}$$

while $< r_\ell \, r_\ell ' >$ vanishes for $\ell \neq \ell'$. It is perhaps worth noting that (4.7) gives a stability limit on the size of a particle for given surface tension, taking $V \to \infty$, this yields the condition $\mu < \frac{3}{2} \rho c^2 a$.

Within an infinite medium, the fluctuations in density are given by [1]

$$<\rho \, (\vec{R}) \, \rho(\vec{R}')> = \bar{\rho}\frac{-kT}{c^2} \, \delta(\vec{R} - \vec{R}') \tag{4.9}$$

Within a finite particle, however, this is only an approximation, since it does not satisfy the constraint (2.12). The way in which (4.9) should be corrected will be considered elsewhere. We shall, in addition, neglect the correlation $<\rho_i \, (\vec{R}) \, r_o>$ also implied by this relation.

With these expressions for the fluctuations, we may calculate the right hand side of equations (3.8), (3.9) :

$$\tilde{\rho}_i \, (\vec{R},o) = b_i \, \frac{\bar{\rho}_i kT}{c_i^2} \, e^{-i \, \vec{\kappa}.\vec{R}} \qquad (R < c) \tag{4.10}$$

$$\tilde{r} \, (\vec{u},o) = (b_1\bar{\rho}_1 - b_o\bar{\rho}_o) \, 4\pi a^2 \, \underset{\ell \neq 1}{\Sigma} \, (2\ell+1)^2 \, (-i)^\ell \, j_\ell \, (\kappa a) \, P_\ell \, (\hat{\vec{\kappa}}.\hat{\vec{u}})$$

$$<r_\ell \, r_\ell> \tag{4.11}$$

5.   SOLUTION OF EQUATIONS

It is now straightforward to obtain the solution of the equations (3.8) - (3.10). Here we give an outline of the solution; mathematical details will be given elsewhere. The general solution of (3.8) may be written as

$$\rho_1 \, (\vec{R},z) = X_1 \, e^{-i\vec{\kappa}.\vec{R}} + \underset{\ell}{\Sigma} \, (2\ell+1) \, (-i)^\ell \, \alpha_\ell(z) \, \frac{j_\ell(i\zeta_1 \frac{R}{a})}{j_\ell(i\zeta_1)} \, P_\ell(\hat{\kappa}.\hat{u}) \tag{5.1}$$

with

$$X_1 = \frac{b_1 \, \bar{\rho}_1 \, kT}{c_1^2} \frac{z + D_1 \, \kappa^2}{z^2 + (c_1^2 + D_1 \, z) \, \kappa^2}$$

$$\zeta_1 = z \, a \, / \, (c_1^2 + D_1 \, z)^{\frac{1}{2}} \tag{5.2}$$

i.e. as a solution of the inhomogeneous equation plus solutions of the homogeneous equation. Similarly $\rho_0(\vec{R}, z)$ may be written in terms of X_0 and coefficients $\beta_\ell(z)$ and Bessel functions $h_\ell(i \, \zeta_i \, R)$, satisfying the boundary conditions at large distances for the particle. $\bar{a} \, \alpha_\ell(z)$ and $\beta_\ell(z)$ are then obtained from the boundary condition equations (3.9), (3.10), together with $r_\ell(z)$, writing

$$r \, (\vec{u}, z) = \Sigma_\ell (-i)^\ell (2\ell+1) \, r_\ell(z) \, P_\ell \, (\hat{\kappa}.\hat{u}) \tag{5.3}$$

These quantities are evaluated in the form ($x = \alpha, \beta, r$)

$$x_\ell(z) = x_\ell / \, [\, \frac{\bar{\rho}_1 c_1^2 \zeta_1^2}{a \lambda_{1\ell}} - \frac{\bar{\rho}_0 c_0^2 \zeta_0^2}{a \lambda_{o\ell}} + \frac{\mu}{a^2} \, (\ell-1)(\ell+2)] \tag{5.4}$$

where the x_ℓ are determined from the inhomogeneous term, $\tilde{r}_\ell$ etc. In the denominators whose   zeros give the frequencies of the free oscillations of the particle in the medium,

$$\lambda_{o\ell} = \frac{i\zeta_o \, h_\ell'(i\zeta_o)}{h_\ell \, (i\zeta_o)} \tag{5.5}$$

$$\lambda_{1\ell} = \frac{i\zeta_1 \, j_\ell'(i\zeta_1)}{j_\ell(i\zeta_1)}$$

Note that the denominator does not depend on κ.

Finally, to obtain the scattering law, we must evaluate $B(\kappa,z)$, the Fourier transform of the solutions. We may write it as

$$\tilde{B}(\kappa,z) = \tilde{B}_0(\kappa,z) + \tilde{B}_1(\kappa,z) \tag{5.6}$$

where

$$\tilde{B}_0(\kappa,z) = b_1^2 \frac{\bar{\rho}_1 kT}{c_1^2} \frac{z + D_1 \kappa^2}{z^2 + (c_1^2 + D_1 z)\kappa^2} \cdot V_1$$

$$+ b_0^2 \frac{\bar{\rho}_0 kT}{c_0^2} \frac{z + D_2 \kappa^2}{z^2 + (c_0^2 + D_0 z)\kappa^2} (V - V_1) \tag{5.7}$$

where V is the total volume and V_1 that occupied by particles. Thus $B_0(\kappa,z)$ is the scattering from a mixture of particles and fluid, neglecting any interaction and boundary effects. It may be expected to give the cross-section for $\kappa a \gg 1$ provided $\kappa\ell \ll 1$ where ℓ is a typical interatomic spacing.

$\bar{B}_1(\kappa,z)$ which contains the effect both of the finite size of the particles, and, for finite surface tension, the interaction with the medium and hence can be described as boundary scattering, is given by the Fourier transform of the terms proportional to α_ℓ, β_ℓ and r_ℓ. By virtue of the fact that these solutions satisfy the wave-equation, their Fourier transforms can be expressed in terms of boundary values of the Bessel functions:

$$\tilde{B}(\kappa,z) = 4\pi a^3 \; N\!\!\underset{\ell \neq 1}{\Sigma} \; (2\ell+1) \; j_\ell \; (\kappa a)$$

$$\{b_1\bar{\rho}_1 \; [\; \frac{(\lambda_{1\ell} - n_\ell)}{(\kappa a)^2 + \zeta_1^{\,2}} \; \frac{\alpha_\ell}{\bar{\rho}_1} \; + \; \frac{r_\ell}{a} \;]$$

$$- \; b_0 \; \bar{\rho}_0 \; [\; \frac{(\lambda_{0\ell} - n_\ell)}{(\kappa a)^2 + \zeta_0^{\,2}} \; \frac{\beta_\ell}{\bar{\rho}_0} \; + \; \frac{r_\ell}{a} \;]\}/\Delta_\ell \qquad\qquad (5.8)$$

where, in addition to symbols already defined, N is the number of particles in volume V,

$$n_\ell = \kappa a \; j_\ell{'} \; (\kappa a)/j_\ell(\kappa a)$$

and Δ_ℓ is the denominator of equation (5.4). Thus each term has poles both of the free oscillations of the surface and of the bulk material.

6. DISCUSSION

We have shown, by a particular example, how the Laplace-Fourier transform method may be used to calculate the scattering law from inhomogeneous media in a hydrodynamic model, for wave-vectors of the order of the inverse particle size (we comment on the longer wave length limit below). The particular advantage of the method over the treatment of [1] is that one can calculate the scattering law directly, without first calculating the normal modes. Given a computer with complex arithmetic, $B_f(\kappa,\omega)$ (equation 2.11) can be calculated directly from (5.7) and (5.8).

Clearly the theory can be generalised to more complex media (e.g. the model of a virus considered in [1] consisting of a fluid core with an elastic shell). The ingredients are (a) a wave-equation in each region of (3.8), (b) a velocity boundary condition, cf (3.9) and (c) a pressure boundary condition, cf (3.10). The solution, giving the scattering law, has (i) a term proportional to the volume of each material present, and its scattering power, given by that for an infinite medium of that material, (ii) a boundary term containing the frequencies of free oscillation of the system.

Each of these terms is Doppler broadened by the motion of the centres of mass of the regions. In section 1, we pointed out that in the region of κ we have considered this is dominated by the diffusive motion of particles in the medium.

At very long wavelengths, however, our analysis must be wrong. This is because we have decoupled the centre of mass motion. For wavelengths long compared to the range of inhomogeneity ($\kappa d \ll 1$, where d is the interparticle separation), one can apply an overall hydrodynamic theory, in which case, in addition to the diffusive mode there will be a Brillouin mode propagating with frequency $\omega = \bar{c}\kappa$, where $\bar{c}$ is the sound velocity of the medium as a whole. $\bar{c}$ may be calculated either by calculating the change in mean density $\Delta\rho$ caused by a change in pressure Δp or equivalently by calculating the volume fluctuation in the system as a whole using the standard method.

In the case of the model considered in this paper, either way one obtains for i particles radius a_i etc.

$$\frac{1}{\bar{\rho}\,\bar{c}^2} = \frac{v_o}{\rho_o\,c_o^2} + \Sigma_i\,\frac{v_i}{\rho_i\,c_i^2 - \frac{2}{3}\frac{\mu_i}{a_i}}$$

where $\bar{\rho}$ is the mean density

$$\bar{\rho} = \rho_o\,v_o + \Sigma\,\rho_i\,v_i$$

where v_i is the specific volume of each particle. The direct derivation of the long wavelength limit, and the transition to the regime discussed in this paper requires further investigation.

ACKNOWLEDGEMENTS

The author wishes to thank Dr. S.W. Lovesey for bringing this problem to his attention and for many helpful discussions and the Directors of the Institut Laue-Langevin for their hospitality during part of the time the work was carried out.

REFERENCES

[1]   LOVESEY, S.W., SCHOFIELD, P., J. Phys. C, 9 (1976) 2843.

[2]   LANDAU, L.D., LIFSCHITZ, E.M., "Fluid Mechanics", Pergamon Press, London (1959) Ch. XVII.

[3]   MARSHALL, W, LOVESEY, S.W., "Theory of Thermal Neutron Scattering", Oxford University Press, Oxford (1971).

[4]   ABRAMOWITZ, M., STEGUN, I.A., "Handbook of Mathematical Functions", Dover Publications Inc., New York, (1965).

[5]   DUBIN, S.B., LUNACEK, J.H., BENEDEK, G.P., Proc. Nat. Acad. Sci. 57 (1967),1164.

[6]   LAMB, H., "Hydrodynamics", Cambridge University Press, (1975).

DISCUSSION

J.W. WHITE: Perhaps I should mention that, undismayed by the lack of success in determining the neutron scattering from interfaces, we are considering using the IN11 spin-echo spectrometer at Grenoble to study the dynamics of long-chain amphiphiles adsorbed on the surface of uniform polystyrene latex spheres.

P. SCHOFIELD: I wish you luck in this undertaking.

S. YIP *(Chairman)*: If you have bulk scattering and surface scattering you should also have interference effects. Can you comment on this?

P. SCHOFIELD: For compressible particles, the free oscillations involve both bulk and surface motion as is seen from the form of the denominator $\Delta \varrho(z)$. I call it 'boundary scattering' because, using Green's theorem, one can obtain the amplitude as an integral over the boundary.

CHAIRMEN OF SESSIONS

Session I	H. RAUCH	Austria
Session II	J.W. WHITE	Institut Laue-Langevin
Session III	K.E. LARSSON	Sweden
Session IV	W. PRESS	Federal Republic of Germany
Session V	S. YIP	United States of America

SECRETARIAT OF THE SYMPOSIUM

Scientific Secretary:	H. REIJONEN	Division of Research and Laboratories, IAEA
Administrative Secretary:	G. SEILER	Division of External Relations, IAEA
Editor:	B. KAUFMANN	Division of Publications, IAEA
Records Officer:	D.J. MITCHELL	Division of Languages, IAEA

The following conversion table is provided for the convenience of readers and to encourage the use of SI units.

FACTORS FOR CONVERTING UNITS TO SI SYSTEM EQUIVALENTS*

SI base units are the metre (m), kilogram (kg), second (s), ampere (A), kelvin (K), candela (cd) and mole (mol).
[For further information, see International Standards ISO 1000 (1973), and ISO 31/0 (1974) and its several parts]

Multiply		by	to obtain
Mass			
pound mass (avoirdupois)	1 lbm	$= 4.536 \times 10^{-1}$	kg
ounce mass (avoirdupois)	1 ozm	$= 2.835 \times 10^{1}$	g
ton (long) (= 2240 lbm)	1 ton	$= 1.016 \times 10^{3}$	kg
ton (short) (= 2000 lbm)	1 short ton	$= 9.072 \times 10^{2}$	kg
tonne (= metric ton)	1 t	$= 1.00 \times 10^{3}$	kg
Length			
statute mile	1 mile	$= 1.609 \times 10^{0}$	km
yard	1 yd	$= 9.144 \times 10^{-1}$	m
foot	1 ft	$= 3.048 \times 10^{-1}$	m
inch	1 in	$= 2.54 \times 10^{-2}$	m
mil (= 10^{-3} in)	1 mil	$= 2.54 \times 10^{-2}$	mm
Area			
hectare	1 ha	$= 1.00 \times 10^{4}$	m^2
(statute mile)^2	1 mile^2	$= 2.590 \times 10^{0}$	km^2
acre	1 acre	$= 4.047 \times 10^{3}$	m^2
yard^2	1 yd^2	$= 8.361 \times 10^{-1}$	m^2
foot^2	1 ft^2	$= 9.290 \times 10^{-2}$	m^2
inch^2	1 in^2	$= 6.452 \times 10^{2}$	mm^2
Volume			
yard^3	1 yd^3	$= 7.646 \times 10^{-1}$	m^3
foot^3	1 ft^3	$= 2.832 \times 10^{-2}$	m^3
inch^3	1 in^3	$= 1.639 \times 10^{4}$	mm^3
gallon (Brit. or Imp.)	1 gal (Brit)	$= 4.546 \times 10^{-3}$	m^3
gallon (US liquid)	1 gal (US)	$= 3.785 \times 10^{-3}$	m^3
litre	1 l	$= 1.00 \times 10^{-3}$	m^3
Force			
dyne	1 dyn	$= 1.00 \times 10^{-5}$	N
kilogram force	1 kgf	$= 9.807 \times 10^{0}$	N
poundal	1 pdl	$= 1.383 \times 10^{-1}$	N
pound force (avoirdupois)	1 lbf	$= 4.448 \times 10^{0}$	N
ounce force (avoirdupois)	1 ozf	$= 2.780 \times 10^{-1}$	N
Power			
British thermal unit/second	1 Btu/s	$= 1.054 \times 10^{3}$	W
calorie/second	1 cal/s	$= 4.184 \times 10^{0}$	W
foot-pound force/second	1 ft·lbf/s	$= 1.356 \times 10^{0}$	W
horsepower (electric)	1 hp	$= 7.46 \times 10^{2}$	W
horsepower (metric) (= ps)	1 ps	$= 7.355 \times 10^{2}$	W
horsepower (550 ft·lbf/s)	1 hp	$= 7.457 \times 10^{2}$	W

* Factors are given exactly or to a maximum of 4 significant figures

Multiply		by	to obtain
Density			
pound mass/inch^3	1 lbm/in^3	= 2.768 × 10^4	kg/m^3
pound mass/foot^3	1 lbm/ft^3	= 1.602 × 10^1	kg/m^3
Energy			
British thermal unit	1 Btu	= 1.054 × 10^3	J
calorie	1 cal	= 4.184 × 10^0	J
electron-volt	1 eV	≃ 1.602 × 10^{-19}	J
erg	1 erg	= 1.00 × 10^{-7}	J
foot-pound force	1 ft·lbf	= 1.356 × 10^0	J
kilowatt-hour	1 kW·h	= 3.60 × 10^6	J
Pressure			
newtons/metre^2	1 N/m^2	= 1.00	Pa
atmosphere^a	1 atm	= 1.013 × 10^5	Pa
bar	1 bar	= 1.00 × 10^5	Pa
centimetres of mercury (0°C)	1 cmHg	= 1.333 × 10^3	Pa
dyne/centimetre^2	1 dyn/cm^2	= 1.00 × 10^{-1}	Pa
feet of water (4°C)	1 ftH$_2$O	= 2.989 × 10^3	Pa
inches of mercury (0°C)	1 inHg	= 3.386 × 10^3	Pa
inches of water (4°C)	1 inH$_2$O	= 2.491 × 10^2	Pa
kilogram force/centimetre^2	1 kgf/cm^2	= 9.807 × 10^4	Pa
pound force/foot^2	1 lbf/ft^2	= 4.788 × 10^1	Pa
pound force/inch^2 (= psi)^b	1 lbf/in^2	= 6.895 × 10^3	Pa
torr (0°C) (= mmHg)	1 torr	= 1.333 × 10^2	Pa
Velocity, acceleration			
inch/second	1 in/s	= 2.54 × 10^1	mm/s
foot/second (= fps)	1 ft/s	= 3.048 × 10^{-1}	m/s
foot/minute	1 ft/min	= 5.08 × 10^{-3}	m/s
mile/hour (= mph)	1 mile/h	= $\begin{cases} 4.470 \times 10^{-1} \\ 1.609 \times 10^{0} \end{cases}$	m/s km/h
knot	1 knot	= 1.852 × 10^0	km/h
free fall, standard (= g)		= 9.807 × 10^0	m/s^2
foot/second^2	1 ft/s^2	= 3.048 × 10^{-1}	m/s^2
Temperature, thermal conductivity, energy/area·time			
Fahrenheit, degrees −32	°F − 32	$\dfrac{5}{9}$	°C
Rankine	°R		K
1 Btu·in/ft^2·s·°F		= 5.189 × 10^2	W/m·K
1 Btu/ft·s·°F		= 6.226 × 10^1	W/m·K
1 cal/cm·s·°C		= 4.184 × 10^2	W/m·K
1 Btu/ft^2·s		= 1.135 × 10^4	W/m^2
1 cal/cm^2·min		= 6.973 × 10^2	W/m^2
Miscellaneous			
foot^3/second	1 ft^3/s	= 2.832 × 10^{-2}	m^3/s
foot^3/minute	1 ft^3/min	= 4.719 × 10^{-4}	m^3/s
rad	rad	= 1.00 × 10^{-2}	J/kg
roentgen	R	= 2.580 × 10^{-4}	C/kg
curie	Ci	= 3.70 × 10^{10}	disintegration/s

^{a} atm abs: atmospheres absolute;
atm (g): atmospheres gauge.

^{b} lbf/in^2 (g) (= psig): gauge pressure;
lbf/in^2 abs (= psia): absolute pressure.

HOW TO ORDER IAEA PUBLICATIONS

 An exclusive sales agent for IAEA publications, to whom all orders
and inquiries should be addressed, has been appointed
in the following country:

UNITED STATES OF AMERICA   UNIPUB, P.O. Box 433, Murray Hill Station, New York, N.Y. 10016

 In the following countries IAEA publications may be purchased from the
sales agents or booksellers listed or through your
major local booksellers. Payment can be made in local
currency or with UNESCO coupons.

ARGENTINA	Comisión Nacional de Energía Atómica, Avenida del Libertador 8250, Buenos Aires
AUSTRALIA	Hunter Publications, 58 A Gipps Street, Collingwood, Victoria 3066
BELGIUM	Service du Courrier de l'UNESCO, 112, Rue du Trône, B-1050 Brussels
C.S.S.R.	S.N.T.L., Spálená 51, CS-113 02 Prague 1
	Alfa, Publishers, Hurbanovo námestie 6, CS-893 31 Bratislava
FRANCE	Office International de Documentation et Librairie, 48, rue Gay-Lussac, F-75240 Paris Cedex 05
HUNGARY	Kultura, Bookimport, P.O. Box 149, H-1389 Budapest
INDIA	Oxford Book and Stationery Co., 17, Park Street, Calcutta, 700016
	Oxford Book and Stationery Co., Scindia House, New Delhi-110001
ISRAEL	Heiliger and Co., 3, Nathan Strauss Str., Jerusalem
ITALY	Libreria Scientifica, Dott. Lucio de Biasio "aeiou".
	Via Meravigli 16, I-20123 Milan
JAPAN	Maruzen Company, Ltd., P.O. Box 5050, 100-31 Tokyo International
NETHERLANDS	Martinus Nijhoff B.V., Lange Voorhout 9-11, P.O. Box 269, The Hague
PAKISTAN	Mirza Book Agency, 65, Shahrah Quaid-e-Azam, P.O. Box 729, Lahore-3
POLAND	Ars Polona-Ruch, Centrala Handlu Zagranicznego,
	Krakowskie Przedmiescie 7, Warsaw
ROMANIA	Ilexim, P.O. Box 136-137, Bucarest
SOUTH AFRICA	Van Schaik's Bookstore (Pty) Ltd., P.O. Box 724, Pretoria 0001
	Universitas Books (Pty) Ltd., P.O. Box 1557, Pretoria 0001
SPAIN	Diaz de Santos, Lagasca 95, Madrid-6
	Diaz de Santos, Balmes 417, Barcelona-6
SWEDEN	AB C.E. Fritzes Kungl. Hovbokhandel, Fredsgatan 2, P.O. Box 16358 S-103 27 Stockholm
UNITED KINGDOM	Her Majesty's Stationery Office, P.O. Box 569, London SE1 9NH
U.S.S.R.	Mezhdunarodnaya Kniga, Smolenskaya-Sennaya 32-34, Moscow G-200
YUGOSLAVIA	Jugoslovenska Knjiga, Terazije 27, POB 36, YU-11001 Belgrade

 Orders from countries where sales agents have not yet been appointed and
requests for information should be addressed directly to:

 **Division of Publications
International Atomic Energy Agency
Kärntner Ring 11, P.O.Box 590, A-1011 Vienna, Austria**